ESSENTIAL ALGEBRA

THIRD EDITION

C. L. Johnston

Alden T. Willis

East Los Angeles College

Wadsworth Publishing Company

Belmont, California
A division of Wadsworth, Inc.

Mathematics Editor: Peter W. Fairchild
Signing Representative: Richard Jones
Production: Greg Hubit Bookworks

Printed in the United States of America

2 3 4 5 6 7 8 9 10—86 85 84 83 82

Library of Congress Cataloging in Publication Data

Johnston, C. L. (Carol Lee).
    Essential algebra.

    Includes index.
    1. Algebra   I. Willis, Alden T.   II. Title.
QA152.2.J63   1982   512.9   81-16480
ISBN 0-534-01124-1   AACR2

Preface

This third edition reflects many helpful comments from users of the first and second editions, as well as our own classroom experience in teaching from the book. Following are the major changes in the third edition.

1. The number of word problem applications has been substantially increased. Several new sections consisting entirely of word problems have been added. Also included are many additional word problems in exercise sets throughout the book. The method used to solve word problems has been retained without change because of the very favorable responses from many users.
2. Metric units have been used more extensively in this edition.
3. A separate set of Cumulative Review Exercises has been added immediately following the Chapter Review Exercises in every chapter (except Chapter 1).
4. The Master Product method for factoring trinomials has been added as an optional section (Sec. 806).
5. The number of exercises requiring the use of a calculator has been increased.
6. There are many other changes throughout the text that have been made to clarify and simplify concepts, explanations, and examples in order to make the book easier for students to read and understand.

Some of the major features of this book are:

1. The contents are arranged in small sections, each with its own examples and exercises. We use a one-step, one-concept-at-a-time approach.
2. After careful and detailed topic explanation, we use many concrete examples that lead up to general algebraic principles which can then be used to work the exercises.
3. Important concepts and algorithms are enclosed in boxes for easy identification and reference.
4. There are over 4700 exercises in this book.

Set I Exercises: The complete solutions for all odd-numbered Set I exercises are included in the back of this text together with the answers for all even-numbered Set I Exercises. In most cases the even-numbered exercises provide practice on problems analogous to the odd-numbered exercises. The student can use the solutions for the odd-numbered Set I exercises as a study aid in doing the even Set I exercises as well as all Set II exercises.

Set II Exercises: Answers to all Set II exercises are included in the instructor's manual. No answers for Set II exercises are given in the text.

5. An instructor's manual is available that contains four different tests for each chapter and two final examinations that may be easily removed and duplicated for class use. These tests are prepared with adequate space for students to work the problems. Answer keys for these tests are provided in the manual.

6. A diagnostic test is included at the end of each chapter. Complete solutions to all problems in these diagnostic tests, together with section references, appear in the answer section.

7. A comprehensive summary is included at the end of each chapter.

8. Our approach to solving word problems is to provide a detailed method for changing a word statement into an algebraic equation.

9. Special attention is given to the operations with zero in a single section of Chapter 1 which includes a discussion of the common errors students make with zero. References are then made to this section throughout the book.

10. Liberal use is made of visual aids such as the number line, shading, and other graphics.

11. In special "Words of Caution" major and common algebraic errors are identified. Attention is drawn to avoiding mistakes that are commonly made by the inexperienced student.

12. The importance of checking solutions is stressed throughout the book.

13. A brief summary of arithmetic is included in Appendix 2 to help students who have trouble with arithmetic in algebra.

14. The basic concepts of Sets are given in Appendix 1 for reference.

This book can be used in three types of instructional programs:

1. The conventional lecture course. This book is particularly easy to fit into a program of regular assignments because it is divided into many small self-contained units. Examinations that can be given for each chapter are provided in the instructor's manual. A diagnostic test is included at the end of each chapter that students may use for review and diagnostic purposes. This book has been class-tested by the authors and many other instructors in the conventional lecture course program.

2. The learning laboratory class. Because of the format of explanation, example, and exercise carried on in each section of the book, together with the diagnostic tests and solutions for the exercises and tests, a wide degree of latitude in the pace at which a student progresses is possible when using this book in the learning laboratory class. A method that instructors have found successful is to give a student one form of a chapter test and grade it. If the student does not pass that test, he is given an opportunity to retake another form of that chapter

test after he has had time to review the material covering those problems that he did incorrectly. The student is not permitted to advance to the next chapter until he has passed one form of the test for the present chapter.

3. <u>Self-study</u>. This book lends itself to self-study because (a) each new topic is short enough to be mastered before continuing, and (b) over 1000 examples and over 1800 completely solved exercises are given, together with all the answers for the even-numbered Set I exercises. A student studying by himself is not apt to repeat incorrect procedures in succeeding problems when he has the correct solutions to show him when and *where* he has made a mistake. In using the book for self-study, a student should begin by taking the diagnostic test for Chapter 1, and then checking answers against the solutions at the back of the book. References given in the solutions will direct the student to specific sections of the book that explain the particular problems done incorrectly. The student can continue in this manner at his own pace throughout the book.

We wish to thank our many friends for their valuable suggestions. In particular we are deeply grateful to Brendan Brown, Antelope Valley College; Anthony Brunswick, Delaware Technical and Community College; Judy Cain, Tompkins-Cortland Community College; Elaine DiPerna, Community College of Allegheny County; Angel Eguaras, Jr., Atlantic City College; Paul Hutchens, Florissant Valley Community College; Mary K. Moynihan, Cape Cod Community College; Dr. William C. Pearce, Kilgore Junior College; Edwin Schultz, Elgin Community College; Pattie Vosgerau, Utah Technical College; Walter I. Weber, Catonsville Community College.

This book is dedicated to our students, who inspired us to do our best to produce a book worthy of their time.

C. L. Johnston

Alden T. Willis

Contents

ONE

Operations with Signed Numbers

Arithmetic is calculation with numbers using fundamental
operations such as addition, subtraction, multiplication,
and division. (See the Appendix for a brief review.)
Algebra deals with the same fundamental operations with
numbers, but uses letters to represent some of the numbers.

Before beginning the study of algebra we review for
your benefit a few basic definitions relating to numbers.

 **Basic Definitions**

NATURAL NUMBERS. The numbers

$$1, 2, 3, 4, 5, 6, 7, 8, 9, 10, 11, 12, \text{ and so on,}$$

are called the *natural numbers* (or *counting numbers*). These
were probably the first numbers invented to enable people
to count their possessions, such as sheep or goats.

NUMBER LINE. Natural numbers can be represented by numbered
points equally spaced along a straight line (Fig. 101A).
Such a line is called a *number line*.

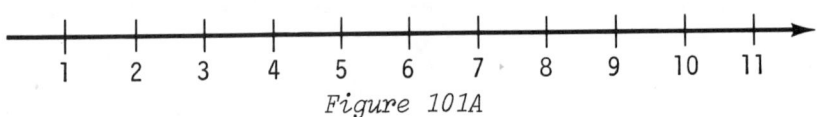

Figure 101A

The arrowhead shows the direction in which numbers get
larger, and also shows that the numbers continue on.
Numbers that follow one another (without interruption) are
called *consecutive numbers*. This means that 6 follows 5;
7 follows 6. Therefore, 5, 6, and 7 are consecutive numbers.
Later we will discuss other kinds of numbers, such as
fractions, which can also be placed on the number line.

The smallest natural number is 1. The largest natural
number can never be found because no matter how far we
count there are always larger natural numbers. Since it is
impossible to write all the natural numbers, it is customary
to represent them as follows:

$$\{1, 2, 3, 4, \boxed{\ldots}\}$$

⎣—Read "and so on."

The three dots to the right of the number 4 indicate that
the remaining numbers are to be found by counting in the
same way we have begun: namely, to add 1 to the preceding
number to find the next number. We call the set of natural
numbers *N*. (Sets are covered in Appendix 1.) So

$$N = \{1, 2, 3, 4, \ldots\}$$

WHOLE NUMBERS. When 0 is included with the natural numbers,
we have the set of numbers known as *whole numbers* (Fig. 101B).

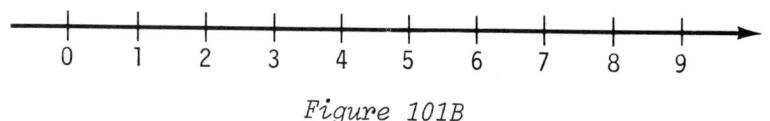

Figure 101B

We call the set of whole numbers W. So

$$W = \{0, 1, 2, 3, \ldots\}$$

INEQUALITY SYMBOLS. The arrowhead on the number line indicates the direction in which numbers get larger. Numbers get larger as we move to the right on the number line; numbers get smaller as we move to the left. For example, 6 is to the right of 3, therefore 6 is *greater than* 3; written 6 > 3 (Example 1). Also 2 is to the left of 7, therefore 2 is *less than* 7; written 2 < 7 (Example 2).

Example 1. 6 > 3

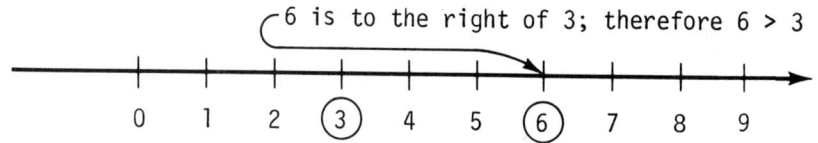

Example 2. 2 < 7

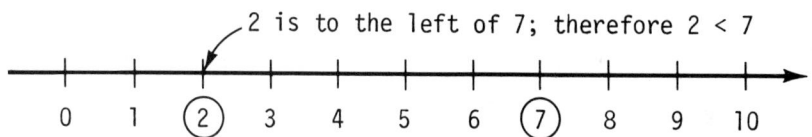

An easy way to remember the meaning of the symbol is to notice that the wide part of the symbol is next to the larger number.

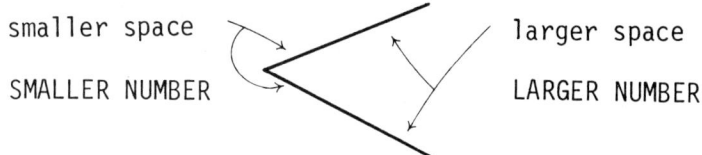

Some people like to think of the symbols > and < as arrowheads that point toward the smaller number.

Example 3. Writing and reading inequalities.

(a) 7 > 6   is read "7 is greater than 6."
(b) 7 > 1   is read "7 is greater than 1."
(c) 5 < 10   is read "5 is less than 10."
(d) 3 < 4 < 5   is read "3 is less than 4 and
                            4 is less than 5."

Note that 7 > 6 and 6 < 7 give the same information even though they are read differently.

Another inequality symbol is $\neq$. A slash line drawn through a symbol puts a *not* in the meaning of the symbol.

Example 4. Showing the use of the slash line

    (a) $=$ is read "is equal to"
         $\neq$ is read "is *not* equal to"
    (b) $<$ is read "is less than"
         $\not<$ is read "is *not* less than"
    (c) $>$ is read "is greater than"
         $\not>$ is read "is *not* greater than"
    (d) $4 \neq 5$ is read "4 is not equal to 5"
    (e) $3 \not< 2$ is read "3 is not less than 2"
    (f) $5 \not> 6$ is read "5 is not greater than 6"

DIGITS. In our number system a digit is any one of the first ten whole numbers: 0, 1, 2, 3, 4, 5, 6, 7, 8, 9. They are shown on the number line in Fig. 101B. Probably because people began counting on their ten fingers (Latin *digitus*, finger), the first ten whole numbers were called *digits*. All numbers are written by using one or more digits.

Numbers are often referred to as *one-digit* numbers, *two-digit* numbers, *three-digit* numbers, and so on.

Example 5. Use of digits.

    (a)   35 is a two-digit number.
    (b)   7 is a one-digit number.
    (c)   275 is a three-digit number.
    (d)   The first digit of 785 is 7.
    (e)   The second digit of 785 is 8.
    (f)   The third digit of 785 is 5.

FRACTIONS. A *fraction* is part of a whole. It is written $\frac{a}{b}$. We call a and b the *terms* of the fraction. The *denominator* b tells us into how many equal parts the whole is divided. The *numerator* a tells us the number of those equal parts indicated by the fraction $\frac{a}{b}$.

The fraction $\frac{a}{b}$ is equivalent to the division $a \div b$.

$$\text{terms of fraction} \rightarrow \left[\begin{array}{l} \text{numerator (any whole number)} \\ \frac{a}{b} \leftarrow \text{fraction line} \\ \text{denominator (cannot be 0)} \end{array} \right.$$

Example 6. In the fraction $\frac{3}{4}$,

$\frac{3}{4}$ 3 indicates the number of fourths;

  the whole is divided into four equal parts called fourths.

The fraction $\frac{3}{4}$ is equivalent to $3 \div 4$.

MIXED NUMBERS. A *mixed number* is made up of both a whole number part and a fraction part.

Example 7. Mixed numbers

$$2\frac{1}{2} , \quad 3\frac{5}{8} , \quad 5\frac{1}{4} , \quad 12\frac{3}{16}$$

DECIMAL FRACTIONS. A *decimal fraction* is a fraction whose
denominator is 10, 100, 1000, and so on.

Example 8. Decimal fractions

    (a) $\dfrac{4}{10} = 0.4$ Read "four-tenths."

    (b) $\dfrac{5}{100} = 0.05$ Read "five-hundredths."

    (c) $\dfrac{6}{1000} = 0.006$ Read "six-thousandths."

    (d) $\dfrac{23}{10} = 2.3$ Read "two and three-tenths."
                                    Read "twenty-three tenths."

Decimal Places. The number of decimal places in a number is
the number of digits written to the right of the decimal
point.

Example 9. Decimal places

    (a)   75.14 (2 decimal places)
    (b)   1.086 (3 decimal places)
    (c)   2.500 (3 decimal places)

REAL NUMBERS. All the numbers that can be represented by
points on the number line are called *real numbers*.
Natural numbers, whole numbers, fractions, decimals, and mixed
numbers are all real numbers and can therefore be represented
by points on the number line. Points representing some fractions, decimals, and mixed numbers are shown in Fig. 101C.

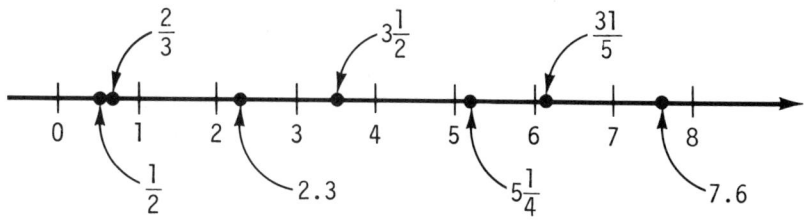

Figure 101C

There are other kinds of real numbers. They are introduced in
Sections 102 and 112.

SET I

1. What is the second digit of the number 159?
2. What is the fourth digit of the number 1975?
3. What is the smallest natural number?
4. What is the smallest digit?
5. What is the largest one-digit natural number?
6. What is the largest two-digit whole number?
7. Write the consecutive natural numbers > 14 and < 17.
8. Write in consecutive order all the digits < 5.
9. What is the smallest two-digit natural number?
10. What is the smallest three-digit whole number?
11. Which of the symbols, < or >, should be used to make the statement, 8 _?_ 7, true?
12. Which of the symbols, < or >, should be used to make the statement, 0 _?_ 1, true?
13. Is 2.3 a real number?
14. Is $\frac{7}{8}$ a real number?

----

15. What is the smallest whole number?
16. What is the smallest digit?
17. Write two different symbols that tell the number of days in a week.
18. Write two different symbols that tell the number of minutes in an hour.
19. Is 1.8 a real number?
20. Is $\frac{9}{5}$ a real number?
21. How many decimal places in the number 7.010?
22. How many decimal places in the number 41.0005?

SET II

1. Is 12 a digit?
2. Is 12 a natural number?
3. What is the largest natural number?
4. What is the largest digit?
5. Write all the whole numbers < 4.
6. Write all the digits > 6.
7. Is 58.4 a real number?
8. How many decimal places are there in the number 50.602?
9. What is the largest three-digit natural number?
10. What is the smallest one-digit natural number?
11. Which of the symbols, < or >, should be used to make the statement, 11 _?_ 6, true?

Negative Numbers

In Sec. 101 we showed how whole numbers could be represented by equally spaced points along the number line. We now extend the number line to the left and continue with the set of equally spaced points.

Numbers used to name the points to the left of 0 on the number line are called *negative numbers*. Numbers used to name the points to the right of 0 on the number line are called *positive numbers*. Zero itself is neither positive nor negative. The positive and negative numbers are referred to as *signed numbers* (Fig. 102A).

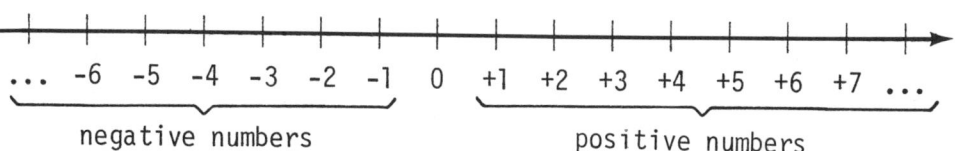

negative numbers   positive numbers

Figure 102A

INTEGERS. The numbers used to name the points shown in Fig. 102A are called *integers*. The set of integers can be represented in the following way:

$$\{..., -3, -2, -1, 0, +1, +2, +3, ...\}$$

Since integers can be represented by points on the number line, integers are real numbers.

Reading Positive and Negative Integers

Example 1.

   (a)   -1   Read "negative one."
   (b)   -575   Read "negative five hundred seventy-five."
   (c)   25   Read "twenty-five" or "positive twenty-five."

When reading or writing positive numbers, we usually omit the word "positive" and the + sign. Therefore, when there is no sign in front of a number, it is understood to be positive.

USING INEQUALITY SYMBOLS WITH INTEGERS. The arrowhead on the number line indicates the direction in which numbers get larger. Numbers get larger as we move to the right on the number line; numbers get smaller as we move to the left. For example, -3 is to the right of -7, therefore -3 is *greater than* -7; written -3 > -7 (Example 2). Also, -5 is to the left of -2, therefore, -5 is *less than* -2; written -5 < -2 (Example 3).

Example 2.   -3 > -7

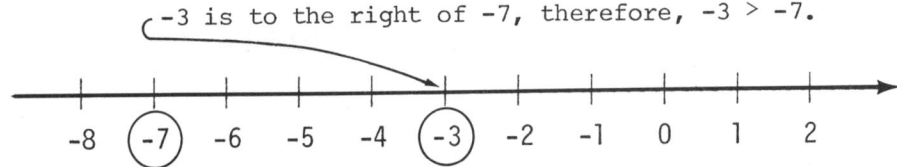

-3 is to the right of -7, therefore, -3 > -7.

Example 3.   -5 < -2

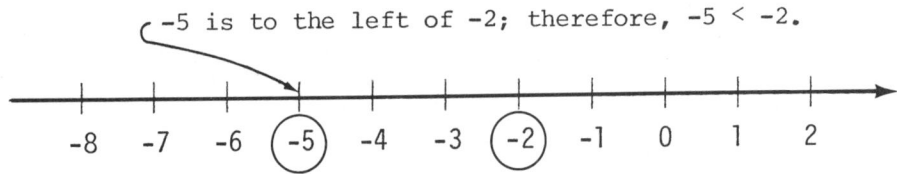

-5 is to the left of -2; therefore, -5 < -2.

Example 4. Verify the following inequalities by noting whether the first number of each pair is to the right or left of the second number (of that pair) on the number line.

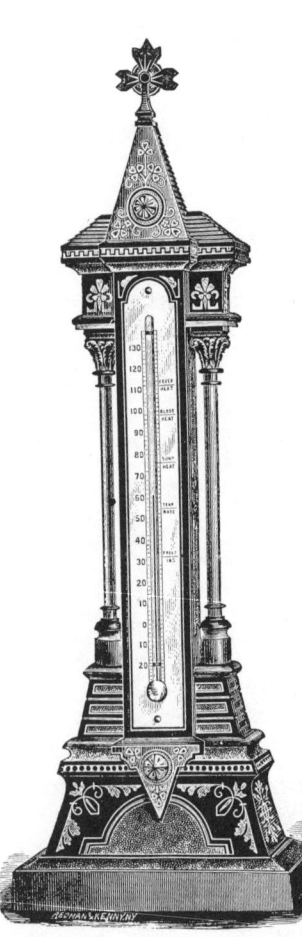

(a)   6 > 4   (b)   0 > -1   (c)   -2 > -5
(d)   -20 < -10   (e)   -5 < 3

In Sec. 101 we stated that a largest natural number could never be found because no matter how far we count there are always larger natural numbers. Similarly, no matter how far we count along the number line to the left of 0 we never reach a smallest negative number.

Showing the Use of Positive and Negative Integers

Example 5. On an unusually cold day in Minnesota, the temperature was -40° F. This means that the temperature was 40° F below 0.

Example 6. The altitudes of some unusual places on earth are as follows:

(a)   Mt. Everest   29,028 ft
      This means that the peak of Mt. Everest
      is 29,028 ft *above* sea level.

(b)   Mt. Whitney (California)   14,494 ft

(c)   Lowest point in Death Valley (California)   -282 ft
      This means that the lowest point in
      Death Valley is 282 ft *below* sea level.

(d)   Dead Sea (Jordan)   -1,299 ft

(e)   World's deepest well (Oklahoma, 1974)   -31,441 ft

(f)   Mariana Trench (Pacific Ocean)   -36,198 ft

Representing Some Negative Numbers Other Than Integers.
Many points exist on the number line to the left of 0 other than those representing the negative integers. Some of these points are shown in Fig. 102B.

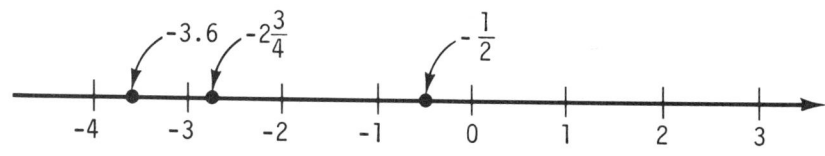

Figure 102B

In Sec. 101 we explained that all the numbers that can be represented by points on the number line are called real numbers. Since negative numbers can be represented by points on the number line, negative numbers are real numbers.

EXERCISES 102

SET I

1. Write -75 in words.
2. Write -49 in words.
3. Use digits to write negative fifty-four.
4. Use digits to write negative one hundred nine.
5. Which is larger, -2 or -4?
6. Which is larger, 0 or -10?
7. A scuba diver descends to a depth of sixty-two feet. Represent this number by an integer.
8. The temperature at Fairbanks, Alaska, was forty-five degrees Fahrenheit below zero. Represent this number by an integer.
9. What is the largest negative integer?
10. What is the smallest negative integer?

In Exercises 11—14, determine which of the two symbols > or < should be used to make each statement true.

11. 0 _?_ -3
12. -2 _?_ -6
13. -5 _?_ 2
14. -7 _?_ -4

----

15. Which is larger, -5 or -10?
16. Which is smaller, -1 or -15?
17. What integers can X be replaced by to make the following statement true? -10 < X < -6
18. What integers can X be replaced by to make the following statement true? -2 < X < 3

SET II

1. Write -17 in words.
2. Use digits to write negative two hundred four.
3. A miner descends to a depth of eighty-five feet. Represent this number by an integer.
4. The temperature at Billings, Montana, was fifty-four degrees Fahrenheit below zero. Represent this number by an integer.

In Exercises 5 and 6 determine which of the two symbols
> or < should be used to make each statement true.

5.   0 _?_ -5   6.   -7 _?_ -3

7.   What is the largest three-digit integer?

8.   What is the smallest two-digit whole number?

 ## Adding Signed Numbers

In this section we show how to add signed numbers. We can
represent a signed number by an arrow beginning at the point
representing 0 and ending at the point representing that
particular number on the number line.

Example 1.   Represent 4 by an arrow.

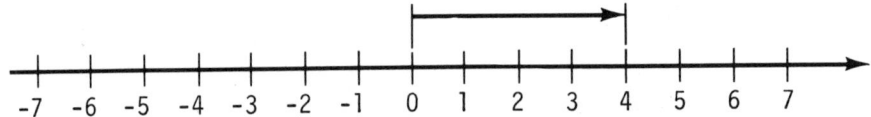

This arrow represents a movement of 4 units to the *right*.
Any *positive* number is represented by an arrow directed to the
right. The arrow need not start at zero so long as it has a
length equal to the number it represents.

Example 2.   Represent -5 by an arrow.

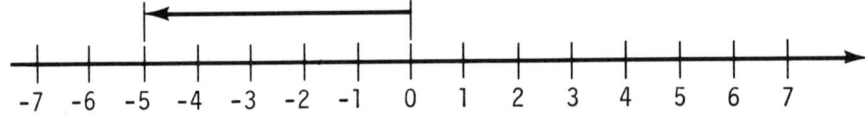

This arrow represents a movement of 5 units to the *left*.
Any *negative* number is represented by an arrow directed to
the *left*.
     We can also represent the addition of signed numbers by
means of arrows.

Example 3.   Add 3 to 2 by means of arrows.

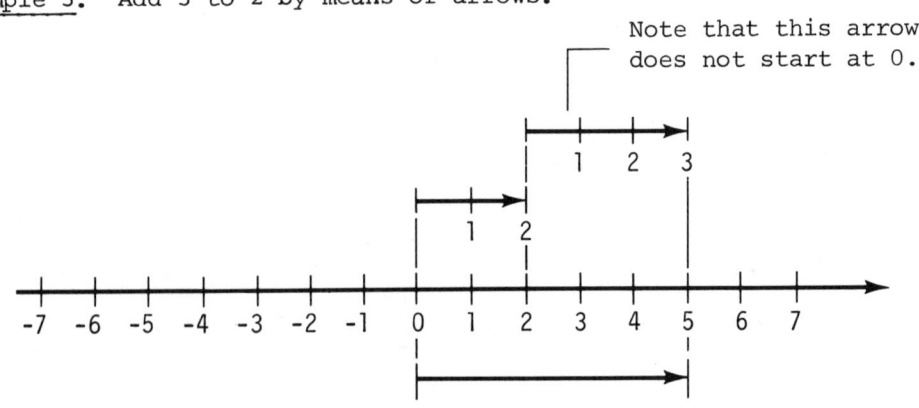

Note that this arrow
does not start at 0.

To add 3 to 2 on the number line, begin by drawing the arrow representing 2. Draw the arrow representing 3 starting at the arrowhead end of the arrow representing 2. These two movements represent a net movement to the right of 5 units. Therefore, 2 + 3 = 5.

Example 4. Add -7 to 5 by means of arrows.

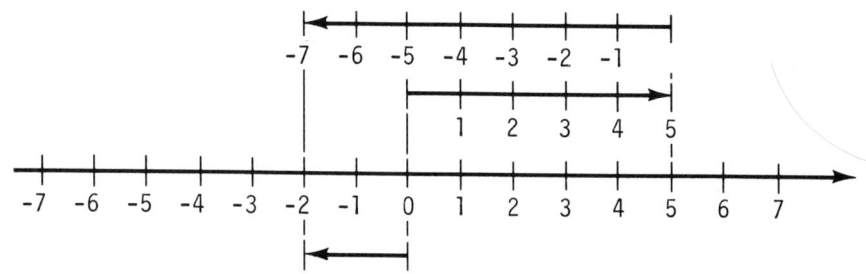

Begin by drawing the arrow representing 5. Draw the arrow representing -7 starting at the arrowhead end of the arrow representing 5. These two movements represent a net movement to the left of 2 units. Therefore, 5 + (-7) = -2.

Example 5. Add -4 to -3 by means of arrows.

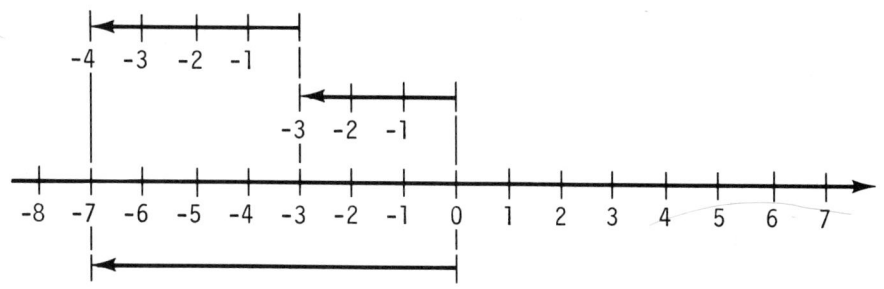

Begin by drawing the arrow representing -3. Draw the arrow representing -4 starting at the arrowhead end of the arrow representing -3. These two movements represent a net movement to the left of 7 units. Therefore, -3 + (-4) = -7.

Example 6. Add +8 to -5 by means of arrows.

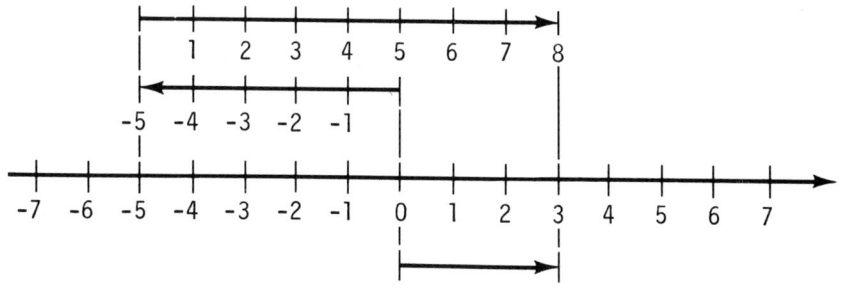

Begin by drawing the arrow representing -5. Draw the arrow representing +8 starting at the arrowhead end of the arrow representing -5. These two movements represent a net movement to the right of 3 units. Therefore, (-5) + (+8) = +3.

<u>ABSOLUTE VALUE</u>. The absolute value of a number is the distance between that number and 0 on the number line *with no regard for direction*. See Figure 103. The absolute value of a real number x is written $|x|$.

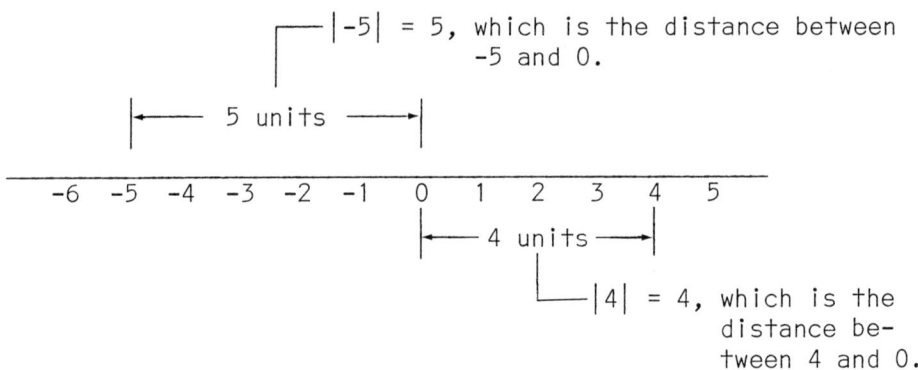

$|-5| = 5$, which is the distance between −5 and 0.

5 units

-6 -5 -4 -3 -2 -1   0   1   2   3   4   5

4 units

$|4| = 4$, which is the distance be-tween 4 and 0.

Figure 103   Absolute Value

<u>Example 7</u>. Absolute value of numbers.

(a) $|9| = 9$ a positive number ⎫   Note that:
                                                   The absolute value of a
(b) $|0| = 0$ zero   ⎬   number can never be
                                                   negative.
(c) $|-4| = 4$ a positive number ⎭

A signed number has two distinct parts: its absolute value, and its sign.

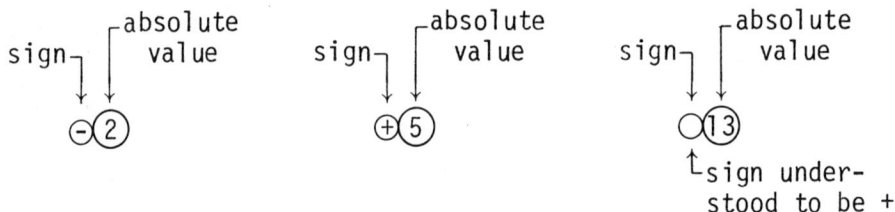

Note that the absolute value of a signed number is the number written without its sign.

Adding signed numbers by means of arrows is easy to understand, but it is a very slow process. The following rules give an easier and faster method for adding signed numbers. The previous four examples can be used to show why the following rules are true.

```
┌─────────────────────────────────────────────────────────────────┐
│                                                                   │
│  TO ADD SIGNED NUMBERS                                            │
│                                                                   │
│   Case I.    When the numbers  ⎰ 1st—Add their absolute values.  │
│              have the *same sign* ⎱ 2nd—The sum has the same sign │
│                                      as both numbers.             │
│                                                                   │
│                                ⎰ 1st—Subtract the smaller abso-   │
│   Case 2.    When the numbers     lute value from the larger.     │
│              have *different*   ⎱ 2nd—The sum has the sign of the │
│              *signs*                 number with the larger       │
│                                      absolute value.              │
│                                                                   │
└─────────────────────────────────────────────────────────────────┘
```

We show how to add signed numbers by means of the rules.

Example 8. Find: (3) + (5)

   Solution: Since 3 and 5 have the same sign, add their
               absolute values: 3 + 5 = 8.
               Sum has the same sign: +
               Therefore, the sum is +8.

Example 9. Find: (-7) + (-11)

   Solution: Since -7 and -11 have the same sign, add their
               absolute values: 7 + 11 = 18.
               Sum has the same sign: -
               Therefore, the sum is -18.

Example 10. Find: (-24) + (17)

   Solution: Since -24 and 17 have different signs, subtract
               their absolute values: 24 - 17 = 7.
               Sum has sign of number with larger absolute
               value (-) since -24 has the larger absolute value.
               Therefore, the sum is -7.

Example 11. Find: (+18) + (-32)

   Solution: Since +18 and -32 have different signs, subtract
               their absolute values: 32 - 18 = 14.
               Sum has sign of number with larger absolute
               value (-) since -32 has the larger absolute value.
               Therefore, the sum is -14.

Example 12. Find: (-29) + (-35)

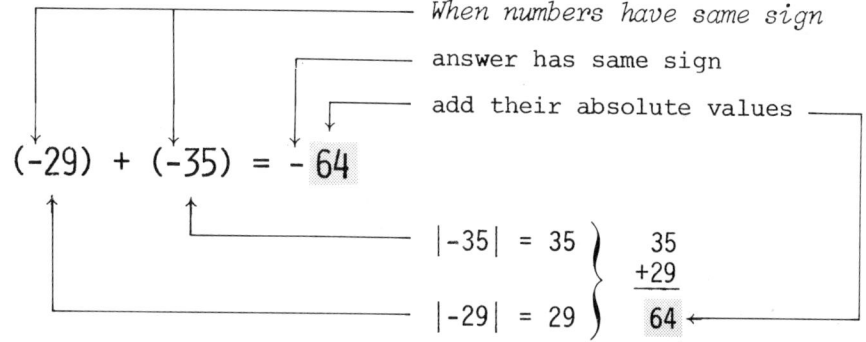

Example 13. Find: (-9) + (+23)

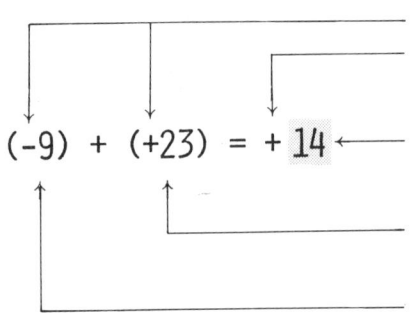

When numbers have different signs answer has sign of number with larger absolute value: + 23

(-9) + (+23) = + 14 ← subtract smaller absolute value from larger absolute value

$|+23| = 23$ ⎫   23
              ⎬   -9
$|-9| = 9$ ⎭   14

EXERCISES 103

SET I

In Exercises 1—22, find the sums.

1. (4) + (5)   2. (6) + (2)

3. (-3) + (-4)   4. (-7) + (-1)

5. (-6) + (5)   6. (-8) + (3)

7. (7) + (-3)   8. (9) + (-4)

9. (15) + (-5)   10. (18) + (-6)

11. (-27) + (-13)   12. (-42) + (-12)

13. (-80) + (121)   14. (-69) + (134)

15. (105) + (-73)   16. (218) + (-113)

----

17. (15) + (21)   18. (24) + (32)

19. $|-6|$ + (-2)   20. $|-8|$ + (-5)

21. (6.075) + (-3.146) 22. (93.118) + (-4.745)

23. At 6 AM the temperature in Hibbing, Minnesota, was -35° F. If the temperature had risen 53° F by 2 PM, what was the temperature at that time?

24. At midnight in Billings, Montana, the temperature was -50° F. By noon the temperature had risen 67° F. What was the temperature at noon?

SET II

In Exercises 1—10, find the sums.

1. (8) + (7)   2. (-9) + (-3)

3. (-5) + (9)   4. (6) + (-10)

5. (-38) + (-17)   6. (214) + (-187)

7. (-17) + $|-4|$ 8. $|-5|$ + $|-2|$

9. (-18.0164) + (2.281) 10. (-9.006) + (-57.356)

11. A team climbing Mt. Everest starts from a camp at 17,018 ft elevation. By evening they had climbed 2759 ft. What is their elevation at that time?

12. An airplane cruising at an altitude of 17,285 ft is ordered by a tower controller to climb 2500 ft. What will the plane's new altitude be?

Subtracting Signed Numbers

THE NEGATIVE OF A NUMBER. The idea of *negative* suggests the opposite of something. For example, the negative of taking two steps to the right would be taking two steps to the left. Since +2 can be thought of as a movement of two units to the right, then the negative of +2 would be thought of as a movement of 2 units to the left. This means the negative of +2 is -2.

Example 1. The negative of a *positive* number.

(a) The negative of 5 is -5.
(b) The negative of 12 is -12, and so on.

Since -3 can be thought of as a movement of 3 units to the left, then the negative of -3 would be thought of as an opposite movement of 3 units to the right. This means that the negative of -3 is +3. This can be written:
-(-3) = +3 = 3.

Example 2. The negative of a *negative* number.

(a) The negative of -10 is +10   written -(-10) = 10.
(b) The negative of -14 is +14   written -(-14) = 14.

Examples 1 and 2 lead to the following rules for finding the negative of a number.

TO FIND THE NEGATIVE OF A NUMBER

Change the sign of the number.

The negative of b = $-b$
The negative of $-b$ = $-(-b)$ = b

The negative of 0 = 0.

The negative of a number is used in the definition of subtraction.

```
┌─────────────────────────────────────────────────────────────┐
│                                                               │
│  DEFINITION OF SUBTRACTION                                     │
│                                                               │
│  (1)                        a - b = a + (-b)                   │
│                                                               │
│  In words: To subtract b from a, add the negative of b        │
│            to a.                                              │
│                                                               │
└─────────────────────────────────────────────────────────────┘
```

This definition leads to the following rule for subtracting signed numbers.

```
┌─────────────────────────────────────────────────────────────┐
│                                                               │
│  TO SUBTRACT ONE SIGNED NUMBER FROM ANOTHER                   │
│                                                               │
│  1.  Change the subtraction symbol to an addition            │
│      symbol, and change the sign of the number being         │
│      subtracted.                                             │
│                                                               │
│  2.  Add the resulting signed numbers as shown in Sec.       │
│      103.                                                     │
│                                                               │
│      For example,   (8) - ( +5 )──── Change the sign of      │
│                   = (8) + ( -5 )     the number being        │
│                                      subtracted.             │
│                   =   3  │                                   │
│                         └─────────── Change the subtraction  │
│                                      symbol to an addition   │
│                                      symbol.                 │
│                                                               │
└─────────────────────────────────────────────────────────────┘
```

Example 3. Subtract (9) from (6).

    Solution: Subtract (9) from (6) means   (6) - (9)
$$= (6) + (-9)$$
$$= -3$$

```
  ( 6)
+ (-9)     These numbers are added as shown in Sec. 103.
  -3
```

Example 4. Subtract (-11) from (-7).

    Solution: Subtract (-11) from (-7) means   (-7) - (-11)
$$= (-7) + (+11)$$
$$=   4$$

```
Or,   (-7)
    + (11)
       4
```

Example 5. Find: (+13) - (-14)

    Solution: (+13) - (-14) = (+13) + (+14) = 27

```
Or,   (+13)
    + (+14)
       27
```

Example 6. Find: $(-147) - (+59)$

Solution: $(-147) - (+59) = (-147) + (-59) = -206$

Or,
$$\begin{array}{r} (-147) \\ + (\ -59) \\ \hline -206 \end{array}$$

Example 7. Find: $\left(-3\frac{1}{2}\right) - \left(+2\frac{1}{4}\right)$

Solution: $\left(-3\frac{1}{2}\right) - \left(+2\frac{1}{4}\right) = \left(-3\frac{1}{2}\right) + \left(-2\frac{1}{4}\right) = -5\frac{3}{4}$

Or,
$$\begin{array}{r} \left(-3\frac{1}{2}\right) = \left(-3\frac{2}{4}\right) \\ + \left(-2\frac{1}{4}\right) = \left(-2\frac{1}{4}\right) \\ \hline \left(-5\frac{3}{4}\right) \end{array}$$

Example 8. Find: $(-4.56) - (-7.48)$

Solution: $(-4.56) - (-7.48) = (-4.56) + (+7.48) = 2.92$

Or,
$$\begin{array}{r} (-4.56) \\ + (+7.48) \\ \hline +2.92 \end{array}$$

EXERCISES 104

SET I

In Exercises 1—18, find the differences.

1. $(10) - (4)$ 2. $(12) - (5)$

3. $(-3) - (-2)$ 4. $(-4) - (-3)$

5. $(-6) - (2)$ 6. $(-8) - (5)$

7. $(9) - (-5)$ 8. $(7) - (-3)$

9. $(2) - (-7)$ 10. $(3) - (-5)$

11. $(-15) - (11)$ 12. $(-24) - (16)$

13. Subtract (-2) from $(+5)$.
14. Subtract (-10) from (-15).

15. $(156) - (-97)$ 16. $(284) - (-89)$

17. $(-354) - (-286)$ 18. $(-484) - (-375)$

19. Mr. Reyes has a balance of $473.29 in his checking account. Find his new balance after he writes a check for $238.43.
20. Beverly made a $45 deposit on a quadraphonic home music system costing $623.89. What is the balance due?

----

21. $(356) - (184)$

22. $(192) - (128)$

23. Subtract $\left(2\frac{1}{2}\right)$ from $\left(-5\frac{1}{4}\right)$.

24. Subtract $\left(3\frac{1}{6}\right)$ from $\left(-7\frac{1}{3}\right)$.

25. $(-7.000) - (-2.009)$

26. $(-15.61) - (-7.89)$

27. At 5 AM the temperature at Mammoth Mountain, California, was $-7°$ F. At noon the temperature was $42°$ F. What was the rise in temperature?

28. At 4 AM the temperature at Massena, New York, was $-5.6°$ F. At 1 PM the temperature was $37.5°$ F. What was the rise in temperature?

29. A scuba diver descends to a depth of 141 ft below sea level. His buddy dives 68 ft deeper. What is his buddy's altitude at the deepest point of his dive?

30. When Fred checked his pocket altimeter at the seashore on Friday afternoon, it read -150 ft. Saturday morning it read 9650 ft when he checked it on the peak of a nearby mountain. Allowing for the obvious error in his altimeter reading, what is the correct height of that peak?

31. Mt. Everest (the highest known point on earth) has an altitude of 29,028 ft. The Mariana Trench in the Pacific Ocean (the lowest known point on earth) has an altitude of $-36,198$ ft. Find the difference in altitude of these two places.

32. An airplane is flying 75 ft above the level of the Dead Sea (elevation -1299 ft). How high must it climb to clear a 2573-ft peak by 200 ft?

SET II

In Exercises 1—9, find the differences.

1. $(9) - (3)$

2. $(-5) - (-1)$

3. $(-8) - (5)$

4. $(7) - (-3)$

5. $(-14) - (10)$

6. $(184) - (-286)$

7. $(-473) - (389)$

8. $(-784) - (-528)$

9. Subtract (-120) from (-285).

10. Subtract $\left(4\frac{1}{4}\right)$ from $\left(-9\frac{1}{2}\right)$.

11. $(-14.685) - (-9.794)$

12. John has a balance of $281.42 in his checking account. Find his new balance after he writes a check for $209.57.

13. A dune buggy starting from the floor of Death Valley $(-282$ ft$)$ is driven to the top of a nearby mountain having an elevation of 5782 ft. What was the change in the dune buggy's altitude?

14. A jeep starting from the shore of the Dead Sea $(-1299$ ft$)$ is driven to the top of a nearby hill having an elevation of 723 ft. What was the change in the jeep's altitude?

15. At 2 PM Cindy's temperature was $103.4°$ F. By 6 PM her temperature had dropped to $99.9°$ F. What was the drop in her temperature?

16. At 5 AM Don's temperature was 101.8° F. By noon his temperature had risen to 103.2° F. What was the increase in his temperature?

Multiplying Signed Numbers

TERMS USED IN MULTIPLICATION

$$6 \times 2 = 12$$

factors ———↑ ↑   ↑—— product

6 and 2 are *factors* of 12; 12 is the *product* of 6 and 2.
3 and 4 are also factors of 12, because 3 × 4 = 12.

IF a IS ANY REAL NUMBER

$$1 \cdot a = a \cdot 1 = a$$

Since multiplying any real number by one gives the identical real number, *one is called the multiplicative identity*.

SYMBOLS USED IN MULTIPLICATION. Multiplication may be shown in several different ways.

1. 3 × 2 = 6
2. 3 • 2 = 6   The multiplication dot "•" is written a little higher than the decimal point.
3. 3(2) = 6   The symbols ( ) are called *parentheses.*
4. (3)(2) = 6   In this kind of multiplication, the double parentheses are not necessary.
5. $ab = a \cdot b$ When two expressions are written next to each other in this way, it is understood that they are to be multiplied. *Exception:* When two *numbers* are written next to each other, they are *not* to be multiplied. For example: 23 does *not* mean 2 • 3 = 6.
6. $3x = 3 \cdot x$

MULTIPLYING TWO SIGNED NUMBERS. Multiplication (by a positive integer) is a short method for doing repeated addition of the same number.

Example 1. 3 × 5 = 3 fives = 5 + 5 + 5 = 15

Example 2. 6 × 2 = 6 twos = 2 + 2 + 2 + 2 + 2 + 2 = 12

Therefore, carrying this same idea over into multiplying signed numbers, we have:

<u>Example 3.</u> $3 \times (-2) = 3$ negative twos $= (-2) + (-2) + (-2) = -6$

<u>Example 4.</u> $4 \times (-6) = 4$ negative sixes
$$= (-6) + (-6) + (-6) + (-6) = -24$$

From Examples 3 and 4 we see that *when two numbers having opposite signs are multiplied, their product is negative.*
The product of two negative numbers is positive. This fact can be seen from the following pattern.

decreasing by 1 →

$4 (-2) = -8$
$3 (-2) = -6$
$2 (-2) = -4$
$1 (-2) = -2$
$0 (-2) = 0$
$-1 (-2) = 2$
$-2 (-2) = 4$
$-3 (-2) = 6$

← increasing by 2

Zero as a factor is discussed in Sec. 109.

The product of two negative numbers is positive.

The rules for multiplying two signed numbers are summarized as follows:

TO MULTIPLY TWO SIGNED NUMBERS

1. Multiply their absolute values.

2. The product is *positive* when the signed numbers have the same sign.
    The product is *negative* when the signed numbers have different signs.

<u>Example 5.</u> Multiply: $(-7)(4)$

<u>Solution:</u> $(-7)(4) = \ominus \, \textcircled{28}$

— Product of their absolute values: $7 \times 4 = 28$

— Product negative because the numbers have different signs.

<u>Example 6.</u> Multiply: $(23)(-11)$

<u>Solution:</u> $(23)(-11) = \ominus \, \textcircled{253}$

— $23 \times 11 = 253$

— Because the numbers have different signs.

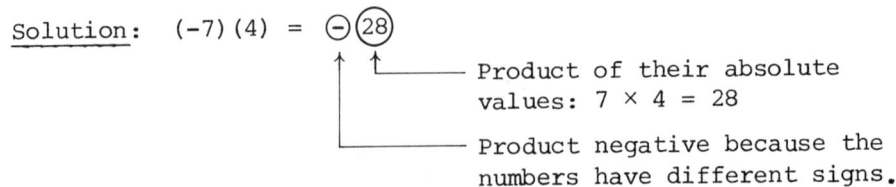

Example 7. Multiply: $(-14)(-10)$

Solution: $(-14)(-10) = \oplus \boxed{140}$

 — $14 \times 10 = 140$

 — Because the numbers have the same sign.

Example 8. Multiply: $\left(4\frac{1}{2}\right)\left(-1\frac{1}{3}\right)$

Solution: $\left(4\frac{1}{2}\right)\left(-1\frac{1}{3}\right) = \left(\frac{9}{2}\right)\left(-\frac{4}{3}\right) = -\left(\frac{\overset{3}{\cancel{9}}}{\underset{1}{\cancel{2}}} \cdot \frac{\overset{2}{\cancel{4}}}{\underset{1}{\cancel{3}}}\right) = -\frac{6}{1} = -6$

Example 9. Multiply: $(-2.7)(-4.6)$

Solution: $(-2.7)(-4.6) = +(2.7 \times 4.6) = 12.42$

The negative of any real number can be found by multiplying it by (-1).

$$(-1) \cdot a = a \cdot (-1) = -a$$

Example 10. The negative of a signed number.

(a) The negative of $5 = (-1)(5) = -5$
(b) The negative of $-7 = (-1)(-7) = 7$

EXERCISES 105. Find the products.

SET I

1. $3(-2)$ 2. $4(-6)$ 3. $(-5)(2)$

4. $(-7)(5)$ 5. $(-8)(-2)$ 6. $(-6)(-7)$

7. $8(-4)$ 8. $9(-5)$ 9. $(-7)(9)$

10. $(-6)(8)$ 11. $(-10)(-10)$ 12. $(-9)(-9)$

13. $(8)(-7)$ 14. $(12)(-6)$ 15. $(-26)(10)$

16. $(-11)(12)$ 17. $(-20)(-10)$ 18. $(-30)(-20)$

----

19. $(75)(-15)$ 20. $(86)(-13)$ 21. $(-30)(+5)$

22. $(-50)(+6)$ 23. $(-7)(-20)$ 24. $(-9)(-40)$

25. $(-3.5)(-1.4)$ 26. $(-4.7)(-1.6)$ 27. $(2.74)(-100)$

28. $(3.04)(-100)$ 29. $\left(2\frac{1}{3}\right)\left(-3\frac{1}{2}\right)$ 30. $\left(-5\frac{1}{4}\right)\left(-2\frac{3}{5}\right)$

SET II

1. $(5)(-4)$ 2. $(-6)(3)$ 3. $(-7)(-3)$

4. $(-4)(8)$ 5. $(-9)(-6)$ 6. $(+8)(+5)$

7. $(-15)(10)$ 8. $(15)(-10)$ 9. $(-300)(-10)$

10. $(400)(-10)$ 11. $(-100)(10)$ 12. $(-5.67)(10)$

🖩 13. $(17.5)(-150)$ 🖩14. $(-3.1416)(5.164)$ 15. $\left(-2\frac{1}{5}\right)\left(3\frac{3}{4}\right)$

Dividing Signed Numbers

Division may be shown in several ways.

$$12 \div 4 = \frac{12}{4} = 4\overline{)12}$$

The quotient in this case is 3.

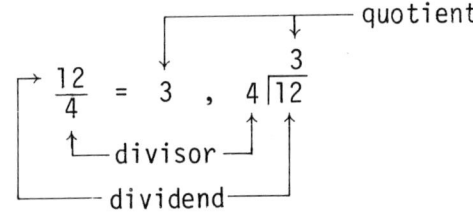

To check the answer in a division problem we use the following relation:

$$divisor \times quotient = dividend$$

$4\overline{)12}^{\,3}$ because $4 \cdot 3 = 12$, then $\frac{12}{4} = 3$

Therefore,

because $4 \cdot 3 = 12$, then $\frac{12}{4} = 3$

because $(-4)(3) = -12$, then $\frac{-12}{-4} = 3$

because $4(-3) = -12$, then $\frac{-12}{4} = -3$

because $(-4)(-3) = 12$, then $\frac{12}{-4} = -3$

From these examples we see that we need the same rules for *dividing* signed numbers that we used for *multiplying* signed numbers.

TO DIVIDE ONE SIGNED NUMBER BY ANOTHER

1. Divide their absolute values.

2. The quotient is *positive* when the signed numbers have the same sign.
   The quotient is *negative* when the signed numbers have different signs.

Example 1. $(-30) \div (5)$

Solution: $(-30) \div (5) = \ominus \,\textcircled{6}$

Quotient of their absolute values: $30 \div 5 = 6$.

Quotient negative because the numbers have different signs.

Example 2. $(-64) \div (-8)$

Solution: $(-64) \div (-8) = \oplus \,\textcircled{8}$

$64 \div 8 = 8$

Because the numbers have the same sign.

Example 3. $\dfrac{35}{-7}$

Solution: $\dfrac{35}{-7} = \ominus \,\textcircled{5}$

$35 \div 7 = 5$

Because the numbers have different signs.

Example 4. $\dfrac{-42}{8}$

Solution: $\dfrac{-42}{8} = -\dfrac{21}{4}$ or $-5\dfrac{1}{4}$ or -5.25

EXERCISES 106.   Find the following quotients.

SET I

1. $(-10) \div (-5)$
2. $(-12) \div (-4)$
3. $(-8) \div (2)$
4. $(-6) \div (3)$
5. $\dfrac{+10}{-2}$
6. $\dfrac{+8}{-4}$
7. $\dfrac{-6}{-3}$
8. $\dfrac{-10}{-2}$
9. $(-40) \div (8)$
10. $(-60) \div (10)$
11. $16 \div (-4)$
12. $25 \div (-5)$
13. $(-15) \div (-5)$
14. $(-27) \div (-9)$
15. $\dfrac{12}{-4}$
16. $\dfrac{24}{-6}$
17. $\dfrac{-18}{-2}$
18. $\dfrac{-49}{-7}$
19. $\dfrac{-150}{10}$
20. $\dfrac{-250}{100}$
21. $36 \div (-12)$
22. $56 \div (-8)$
23. $(-45) \div 15$
24. $(-39) \div 13$

----

25. $\dfrac{-15}{6}$ 26. $\dfrac{-27}{12}$ 27. $\dfrac{7.5}{-0.5}$

28. $\dfrac{1.25}{-0.25}$ 29. $\dfrac{-6.3}{-0.9}$ 30. $\dfrac{-4.8}{-0.6}$

31. $\dfrac{-367}{100}$ 32. $\dfrac{-4860}{1000}$ 33. $\dfrac{78.5}{-96.5}$

34. $\dfrac{98.5}{-84.3}$ 35. $\dfrac{2\frac{1}{2}}{-5}$ 36. $\dfrac{3\frac{2}{5}}{-17}$

SET II

1. $(-8) \div (-2)$ 2. $(-10) \div (5)$ 3. $(12) \div (-6)$

4. $\dfrac{14}{-7}$ 5. $\dfrac{-8}{2}$ 6. $\dfrac{-50}{-10}$

7. $(36) \div (-12)$ 8. $(-18) \div (-9)$ 9. $(-16) \div (4)$

10. $\dfrac{-15.6}{10}$ 11. $\dfrac{13.8}{-10}$ 12. $\dfrac{-6.3}{-0.7}$

13. $(-8.4) \div (0.6)$ 14. $(-9.6) \div (-0.8)$ 15. $(18.5) \div (-3.7)$

16. $\dfrac{7.2}{-2.5}$ 17. $\dfrac{1\frac{1}{2}}{-3}$ 18. $\dfrac{2\frac{3}{4}}{-2}$

107 Commutative Properties

ADDITION. If you change the order of the two numbers in an
addition problem, you get the same sum. This is called the
Commutative Property of Addition.

In Fig. 107 we use the number line to show that
2 + 3 = 3 + 2.

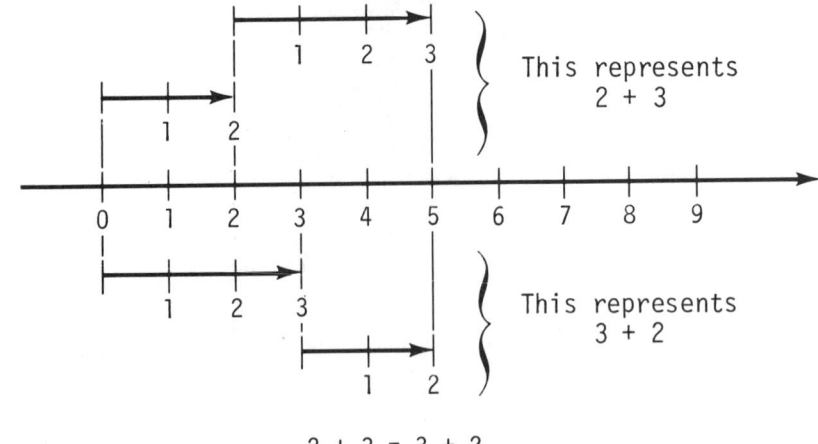

2 + 3 = 3 + 2

Figure 107

Since a diagram such as this can be drawn when any two
integers are added, it is assumed that this property of addition is true when any two *real* numbers are added.

```
┌─────────────────────────────────────────────────────────┐
│                                                           │
│   COMMUTATIVE PROPERTY OF ADDITION                        │
│                                                           │
│   If $a$ and $b$ represent any real numbers, then         │
│                                                           │
│                   $a + b = b + a$                         │
│                                                           │
└─────────────────────────────────────────────────────────┘
```

Example 1. Addition is commutative.

(a) $\begin{cases} (+7) + (5) = 12 \\ (5) + (+7) = 12 \end{cases}$ Therefore, $(+7) + (5) = (5) + (+7)$

(b) $\begin{cases} (-6) + (2) = -4 \\ (2) + (-6) = -4 \end{cases}$ Therefore, $(-6) + (2) = (2) + (-6)$

(c) $\begin{cases} (-4) + (-8) = -12 \\ (-8) + (-4) = -12 \end{cases}$ Therefore, $(-4) + (-8) = (-8) + (-4)$

SUBTRACTION. If you change the order of the two numbers in a
    subtraction problem, you *do not* get the same difference
    (except when the two numbers are equal). Therefore,
    subtraction is not commutative.

Example 2. Subtraction is *not* commutative.

(a) $\begin{cases} 3 - 2 = 1 \\ 2 - 3 = -1 \end{cases}$ Therefore, $3 - 2 \neq 2 - 3$

(b) $\begin{cases} (-4) - (6) = -10 \\ (6) - (-4) = 10 \end{cases}$ Therefore, $(-4) - (6) \neq (6) - (-4)$

MULTIPLICATION. If you change the order of the two numbers in
    a multiplication problem, you get the same product. This is
    called the *Commutative Property of Multiplication.*

Example 3. Multiplication is commutative.

(a) $\begin{cases} (4)(5) = 20 \\ (5)(4) = 20 \end{cases}$ Therefore, $(4)(5) = (5)(4)$

(b) $\begin{cases} (-9)(3) = -27 \\ (3)(-9) = -27 \end{cases}$ Therefore, $(-9)(3) = (3)(-9)$

```
┌─────────────────────────────────────────────────────────┐
│                                                           │
│   COMMUTATIVE PROPERTY OF MULTIPLICATION                  │
│                                                           │
│   If $a$ and $b$ are real numbers, then                   │
│                                                           │
│                   $a \cdot b = b \cdot a$                 │
│                                                           │
└─────────────────────────────────────────────────────────┘
```

DIVISION. If you change the order of the two numbers in a division problem, you *do not* get the same quotient (except when the two numbers are equal). Therefore, *division is not commutative.*

Example 4. Division is *not* commutative.

(a)
$$\left\{ \begin{array}{l} 10 \div 5 = 2 \\ 5 \div 10 = \frac{1}{2} \end{array} \right\}$$
Therefore, $10 \div 5 \neq 5 \div 10$

(b)
$$\left\{ \begin{array}{l} (6) \div (-2) = -3 \\ (-2) \div (6) = -\frac{1}{3} \end{array} \right\}$$
Therefore, $(6) \div (-2) \neq (-2) \div (6)$

Associative Properties

ADDITION. *In adding three numbers*, we can do either of the following:

1. Find the sum of the first two numbers, then add that sum to the third number.
2. Find the sum of the last two numbers, then add that sum to the first number.

Parentheses ( ) can be used to show which two numbers are to be added first.

Example 1. Add: 2 + 3 + 4

(a)   (2 + 3) + 4   The parentheses mean that
    =   5   + 4 = 9   2 and 3 are to be added first.

(b)   2 + (3 + 4)   Here, the parentheses mean that
    = 2 +   7   = 9   3 and 4 are to be added first.

Therefore, 2 + 3 + 4 = (2 + 3) + 4 = 2 + (3 + 4)
                   =   5   + 4 = 2 +   7
                   =   9   =   9

   In this example, the sum of three numbers was unchanged no matter how we grouped the numbers. It is assumed that this property of addition is true when any three real numbers are added. This is called the *Associative Property of Addition.*

ASSOCIATIVE PROPERTY OF ADDITION

If a, b, and c represent any real numbers, then

$$a + b + c = (a + b) + c = a + (b + c)$$

SUBTRACTION. A single example will show that *subtraction is not associative.*

Example 2. Subtraction is *not* associative.

$$\left.\begin{array}{l} (7 - 4) - 8 = 3 - 8 \quad = -5 \\ 7 - (4 - 8) = 7 - (-4) = 11 \end{array}\right\} \quad \begin{array}{l} \text{Therefore,} \\ (7 - 4) - 8 \neq 7 - (4 - 8) \end{array}$$

MULTIPLICATION. *In multiplying three numbers*, we can do either of the following:

    1. Find the product of the first two numbers, then multiply that product by the third number.
    2. Find the product of the last two numbers, then multiply that product by the first number.

Example 3. Multiplication *is* associative.

$$\left.\begin{array}{l} (3 \cdot 4) \cdot 2 = 12 \cdot 2 = 24 \\ 3 \cdot (4 \cdot 2) = 3 \cdot 8 \quad = 24 \end{array}\right\} \quad \begin{array}{l} \text{Therefore,} \\ (3 \cdot 4) \cdot 2 = 3 \cdot (4 \cdot 2) \end{array}$$

Brackets [ ] as well as parentheses ( ) can be used to show which two numbers are to be multiplied first.

Example 4. Use of brackets and parentheses in multiplication.

$$\left.\begin{array}{l} [(-6) \cdot (+2)] \cdot (-5) = [-12] \cdot (-5) = 60 \\ (-6) \cdot [(+2) \cdot (-5)] = (-6) \cdot [-10] = 60 \end{array}\right\}$$

Therefore,

$$[(-6) \cdot (+2)] \cdot (-5) = (-6) \cdot [(+2) \cdot (-5)]$$

In these examples, the product of three numbers was unchanged no matter how we grouped the numbers. It is assumed that this property of multiplication is true when any three real numbers are multiplied. This is called the *Associative Property of Multiplication.*

ASSOCIATIVE PROPERTY OF MULTIPLICATION

If a, b, and c are real numbers, then

$$a \cdot b \cdot c = (a \cdot b) \cdot c = a \cdot (b \cdot c)$$

DIVISION. We found that the operations of addition and multiplication are both associative. That is,

$$(a + b) + c = a + (b + c)$$

and

$$(a \cdot b) \cdot c = a \cdot (b \cdot c)$$

On the other hand, we found that the operation of subtraction is not associative. That is,

$$(a - b) - c \neq a - (b - c)$$

What is the case with division? A single example will show that *division is not associative*.

<u>Example 5</u>. Division is *not* associative.

$$\left\{ \begin{array}{l} [(-16) \div (4)] \div (-2) = [-4] \div (-2) = 2 \\ (-16) \div [(4) \div (-2)] = (-16) \div [-2] = 8 \end{array} \right\}$$

Therefore,

$$[(-16) \div (4)] \div (-2) \neq (-16) \div [(4) \div (-2)]$$

SUMMARY

1. *The Commutative Property* says that *changing the order* of the numbers in an addition or multiplication problem gives the same answer.

2. *The Associative Property* says that *changing the grouping* of the numbers in an addition or multiplication problem gives the same answer.

<u>Example 6</u>. State whether each of the following is true or false, and give the reason.

(a) $(-7) + 5 = 5 + (-7)$ *True* because of the Commutative Property of Addition. (*Order* of numbers changed.)

(b) $(+6)(-8) = (-8)(+6)$ *True* because the Commutative Property of Multiplication. (*Order* of numbers changed.)

(c) $[(-3) + 5] + (-2)$
     $= (-3) + [5 + (-2)]$ *True*. Associative Property of Addition. (*Grouping* changed.)

(d) $[(7) \cdot (-4)] \cdot (2)$
     $= (7) \cdot [(-4) \cdot (2)]$ *True*. Associative Property of Multiplication. (*Grouping* changed.)

(e) $(+8) - (-7)$
     $= (-7) - (+8)$ *False*. Subtraction is *not* commutative.

(f) $a + (b + c) = (a + b) + c$ *True*. Associative Property of Addition. (*Grouping* changed.)

(g) $y \div z = z \div y$ *False*. Division is *not* commutative.

(h) $(p \cdot r) \cdot s = p \cdot (r \cdot s)$ *True*. Associative Property of Multiplication. (*Grouping* changed.)

The fact that the product of two negative numbers is positive can be justified by using the commutative and associative properties.

Example 7. $(-5)(-4) = (-1)(5)(-4)$ Because $-5 = (-1)(5)$.
                    $= (-1)(-20)$ Because $(5)(-4) = -20$.
                    $=$ negative of -20 Because -1 times a
                                            number gives the nega-
                                            tive of that number.
                    $= 20$ Because the negative
                                            of a number is found
                                            by changing its sign
                                            (Sec. 104).

EXERCISES 108. State whether each of the following is true or false, and give the reason.

SET I

1. $7 + 5 = 5 + 7$ 2. $9 + 4 = 4 + 9$

3. $(2 + 6) + 3 = 2 + (6 + 3)$ 4. $(1 + 8) + 7 = 1 + (8 + 7)$

5. $6 - 2 = 2 - 6$ 6. $4 - 7 = 7 - 4$

7. $(a \cdot b) \cdot c = a \cdot (b \cdot c)$ 8. $(p \cdot q) \cdot r = p \cdot (q \cdot r)$

9. $8 \div 4 = 4 \div 8$ 10. $3 \div 6 = 6 \div 3$

11. $(p)(t) = (t)(p)$ 12. $(m)(n) = (n)(m)$

13. $(4)(-5) = (-5) + (4)$ 14. $(-7)(2) = (2) + (-7)$

15. $5 + (3 + 4) = 5 + (4 + 3)$ 16. $6 + (8 + 2) = 6 + (2 + 8)$

17. $e + f = f + e$ 18. $j + k = k + j$

----

19. $9 + (5 + 6) = (9 + 6) + 5$ 20. $3 \cdot (8 \cdot 4) = (3 \cdot 4) \cdot 8$

21. $x - 4 = 4 - x$ 22. $5 - y = y - 5$

23. $4(a \cdot 6) = 4a(6)$ 24. $m(7 \cdot 5) = (m \cdot 7)5$

25. $H + 8 = 8 + H$ 26. $4 + P = P + 4$

SET II

1. $5 + 3 = 3 + 5$ 2. $(3 + 1) + 5 = 3 + (1 + 5)$

3. $8 - 2 = 2 - 8$ 4. $(x \cdot y) \cdot z = x \cdot (y \cdot z)$

5. $10 \div 2 = 2 \div 10$ 6. $(3)(-2) = (-2)(3)$

7. $2 + (3 + 4) = 2 + (4 + 3)$ 8. $x + y = y + x$

9. $8 + (2 + 5) = (8 + 5) + 2$ 10. $a - 2 = 2 - a$

11. $(4 \cdot c)(3) = 4(3 \cdot c)$ 12. $3 \div x = x \div 3$

 **Operations with Zero**

ADDITION INVOLVING ZERO. It was shown in Fig. 102A that zero is neither a positive nor a negative number.

> IF a IS ANY REAL NUMBER, THEN
>
> $$a + 0 = 0 + a = a$$

Since adding zero to a number gives the identical number for the sum, *zero is called the additive identity.*

SUBTRACTION INVOLVING ZERO. Since the subtraction $a - b$ has been defined as $a + (-b)$, the rules for subtractions involving zero are derived from the rules for addition.

> IF a IS ANY REAL NUMBER, THEN
>
> 1. $a - 0 = a$
> 2. $0 - a = 0 + (-a) = -a$

MULTIPLICATION INVOLVING ZERO. Since multiplication is a method for doing repeated addition of the same number, multiplying a number by zero gives a product of zero.

Example 1

    (a) $3 \cdot 0 = 0 + 0 + 0 = 0$
    (b) $4 \cdot 0 = 0 + 0 + 0 + 0 = 0$

Because of the Commutative Property of Multiplication, it follows that

$$3 \cdot 0 = 0 \cdot 3 = 0$$

and

$$4 \cdot 0 = 0 \cdot 4 = 0$$

> IF a IS ANY REAL NUMBER, THEN
>
> $$a \cdot 0 = 0 \cdot a = 0$$

DIVISION INVOLVING ZERO. *Division of zero by a number other than zero is possible.*

Example 2. Dividing zero by a nonzero number.

(a) $\frac{0}{2} = 0 \div 2 = 2\overline{)0}^{\,0}$ Because $2 \cdot 0 = 0$
(divisor × quotient = dividend).

(b) $\frac{0}{-5} = 0 \div (-5) = -5\overline{)0}^{\,0}$ Because $(-5)(0) = 0$.

Division of a nonzero number by zero is impossible.

Example 3. $\frac{4}{0} = 4 \div 0 = 0\overline{)4}^{\,?}$

Suppose the quotient is some unknown number we call x. Then,

$0\overline{)4}^{\,x}$ means $0 \cdot x = 4$, which is certainly false.

$0 \cdot x \neq 4$ because any number multiplied by zero = 0.

Therefore, dividing any nonzero number by zero is impossible.

Division of zero by zero cannot be determined.

Example 4. Can zero be divided by *zero*?

$\frac{0}{0} = 0\overline{)0}^{\,1}$ means $0 \cdot 1 = 0$, which is true.

$\frac{0}{0} = 0\overline{)0}^{\,17}$ means $0 \cdot 17 = 0$, which is true.

$\frac{0}{0} = 0\overline{)0}^{\,156}$ means $0 \cdot 156 = 0$, which is true.

In other words, $0 \div 0 = 1$, 17, and also 156. In fact, it can be any number. But any operation with signed numbers can have only one answer. For this reason we say $0 \div 0$ cannot be determined.

IF a IS ANY REAL NUMBER *EXCEPT* 0, THEN

1. $\frac{0}{a} = 0$

2. $\frac{a}{0}$ is not possible

3. $\frac{0}{0}$ cannot be determined

EXERCISES 109. Find the value of each of the following (if it has one). If an expression does not have a value, give a reason.

SET I

1. 5 • 0   2. 0 • 7   3. 4 + 0

4. 0 + 9   5. 0 - 6   6. 0 - 10

7. 0 ÷ 12   8. 0 ÷ 15   9. 5 + (0 + 6)

10. (3 + 0) + 7   11. $\frac{4}{0}$ 12. $\frac{8}{0}$

13. (0)(-15)   14. (-13)(0)   15. $\frac{0}{0}$

16. $-\left(\frac{0}{0}\right)$ 17. 0 + (-789)   18. (-546) + 0

19. $\frac{-1}{0}$ 20. $\frac{-156}{0}$

SET II

1. 4 • 0   2. 5 + 0   3. 0 - 2

4. 0 ÷ 6   5. 8 ÷ 0   6. (0)(8)

7. $-\frac{0}{0}$ 8. 0 ÷ (-10)   9. (2 + 0) + 5

10. (2 • 0)(-5)

Powers of Signed Numbers

Now that we have learned to multiply signed numbers, it is possible to consider products in which the same number is repeated as a factor. For example:

$$3 \cdot 3 \cdot 3 \cdot 3 = 3^4 = 81$$

In the symbol 3^4, the 3 is called the *base*. The 4 is called the *exponent* and is written above and to the right of the base 3. The entire symbol 3^4 is called the *fourth power of three* and is commonly read "three to the fourth power" (Fig. 110).

$$\overset{\text{exponent}}{\underset{\text{base}}{3^4}} = \underset{\text{fourth power of 3}}{81}$$

Figure 110

Note. $3^4 \neq 3 \cdot 4$

$$3^4 = \underbrace{3 \cdot 3 \cdot 3 \cdot 3}_{4 \text{ factors}} = 81$$ ∎

EVEN POWER.   If a base has an exponent that is exactly divisible by two, we say that it is an even power of the base. For example: 3^2, 5^4, $(-2)^6$ are even powers.

ODD POWER.   If a base has an exponent that is *not* exactly divisible by two, we say that it is an odd power of the base. For example: 3^1, 10^3, $(-4)^5$ are odd powers.

Example 1.   Powers of signed numbers.

(a) $2^3 = 2 \cdot 2 \cdot 2 = 8$

(b) $4^2 = 4 \cdot 4 = 16$

(c) $1^4 = 1 \cdot 1 \cdot 1 \cdot 1 = 1$

(d) $(-3)^2 = (-3)(-3) = 9$

(e) $(-1)^4 = (-1)(-1)(-1)(-1) = 1$ Notice: An *even* power of a negative number is positive.

(f) $(-2)^3 = (-2)(-2)(-2) = -8$

(g) $(-1)^5 = (-1)(-1)(-1)(-1)(-1) = -1$ Notice: An *odd* power of a negative number is negative.

(h) $(-36)^3 = (-36)(-36)(-36) = -46,656$

A word of caution.   Students often think that expressions such as $(-6)^2$ and -6^2 are the same. They are *not* the same. The exponent applies only to the symbol immediately preceding it.

$(-6)^2 = (-6)(-6) = 36$ The exponent applies to the ( ).

$-6^2 = -(6 \cdot 6) = -36$ The exponent applies to the 6.

Therefore, $-6^2 \neq (-6)^2$.   ∎

POWERS OF ZERO

IF a IS ANY POSITIVE REAL NUMBER
Except 0
$0^a = 0$

Example 2

(a) $0^2 = 0 \cdot 0 = 0$

(b) $0^5 = 0 \cdot 0 \cdot 0 \cdot 0 \cdot 0 = 0$

Cases where 0 appears as an exponent, such as 5^0, or where 0 appears as both exponent and base, 0^0, are discussed in Chapter 6.

EXERCISES 110. Find the value of each of the following
expressions (if it has a value).

SET I

1. 3^3 2. 2^4 3. $(-5)^2$
4. $(-6)^3$ 5. 7^2 6. 3^4
7. 0^3 8. 0^4 9. $(-10)^1$
10. $(-10)^2$ 11. 10^3 12. 10^4
13. $(-10)^5$ 14. $(-10)^6$ 15. 2^4
16. 2^5 17. $(-2)^6$ 18. $(-2)^7$
19. 2^8 20. 25^2

----

21. 40^3 22. 0^4 23. $(-12)^3$
24. $(-15)^2$ 25. $(-1)^5$ 26. $(-1)^7$
27. -2^2 28. -3^2 29. $(-1)^{99}$
30. $(-1)^{98}$  31. $(12.7)^2$ 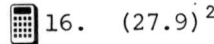 32. $(15.4)^2$

SET II

1. $(-2)^3$ 2. 6^2 3. $(-10)^2$
4. -10^2 5. 0^5 6. $(-1)^{35}$
7. $-(-5)^2$ 8. $(-1)^{50}$ 9. 10^5
10. 8^2 11. 4^3 12. -3^4
13. $(-3)^4$ 14. 20^3 15. 24^2
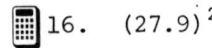 16. $(27.9)^2$

Inverse Operations

SUBTRACTION. Subtraction is called the *inverse* of addition
    because it "undoes" addition.

Example 1. Subtraction is the inverse of addition.

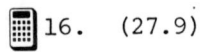

┌─Note that 5 is where we begin
│ and 5 is where we end.─────────┐
↓   ↓
5 + 4 = 9,   9 - 4 = 5
    ↑   ↑
    └──Addition   └── Subtraction
        of 4.   of 4.

It is also true that addition is the inverse of subtraction
because it "undoes" subtraction.

<u>DIVISION</u>. Division is the inverse of multiplication because it "undoes" multiplication.

<u>Example 2</u>. Division is the inverse of multiplication.

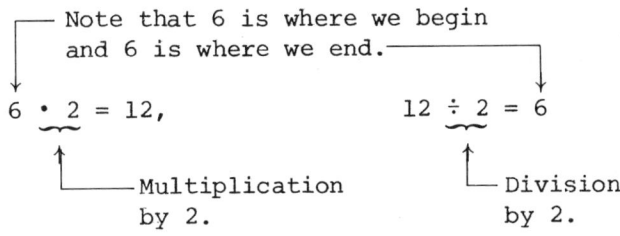

Note that 6 is where we begin and 6 is where we end.

$$6 \cdot 2 = 12, \qquad\qquad 12 \div 2 = 6$$

Multiplication by 2.

Division by 2.

It is also true that multiplication is the inverse of division because it "undoes" division.

In the following section, we will find that the operation of raising a number to a power also has an inverse operation, which is called *finding the root of a number*.

Roots of Signed Numbers

Finding the root of a real number is the inverse of raising a number to a power.

<u>FINDING SQUARE ROOTS BY INSPECTION</u>. Study the following examples.

<u>Example 1</u>

$$3^2 = 3 \cdot 3 = 9$$

3 is called the square root of 9, written $\sqrt{9} = 3$.

9 is called the square of 3 (second power of 3), written $3^2 = 9$.

<u>Example 2</u>

$$10^2 = 10 \cdot 10 = 100$$

10 is the square root of 100, written $\sqrt{100} = 10$.

100 is the square of 10 (second power of 10), written $10^2 = 100$.

The square root of a number is written by using the symbol $\sqrt{\ }$.

<u>Example 3</u>. Find the square root of 25, written $\sqrt{25}$.

$$\sqrt{25} = 5 \text{ because } 5^2 = 25$$

<u>Example 4</u>. Find the square root of 16, written $\sqrt{16}$.

$$\sqrt{16} = 4 \text{ because } 4^2 = 16$$

Example 5. Square roots by inspection.

(a) $\sqrt{4} = 2$ because $2^2 = 4$

(b) $\sqrt{9} = 3$ because $3^2 = 9$

(c) $\sqrt{36} = 6$ because $6^2 = 36$

(d) $\sqrt{0} = 0$ because $0^2 = 0$

(e) $\sqrt{1} = 1$ because $1^2 = 1$

Note.

The *square* of $4 = 4^2 = 16$.

The *square root* of $4 = \sqrt{4} = 2$ because $2^2 = 4$. ■

PRINCIPAL SQUARE ROOTS. All the square roots discussed so far have been what are usually called *principal square roots*.

Every positive number has both a positive and a negative square root. The positive square root is called the principal square root.

Example 6. The number 9 has two square roots: +3 and -3.

+3 is a square root of 9 because $3^2 = 9$.

-3 is a square root of 9 because $(-3)^2 = 9$.

3 is the principal square root of 9 indicated by $\sqrt{9}$;
-3 is the other square root of 9 indicated by $-\sqrt{9}$.

When the symbol $\sqrt{N}$ is used, it *always* represents the *principal square root* of N.

In all the examples given so far, we have only found the square root of numbers greater than or equal to zero. Square roots of negative numbers are *complex numbers* and are not discussed in this book.

EXERCISES 112A. Find the following square roots by inspection.

SET I

1. $\sqrt{16}$	2. $\sqrt{25}$	3. $-\sqrt{4}$
4. $-\sqrt{9}$	5. $\sqrt{81}$	6. $\sqrt{36}$

----

7. $\sqrt{100}$	8. $\sqrt{144}$	9. $-\sqrt{81}$
10. $-\sqrt{121}$	11. $\sqrt{64}$	12. $\sqrt{169}$

SET II

1. $-\sqrt{100}$	2. $-\sqrt{144}$	3. $\sqrt{49}$
4. $\sqrt{196}$	5. $\sqrt{225}$	6. $-\sqrt{36}$

FINDING SQUARE ROOTS BY TRIAL AND ERROR.   Suppose you were asked to find $\sqrt{196}$.   You know $\sqrt{100} = 10$, because $10^2 = 100$. Therefore, $\sqrt{196} > 10$.

Try 12; $12^2 = 144$.   Therefore, 12 is too small.

Try 13; $13^2 = 169$.   Therefore, 13 is too small.

Try 14; $14^2 = 196$.   Therefore, $\sqrt{196} = 14$.

This is what we mean by "finding the square root by trial and error."

Example 7.   Find $\sqrt{576}$ by trial and error.

$\sqrt{400} = 20$, because $20^2 = 400$.

$\sqrt{900} = 30$, because $30^2 = 900$.

Since $400 < 576 < 900$, therefore, $20 < \sqrt{576} < 30$.   This tells us that $\sqrt{576}$ is a number between 20 and 30.   Note: Since the last digit of 576 is 6, the last digit of the square root must be 4 or 6 (if the square root is an integer), because $4 \cdot 4 = 16$ and $6 \cdot 6 = 36$.   Therefore, 24 or 26 are the only possible square roots.

Try 24; $24^2 = 576$.   Therefore, $\sqrt{576} = 24$.

EXERCISES 112B.   Find the following square roots by trial and error.

SET I

1. $\sqrt{256}$ 2. $\sqrt{361}$ 3. $\sqrt{441}$ 4. $\sqrt{625}$

----

5. $\sqrt{289}$ 6. $\sqrt{324}$ 7. $\sqrt{729}$ 8. $\sqrt{1296}$

SET II

1. $\sqrt{400}$ 2. $\sqrt{484}$ 3. $\sqrt{676}$ 4. $\sqrt{1024}$

FINDING SQUARE ROOTS BY TABLE.   Find $\sqrt{3}$ by trial and error.

$\sqrt{1} = 1$, because $1^2 = 1$

$\sqrt{4} = 2$, because $2^2 = 4$

Since $1 < 3 < 4$, therefore, $1 < \sqrt{3} < 2$.   This tells us that $\sqrt{3}$ is a number between 1 and 2, and therefore cannot be an integer.   The $\sqrt{3}$ can be found by referring to Table I, inside back cover.

Locate 3 in the column headed N.

Read the value of $\sqrt{3} \doteq 1.732$ to the right of 3 in the column headed $\sqrt{N}$.

Example 8. Find $\sqrt{94}$ using Table I.
Locate 94 in the column headed N ────────┐
Then read the value of $\sqrt{94}$ = 9.695
in the column headed $\sqrt{N}$.
Table I gives the roots rounded
off to three decimal places.

N	$\sqrt{N}$
81	9.000
82	9.055
92	9.592
93	9.644
94	9.695
95	9.747
96	9.798

Further use of Table I for
finding square roots is made in
Sec. 1204.
There are methods for calculating
square roots. However, calculating
square roots is rarely necessary
today because of the ready availability
of tables, calculators, and computers.
For example, a calculator with a square root key $\boxed{\sqrt{}}$ gives
$\sqrt{94} \doteq 9.695359714$. When 9.695359714 is rounded off to three
decimal places we get 9.695, which is the same number obtained
from Table I.

EXERCISES 112C. Find the following square roots using Table I,
    inside back cover (or a calculator).

SET I

1. $\sqrt{13}$ 2. $\sqrt{18}$ 3. $\sqrt{37}$ 4. $\sqrt{50}$

----

5. $\sqrt{79}$ 6. $\sqrt{60}$ 7. $\sqrt{86}$ 8. $\sqrt{92}$

SET II

1. $\sqrt{31}$ 2. $\sqrt{69}$ 3. $\sqrt{92}$ 4. $\sqrt{184}$

REAL NUMBERS. All the numbers that can be represented by points
    on the number line are called real numbers. In Secs. 101
    and 102 we showed that integers, fractions, mixed numbers,
    and decimals are real numbers. Square roots of positive
    numbers (and zero) are also real numbers and therefore can be
    represented by points on the number line (Fig. 112).

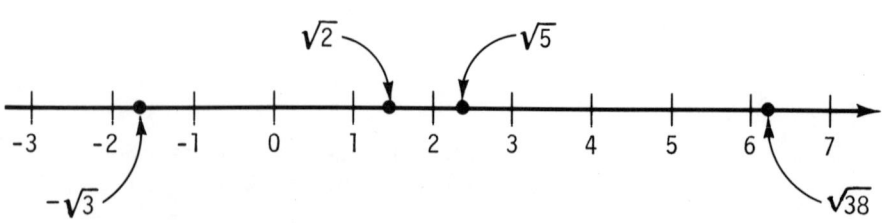

Figure 112

HIGHER ROOTS. Roots other than square roots are called *higher
    roots*. The following are examples of such roots.

Example 9. Higher roots.

(a) In the expression 2^3

2 is called the cube root of 8, written $\sqrt[3]{8} = 2$.

$$2^3 = 2 \cdot 2 \cdot 2 = 8$$

8 is called the cube of 2 (third power of 2), written $2^3 = 8$.

(b) In the expression $(-2)^3$

-2 is called the cube root of -8, written $\sqrt[3]{-8} = -2$.

$$(-2)^3 = (-2)(-2)(-2) = -8$$

-8 is called the cube of -2, written $(-2)^3 = -8$ (third power of -2).

(c) In the expression 2^4

2 is called the fourth root of 16, written $\sqrt[4]{16} = 2$.

$$2^4 = 2 \cdot 2 \cdot 2 \cdot 2 = 16$$

16 is called the fourth power of 2, written $2^4 = 16$.

(d) In the expression $(-1)^5$

-1 is the fifth root of -1, written $\sqrt[5]{-1} = -1$.

$$(-1)^5 = (-1)(-1)(-1)(-1)(-1) = -1$$

-1 is the fifth power of -1, written $(-1)^5 = -1$.

Taking a square root is the inverse of squaring a number.

Example 10. Roots preceded by a minus sign.

(a) $-\sqrt{16} = -(4) = -4$

(b) $-\sqrt[3]{8} = -(2) = -2$

(c) $-\sqrt[3]{-8} = -(-2) = 2$

There is an inverse relation between any like power and root. Finding the root of a number is the inverse of raising that number to a power.

Example 11. Taking the square root of a number is the inverse of squaring a number.

$$4^2 = 16 \quad , \quad \sqrt{16} = 4$$
squaring   taking square root

inverse operations

Since 4 is where we began and 4 is where we ended, the operation of squaring was "undone" by the operation of taking the square root.

EXERCISES 112D. Find each of the indicated roots by trial and error.

SET I

1. $\sqrt[3]{64}$ 2. $\sqrt[4]{81}$ 3. $\sqrt[3]{27}$ 4. $\sqrt[3]{125}$

5. $-\sqrt[3]{27}$ 6. $-\sqrt{25}$ 7. $-\sqrt[4]{1}$ 8. $-\sqrt[5]{-32}$

9. $\sqrt[3]{-125}$ 10. $\sqrt[3]{-8}$ 11. $-\sqrt[4]{-16}$ 12. $-\sqrt{-16}$

----

13. $\sqrt[3]{-1000}$ 14. $\sqrt[3]{-64}$ 15. $\sqrt[7]{-1}$ 16. $\sqrt[5]{-32}$

17. $\sqrt[4]{81}$ 18. $-\sqrt[3]{-216}$ 19. $\sqrt{-25}$ 20. $\sqrt{-36}$

SET II

1. $-\sqrt[3]{-8}$ 2. $-\sqrt[3]{-64}$ 3. $\sqrt[5]{-1}$ 4. $\sqrt[4]{16}$

5. $\sqrt[3]{1000}$ 6. $\sqrt[5]{32}$ 7. $\sqrt[3]{216}$ 8. $\sqrt[6]{64}$

9. $\sqrt[4]{256}$ 10. $\sqrt[5]{243}$

Chapter Summary

Natural Numbers (Sec. 101)

   {1, 2, 3, ...}

Whole Numbers (Sec. 101)

   {0, 1, 2, ...}

Integers (Sec. 102)

   {..., -3, -2, -1, 0, 1, 2, 3, ...}

Digits (Sec. 101)

   {0, 1, 2, 3, 4, 5, 6, 7, 8, 9}

Fractions (Sec. 101)

   Numbers having the form $\frac{a}{b}$, where a and b are integers and $b \neq 0$.

Decimal Fractions (Sec. 101)

   A decimal fraction is a fraction whose denominator is a power of 10. (10, 100, 1000, ...)

Mixed Numbers (Sec. 101)

   A mixed number is made up of both a whole number part and a fraction part.

Real Numbers (Secs. 101, 102, 112)

All the numbers that can be represented by points on the number line are called real numbers.

Positive Numbers (Sec. 102)

All real numbers $b < 0$.

Negative Numbers (Sec. 102)

All real numbers $b > 0$.

Operations Involving Zero (Secs. 109, 110)

Zero is the real number that is neither a positive number nor a negative number.

If a is any real number:

(a) $a + 0 = 0 + a = a$

(b) $a - 0 = a$

(c) $0 - a = 0 + (-a) = -a$

(d) $a \cdot 0 = 0 \cdot a = 0$

If a is any real number $\neq 0$:

(e) $\dfrac{0}{a} = 0$

(f) $\dfrac{a}{0}$ is not possible

(g) $\dfrac{0}{0}$ cannot be determined

(h) $0^{a} = 0$

Zero is the additive identity. (Sec. 109)

One is the multiplicative identity. (Sec. 105)

$1 \cdot a = a \cdot 1 = a$

Absolute Value (Sec. 103)

The absolute value of a number is the distance between that number and 0 on the number line with no regard for direction.
The absolute value of a number can never be negative.
The absolute value of a real number X is written $|X|$.

To Add Signed Numbers (Sec. 103)

Case 1. When the numbers have the *same sign*
- 1st—Add their absolute values.
- 2nd—The sum has the same sign as both numbers.

Case 2. When the numbers have *different signs*
- 1st—Subtract the smaller absolute value from the larger.
- 2nd—The sum has the sign of the number with the larger absolute value.

To Subtract One Signed Number from Another (Sec. 104)

1. Change the subtraction symbol to an addition symbol, and change the sign of the number being subtracted.
2. Add the resulting signed numbers as shown in Sec. 103.

To Multiply Two Signed Numbers (Sec. 105)

1. Multiply their absolute values.
2. The product is *positive* when the signed numbers have the same sign.
   The product is *negative* when the signed numbers have different signs.

To Divide One Signed Number by Another (Sec. 106)

1. Divide their absolute values.
2. The quotient is *positive* when the signed numbers have the same sign.
   The quotient is *negative* when the signed numbers have different signs.

Powers of Signed Numbers (Sec. 110)

exponent

$$3^4 = 3 \cdot 3 \cdot 3 \cdot 3 = 81$$

base ——— fourth power of 3

Roots of Signed Numbers (Sec. 112)

$$\sqrt[3]{-8} = -2 \qquad \text{because} \quad (-2)^3 = (-2)(-2)(-2) = -8$$

cube root of -8

Inverse Operations (Secs. 111, 112)

Addition and subtraction are inverse operations.
Multiplication and division are inverse operations.
Like powers and roots are inverse operations.

REVIEW EXERCISES 113

SET I

1. Write all the digits greater than 7.
2. Write all the whole numbers less than 3.
3. Write the largest two-digit natural number.
4. Write the smallest two-digit natural number.
5. Write the smallest one-digit integer.
6. Write the largest one-digit integer less than zero.
7. Write all the integers that can be put in place of x that will make each of the following statements true.

   (a) $11 < x < 15$ (b) $-3 < x < 3$ (c) $-21 < x < -17$

8. Write all the integers that can be put in place of x that will make each of the following statements true.

   (a) $17 < x < 20$ (b) $-4 < x < 2$ (c) $-18 < x < -14$

In Exercises 9—48, perform the indicated operations.

9. $(-2) + (+3)$ 10. $(-5) + (+4)$

11. $(-6) \div (-2)$ 12. $(-8) \div (-4)$

13. $(-5) - (-3)$ 14. $(-7) - (-2)$

15. $(+5) - |-2|$ 16. $(+8) - |-3|$

17. $(-3)(-4)$ 18. $(-5)(-4)$

19. -3^2 20. -4^2

21. Subtract (-6) from (-10).

22. Subtract (-8) from (-5).

23. $(-6) \div (2)$ 24. $(-12) \div (4)$

25. 0^3 26. 0^4

27. $(-5)^2$ 28. $(-4)^2$

29. $(-10) + (-2)$ 30. $(-8) + (-3)$

31. $(-4)(6)$ 32. $(-5)(7)$

33. $\dfrac{-25}{-5}$ 34. $\dfrac{-16}{-2}$

35. $0 \div (-4)$ 36. $0 \div (-3)$

37. $\sqrt{36}$ 38. $\sqrt{64}$

39. -2^4 40. -2^6

41. $\sqrt[3]{-8}$ 42. $\sqrt[3]{-64}$

43. $(0)(-5)$ 44. $(0)(-2)$

45. $\dfrac{-14.25}{2.85}$ 46. $\dfrac{-24.15}{3.45}$

Use Table I, or a calculator, to work Exercises 47 and 48.

47. $\sqrt{153}$ 48. $\sqrt{185}$

49. State whether each of the following is true or false, and give the reason.

   (a) $[(-2) \cdot 3] \cdot 4 = (-2)(3 \cdot 4)$

   (b) $5 + (-2) = (-2) + 5$

   (c) $5 - (-2) = (-2) - 5$

   (d) $a + (b + c) = (a + b) + c$

   (e) $(c \cdot d) \cdot e = e \cdot (c \cdot d)$

   (f) $5 + (x + 7) = (x + 7) + 5$

50. State whether each of the following is true or false, and give the reason.

  (a) $5 \cdot [2(-4)] = [5 \cdot 2] \cdot (-4)$

  (b) $(-6) + (-3) = (-3) + (-6)$

  (c) $(-6) \div (-3) = (-3) \div (-6)$

  (d) $(x + y) + z = x + (y + z)$

  (e) $c \cdot (d \cdot e) = (d \cdot e) \cdot c$

SET II

1. Write all the digits greater than 5.
2. Write all the whole numbers less than 4.
3. Write the largest two-digit integer.
4. Write all the integers that can be put in the place of x that will make the statement, $-4 < x < 2$, true.

In Exercises 5—18, perform the indicated operations.

5. $(-5) + (+2)$ 6. $(-8)(-2)$

7. $(-10) \div (5)$ 8. $(6) - (-3)$

9. -5^2 10. $\sqrt[3]{-125}$

11. $\sqrt{81}$ 12. $(-4)^2$

13. $-(-7)^3$ 14. $-(-2)^4$

15. $24 \div 0$ 16. 0^5

17. $-|-3|$ 18. $0 \div (-6)$

19. $|-4| - |6|$ 20. $|0| + |-5|$

21. $0 \div 0$ 22. $(-9)(2)$

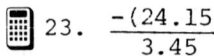 23. $\dfrac{-(24.15)}{3.45}$

24. Use Table I, or a calculator, to find $\sqrt{176}$.

25. State whether each of the following is true or false, and give a reason.

  (a) $(6) - (-2) = (-2) - (6)$

  (b) $5 \cdot (2 \cdot 3) = (5 \cdot 2) \cdot 3$

  (c) $(-7) + (4 + 3) = [(-7) + (4)] + 3$

Chapter One Diagnostic Test

Name_____

_____

The purpose of this test is to see how well you understand the operations with signed numbers. We recommend that you work this diagnostic test *before* your instructor tests you on this chapter. Allow yourself about twenty-five minutes to do this test.

Complete solutions for all the problems on this test, together with section references, are given in the Answer Section. We suggest that you study the sections referred to for the problems you do incorrectly.

Write the correct symbol, < or >, that should be used in Problems 1-3 to make the statement true.

1. 3 ___ 5   2. 0 ___ -4   3. -5 ___ -4

---

4. Write the largest two-digit natural number. (4)_____

5. Write the smallest one-digit integer.   (5)_____

6. Write all the digits less than 3.   (6)_____

7. Write -35 in words.   (7)_____

---

8. At 5 AM the temperature at Denver, Colorado, was -20° F. At noon the temperature was 38° F. What was the rise in temperature?

(8)_____

In Problems 9-11 state whether each is true or false, and give the reason.

9. $(-9)(3) = (3) + (-9)$

(9)_____

10. $(3 + 5) + 6 = 3 + (5 + 6)$

(10)_____

11. $a \cdot (b \cdot c) = a \cdot (c \cdot b)$

(11)_____

In each of the following, perform the indicated operation. If the indicated operation cannot be done, give a reason.

12. Add -6 and 2. (12)_____

13. Subtract -10 from 20. (13)_____

14. (-10)(-5) (14)_____

15. (42) ÷ (-14) (15)_____

16. 6^2 (16)_____

17. (8) + (-5) (17)_____

18. (-12)(0) (18)_____

19. Subtract 5 from -10. (19)_____

20. $\frac{2}{0}$ (20)_____

21. (-5)(8) (21)_____

22. $\frac{15}{-18}$ (22)_____

23. $(-4)^3$ (23)_____

24. (-24) ÷ (-6) (24)_____

25. (-10) + (-4) (25)_____

26. 0^2 (26)_____

27. $\frac{-33}{11}$ (27)_____

28. 0 ÷ (-12) (28)_____

29. 6(-4) (29)_____

30. $-\left(\frac{0}{0}\right)$ (30)_____

31. $(-2)^4$ (31)_____

_____

In Problems 32-35 find each of the indicated roots by trial and error.

32. $\sqrt{49}$ (32)_____   33. $\sqrt{81}$ (33)_____

34. $\sqrt[3]{64}$ (34)_____   35. $\sqrt[3]{-8}$ (35)_____

_____

TWO

Evaluation of Expressions Containing Numbers and Letters

One of the first places a student uses algebra is in the evaluation of formulas in courses taken in science, business, and so on. In this chapter we apply the operations with signed numbers discussed in Chapter 1 to evaluate algebraic expressions and formulas.

In Chapter 1 we learned how to perform all six arithmetic operations with signed numbers: addition, subtraction, multiplication, division, taking powers, and finding roots; but each problem dealt with only one kind of operation.

Example 1. Problems involving only one kind of operation.

(a) $2 + (-4) = -2$ Addition only.
(b) $(-3) \cdot [4 \cdot (-5)] = (-3)(-20) = 60$ Multiplication only.
(c) $(-7) - 4 = -11$ Subtraction only.

In this chapter we will evaluate expressions in which more than one kind of operation is used.

Example 2. $5 + 4 \cdot 6$ Multiplication *and* addition.

If the addition is done first,
we get $5 + 4 \cdot 6 \overset{?}{=} 9 \cdot 6 = 54$.

If the multiplication is done first,
we get $5 + 4 \cdot 6 \overset{?}{=} 5 + 24 = 29$.

Which is correct?

Obviously, both answers cannot be correct. In the next section we show the accepted order in which the operations are done.

Order of Operations

In evaluating expressions with more than one operation, the following order of operations is used.

ORDER OF OPERATIONS

1. If there are any parentheses in the expression, that part of the expression within a pair of parentheses is evaluated first. Then the entire expression is evaluated.

2. Any evaluation always proceeds in three steps:
    First: Powers and roots are done in any order.
    Second: Multiplication and division are done in order from left to right.
    Third: Addition and subtraction are done in order from left to right.

It is important for students to realize that an expression
such as

$$8 - 6 - 4 + 7$$

is evaluated by doing the additions and subtractions in order
from left to right (because subtraction is not commutative
or associative).

This same expression may also be considered as a sum
by changing the sign of any number being subtracted.

$$(8) + (-6) + (-4) + (7).$$

If the expression is considered as a sum, then the terms can
be added in any order (because addition is commutative and
associative).

Only evaluated left to right	*Added in any order*
$8 - 6 - 4 + 7$	$(8) + (-6) + (-4) + (7)$
$= \quad 2 \quad -4 + 7$	$= (8) + (7) + (-6) + (-4)$
$= \qquad -2 \quad + 7$	$= \quad 15 \quad + \quad (-10)$
$= \qquad\qquad 5$	$= \qquad 5$

Example 1. $(7 + 3) \cdot 5$ We do the part in
              $10 \quad \cdot 5 = 50$ parentheses first.

Example 2. $7 + 3 \cdot 5$ Multiplication is done
              $7 + \quad 15 = 22$ before addition.

Example 3. $4^2 + \sqrt{25} - 6$ Powers and roots are
              $16 + \quad 5 \quad - 6$ done first.
                 $21 \qquad - 6 = 15$

Example 4. $16 \div 2 \cdot 4$ Here, division is done
              $8 \quad \cdot 4 = 32$ first because in reading
                                     from left to right the
                                     division comes first.

Example 5. $\sqrt{16} - 4(2 \cdot 3^2 - 12 \div 2)$ First, evaluate the expres-
                                              sion inside the parentheses.

$\sqrt{16} - 4(2 \cdot 9 - 12 \div 2)$ Do the power inside ( ).

$\sqrt{16} - 4(18 \quad - \quad 6)$ Do the $\times$ and $\div$ inside ( ).

$\sqrt{16} - 4(12)$ Do the $-$ inside ( ).

$4 \quad - 4(12)$ Root next.

$4 \quad - \quad 48 \quad = -44$

Example 6. $(-8) \div 2 - (-4)$ Division is done before
                 $-4 \quad - \quad (-4)$ subtraction.
                 $-4 \quad + \quad 4 \quad = 0$

Example 7. $\sqrt[3]{-8}(-3)^2 - 2(-6)$ Roots and powers are
                                        done first.
                 $-2(9) \quad - \quad 2(-6)$ Multiplication is done
                 $-18 \qquad - \quad (-12)$ before subtraction.
                 $-18 \quad + \quad 12 = -6$

<u>EXERCISES 201</u>. In working the following exercises, be sure to perform the operations in the correct order.

SET I

1. $12 - 8 - 6$
2. $15 - 9 - 4$
3. $17 - 11 + 13 - 9$
4. $12 - 8 + 14 - 6$
5. $7 + 2 \cdot 4$
6. $10 + 3 \cdot 6$
7. $9 - 3 \cdot 2$
8. $14 - 8 \cdot 3$
9. $10 \div 2 \cdot 5$
10. $20 \cdot 15 \div 5$
11. $12 \div 6 \div 2$
12. $24 \div 12 \div 6$
13. $(-12) \div 2 \cdot (-3)$
14. $(-18) \div (-3) \cdot (-6)$
15. $(8 - 2) \cdot 6$
16. $(10 - 6) \cdot 4$
17. $(-485)^2 \cdot 0 \cdot (-5)^2$
18. $(-589)^2 \cdot 0 \cdot (-3)^2$
19. $12 \cdot 4 + 16 \div 8$
20. $4 \cdot 3 + 15 \div 5$
21. $28 \div 4 \cdot 2(6)$
22. $48 \div 16 \cdot 2(-8)$

----

23. $(-2)^2 + (-4)(5) - (-3)^2$
24. $(-5)^2 + (-2)(6) - (-4)^2$
25. $2 \cdot 3 + 3^2 - 4 \cdot 2$
26. $100 \div 5^2 \cdot 6 + 8 \cdot 75$
27. $(10^2)\sqrt{16} + 5(4) - 80$
28. $(5^2)\sqrt{9} + 4(6) - 60$
29. $2\sqrt{9}(2^3 - 5)$
30. $5\sqrt{36}(4^2 - 8)$
31. $(3 \cdot 5^2 - 15 \div 3) \div (-7)$
32. $(3 \cdot 4^3 - 72 \div 6) \div (-9)$
33. $2.573 - 5.846(1.098)$
34. $5.362 - 7.604(2.188)$
35. $82.49 \div 23.06(51.73)$
36. $72.81 \div 35.04(40.63)$

SET II

1. $18 - 10 - 5$
2. $13 - 9 + 16 - 8$
3. $2 + 5 \cdot 3$
4. $15 \div 3 \cdot 5$
5. $-18 \div (- \sqrt{81})$
6. $18 \div 6 \div 3$
7. $10 \cdot 15^2 - 4^3$
8. $(-10)^2 \cdot 10 + 0(-20)$
9. $(785)^3(0) + 1^5$
10. $(-5)^2 - (2)(-6) + (-2)^2$
11. $2 + 3(100) \div 25 - 10$
12. $7^2 + \sqrt{64} - 14$
13. $(-12) \div 6 - (-4)$
14. $(10^2)\sqrt{4} - 5 + 36$
15. $4(-8) - (-5)^2\sqrt[3]{-1}$
16. $5(3 \cdot 2^3 - 14 \div 7) - \sqrt{36}$
17. $5.907 - 8.628(2.054)$
18. $27.93 \div 18.06(42.81)$

Grouping Symbols

Here are the grouping symbols that we have already used.

( ) Parentheses
[ ] Brackets
{ } Braces
——— Bar

Fraction line ⟶ $\dfrac{3(-5) + 7}{9 - 4(-2)}$

Bar in a square root ⟶
$\sqrt{7(+4) - 8}$

Grouping symbols are used to change the normal order of operations. Operations indicated within grouping symbols are carried out before operations outside the grouping symbols. *All grouping symbols have the same meaning.*

$$(8 + 4) - (9 - 7) = [8 + 4] - [9 - 7]$$
$$= \{8 + 4\} - \{9 - 7\} = \overline{8 + 4} - \overline{9 - 7}$$
$$= \quad 12 \quad - \quad 2$$
$$= 10$$

Different grouping symbols can be used in the same expression.

$$(8 + 4) - \{9 - 7\} = [8 + 4] - (9 - 7)$$
$$= \{8 + 4\} - [9 - 7]$$
$$= \quad 12 \quad - \quad 2$$
$$= 10$$

In this section we will make more extensive use of these symbols than was done in previous sections.

Example 1. $5(-4) \div 2(6 - 8)$ The expression within the
$5(-4) \div 2(-2)$ parentheses is evaluated
$-20 \quad \div 2(-2)$ first.
$\quad\quad -10\,(-2) = 20$
$\quad\quad 20$

Example 2. $10 - [3 - (2 - 7)]$ When grouping symbols appear
                                      within other grouping symbols,
$10 - [3 - \quad (-5)]$ evaluate the inner grouping
                                      first.
$10 - [3 + \quad\quad 5]$ $3 - (-5) = 3 + (+5) = 3 + 5$
                                      because of the definition of
$10 - \quad\quad [8] \quad = 2$ subtraction: "To subtract a
                                      signed number, change its
                                      sign and add."

Example 3. $\dfrac{(-4) + (-2)}{8 - 5}$ ⟵ —— This bar is a grouping symbol for both $\underline{(-4) + (-2)}$ and for $\overline{8 - 5}$. Notice that the bar can be used either above or below the numbers being grouped.

$$= \dfrac{-6}{3} = -2$$

Example 4. $20 - 2\{5 - [3 - 5(6 - 2)]\}$

$20 - 2\{5 - [3 - 5(4)]\}$

$20 - 2\{5 - [3 - 20]\}$

$20 - 2\{5 - [-17]\}$

$20 - 2\{5 + 17\}$

$20 - 2\{22\}$

$20 - 44 = -24$

Example 5.

(a) $5 + 4 \cdot 6 = 5 + 24 = 29$ ⎫ Grouping symbols provide
(b) $(5 + 4) \cdot 6 = 9 \cdot 6 = 54$ ⎬ a means for changing the
                                       ⎭ normal order of operations.

Example 6. $27 \div (-3)^2 - 5\left\{6 - \dfrac{8 - 4}{5}\right\}$

$27 \div (-3)^2 - 5\left\{6 - \dfrac{4}{5}\right\}$ ———— $6 = \dfrac{30}{5}$

$27 \div (-3)^2 - 5\left\{\dfrac{26}{5}\right\}$ ———— $6 - \dfrac{4}{5} = \dfrac{30}{5} - \dfrac{4}{5} = \dfrac{26}{5}$

$27 \div 9 - 5\left\{\dfrac{26}{5}\right\}$

$3 - 26 = -23$

Approximately Equal. The symbol $\doteq$ (read "*approximately equal to*") is used to show that two numbers are approximately equal to each other. The use of this symbol is shown in the following example.

Example 7. $(2.5)^2 \div (5.6 - 11.4)$

$(2.5)^2 \div (-5.8)$

$6.25 \div (-5.8) = -1.077586207$

$\doteq -1.08$ (Rounded off to 2 decimal places.)

Example 8. $\sqrt{13^2 - 12^2}$ ⟵ Since this bar is a grouping symbol, the expression under it is evaluated first. Then the square root is taken.

$\sqrt{169 - 144}$

$\sqrt{25} = 5$

Note: $\sqrt{13^2 - 12^2} \neq \sqrt{13^2} - \sqrt{12^2}$

$\sqrt{169 - 144} \neq 13 - 12$

$\sqrt{25} \neq 1$ ■

EXERCISES 202. Evaluate each of the following expressions.

SET I

1. $2(-6) \div 3(8 - 4)$ 2. $5(-4) \div 2(9 - 4)$
3. $24 - [(-6) + 18]$ 4. $17 - [(-9) + 15]$
5. $[12 - (-19)] - 16$ 6. $[21 - (-14)] - 29$
7. $[11 - (5 + 8)] - 24$ 8. $[16 - (7 + 12)] - 22$
9. $20 - [5 - (7 - 10)]$ 10. $16 - [8 - (2 - 7)]$
11. $\dfrac{7 + (-12)}{8 - 3}$ 12. $\dfrac{(-14) + (-2)}{9 - 5}$

----

13. $15 - \{4 - [2 - 3(6 - 4)]\}$
14. $17 - \{6 - [9 - 2(2 - 7)]\}$
15. $32 \div (-2)^3 - 5\left\{7 - \dfrac{6 - 2}{5}\right\}$
16. $36 \div (-3)^2 - 6\left\{4 - \dfrac{9 - 7}{3}\right\}$
17. $\sqrt{3^2 + 4^2}$ 18. $\sqrt{13^2 - 5^2}$
19. $\sqrt{16.3^2 - 8.35^2}$ 20. $\sqrt{23.9^2 + 38.6^2}$
21. $(1.5)^2 \div (-2.5) + \sqrt{35}$ 22. $(-0.25)^2(-10)^3 + \sqrt{54}$
23. $18.91 - [64.3 - (8.6^2 + 14.2)]$
24. $[\sqrt{101.4} - (73.5 - 19.6^2)] \div 38.2$

SET II

1. $4(11 - 17) \div 3(-2)$ 2. $[18 - (-15)] - 13$
3. $33 - [(-16) + 11]$ 4. $[22 - (7 + 12)] - 14$
5. $26 - [8 - (6 - 15)]$ 6. $\dfrac{(-2) + (-7)}{18 + (-15)}$
7. $23 - \{6 - [5 - 2(8 - 3)]\}$
8. $28 \div (-2)^2 - 6\left\{8 - \dfrac{9 - 4}{3}\right\}$
9. $\sqrt{10^2 - 6^2}$ 10. $\sqrt{34.5^2 - 17.8^2}$
11. $(1.7)^2 \div (-3.2) + \sqrt{43}$
12. $[\sqrt{126.3} - (89.7 - 46.5^2)] \div 52.6$

Finding the Value of Expressions Having Letters and Numbers   53

 **Finding the Value of Expressions Having Letters and Numbers**

In algebra we use letters to represent numbers. In this section we make use of what we have already learned about signed numbers to help us find the value of expressions having letters as well as numbers.

TO FIND THE VALUE OF AN EXPRESSION HAVING LETTERS AND NUMBERS

1. Replace each letter by its number value.

2. Carry out all arithmetic operations using the correct order of operations (Sec. 201).

Example 1. Find the value of $3x - 5y$ if $x = 10$ and $y = 4$.

Solution:
$$
\begin{aligned}
&3x \quad - \;5y \qquad\qquad 3x = 3 \cdot x; \quad 5y = 5 \cdot y\\
&= 3(10) - 5(4)\\
&= \;30 \quad - \;20 \;= 10
\end{aligned}
$$

Notice that we simply replace each letter by its number value, then carry out the arithmetic operations as we have done before.

A word of caution. When replacing a letter by a number, enclose the number in parentheses to avoid the following common errors.

Evaluate $3x$ when $x = -2$.

Correct	*Common Error*
$3x = 3(-2) = -6$	$3x \neq 3 - 2 = 1$

Evaluate $4x^2$ when $x = -3$.

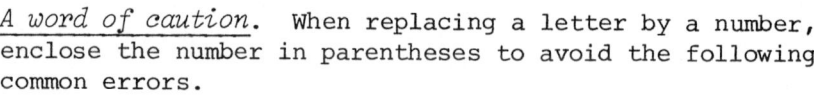

Correct	*Common Errors*
$4x^2 = 4(-3)^2 = 4 \cdot 9 = 36$	$4x^2 \neq 4 - 3^2 = 4 - 9 = -5$
	or $4x^2 \neq 4 - 3^2 = 4 + 9 = 13$ ∎

Example 2. Evaluate $3x - 5y$ if $x = -4$ and $y = -6$.

Solution:
$$
\begin{aligned}
&3x \quad - \;5y\\
&= 3(-4) - 5(-6)\\
&= -12 \quad + \;30 \quad = 18
\end{aligned}
$$

Example 3. Find the value of $\dfrac{2a - b}{10c}$ if $a = -1$, $b = 3$, and $c = -2$.

Remember this bar is a grouping symbol.

Solution: $\dfrac{2a - b}{10c} = \dfrac{2(-1) - (3)}{10(-2)} = \dfrac{-2 - 3}{-20} = \dfrac{-5}{-20} = \dfrac{1}{4} = 0.25$

Example 4. Evaluate $\dfrac{5hgk}{2m}$ if $h = -2$, $g = 3$, $k = -4$, $m = 6$.

Solution: $\dfrac{5hgk}{2m} = \dfrac{5(-2)(3)(-4)}{2(6)} = \dfrac{120}{12} = 10$

Example 5. Find the value of $2a - [b - (3x - 4y)]$ for $a = -3$, $b = 4$, $x = -5$, and $y = 2$.

Solution: $2a\quad - [b - (3x\quad - 4y)]$

   $= 2(-3) - [4 - \{3(-5) - 4(2)\}]$ Notice { } were used in place of ( ) to clarify the grouping.

   $= 2(-3) - [4 - \{-15 - 8\}]$

   $= 2(-3) - [4 - \{-23\}]$

   $= 2(-3) - [4 + 23]$

   $= \ \ -6\quad - \ \ [27]$

   $= \ \ -6\quad - \quad 27\quad = -33$

Example 6. Evaluate $b - \sqrt{b^2 - 4ac}$ when $a = 3$, $b = -7$, and $c = 2$.

Solution: $b\ \ - \sqrt{b^2 - 4ac}$ This bar is a grouping symbol for $b^2 - 4ac$.

   $= (-7) - \sqrt{(-7)^2 - 4(3)(2)}$

   $= (-7) - \sqrt{49 - 24}$

   $= (-7) - \sqrt{25}$

   $= (-7) - \ \ 5\ \ = -12$

A Word of Caution. A common error often made in evaluation problems is to mistake $(-3)^2$ for -3^2.

   $(-3)^2 = (-3)(-3) = 9$ The exponent 2 applies to -3.

   $-3^2 \ \ = -(3)(3) \ \ = -9$ The exponent 2 applies to 3.

SET I

In Exercises 1—20, evaluate the expression when $a = 3$, $b = -5$, $c = -1$, $x = 4$, and $y = -7$.

1. b^2 2. $-y^2$

3. $2a - 3b$ 4. $3x - 2y$

5. $x - y - 2b$ 6. $a - b - 3y$

7. $3b - ab + xy$ 8. $4c + ax - by$

9. $x^2 - y^2$ 10. $b^2 - c^2$

11. $4 + a(x + y)$ 12. $5 - b(a + c)$

13. $2(a - b) - 3c$ 14. $3(a - x) - 4b$

15. $3x^2 - 10x + 5$ 16. $2y^2 - 7y + 9$

17. $a^2 - 2ab + b^2$ 18. $x^2 - 2xy + y^2$

19. $\dfrac{3x}{y + b}$ 20. $\dfrac{4a}{c - b}$

In Exercises 21—30, find the value of the expression when $E = -1$, $F = 3$, $G = -5$, $H = -4$, and $K = 0$.

21. $\dfrac{E + F}{EF}$ 22. $\dfrac{G + H}{GH}$

23. $\dfrac{(1 + G)^2 - 1}{H}$ 24. $\dfrac{1 - (1 + E)^2}{F}$

25. $2E - [F - (3K - H)]$ 26. $3H - [K - (4F - E)]$

27. $G - \sqrt{G^2 - 4EH}$ 28. $H - \sqrt{H^2 - 4EF}$

29. $\dfrac{\sqrt{2H - 5G}}{0.2F^2}$ 30. $\dfrac{\sqrt{5HG}}{0.5E^2}$

SET II

In Exercises 1—15, evaluate the expression when $a = -2$, $b = 4$, $c = -5$, $x = 3$, and $y = -1$.

1. $-a^2$ 2. $4c - 5y$

3. $a - b - 2c$ 4. $6x - xy + ab$

5. $c^2 - x^2$ 6. $7 - x(a + b)$

7. $3(x - y) - 4c$ 8. $b^2 - 4ac$

9. $b^2 - 2bc + c^2$ 10. $\dfrac{5b}{x - y}$

11. $\dfrac{a - b}{ab}$ 12. $\dfrac{(1 - x)^2 - 1}{y}$

13. $3a - [b - (5x - y)]$ 14. $x - \sqrt{x^2 - 4ay}$

In Exercises 15, 16, a = -19.32, b = 25.73, and c = 47.02

15. $\dfrac{\sqrt{3b - 4a}}{0.7c^2}$ 16. $\dfrac{-b - \sqrt{b^2 - 4ac}}{2a}$

56   Chapter 2:   Evaluation of Expressions Containing Numbers and Letters

Evaluating Formulas

One reason for studying algebra is to prepare us to use formulas. Students will encounter formulas in many courses they take, as well as in real-life situations. In the examples and exercises we have listed the subject areas where the formulas are used.

Formulas are evaluated in the same way any expression having numbers and letters is evaluated.

Example 1. Given the formula $A = \frac{1}{2}bh$, find A when $b = 17$ and $h = 12$. (Geometry)

Solution: $A = \frac{1}{2}bh$

$\qquad = \frac{1}{2}(17)(12)$

$\qquad = \frac{(17)(12)}{2} = 102$

Example 2. Given the formula $A = P(1 + rt)$, find A when $P = 1000$, $r = 0.08$, and $t = 1.5$. (Business)

Solution: $A = P(1 + rt)$

$\qquad = 1000[1 + (0.08)(1.5)]$ Notice [ ] were used in place of ( ) to clarify the grouping.

$\qquad = 1000[1 + 0.12] = 1000[1.12] = 1120$

Example 3. Given the formula $s = \frac{1}{2}gt^2$, find s when $g = 32$ and $t = 5\frac{1}{2}$. (Physics)

Solution: $s = \frac{1}{2}gt^2$

$\qquad = \frac{1}{2}(32)\left(\frac{11}{2}\right)^2$

$\qquad = \frac{1}{2}\left(\frac{32}{1}\right)\left(\frac{121}{4}\right) = 484$

Example 4. Given the formula $C = \frac{5}{9}(F - 32)$, find C when $F = -13$. (Science)

Solution: $C = \frac{5}{9}(F - 32)$

$\qquad = \frac{5}{9}(-13 - 32)$

$\qquad = \frac{5}{9}(-45) = -25$

Example 5. Given the formula $T = \pi\sqrt{\dfrac{L}{g}}$, find T when $\pi \doteq 3.14$, $L = 96$, and $g = 32$. (Physics)

Solution: $T = \pi\sqrt{\dfrac{L}{g}}$

$$\doteq (3.14)\sqrt{\dfrac{96}{32}}$$

$$\doteq (3.14)\sqrt{3} \doteq (3.14)(1.732)$$

$$\doteq 5.44 \qquad \text{(Rounded off to 2 decimal places.)}$$

Example 6. Given the formula $S = \dfrac{a(1 - r^n)}{1 - r}$, find S when $a = -4$, $r = \dfrac{1}{2}$, and $n = 3$. (Mathematics)

Solution: $S = \dfrac{a(1 - r^n)}{1 - r}$

$$= \dfrac{(-4)\left[1 - \left(\dfrac{1}{2}\right)^3\right]}{1 - \dfrac{1}{2}} \qquad \left(\dfrac{1}{2}\right)^3 = \left(\dfrac{1}{2}\right)\left(\dfrac{1}{2}\right)\left(\dfrac{1}{2}\right) = \dfrac{1}{8}$$

$$= \dfrac{(-4)\left[1 - \dfrac{1}{8}\right]}{1 - \dfrac{1}{2}} = \dfrac{(-4)\left[\dfrac{7}{8}\right]}{\dfrac{1}{2}} = -7$$

Formulas will be discussed further in Sec. 909.

EXERCISES 204. Evaluate each formula using the values of the letters given with the formula.

SET I

(Geometry)	1. $A = \dfrac{1}{2}bh$	$b = 15,\ h = 14$
	2. $A = \dfrac{1}{2}bh$	$b = 27,\ h = 36$
(Electricity)	3. $I = \dfrac{E}{R}$	$E = 110,\ R = 22$
	4. $I = \dfrac{E}{R}$	$E = 220,\ R = 33$
(Business)	5. $I = prt$	$p = 600,\ r = 0.09,\ t = 4.5$
	6. $I = prt$	$p = 700,\ r = 0.08,\ t = 2.5$
(Nursing)	7. $q = \dfrac{DQ}{H}$	$D = 5,\ H = 30,\ Q = 420$
	8. $q = \dfrac{DQ}{H}$	$D = 25,\ H = 90,\ Q = 450$
(Business)	9. $S = P(1 + i)^n$	$P = 1000,\ i = 0.06,\ n = 2$
	10. $S = P(1 + i)^n$	$P = 2000,\ i = 0.08,\ n = 2$

(Geometry)	11.	$A = \pi R^2$	$\pi \doteq 3.14$, $R = 10$
	12.	$A = \pi R^2$	$\pi \doteq 3.14$, $R = 20$
(Chemistry)	13.	$F = \dfrac{9}{5} C + 32$	$C = -25$
	14.	$F = \dfrac{9}{5} C + 32$	$C = -35$
(Business)	15.	$A = P(1 + rt)$	$P = 500$, $r = 0.09$, $t = 2.5$
	16.	$A = P(1 + rt)$	$P = 400$, $r = 0.07$, $t = 3.5$

(Physics)	17.	$C = \dfrac{5}{9}(F - 32)$	$F = -10$
	18.	$C = \dfrac{5}{9}(F - 32)$	$F = -7$
(Geometry)	19.	$V = \dfrac{4}{3} \pi R^3$	$\pi \doteq 3.14$, $R = 3$
	20.	$V = \dfrac{4}{3} \pi R^3$	$\pi \doteq 3.14$, $R = 6$
(Nursing)	21.	$C = \dfrac{a}{a + 12} \cdot A$	$a = 6$, $A = 30$
	22.	$C = \dfrac{a}{a + 12} \cdot A$	$a = 4$, $A = 48$
(Business)	23.	$S = R\left[\dfrac{(1 + i)^n - 1}{i}\right]$	$R = 100$, $n = 2$, $i = 0.01$
	24.	$S = R\left[\dfrac{(1 + i)^n - 1}{i}\right]$	$R = 50$, $n = 3$, $i = 0.01$
(Forestry)	25.	$Y = 0.2Q - 0.015Q^2$	$Q = 4.7$
	26.	$Y = 0.2Q - 0.015Q^2$	$Q = 5.4$
(Aerial Photography)	27.	$M = \dfrac{17.6Vtf}{H}$	$V = 145$, $t = \dfrac{1}{125}$, $f = 5.89$, $H = 3250$
	28.	$M = \dfrac{17.6Vtf}{H}$	$V = 205$, $t = \dfrac{1}{250}$, $f = 6.02$, $H = 3850$

SET II

(Geometry)	1.	$A = \dfrac{1}{2} bh$	$b = 24$, $h = 19$
(Electricity)	2.	$I = \dfrac{E}{R}$	$E = 12$, $R = 200$
(Business)	3.	$I = prt$	$p = 800$, $r = 0.06$, $t = 3.5$
(Nursing)	4.	$q = \dfrac{DQ}{H}$	$D = 12$, $Q = 450$, $H = 60$
(Business)	5.	$S = P(1 + i)^n$	$P = 500$, $i = 0.07$, $n = 2$
(Geometry)	6.	$A = \pi R^2$	$\pi \doteq 3.14$, $R = 50$
(Chemistry)	7.	$F = \dfrac{9}{5} C + 32$	$C = -15$

(Business)	8.	$A = p(1 + rt)$	$p = 800,\ r = 0.08,\ t = 2.5$
(Physics)	9.	$C = \dfrac{5}{9}(F - 32)$	$F = 17$
(Geometry)	10.	$V = \dfrac{4}{3}\pi R^3$	$\pi \doteq 3.14,\ R = 16$
(Nursing)	11.	$C = \dfrac{a}{a + 12} \cdot A$	$a = 8,\ A = 20$
(Business)	12.	$S = R\left[\dfrac{(1 + i)^n - 1}{i}\right]$	$R = 80,\ n = 2,\ i = 0.006$
(Forestry)	13.	$Y = 0.2Q - 0.015Q^2$	$Q = 6.3$
(Aerial Photography)	14.	$M = \dfrac{17.6Vtf}{H}$	$V = 115,\ t = \dfrac{1}{125},\ f = 5.37,$ $H = 3750$

205 Chapter Summary

Grouping Symbols (Sec. 202)

( ) Parentheses
[ ] Brackets
{ } Braces
—— Bar

Fraction line $\longrightarrow \dfrac{3x - 2}{5 + 7y}$

Bar in a square root $\longrightarrow$
$$\sqrt{5x - 12}$$

Order of Operations (Sec. 201)

1. If there are any parentheses in the expression, that part of the expression within a pair of parentheses is evaluated first, then the entire expression.
2. Any evaluation always proceeds in three steps:
   First: Powers and roots are done in any order.
   Second: Multiplication and division are done in order from left to right.
   Third: Addition and subtraction are done in order from left to right.

To Evaluate an Expression or Formula (Sec. 203)

1. Replace each letter by its number value.
2. Carry out all arithmetic operations using the correct order of operations.

REVIEW EXERCISES 205

SET I

In Exercises 1—16, evaluate each expression.

1. $26 - 14 + 8 - 11$ 2. $18 - 22 - 15 + 6$

3. $11 - 7 \cdot 3$ 4. $(11 - 7) \cdot 3$

5. $15 \div 5 \cdot 3$ 6. $3 \cdot 12 \div 4$

7. $[16 - (-8)] - 22$ 8. $36 - [(-7) - 15]$

9. $6 - [8 - (3 - 4)]$ 10. $10 - [-4 - (5 - 6)]$

11. $(56)^2(0) - 8 \div (-2)$ 12. $(35)^2(0) + 18 \div (-6)$

13. $\dfrac{6 + (-14)}{3 - 7}$ 14. $\dfrac{10 - (-2)}{9 - 12}$

15. $\sqrt{6^2 + 8^2}$ 16. $\sqrt{10^2 - 8^2}$

In Exercises 17—28, find the value of each expression when $x = -2$, $y = 3$, and $z = -4$.

17. $3x - y + z$ 18. $x - 2y + 3z$

19. $6 - x(y - z)$ 20. $7 - y(x + z)$

21. $5x^2 - 3x + 10$ 22. $3y^2 + 7y - 15$

23. $y^2 - 2yz + z^2$ 24. $x^2 + 2xy - y^2$

----

25. $x - 2[y - x(y + z)]$ 26. $y - 3[x - y(x - z)]$

27. $\dfrac{(x + y)^2 - z^2}{x - 2y}$ 28. $\dfrac{(x - y)^2 + z^2}{x - 2z}$

In Exercises 29-38, evaluate each formula using the values of the letters given with the formula.

29. $C = \dfrac{a}{a + 12} \cdot A$ $a = 8$, $A = 35$

30. $C = \dfrac{a}{a + 12} \cdot A$ $a = 5$, $A = 34$

31. $I = Prt$ $P = 100$, $r = 0.07$, $t = 4.5$

32. $I = Prt$ $P = 400$, $r = 0.10$, $t = 2.75$

33. $C = \dfrac{5}{9}(F - 32)$ $F = 15\frac{1}{2}$

34. $C = \dfrac{5}{9}(F - 32)$ $F = 21\frac{1}{2}$

35. $S = P(1 + i)^n$ $P = 700$, $n = 2$, $i = 0.05$

36. $S = P(1 + i)^n$ $P = 500$, $n = 3$, $i = 0.1$

37. $Y = 0.2Q - 0.015Q^2$ $Q = 5.8$

38. $H = \dfrac{17.6Vtf}{M}$ $V = 135$, $t = \dfrac{1}{125}$, $f = 5.16$, $M = 0.0175$

SET II

In Exercises 1—8, evaluate each expression.

1. $13 - 25 - 8 + 17$ 2. $19 - 8 \cdot 4$

3. $21 \div 7 \cdot 3$ 4. $[(-9) - 14] + 21$

5. $12 - [14 - (6 - 8)]$ 6. $16 \div (-8) - (25)^2(0)$

7. $\dfrac{28 + (-7)}{9 - 12}$ 8. $\sqrt{13^2 - 5^2}$

In Exercises 9—14, find the value of each expression when $x = -3$, $y = 5$, and $z = -2$.

9. $4x - y + 2z$ 10. $11 - y(x - z)$

11. $3z^2 - 8z + 13$ 12. $x^2 + 3xy - y^2$

13. $z - 5[z(x - y) - 2x]$ 14. $\dfrac{x^2 - (y - z)^2}{2z - x}$

In Exercises 15-20, evaluate each formula using the values of the letters given with the formula.

15. $q = \dfrac{DQ}{H}$ $D = 8$, $Q = 500$, $H = 40$

16. $I = Prt$ $P = 500$, $r = 0.09$, $t = 1.75$

17. $C = \dfrac{5}{9}(F - 32)$ $F = 39\frac{1}{2}$

18. $S = P(1 + i)^n$ $P = 2000$, $n = 4$, $i = 0.15$

19. $Y = 0.2Q - 0.015Q^2$ $Q = 6.2$

20. $M = \dfrac{17.6Vtf}{H}$ $V = 125$, $t = \dfrac{1}{250}$, $f = 4.97$,

                                        $H = 5040$

REVIEW EXERCISES FROM CHAPTER 1

In each of the following, perform the indicated operation. If the indicated operation cannot be done, give a reason.

1. $(-16)(-2)$ 2. $(-13) + (-8)$ 3. $(-5) - (-11)$

4. $(+28) \div (-7)$ 5. $(-15)(0)(4)$ 6. $(-2)^3$

7. $(-27) + (10)$ 8. $\sqrt{16}$ 9. $\dfrac{-48}{-12}$

10. $(0) \div (-6)$ 11. $(25)^2$ 12. $(-15)(3)$

13. -2^4 14. Subtract -9 from -13

15. $\dfrac{-12}{0}$ 16. $\sqrt[3]{8}$ 17. $\sqrt{64}$

18. 0^4 19. $(8) - (17)$ 20. $(-20) - (9)$

Chapter Two Diagnostic Test

Name_____

_____

The purpose of this test is to see how well you understand the evaluation of expressions containing numbers and letters. We recommend that you work this diagnostic test *before* your instructor tests you on this chapter. Allow yourself about fifty minutes to do this test.

Complete solutions for all the problems on this test, together with section references, are given in the Answer Section. We suggest that you study the sections referred to for the problems you do incorrectly.

Evaluate each of the following expressions. (You may need to review the correct order of operations before working these problems.)

1. $17 - 9 - 6 + 11$ (1)_____

2. $5 + 2 \cdot 3$ (2)_____

3. $12 \div 2 \cdot 3$ (3)_____

4. $-5^2 + (-4)^2$ (4)_____

5. $(2) \cdot 3^2 - 4$ (5)_____

6. $3\sqrt{25} - 5(-4)$ (6)_____

7. $\dfrac{8 - 12}{-6 + 2}$ (7)_____

8. $(2^3 - 8)(5^2 + 4^2)$ (8)_____

9. $10 - [6 - (5 - 7)]$

                                         (9)_____

10. $\{-10 - [5 + (4 - 7)]\} - 3$

                                         (10)_____

11. $\sqrt{10^2 - 6^2}$

                                         (11)_____

12. $48 \div (-4)^2 - 3\left[10 - \dfrac{10}{-2}\right]$

                                         (12)_____

_____

Find the value of each of the following expressions when $a = -2$, $b = 4$, $c = -3$, $x = 5$, and $y = -6$.

13. $3a + bx - cy$

(13) _____

14. $4x - [a - (3c - b)]$

(14) _____

15. $x^2 + 2xy - y^2$

(15) _____

Evaluate each formula using the values of the letters given with the formula.

16. $C = \frac{5}{9}(F - 32)$ $F = -4$

(16) _____

17. $A = \pi R^2$ $\pi \doteq 3.14$, $R = 20$

(17) _____

18. $C = \frac{a}{a + 12} \cdot A$ $a = 7$, $A = 38$

(18) _____

19. $A = P(1 + rt)$ $P = 600, r = 0.10, t = 2.5$

(19) _____

20. $Y = 0.2Q - 0.015Q^2$ $Q = 6$

(20) _____

_____

THREE

Simplifying Algebraic Expressions

301 Basic Definitions

ALGEBRAIC EXPRESSIONS. An *algebraic expression* consists only of numbers, letters, signs of operation, and signs of grouping. Not *all* of these need be present.

Example 1. The following are examples of algebraic expressions.

(a) $2x - 3y$

(b) $5x^3 - 7x^2 + 4$

(c) $\dfrac{5a^2 - 2b^3}{\sqrt{3ab}}$

(d) $\sqrt{b^2 - 4ac}$

(e) $(a - b)^2 + (c - d)^2$

CONSTANTS. A *constant* is an object or symbol that does not change its value in a particular problem or discussion. It is usually represented by a number symbol. In the algebraic expression, $4x^2 - 3y$, the constants are 4, 2, and -3.

VARIABLES. A *variable* is an object or symbol that changes its value in a particular problem or discussion. It is represented by a letter. In the algebraic expression $2x - 3y$, the variables are x and y.

TERMS. The + and - signs in an algebraic expression break it into smaller pieces called *terms*. Each + and - sign is part of the term that follows it. *Exception*: An expression within grouping symbols is considered as a single piece even though it may contain + and - signs. See Examples 2(c), 2(d), and Example 3.

Example 2

(a) In the algebraic expression $2a + 5c$,

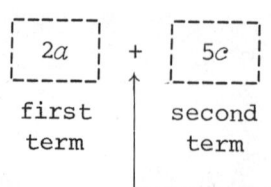

first term   second term

The + sign separates the algebraic expression into two terms.

(b) In the algebraic expression $3x^2y - 5xy^3 + 7xy$:

The - and + signs separate the algebraic expression into three terms.

┌─The minus sign is part of the second term.

$$\boxed{3x^2y} + \boxed{-5xy^3} + \boxed{7xy}$$

first   second   third
term   term   term

(c)   In the algebraic expression $3x^2 - 9x(2y + 5z)$,

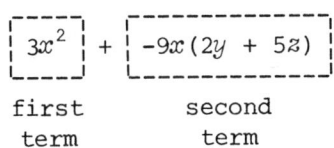

first   second
term   term

(d)   In the algebraic expression $\dfrac{2 - x}{xy} + 5(2x^2 - y)$,

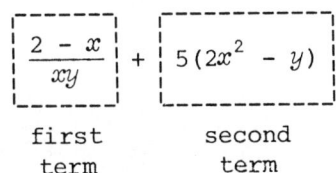

first   second
term   term

Example 3. The number of terms in an algebraic expression.

(a) $3 + 2x - 1$ has three terms.

(b) $3 + (2x - 1)$ has two terms.

(c) $(3 + 2x - 1)$ has one term.

FACTORS. The numbers that are multiplied together to give a
product are called the *factors* of that product. One (1)
is a factor of any number. Even though 1 is a factor of
every number, it is often omitted. More information on
factors is given in Chapter 8.

Example 4. Factors of a product.

(a) $(3)(5) = 15$ 3 and 5 are factors of 15.

                                          ─ factors of 15

(b) $(2)(x) = 2x$

                                          ─ factors of $2x$

(c) $(7)(a)(b)(c) = 7abc$

                                    └─ product of factors

                                      ─ factors of $7abc$

COEFFICIENTS. In a term having *two* factors, the *coefficient* of
one factor is the other factor. In a term having *more than
two* factors, the coefficient of each factor is the product
of all the other factors in that term.

Example 5. Coefficients.

(a)   (3)(5)

           5 is the coefficient of 3.

           3 is the coefficient of 5.

(b) $\frac{3}{4}\, y$

           y is the coefficent of $\frac{3}{4}$.

           $\frac{3}{4}$ is the coefficient of y.

(c) $3xy = 3(xy) = (3x)y = (3y)x$

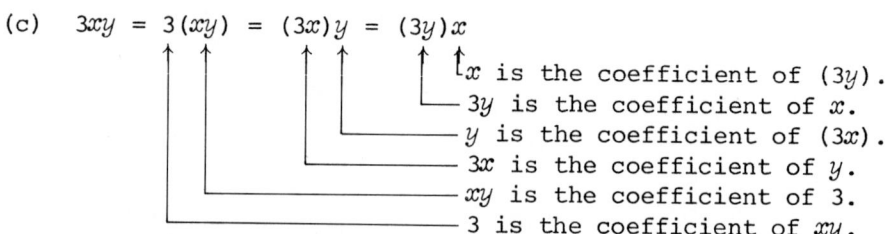

           x is the coefficient of $(3y)$.

           $3y$ is the coefficient of x.

           y is the coefficient of $(3x)$.

           $3x$ is the coefficient of y.

           xy is the coefficient of 3.

           3 is the coefficient of xy.

Numerical Coefficients. A *numerical coefficient* is a coefficient that is a number. If we say "*the* coefficient" of a term, it is understood to mean the *numerical* coefficient of that term.

Literal Coefficients. A *literal coefficient* is a coefficient that is a letter or product of letters.

Example 6. Literal and numerical coefficients.

(a) $6w$

           Literal coefficient of 6.

           Numerical coefficient of w.

(b) $12xy^2$

           xy^2 is the literal coefficient of 12.

           12 is the numerical coefficient of xy^2.

(c) $\dfrac{3xy}{4} = \dfrac{3}{4}xy$

           $\frac{3}{4}$ is the numerical coefficient of xy.

(d) xy

           Even though there is no number written, the numerical coefficient can be considered to be 1 because $xy = 1(xy)$ Also see part (e).

(e) $-a^2$

           −1 is the numerical coefficient of a^2.

(f) $\dfrac{c}{5} = \dfrac{1}{5}c$

$\dfrac{1}{5}$ is the numerical coefficient of c.

(g) $3x^2 - 9x(2y + 5z)$

-9 is the numerical coefficient of $x(2y + 5z)$.

EXERCISES 301

SET I

In Exercises 1-4, list (a) the different constants, and (b) the different variables.

1. $2x + 4y + 2$ 2. $7a + 3b + 7$

3. $7u - 8v + 2v$ 4. $3x - 5y - 2x$

In Exercises 5—10, (a) determine the number of terms;
(b) write the second term if there is one.

5. $7xy$ 6. $5ab$

7. $E + 5F - 3$ 8. $R - 2T - 6$

9. $3x^2y + \dfrac{2x + y}{3xy} + 4(3x^2 - y)$

10. $5xy^2 + \dfrac{5x - y}{7xy} + 3(x^2 - 4y)$

In Exercises 11—14, write (a) the numerical coefficient of
the first term, and (b) the literal part of the second term.

11. $3x + 7y$ 12. $4R + 3T$

13. $x^2 - 3xy$ 14. $x^2 + 5xy$

15. In the expression $3xyz$,
     (a) What is the numerical coefficient of the term?
     (b) What is the coefficient of z?
     (c) What is the coefficient of xy?
16. In the expression $12abc$,
     (a) What is the numerical coefficient of the term?
     (b) What is the coefficient of c?
     (c) What is the coefficient of ab?

In Exercises 17 and 18, list (a) the constants, and
(b) the variables.

17. $\dfrac{3x^5 - 4y}{6y^2}$ 18. $\dfrac{5x - 2y^3}{4x^6}$

In Exercises 19—22, (a) determine the number of terms;
(b) write the second term if there is one.

19. $5u^2 - 6u(2u + v^2)$ 20. $3E^3 - 2E(8E + F^2)$

21. $[(x + y) - (x - y)]$ 22. $\{x - [y - (x - y)]\}$

In Exercises 23 and 24, write (a) the numerical coefficient of the first term, and (b) the literal part of the second term.

23. $x^2 + 2xy + y^2$ 24. $-x^2 + 3xy + 3y^2$

SET II

In Exercises 1 and 2, list (a) the different constants, and (b) the different variables.

1. $4x - 7y + 4$ 2. $8u - 5v + 3u$ 3. $\dfrac{7a^3 - 4b}{5c^2}$

In Exercises 4-8, (a) determine the number of terms; (b) write the second term if there is one.

4. $3ab$ 5. $5 - (x + y)$
6. $[x^2 - (x + y)]$ 7. $[a + (b - c)]$
8. $3x(10x + y^2) - 6y^2$

In Exercises 9-12, write (a) the numerical coefficient of the first term, and (b) the literal part of the second term.

9. $-x^2 + 5xy$ 10. $-y^2 + 3(x + y)$ 11. $-2a^2 - 5ab + b^3$

12. In the expression $5abc$,
     (a) Write the numerical coefficient of the term.
     (b) Write the coefficient of a.
     (c) Write the coefficient of b.

First Basic Rule of Exponents

In Sec. 110 we discussed bases, exponents, and powers of signed numbers.

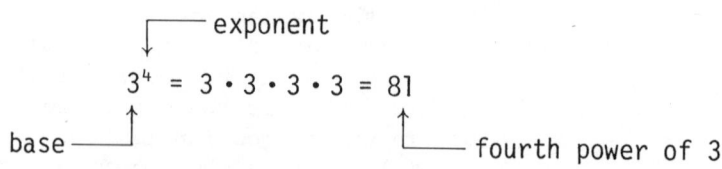

exponent

$$3^4 = 3 \cdot 3 \cdot 3 \cdot 3 = 81$$

base ⟶   ⟶ fourth power of 3

The same definitions are carried over to expressions with letters.

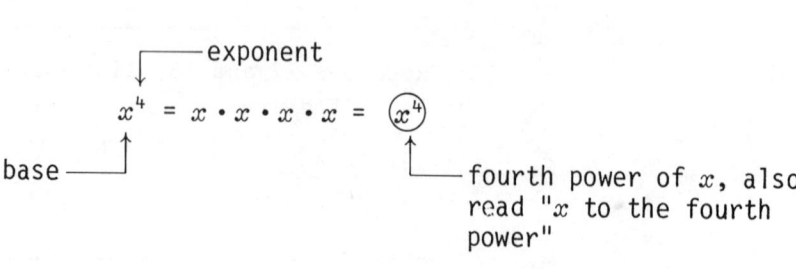

exponent

$$x^4 = x \cdot x \cdot x \cdot x = \boxed{x^4}$$

base ⟶   ⟶ fourth power of x, also read "x to the fourth power"

Consider the product $x^3 \cdot x^2$

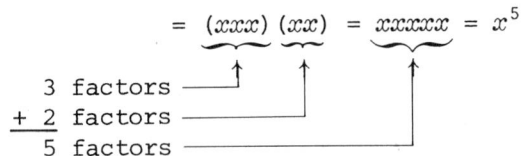

$$= \underbrace{(xxx)}_{} \; \underbrace{(xx)}_{} \; = \; \underbrace{xxxxx}_{} \; = \; x^5$$

3 factors ⎯⎯⎯⎯
+ 2 factors ⎯⎯⎯⎯
5 factors ⎯⎯⎯⎯

Therefore, $x^3 \cdot x^2 = x^{3+2} = x^5$

This leads to the following rule of exponents:

FIRST BASIC RULE OF EXPONENTS

$$x^a \cdot x^b = x^{a+b}$$

The first basic rule of exponents can be extended to include more factors.

$$x^a x^b x^c \; \cdots \; = \; x^{a+b+c+\cdots}$$

Note. When *multiplying* powers of the *same* base, *add* the exponents but keep the *same* base. Do not multiply the bases. ∎

Example 1. Using the first basic rule of exponents.

(a) $\quad x^5 \cdot x^2 = x^{5+2} = x^7$

(b) $\quad x \cdot x^2 = x^{1+2} = x^3$

$\quad \uparrow\!\!\rule{0pt}{0pt}\,x = x^1 \qquad$ (When no exponent is written, the exponent is understood to be 1.)

(c) $\quad x^3 \cdot x^7 \cdot x^4 = x^{3+7+4} = x^{14}$

(d) $\quad 10^7 \cdot 10^5 = 10^{7+5} = 10^{12} = 1,\!\underbrace{000,\!000,\!000,\!000}_{}$

$\qquad\qquad\qquad\qquad\qquad\qquad\qquad$ 12 zeros

(e) $\quad 2 \cdot 2^3 \cdot 2^2 = 2^{1+3+2} = 2^6 = 64$

(f) $\quad a^4 \cdot a \cdot a^5 = a^{4+1+5} = a^{10}$

(g) $\quad a^x \cdot a^y = a^{x+y}$

(h) $\quad x^3 \cdot y^2 \qquad$ Notice: *The rule does not apply* because the bases are different.

EXERCISES 302. Find the following products using the first basic rule of exponents.

SET I

1. $x^3 \cdot x^4$	2. $x^2 \cdot x^9$	3. $y \cdot y^3$
4. $z \cdot z^4$	5. $m^2 \cdot m$	6. $a^3 \cdot a$
7. $10^2 \cdot 10^3$	8. $10^4 \cdot 10^3$	9. $2 \cdot 2^3 \cdot 2^2$

10. $3 \cdot 3^2 \cdot 3^3$ 11. $x \cdot x^3 \cdot x^4$ 12. $y \cdot y^5 \cdot y^3$

13. $x^2 y^5$ 14. $a^3 b^2$ 15. $3^2 \cdot 5^3$

16. $2^3 \cdot 3^2$

----

17. $a^x \cdot a^w$ 18. $x^a \cdot x^b$ 19. $x^y \cdot y^x$

20. $a^b \cdot b^a$ 21. $x^2 y^3 x^5$ 22. $z^3 z^4 w^2$

23. $a^2 b^3 a^5$ 24. $x^8 y x^4$

SET II

1. $x^2 \cdot x^5$ 2. $y \cdot y^4$ 3. $u^2 \cdot u$

4. $10^3 \cdot 10^4$ 5. $3 \cdot 3^2 \cdot 3^3$ 6. $a \cdot a^3 \cdot a^2$

7. $x^3 y^3$ 8. $x^a \cdot x^b$ 9. $x^2 \cdot x^y \cdot x^3$

10. $3^2 \cdot 4^3$ 11. $a^4 \cdot a^2$ 12. $xy^2 x^3$

Simplifying Products of Factors

In working with algebraic expressions, you must be able to
simplify a product of factors.

TO SIMPLIFY A PRODUCT OF FACTORS

1. *Write the sign.* The sign is negative if there are
an odd number of negative factors. The sign is
positive if there are an even number of negative
factors (or no negative factor).

2. *Write the number.* (Its sign was found in Step 1.)
The number is the product of all the absolute
values of the numbers.

3. *Write the letters.* (Usually in alphabetical
order.) Use the first rule of exponents to determine the exponent of each letter.

Example 1. Simplify the following products.

(a) $(6x)(-2x^3)$

   $= -(6 \cdot 2)(xx^3)$

   $= -(12)(x^4) = -12x^4$

         └─ First basic rule of exponents.

       └─ 12 is the product of the absolute
values of the numbers in the factors.

     └─ The sign is negative because there
is an odd number of negative factors.

(b) $(-2a^2b)(5a^3b^3)$

$= -(2 \cdot 5)(a^2a^3)(bb^3)$

$= -(10)(a^5)(b^4) = -10a^5b^4$

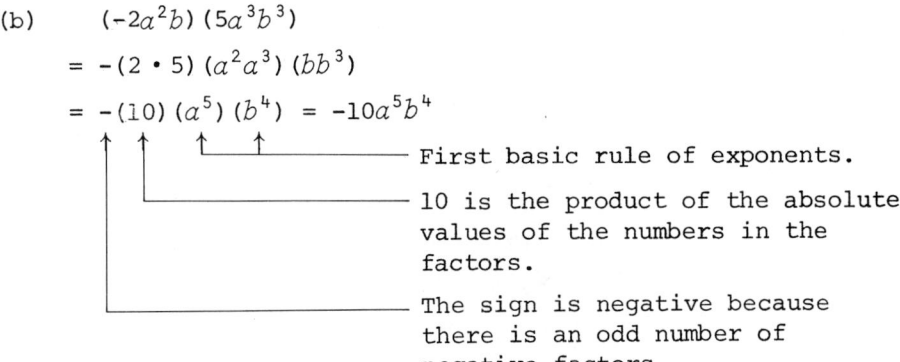

First basic rule of exponents.

10 is the product of the absolute values of the numbers in the factors.

The sign is negative because there is an odd number of negative factors.

(c) $(-5y^2)(2y)(-4y^3)$

$= +(5 \cdot 2 \cdot 4)(y^2yy^3)$

$= +(40)(y^6) = 40y^6$

Positive, because there is an even number of negative factors.

(d) $(4xy^2)(-3x^2y^3)(-2x^3y)$

$= +(4 \cdot 3 \cdot 2)(xx^2x^3)(y^2y^3y)$

$= +(24)(x^6)(y^6) = 24x^6y^6$

Positive, because there is an even number of negative factors.

This method of simplifying products of factors makes use of the Associative and Commutative Properties of Multiplication.

EXERCISES 303. Simplify the following products of factors.

SET I

1. $(-2a)(4a^2)$ 2. $(-3x)(5x^3)$
3. $(-5h^2)(-6h^3)$ 4. $(-6k^3)(-8k)$
5. $(-5x^3)^2$ 6. $(-7y^4)^2$
7. $(-2a^3)(-4a)(3a^4)$ 8. $(-6b^2)(-2b)(-4b^3)$
9. $(-9m)(m^5)(-2m^2)$ 10. $(4n^4)(-7n^2)(-n)$
11. $(5x^2)(-7y)$ 12. $(-3x^3)(4y)$
13. $(-6m^3n^2)(-4mn^2)$ 14. $(-8h^4k)(5h^2k^3)$
15. $(2x^{10}y^2)(-3x^{12}y^7)$ 16. $(-2a^2b^5)(-5a^{10}b^{10})$
17. $(3xy^2)^2$ 18. $(4x^2y^3)^2$
19. $(5x^4y^5z)(-y^4z^7)$ 20. $(-7E^2F^5G^8)(3F^6G^{10})$
21. $(2^3RS^2)(-2^2R^5T^4)$ 22. $(-3^2xy)(3^3x^8z^5)$

- - - - - - - - - - - - - - - - - -

23. $(-c^2 d)(5d^1 e^3)(-4c^5 e^2)$ 24. $(3m^1 n^2)(-m^3 r^4)(-8n^5 r)$

25. $(-2x^2)(-3xy^2 z)(-7yz)$ 26. $(14y^2)(-5x^3 z^4)(-6xyz)$

27. $(3xy)(x^2 y^2)(-5x^3 y^3)$ 28. $(xy)(-2xz)(3yz)$

29. $(-2ab)(5bc)(ac)$ 30. $(3xyz)(-2x^2 y)(-yz^2)$

31. $(-5x^2 y)(2yz^3)(-xz)$ 32. $(2a^2 b^3)(-3ab^2)(-a^2 b^2)$

33. $(-5x^2 y^2 z)(x^5 y^3 z)(7xyz^5)$

34. $(-4R^2 S^3 T^4)(-8RS^3 T^4)(-R^6 S^1 T^5)$

35. $(-3h^2 k)(7)(-m^3 k^5)(-mh^4)$ 36. $(-km^2)(-6n^3)(8)(-k^2 m)$

SET II

1. $(-3x)(5x^3)$ 2. $(3a^2)(-2a^4)$

3. $(4x^2)^3$ 4. $(3x^2)^2$

5. $(-4b^2)(-2b)(-6b^5)$ 6. $(-3t^4)(5t^3)(-10t)$

7. $(15x^3)(-3y^2)$ 8. $(-12a^4)(-5b)$

9. $(-4c^2 d)(-13cd^3)$ 10. $(-6e^5 f^3)(11e^2 f^3)$

11. $(2mn^2)(-4m^2 n^2)(2m^3 n)$ 12. $(5x^2 y)(-2xy^2)(-3xy)$

13. $(2m^5 n)(-4mn^3)(3m^2 n^6)$ 14. $(7ab^4)(2a^2 b)(-5a^2 b^3)$

15. $(2H^2 K^4 M)(-2^2 H^4 K^5 N)(2^3 M^6 K^7 N)$

16. $(-10x^3 y^2 z)(-10^2 xk^{10} z^1)(-10ky)$

17. $(-2e^1 f^2)(-3e^3 h)(-6fh)(-5e^2 h)$

18. $(-4x^2 y)(-7y^2 z^2)(-5xy^4 z)(-2x^3 z^5)$

The Distributive Rule

The formula for finding the area of a rectangle is:

Area of rectangle = Length × Width

$$A = LW$$

Consider Fig. 304:

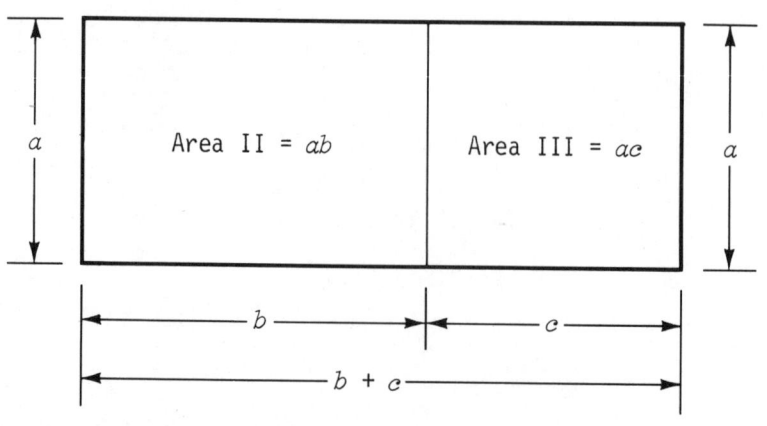

Figure 304

There are three rectangles in the figure.

I.   The large rectangle: Length = $b + c$, Width = a,
                            Area I = $a(b + c)$
II. The left rectangle: Length = b, Width = a,
                            Area II = ab
III. The right rectangle: Length = c, Width = a,
                            Area III = ac

Area of large rectangle	=	Area of left rectangle	+	Area of right rectangle
Area I	=	Area II	+	Area III
$a(b + c)$	=	ab	+	ac

This is one of the fundamental properties of real numbers and is called *the Distributive Rule*.

THE DISTRIBUTIVE RULE

$$a(b + c) = ab + ac$$

By dividing the rectangle into any number of smaller rectangles, we can extend the distributive rule to the following more general rule:

$$a(b + c + d + \cdots) = ab + ac + ad + \cdots$$

<u>Meaning of the Distributive Rule</u>. When a factor is multiplied by an expression enclosed within grouping symbols, the factor must be multiplied by *each term* within the grouping symbol; then the products are added.

$$-5(2 - 7) = (-5)(\boxed{2} + \boxed{-7})$$

first product + second product

Each term inside the parentheses is multiplied by the factor outside the parentheses; then these products are added.

$$= \quad (-5)(2) \quad + \quad (-5)(-7)$$
$$= \quad -10 \quad + \quad 35 \quad = 25$$

<u>Example 1</u>. Using the distributive rule.

(a) $4(3 + 6) = (4)(3) + (4)(6)$
$$= \quad 12 \quad + \quad 24 \quad = 36$$

(b) $\quad 2(3 - 7) = \left(\!2\!\right) \left(\boxed{\;3\;} + \boxed{\;-7\;} \right)$

$\qquad\qquad\qquad = \quad (2)(3) \quad + (2)(-7)$

$\qquad\qquad\qquad = \qquad 6 \qquad + \quad (-14) \quad = -8$

(c) $\quad 2(x + y) = (2)(x) + (2)(y)$

$\qquad\qquad\qquad = \quad 2x \quad + \quad 2y$

(d) $\quad a(x - y) = (a)(x) + (a)(-y)$

$\qquad\qquad\qquad = \quad ax \quad + \quad (-ay) = ax - ay$

(e) $\quad x(x^2 + y) = (x)(x^2) + (x)(y)$

$\qquad\qquad\qquad = \quad x^3 \quad + \quad xy$

(f) $\quad 3x(4x + x^3 y) = (3x)(4x) + (3x)(x^3 y)$

$\qquad\qquad\qquad\qquad = \quad 12x^2 \quad + \quad 3x^4 y$

Example 2. Using the distributive rule when more than two terms appear within the parentheses.

$-5a(4a^3 - 2a^2 b + b^2) = \left(\!-5a\!\right) \left(\boxed{\;4a^3\;} + \boxed{\;-2a^2 b\;} + \boxed{\;b^2\;} \right)$

$\qquad\qquad\qquad\qquad = (-5a)(4a^3) + (-5a)(-2a^2 b) + (-5a)(b^2)$

$\qquad\qquad\qquad\qquad = \quad -20a^4 \quad + \quad 10a^3 b \quad - \quad 5ab^2$

FURTHER EXTENSIONS OF THE DISTRIBUTIVE RULE. Using the distributive rule, the definition of subtraction, and the Commutative Rule of Multiplication, it follows that

$$(b + c)a = a(b + c) = ab + ac = ba + ca$$

Therefore, $(b + c)a = ba + ca$.
This can be extended to include more terms.

$$(b + c + d + \cdots)a = ba + ca + da + \cdots$$

In Example 3 we show how to use the distributive rule when the factor appears on the right.

Example 3. Using the distributive rule when the factor appears on the right.

(a) $\quad (2x - 5)(-4x) = \left(\boxed{\;2x\;} + \boxed{\;-5\;} \right) \left(\!-4x\!\right)$

$\qquad\qquad\qquad = (2x)(-4x) + (-5)(-4x)$

$\qquad\qquad\qquad = \quad -8x^2 \quad + \quad 20x$

Note. $-8x^2$ and $20x$ are *unlike* terms and can *not* be combined.

(b) $(-2x^2 + xy - 5y^2)(-3xy)$

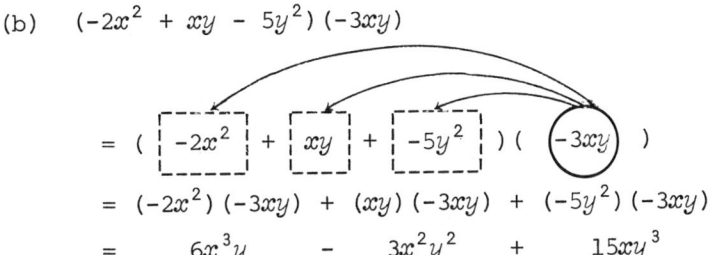

$$= (\,\boxed{-2x^2}\, + \,\boxed{xy}\, + \,\boxed{-5y^2}\,)(\,\boxed{-3xy}\,)$$

$$= (-2x^2)(-3xy) + (xy)(-3xy) + (-5y^2)(-3xy)$$

$$= \quad 6x^3y \quad - \quad 3x^2y^2 \quad + \quad 15xy^3$$

A word of caution. A common mistake students make is to think that the distributive rule applies to expressions like $2(3 \cdot 4)$.

└──────The distributive rule only applies when this is an addition.

$$2(3 \cdot 4) \neq (2 \cdot 3)(2 \cdot 4)$$
$$2(12) \neq 6 \cdot 8$$
$$24 \neq 48$$

EXERCISES 304. Find each of the following products using the Distributive Rule.

SET I

1. $5(a + 6)$ 2. $4(x + 10)$
3. $7(x + y)$ 4. $5(m + n)$
5. $3(m - 4)$ 6. $3(a - 5)$
7. $4(x - y)$ 8. $9(m - n)$
9. $a(6 + x)$ 10. $b(7 + y)$
11. $-2(x - 3)$ 12. $-3(x - 5)$
13. $-3(2x^2 - 4x + 5)$ 14. $-5(3x^2 - 2x - 7)$
15. $4x(3x^2 - 6)$ 16. $3x(5x^2 - 10)$
17. $-2x(5x^2 + 3x - 4)$ 18. $-4x(2x^2 - 5x + 3)$
19. $(x - 4)6$ 20. $(3 - 2x)(-5)$
21. $(y^2 - 4y + 3)7$ 22. $(-9 + z - 2z^2)(-7)$
23. $(2x^2 - 3x + 5)4x$ 24. $(3w^2 + 2w - 8)5w$
25. $x(xy - 3)$ 26. $a(ab - 4)$
27. $3a(ab - 2a^2)$ 28. $4x(3x - 2y^2)$

----

29. $(-2x + 4x^2y)(-3y)$ 30. $(-3a + 2a^2z)(-2z)$
31. $-2xy(x^2y - y^2x - y - 5)$ 32. $-3ab(8 - a^2 - b^2 + ab)$
33. $-3(x - 2y + 2)$ 34. $-2(x - 3y + 4)$
35. $(3x^3 - 2x^2y + y^3)(-2xy)$ 36. $(4z^3 - z^2y - y^3)(-2yz)$
37. $(2xy^2z - 7x^2z^2)(-5xz^3)$ 38. $(3a^2bc^2 - 4ab^3c)(-3ac^2)$
39. $(5x^2y^3z - 2xz^3 + y^4)(-4xz^2)$
40. $(-2xy^2z^2)(6x^2y - 3yz - 4xz^2)$

1. $3(x + 4)$

2. $2(m - 5)$

3. $x(4 + y)$

4. $-3(x - 4)$

5. $(M + N)(3)$

6. $(x - y)(-4)$

7. $-5(3x^2 + 4x - 7)$

8. $6x(5x^2 - 4)$

9. $-3x(4x^2 - 6x + 8)$

10. $(9 - 5x)(-2)$

11. $(3z^2 - 5z + 4)(-6)$

12. $(2u - 5u^2 + 11)6$

13. $x(xy - 6)$

14. $4a(ab - b^2)$

15. $4x(3xy^2 - 2x^2y)$

16. $(6s^2t - 5st)(-3t)$

17. $(x^2 - 4xy + y^2)(-2x)$

18. $3x^2y(x^3 - 3x^2y + 3xy^2 - y^3)$

19. $(-5a^2bc)(2b^2c - 5ac^3 - 3a^2b^3)$

20. $(2a^3bc^2 - 3ac + b^3)(-5ab^2)$

Removing Grouping Symbols

To simplify algebraic expressions, grouping symbols must be removed. The distributive rule can be used to remove grouping symbols.

Multiplying a number by 1 does not change its value.

$(3x - 5) = \boxed{1}(3x - 5) = (1)(3x) + (1)(-5) = 3x - 5$

$+(4y + 7) = + \boxed{1}(4y + 7) = (+1)(4y) + (+1)(+7) = +4y + 7$

$-(8 - 6z) = - \boxed{1}(8 - 6z) = (-1)(8) + (-1)(-6z) = -8 + 6z$

$-2x(4 - 5x) = (-2x)(4) + (-2x)(-5x) = -8x + 10x^2$

All grouping symbols may be removed by using the distributive rule as just shown. Grouping symbols may also be removed by using the following rules which result from these applications of the distributive rule.

REMOVING GROUPING SYMBOLS

First, write a + sign for any enclosed term having no written sign.   Then,

1. *When removing a grouping symbol preceded by a + sign (or no sign):*

    Leave the enclosed terms unchanged. Drop the grouping symbol and the + sign (if there is one) preceding it.

    $a + (b - c)$ $(a - b) + c$

                 — + sign   — + sign
    $= a + (+b - c)$ added. $= (+a - b) + c$ added.

              — Drop   — Drop
    $= a \quad + b - c$ these. $= +a - b + c$ these.

2. *When removing a grouping symbol preceded by a – sign:*

    Change the sign of each enclosed term. Drop the grouping symbol and the – sign preceding it.

    $a - (b - c)$ — + sign added.

    $= a - (+b - c)$

            — Drop these.

    $= a \quad - b + c$ Sign of each enclosed term changed.

3. *When removing a grouping symbol preceded by a factor:*

    Multiply each enclosed term by the factor, and add these products. Drop the grouping symbol and the factor.

    $a(b - c)$ — + sign added.

    $= a(+b - c)$

    $= (a)(+b) + (a)(-c)$

    $= \quad ab \quad - \quad ac$

Example 1.   Removing grouping symbols.

(a) Removing a grouping symbol preceded by no sign.

   $(3x - 5) - y$

$= (+3x - 5) - y$ Write + sign when enclosed term has no sign.

$= \quad +3x - 5 - y$ Drop the ( ).

(b)   Removing a grouping symbol preceded by a + sign.

$$5z + (4y + 7)$$

$$= 5z + (+4y + 7)$$ Write + sign when enclosed term has no sign.

$$= 5z \quad +4y + 7$$ Drop the ( ) and the + sign preceding it.

(c)   Removing a grouping symbol preceded by a - sign.

$$2x - (8 - 6z)$$

$$= 2x - (+8 - 6z)$$ Write + sign when enclosed term has no sign.

$$= 2x \quad - 8 + 6z$$ Change the sign of each enclosed term, *and* drop the ( ) and the - sign preceding it.

(d)   Removing a grouping symbol preceded by a factor.

$$-2x(4 - 5x)$$

$$= -2x(+4 - 5x)$$ Write + sign when enclosed term has no sign.

$$= (-2x)(+4) + (-2x)(-5x)$$ Multiply each enclosed term by the factor and add the products.

$$= \quad -8x \quad + \quad 10x^2$$

WHEN GROUPING SYMBOLS OCCUR *WITHIN* OTHER GROUPING SYMBOLS

It is usually easier to remove the *innermost* grouping symbols first.

$$a - [b + (c - d) + e]$$ + sign added.

$$= a - [+b + (+c - d) + e]$$

$$= a - [+b \quad + c - d \quad + e]$$ Removed inner ( ).

$$= a \quad - b \quad - c + d - e$$ Removed outer [ ].

Example 2.   Removing grouping symbols within other grouping symbols.

(a) $x - [y + (a - b)]$
$= x - [y + a - b]$ Removed ( ) preceded by + sign.
$= x - y - a + b$ Removed [ ] preceded by - sign.

(b) $3 + 2[a - 5(x - 4y)]$
$= 3 + 2[a - 5x + 20y]$ Removed ( ) using the Distributive Rule.
$= 3 + 2a - 10x + 40y$ Removed [ ] using the Distributive Rule.

(c) $(3a - b) - 2\{x - [(y - 2) - z]\}$

  = $(3a - b) - 2\{x - [y - 2 - z]\}$ Removed ( ) preceded by no sign.

  = $(3a - b) - 2\{x - y + 2 + z\}$ Removed [ ] preceded by − sign.

  = $(3a - b) - 2x + 2y - 4 - 2z$ Removed { } using the Distributive Rule.

  = $3a - b - 2x + 2y - 4 - 2z$ Removed ( ) preceded by no sign. These ( ) could have been removed as early as the first step.

EXERCISES 305.   Remove the grouping symbols.

SET I

1. $8 + (a - b)$ 2. $7 + (m - n)$

3. $5 - (x - y)$ 4. $6 - (a - b)$

5. $12 - 3(m - n)$ 6. $14 - 5(x - y)$

7. $(R - S) - 8$ 8. $(x - y) - 2$

9. $10 - 2(a - b)$ 10. $12 - 5(x - 2y)$

11. $2(x - y) + 3$ 12. $4(a - 2b) + 5$

13. $2a - 3(x - y)$ 14. $5x - 2(a - b)$

15. $a - [x - (b - c)]$ 16. $a - [x - (-b + c)]$

----

17. $4 - 2[a - 3(x - y)]$ 18. $8 - 3[x - 2(3a - b)]$

19. $3(a - 2x) - 2(y - 3b)$ 20. $2(2x - b) - 3(y - 5a)$

21. $-10[-2(x - 3y) + a] - b$ 22. $-5[-3(2x - y) + a] - c$

23. $(a - b) - \{[x - (3 - y)] - R\}$

24. $(x - y) - \{[a - (c - 5)] - b\}$

SET II

1. $5 + (x + y)$ 2. $3 - (x - y)$

3. $12 - 2(a + b)$ 4. $(a - b) - c$

5. $2x - 3(a - b)$ 6. $4(x - 2y) - 3a$

7. $-(x - y) + (2 - a)$ 8. $(a + b)(2) - 6$

9. $x - [a + (y - b)]$ 10. $x - [-(y - b) + a]$

11. $P - \{x - [y - (4 - z)]\}$ 12. $-\{-[-(-2 - x) + y]\} - a$

Combining Like Terms

LIKE TERMS. Terms having identical literal parts are called *like terms*.

UNLIKE TERMS. Terms having different literal parts are called *unlike terms*.

Example 1. Examples of like terms.

(a) $3x$, $4x$, x, $\frac{1}{2}x$, $0.7x$ are like terms. They are called "x-terms."

(b) $2x^2$, $10x^2$, $\frac{3}{4}x^2$, $2.3x^2$ are like terms. They are called "x^2-terms."

(c) $5xy$, $2xy$, xy, $\frac{2}{3}xy$, $5.6xy$ are like terms. They are called "xy-terms."

(d) $4x^2y$, $8x^2y$, x^2y, $\frac{1}{5}x^2y$, $2.8x^2y$ are like terms. They are called "x^2y-terms."

Example 2. Examples of unlike terms.

(a) $2x$, $3y$ are unlike terms.

(b) $5x^2$, $7x$ are unlike terms.

$$5x^2 = 5(xx)$$
$$7x \; = 7(x)$$
The literal parts are different.

(c) $4x^2y$, $10xy^2$ are unlike terms.

$$4x^2y = 4(xxy)$$
$$10xy^2 = 10(xyy)$$
The literal parts are different.

COMBINING LIKE TERMS

3 dollars + 5 dollars = (3 + 5)dollars = 8 dollars

3 cars   + 5 cars   = (3 + 5)cars   = 8 cars

$3x$ + $5x$ = $(3 + 5)x$ = $8x$

⌐———————— This is an application of the Distributive Rule.

When we combine like terms, we are usually changing the grouping and the order in which the terms appear. The Commutative and Associative Properties of Addition guarantee that when we do this, the sum remains unchanged.

TO COMBINE LIKE TERMS

1. Identify the like terms by their identical literal parts.

2. Find the sum of each group of like terms by adding their numerical coefficients (then multiply that sum by the literal part of those like terms). When no coefficient is written, it is understood to be 1.

Example 3. Combining like terms.

(a) $2x + 4x = (2 + 4)x = 6x$

(b) $8y - 3y = (8 - 3)y = 5y$

(c) $e - 9e = (1 - 9)e = -8e$

    ↑_____↑_____ When no coefficient is written, it is understood to be 1.

(d) $5x^2y - 7x^2y = (5 - 7)x^2y = -2x^2y$

(e) $4ab - 3ab + 6ab = (4 - 3 + 6)ab = 7ab$

(f) $\underbrace{9x - 3x} + 5y = (9 - 3)x + 5y = 6x + 5y$

    ↑____ These are the only like terms in the expression. Unlike terms cannot be combined.

(g) $12a - 7b - 9a + 4b$

  $= (12a - 9a) + (-7b + 4b)$ Only like terms can be combined.

  $= (12 - 9)a + (-7 + 4)b$

  $= \quad 3a \quad + \quad (-3b) \quad = 3a - 3b$

(h) $7x - 2y + 9 - 11x + 3 - 4y$

  $= (7x - 11x) + (-2y - 4y) + (9 + 3)$

  $= \quad -4x \quad + \quad (-6y) \quad + \quad 12 \quad = -4x - 6y + 12$

(i) $3x^2 - 5x + 5 - 2x^2 + 7x + 11$

  $= (3x^2 - 2x^2) + (-5x + 7x) + (5 + 11)$

  $= \quad x^2 \quad + \quad 2x \quad + \quad 16$

Note. It is important for a student to realize that in an expression such as

$$3x - 7x + 10x$$

$$3, \quad -7, \quad 10 \quad \text{can be thought of as}$$

the coefficients in the *sum*

$$(3x) + (-7x) + (10x). \quad \text{For this reason, we}$$

can add as follows:

        ③x ⑺x ⑽x $= 6x$

        |___|____|_____ Add these.   ■

EXERCISES 306. Combine like terms.

SET I

1. $15x - 3x$ 2. $12a - 9a$

3. $5a - 12a$ 4. $10x - 24x$

5. $2a - 5a + 6a$ 6. $3y - 4y + 5y$

7. $5x - 8x + x$ 8. $3a - 5a + a$

9. $3x + 2y - 3x$ 10. $4a - 2b + 2b$

11. $4y + y - 10y$ 12. $3x - x - 5x$

13. $3mn - 5mn + 2mn$ 14. $5cd - 8cd + 3cd$

15. $2xy - 5yx + xy$ 16. $8mn - 7nm + 3nm$

17. $8x^2y - 2x^2y$ 18. $10ab^2 - 3ab^2$

19. $a^2b - 3a^2b$ 20. $x^2y^2 - 5x^2y^2$

----

21. $5ab + 2c - 2ba$ 22. $7xy - 3z - 4yx$

23. $5xyz^2 - 2xyz^2 - 4xyz^2$ 24. $7a^2bc - 4a^2bc - a^2bc$

25. $5u - 2u + 10v$ 26. $8w - 4w + 5v$

27 $8x - 2y - 4x$ 28. $9x - 8y + 2x$

29. $7x^2y - 2xy^2 - 4x^2y$ 30. $4xy^2 - 5x^2y - 2xy^2$

31. $5x^2 - 3x + 7 - 2x^2 + 8x - 9$

32. $7y^2 + 4y - 6 - 9y^2 - 2y + 7$

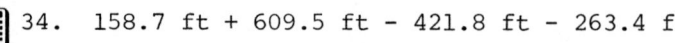 33. 12.67 sec $+ 9.08$ sec $- 6.73$ sec

34. 158.7 ft $+ 609.5$ ft $- 421.8$ ft $- 263.4$ ft

SET II

1. $12a - 4a$ 2. $5x - 10x$

3. $3x - 2x + 10x$ 4. $7y - 5y - 2y$

5. $7ab + c - 2ba$ 6. $8xy - 2xz - 2yz$

7. $6x - 6 + 4y - 3$ 8. $5a - 4 + 3b - 3$

9. $2x^3 - 2x^2 + 3x - 5x$ 10. $5y^2 - 3y^3 + 2y - 4y$

11. $4x - 3y + 7 - 2x + 4 - 6y$

12. $3b - 5a - 9 - 2a + 4 - 5b$

13. $x - 3x^3 + 2x^2 - 5x - 4x^2 + x^3$

14. $y - 2y^2 - 5y^3 - y + 3y^3 - y^2$

15. $a^2b - 11ab + 12ab^2 - 3a^2b + 4ab$

16. $xy^2 + y - 5x^2y + 3xy^2 + x^2y$

17. $4z^2 - 6z + 5 - z^2 + 9z - 10$

18. 37.9cm $- 13.5$cm $+ 24.8$cm $- 19.3$cm

Simplifying Algebraic Expressions

> TO SIMPLIFY AN ALGEBRAIC EXPRESSION
> 1. Remove grouping symbols (Sec. 305).
> 2. Combine like terms (Sec. 306).

<u>Example 1.</u> Simplify the following algebraic expressions.

(a) $a - 2(a + b)$
   $= a - 2a - 2b$ Removing grouping symbol.
   $= -a - 2b$ Combining like terms.

(b) $3(5x - 2y) - 4(3x - 6y)$

   $= \underline{15x} - \underline{6y} - \underline{12x} + \underline{24y}$ Removing grouping symbols.

   $= \underline{15x - 12x} - \underline{6y + 24y}$ Collecting like terms.

   $= 3x + 18y$ Combining like terms.

(c) $x(x^2 + xy + y^2) - y(x^2 + xy + y^2)$
   $= x^3 + \underline{x^2 y} + \underline{xy^2} - \underline{x^2 y} - \underline{xy^2} - y^3$ Using the first
   $= x^3 + \underline{x^2 y - x^2 y} + \underline{xy^2 - xy^2} - y^3$ rule of exponents.
   $= x^3 + \quad 0 \quad + \quad 0 \quad - y^3$
   $= x^3 - y^3$

It often helps to underline like terms when combining them.

(d) $2x^2 y(4xy - 3xy^2) - 5xy(3x^2 y^2 - 2x^2 y)$
   $= \underline{8x^3 y^2} - \underline{6x^3 y^3} - \underline{15x^3 y^3} + \underline{10x^3 y^2}$
   $= \underline{8x^3 y^2 + 10x^3 y^2} - \underline{6x^3 y^3 - 15x^3 y^3}$
   $= \quad 18x^3 y^2 \quad - \quad 21x^3 y^3 \quad = 18x^3 y^2 - 21x^3 y^3$

Sometimes it is helpful to combine like terms within a pair of grouping symbols *before* removing that pair of grouping symbols as is done in parts (e) and (f).

(e) $-8[-5(3x - 2) + 13] - 11x$

   $= -8[-15x + \underline{10} + \underline{13}] - 11x$ Remove innermost
   $= -8[-15x + 23] \quad - 11x$ grouping symbol first.

   $= \underline{+120x} - 184 \quad - \underline{11x}$

   $= 109x - 184$

(f) $(8x + 10y) - 2\{[4x - 5(8 - y)] - 15\}$
   $= (8x + 10y) - 2\{[4x - 40 + 5y] - 15\}$

$$= (8x + 10y) - 2\{4x - \underline{40} + 5y - \underline{15}\}$$
$$= (8x + 10y) - 2\{4x \qquad + 5y - 55\}$$
$$= \underline{8x} + \underline{10y} - \underline{8x} \qquad - \underline{10y} + 110 = 110$$

EXERCISES 307. Simplify the following algebraic expressions.

SET I

1. $x - 3(x + y)$ 2. $y - 2(y + z)$
3. $2a - 4(a - b)$ 4. $3c - 2(c - d)$
5. $u(u^2 + 2u + 4) - 2(u^2 + 2u + 4)$
6. $x(x^2 - 3x + 9) + 3(x^2 - 3x + 9)$
7. $x^2(x^2 + y^2) - y^2(x^2 + y^2)$
8. $w^2(w^2 - 4) + 4(w^2 - 4)$
9. $2x(3x^2 - 5x + 1) - 4x(2x^2 - 3x - 5)$
10. $3x(4x^2 - 2x - 3) - 2x(3x^2 - x + 1)$
11. $-3(a - 2b) + 2(a - 3b)$ 12. $-2(m - 3n) + 4(m - 2n)$
13. $-5(2x - 3y) - 10(x + 5y)$
14. $-4(3s - 7t) - 8(3s - 4t)$

----

15. $x^2y(3xy^2 - y) - 2xy^2(4x - x^2y)$
16. $ab^2(2a - ab) - 3ab(2ab - ab^2)$
17. $2h(3h^2 - k) - k(h - 3k^3)$
18. $4x(2y^2 - 3x) - x(2x - 3y^2)$
19. $3f(2f^2 - 4g) - g(2f - g^2)$
20. $4a(b^2 - 2b) - b(ab - a)$
21. $2x - [3a + (4x - 5a)]$ 22. $2y - [5c + (3y - 4c)]$
23. $5x + [-(2x - 10) + 7]$ 24. $4x + [-(3x - 5) + 4]$
25. $25 - 2[3g - 5(2g - 7)]$ 26. $40 - 3[2h - 8(3h - 10)]$
27. $-2\{-3[-5(-4 - 3z) - 2z] + 30z\}$
28. $-3\{-2[-3(-5 - 2z) - 3z] - 40z\}$

SET II

1. $a - 4(a + b)$ 2. $2x - 3(x - y)$
3. $5x - 2(4x - 3y)$ 4. $2(a - 3b) - 3(4a - b)$
5. $2h(4h^2 - k) - 3k(h - 2k^2)$
6. $x(x^2 + 2x + 4) - 2(x^2 + 2x + 4)$
7. $a^2(a^2 - b^2) + b^2(a^2 - b^2)$
8. $2x^2y(3xy^2 - 2y) - 3xy^2(2x^2y - 5x)$
9. $3xy^2(2x - xy + 4) + x(3xy^3 - 12y^2)$
10. $5r^2s(3r - 5 - 2s) + 5r^2s(5 + 2s)$

11. $-10[-2(3x - 5) + 17] - 4x$

12. $(2x - y) - \{[3x - (7 - y)] - 10\}$

13. $100 - \{2z - [3z - (4 - z)]\}$

14. $60x - 2\{-3[-5(-5 - x) - 6x]\}$

Chapter Summary

Algebraic Expressions (Sec. 301). An algebraic expression consists only of numbers, letters, signs of operation, and signs of grouping. Not all of these need be present.

Constants (Sec. 301). A constant is an object or symbol that does not change its value in a particular problem or discussion. It is usually represented by a number symbol.

Variables (Sec. 301). A variable is an object or symbol that changes its value in a particular problem or discussion. It is represented by a letter.

Terms (Sec. 301). The + and - signs in an algebraic expression break it up into smaller pieces called *terms*. A minus sign is part of the term that follows it. *Exception*: An expression within grouping symbols is considered as a single piece even though it may contain + and - signs.

Like terms (Sec. 306). Terms having identical literal parts are called *like terms*.

Unlike terms (Sec. 306). Terms having different literal parts are called *unlike terms*.

Factors (Sec. 301). The numbers that are multiplied together to give a product are called the *factors* of that product.

A product of factors (Sec. 303) is negative if there are an odd number of negative factors; the product of factors is positive if there are an even number or no negative factors.

Coefficients (Sec. 301). The coefficient of one factor in a term is the product of all the other factors in that term.

Numerical coefficient (Sec. 301). A numerical coefficient is a coefficient that is a number. If we say "*the* coefficient" of a term, it is understood to mean the *numerical* coefficient of that term.

Literal coefficient (Sec. 301). A literal coefficient is a coefficient that is a letter or product of letters.

First Basic Rule of Exponents (Sec. 302). $x^a \cdot x^b = x^{a+b}$

The Distributive Rule (Sec. 304). $a(b + c) = ab + ac$
When a factor is multiplied by an expression enclosed within grouping symbols, the factor must be multiplied by each term within the grouping symbol, then those products are added.

Removing Grouping Symbols (Sec. 305)

First, write a + sign for any enclosed term having no written sign. Then,

1. *When removing a grouping symbol preceded by a + sign (or no sign):*

   Leave the enclosed terms unchanged. Drop the grouping symbol and the + sign (if there is one) preceding it.

2. *When removing a grouping symbol preceded by a - sign:*

   Change the sign of each enclosed term. Drop the grouping symbol and the - sign preceding it.

3. *When removing a grouping symbol preceded by a factor:*

   Multiply each enclosed term by the factor, and add these products. Drop the grouping symbol and the factor.

When grouping symbols occur within other grouping symbols (Sec. 305), it is usually easier to remove the innermost grouping symbols first.

To Combine Like Terms (Sec. 306)

1. Identify the like terms by their identical literal parts.
2. Find the sum of each group of like terms by adding their numerical coefficients; then multiply that sum by the literal part of those like terms. When no coefficient is written, it is understood to be 1.

To Simplify an Algebraic Expression (Sec. 307)

1. Remove grouping symbols.
2. Combine like terms.

REVIEW EXERCISES 308

SET I

In Exercises 1 and 2, list (a) the different constants and (b) the different variables.

1. $12xy - 7$

2. $9 - 6ab$

In Exercises 3—6, (a) determine the number of terms; (b) write the second term if there is one.

3. $a^2 + 2ab + b^2$

4. $x^3 - y^3$

5. $6x - 2(x^2 + y^2)$

6. $2(m^2 - n^2) + 5mn$

7. In the expression $5x^2y$,
   (a) What is the numerical coefficient?
   (b) What is the coefficient of y?

8. In the expression $10xy^2z$,
   (a) What is the numerical coefficient?
   (b) What is the coefficient of xz?

In Exercises 9—14, find the products.

9. m^2m^3

10. p^4p^5

11. xx^3

12. yy^7

13. $2 \cdot 2^2$

14. $10 \cdot 10^3$

In Exercises 15—22, simplify the products.

15. $(-5p)(4p^3)$

16. $(-7m^2)(8m)$

17. $(9x^8y^3)(-7x^4y^5)$

18. $(9x^3y^2)(-6x^5y^6)$

19. $(-5a^5b^6)(-8b^4c^3)$

20. $(-4p^2q^8)(-11q^9r^4)$

21. $(-5e^1f^2)(-f^7g^3)(-10e^4g^2)(-2ef)$

22. $(-4h^1j^5)(-j^3k^4)(-5hk)(-10j^2h^7)$

In Exercises 23—28, simplify the algebraic expressions.

23. $x - 2(x - y)$

24. $m - 3(m - n)$

25. $2x(3x^2 - x) - x^2(3x - 4)$

26. $3y^2(2y - 5) - 2y(4y^2 - 3y)$

27. $2m^2n(3mn^2 - 2n) - 5mn^2(2m - 3m^2n)$

28. $3xy^2(8x - 2xy) - 5xy(10xy - 3xy^2)$

In exercises 29 and 30, list (a) the different constants, and (b) the different variables.

29. $4uv + 5u$

30. $2x^3 - 5xy + 2x$

In Exercises 31 and 32, (a) determine the number of terms; (b) write the second term if there is one.

31. $[5 - (x + y)] + 4$

32. $\dfrac{x + x^2}{4} - 2(x^3 + 1)$

In Exercises 33—42, find the products.

33. $10^2 \cdot 10 \cdot 10^5$

34. $3^3 \cdot 3 \cdot 3^2$

35. $r^2r^5r^{10}$

36. $x^3x^{10}x^5$

37. x^ax^{2a}

38. $x^{2y}x^{5y}$

39. $10^a \cdot 10^b$

40. $5^x \cdot 5^y$

41. $4 \cdot 4^x$

42. $10 \cdot 10^y$

In Exercises 43—48, simplify the algebraic expressions.

43. $2x(4x^2 + 6xy + 9y^2) - 3y(4x^2 + 6xy + 9y^2)$

44. $4v(16v^2 - 12vw + 9w^2) + 3w(16v^2 - 12vw + 9w^2)$

45. $4(2m - 3n) - \{5[4m - 2(m - 3n)] - 10n\}$

46. $6(7a - 2b) - \{4[6a - 3(2a - b)] - 14b\}$

47. $-5\{-2[-3(4 - 2x) - 7x] - 3x\} - 15x$

48. $-4\{-5[-2(7 - 3x) - 8x] - 8x\} - 20x$

SET II

In Exercises 1 and 2, list (a) the different constants, and (b) the different variables.

1. $\dfrac{2m + n}{5}$

2. $9 - 6ab$

In Exercises 3 and 4, (a) determine the number of terms; (b) write the second term if there is one.

3. $\dfrac{p + q}{2} + \dfrac{p}{4} + 3(p^2 - q)$

4. $5 - \{4 - (p - q)\}$

5. In the expression $6xy^2$,
   (a) What is the numerical coefficient?
   (b) What is the coefficient of x?

In Exercises 6—14, find the products.

6. x^3y^5

7. a^2b^7

8. $t^3u^2t^6$

9. u^2v^4u

10. $m^x m^y$

11. $(4r^2s^5)(-3r^3s^2)(5r^4s)$

12. $(2c^2d^8)(8c^5d)(-5c^4d^3)$

13. $(-10x^2y^3)(-8x^3)(-xy^2z^4)$

14. $(-9w^2z^3)(-7z^4)(-wx^2z^4)$

In Exercises 15—24, simplify the algebraic expressions.

15. $2p - 3(2p - 3q)$

16. $4a - 2(3a - 2b)$

17. $5(2h - 3k) - 2(h - 2k)$

18. $4(3x - 2y) - 5(2x - y)$

19. $10k(4k^2 - 3k - 5) - 2k(5k^2 - 4k + 10)$

20. $7x(6x^2 - 5x - 4) - 8x(9x^2 - 3x - 7)$

21. $6y - 2[-8y - 3(y - 4)]$

22. $7h - 3[-5h - 4(2h - 3)]$

23. $-8[3(7 - 2z) - 12z] + 20z$

24. $-6[2(5w - 8) - 10w] + 30w$

CUMULATIVE REVIEW EXERCISES: CHAPTERS 1 and 2

In Exercises 1-7, evaluate each expression.

1. $\dfrac{14 - 23}{-8 + 11}$

2. $\sqrt{13^2 - 5^2}$

3. $-4^2 + (-4)^2$

4. $(27 - 3^3)(8^2 + 5^2)$

5. $6(-3) - 4\sqrt{36}$ 6. $\{-12 - [7 + (3 - 9)]\} - 15$

7. $\dfrac{0}{-11}$

In Exercises 8-10, evaluate each formula using the values of the letters given with the formula.

8. $C = \dfrac{5}{9}(F - 32)$ $F = -13$

9. $A = P(1 + rt)$ $P = 1200,\ r = 0.15,\ t = 4$

10. $S = 4\pi R^2$ $\pi \doteq 3.14,\ R = 10$

Chapter Three Diagnostic Test

Name_____

_____

The purpose of this test is to see how well you understand the simplification of algebraic expressions. We recommend that you work this diagnostic test *before* your instructor tests you on this chapter. Allow yourself about forty minutes to do this test.

Complete solutions for all the problems on this test, together with section references, are given in the Answer Section. We suggest that you study the sections referred to for the problems you do incorrectly.

---

1. The expression $2x + \dfrac{4x + 5y}{3} + 7$ has:

   (a) How many terms?   (1a)_____

   (b) How many different variables? (1b)_____

   (c) How many different constants? (1c)_____

Find the following products.

2. $(-2x)(3x^4)$

                                       (2)_____

3. $(-3xy)(5x^3y)(-2xy^4)$

                                       (3)_____

4. $2(x - 3y)$

                                       (4)_____

5. $(x - 4)(-5)$

                                       (5)_____

6. $2xy^2(x^2 - 3y - 4)$

                                       (6)_____

Remove the grouping symbols in each of the following.

7. $5 - (x - y)$

                                       (7)_____

8. $h - k + (m - n)$

(8) _____

9. $-2[-4(3c - d) + a] - b$

(9) _____

_____

Combine like terms in each of the following.

10. $4x - 3x + 5x$

(10) _____

11. $8mn - nm + 3nm$

(11) _____

12. $6p - 7q + 2p$

(12) _____

13. $2a - 5b - 7 - 3b + 4 - 5a$

(13) _____

_____

Simplify each of the following agebraic expressions.

14. $5x - 3(y - x)$

(14) _____

15. $4(a - 2b) - 2(a - 3b)$

(15) _____

16. $3h(2k^2 - 5h) - h(2h - 3k^2)$

(16) _____

17. $ef^2(2e - ef) - 3ef(2ef - ef^2)$

(17) _____

18. $x(x^2 + 2x + 4) - 2(x^2 + 2x + 4)$

(18) _____

19. $7m - [5n + (4m - 3n)]$

(19) _____

20. $25 - \{-3x - [5x - (7 - 2x)]\}$

(20) _____

_____

FOUR

Equations

The main reason for studying algebra is to equip oneself with the tools necessary for solving problems. Most problems are solved by the use of equations. In this chapter we show how to solve simple equations. Methods for solving more difficult equations will be given in later chapters.

401 The Parts of an Equation

In algebra, an *equation* is a statement that two algebraic expressions are equal. The following is an example of an equation.

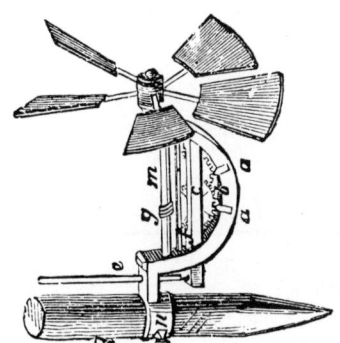

$$5x - 8 \; = \; 3x + 2$$

left side ⟶↑   ↑   ↳ right side

equal sign

An equation is made up of three parts:

1. The equal sign (=).
2. The expression to the left of the = sign, called the left side (or left member) of the equation.
3. The expression to the right of the = sign, called the right side (or right member) of the equation.

The letter x represents an *unknown number*. Letters other than x may be used in equations to represent the unknown number.

Example 1. Identify the members of the equation: $2x - 3 = 7$

The left side of the equation is $2x - 3$.
The right side of the equation is 7.

Example 2. Identify the members of the equation: $5x - 2 = 10x + 3$

The Meaning of the Equal Sign in an Equation. The equal sign (=) in an equation means that the number represented by the left side *is the same* as the number represented by the right side.

Example 3. $\left. \begin{array}{l} x = -2 \\ \\ \text{and} \quad -2 = x \end{array} \right\}$ Both say that x and -2 are the same number.

402 Solving Equations by Adding the Same Signed Number to Both Sides

If we add the same signed number to both sides of an equation, the resulting sums must be equal.

Example 1.
$$\begin{array}{r} 7 \; = \; 7 \\ \underline{+\,5} \quad \underline{+\,5} \\ 12 \; = \; 12 \end{array}$$
We are adding +5 to both sides.
The resulting sums are equal.

Example 2.

$$
\begin{array}{rcr}
7 & = & 7 \\
-5 & & -5 \\
\hline
2 & = & 2
\end{array}
$$

We are adding -5 to both sides.
The resulting sums are equal.

Example 3.

$$
\begin{array}{rcr}
x - 3 & = & 6 \\
+ 3 & & + 3 \\
\hline
x & = & 9
\end{array}
$$

We call 9 the *solution* (or *root*) of the equation $x - 3 = 6$. A solution of an equation is a number that, when put in place of the letter, makes the two sides of the equation equal. To *solve an equation* means to find the value of the unknown letter. An equation is solved when we succeed in getting the unknown letter by itself on one side of the equal sign, and only a single number on the other side.

In this section, we show how to solve equations in which the unknown letter appears on only one side of the equation, and has a coefficient of one (1).

TO SOLVE AN EQUATION USING ADDITION WHEN THE COEFFICIENT OF THE UNKNOWN LETTER IS ONE (1)

If the equation contains a number added to the unknown letter:

1. Add the negative of that number to both sides of the equation.

2. The resulting equation gives the solution.

Example 4. Solve the equation: $2 + m = 7$

Solution:
$$
\begin{array}{rcr}
2 + m & = & 7 \\
-2 & & -2 \\
\hline
m & = & 5
\end{array}
$$

Adding -2 to both sides gets m by itself on the left side.

└── Solution

Example 5. Solve the equation: $8 = H - 4$

Solution:
$$
\begin{array}{rcr}
8 & = & H - 4 \\
+4 & & +4 \\
\hline
12 & = & H
\end{array}
$$

Adding +4 to both sides gets H by itself on the right side.

── Since this means that 12 and H are symbols for the same number, we can also say $H = 12$.

TO CHECK THE SOLUTION OF AN EQUATION

1. Replace the unknown letter in the given equation by the number obtained as a solution.

2. Perform the indicated operations on both sides of the = sign.

3. If the resulting number on each side of the = sign is the same, the solution is correct.

Example 6. Solve and check: $x - 5 = 3$

Remove by adding 5 to both sides

Solution:
$$
\begin{array}{rcr}
x - 5 &=& 3 \\
+ 5 && + 5 \\
\hline
x &=& 8
\end{array}
$$

Check:
$$
\begin{array}{rcl}
x - 5 &=& 3 \\
(8) - 5 &=& 3 \\
3 &=& 3
\end{array}
$$
x was replaced by the solution 8. The solution is correct.

Example 7. Solve and check: $\frac{1}{4} + x = 3\frac{1}{4}$

Remove by adding $-\frac{1}{4}$ to both sides.

Solution:
$$
\begin{array}{rcr}
\frac{1}{4} + x &=& 3\frac{1}{4} \\
-\frac{1}{4} && -\frac{1}{4} \\
\hline
x &=& 3
\end{array}
$$

Check:
$$
\frac{1}{4} + x = 3\frac{1}{4}
$$
$$
\frac{1}{4} + (3) = 3\frac{1}{4}
$$
x was replaced by the solution 3.
$$
3\frac{1}{4} = 3\frac{1}{4}
$$

Example 8. Solve: $9.08 = x - 5.47$

Solution:
$$
\begin{array}{rcl}
9.08 &=& x - 5.47 \\
+ 5.47 && + 5.47 \\
\hline
14.55 &=& x
\end{array}
$$
or $\qquad\qquad x = 14.55$

In problems like Example 8, it is convenient to use a calculator for addition and subtraction of decimals.

EXERCISES 402. Solve and check the following equations.

SET I

1. $x + 5 = 8$ 2. $x + 4 = 9$

3. $x - 3 = 4$ 4. $x - 7 = 2$

5. $3 + x = -4$ 6. $2 + x = -5$

7. $x + 4 = 21$ 8. $x + 15 = 24$

9. $x - 35 = 7$ 10. $x - 42 = 9$

11. $9 = x + 5$ 12. $11 = x + 8$

13. $12 = x - 11$ 14. $14 = x - 15$

15. $-17 + x = 28$ 16. $-14 + x = 33$

----

17. $-28 = -15 + x$ 18. $-47 = -18 + x$

19. $x + \frac{1}{2} = 2\frac{1}{2}$ 20. $x + \frac{3}{4} = 5\frac{3}{4}$

21. $5.6 + x = 2.8$ 22. $3.04 + x = 2.96$

 23. $7.84 = x - 3.98$  24. $4.99 = x - 2.08$

SET II

1. $x + 7 = 12$ 2. $x - 5 = 8$

3. $6 + x = -9$ 4. $x + 11 = 25$

5. $x - 18 = 13$ 6. $14 = x + 6$

7. $17 = x - 11$ 8. $-21 + x = -42$

9. $-51 = -37 + x$ 10. $x + 2\frac{1}{4} = 8\frac{1}{4}$

11. $8.4 + x = 6.2$ 12. $5.36 = x - 4.82$

403 Solving Equations by Dividing Both Sides by the Same Signed Number

If we divide both sides of an equation by the same signed number (not zero), the resulting quotients must be equal.

Example 1. $8 = 8$

$\frac{8}{4} = \frac{8}{4}$ We are dividing both sides by 4.

$2 = 2$ The resulting quotients are equal.

Example 2. $6 = 6$

$\frac{6}{-2} = \frac{6}{-2}$ We are dividing both sides by -2.

$-3 = -3$ The resulting quotients are equal.

100   Chapter 4: Equations

Example 3. $2x = 10$ ────── Remove by dividing both sides by 2.

$$\frac{2x}{2} = \frac{10}{2}$$

$x = 5$ Solution

Example 4. $9x = -27$ ────── Remove by dividing both sides by 9.

$$\frac{9x}{9} = \frac{-27}{9}$$

$x = -3$ Solution

Example 5. $12x = 8$ ────── Remove by dividing both sides by 12.

$$\frac{12x}{12} = \frac{8}{12}$$

$x = \dfrac{2}{3}$ Solution

Example 6. $16 = 2x$

$$\frac{16}{2} = \frac{2x}{2}$$

$8 = x$ Solution

Example 7. $3x - 2 = 10$

$\quad\quad\quad\quad \underline{+ 2 \quad\quad + 2}$ Adding 2 to both sides.

$\quad\quad 3x \quad\quad = \quad 12$

$$\frac{3x}{3} = \frac{12}{3}$$ Dividing both sides by 3.

$x = 4$ Solution

In the last example, two numbers had to be removed: 3 and -2. When more than one number must be removed, use the following procedure.

TO SOLVE AN EQUATION USING ADDITION AND DIVISION

All numbers on the same side as the unknown letter must be removed.

1. Remove those numbers being added or subtracted using the method of the last section.

2. Remove the number multiplied by the unknown letter by dividing both sides by that signed number.

Example 8. Solve the equation: $2x + 3 = 11$

Solution: The numbers 2 and 3 must be removed from the side with the x.

1. Since the 3 is added, it is removed first.

$$
\begin{array}{rcl}
2x + 3 &=& 11 \\
-\ 3 & & -\ 3 \\
\hline
2x &=& 8
\end{array}
$$
Adding -3 to both sides.

2. Since the 2 is multiplied by the x, it is removed by dividing both sides by 2.

$$2x = 8$$

$$\frac{2x}{2} = \frac{8}{2}$$ Dividing both sides by 2.

$$x = 4$$

Check:
$$
\begin{array}{rcl}
2x + 3 &=& 11 \\
2(4) + 3 &=& 11 \\
8 + 3 &=& 11 \\
11 &=& 11
\end{array}
$$

Example 9. Solve the equation: $-12 = 3x + 15$

Solution: 15 and 3 must be removed from the side with the x.

1.
$$
\begin{array}{rcl}
-12 &=& 3x + 15 \\
-15 & & -\ 15 \\
\hline
-27 &=& 3x
\end{array}
$$
Adding -15 to both sides.

2. $$\frac{-27}{3} = \frac{3x}{3}$$ Dividing both sides by 3.

$$-9 = x$$

Check:
$$
\begin{array}{rcl}
-12 &=& 3x + 15 \\
-12 &=& 3(-9) + 15 \\
-12 &=& -27 + 15 \\
-12 &=& -12
\end{array}
$$

PROCEDURE WHEN THE UNKNOWN LETTER HAS A NEGATIVE COEFFICIENT

Example 10. Solve: $3 - 2x = 9$

Solution:
$$
\begin{array}{rcl}
3 - 2x &=& 9 \\
-\ 3 & & -\ 3 \\
\hline
-\ 2x &=& 6
\end{array}
$$
Since x is multiplied by -2, we divide both sides by -2.

$$\frac{(-2)x}{(-2)} = \frac{6}{-2}$$

$$x = -3 \qquad \text{Solution}$$

Check: 3 - 2x = 9
                3 - 2(-3) = 9
                    3 + 6 = 9
                        9 = 9

EXERCISES 403. Solve and check the following equations.

SET I

1. $2x = 8$ 2. $3x = 15$

3. $21 = 7x$ 4. $42 = 6x$

5. $11x = 33$ 6. $12x = 48$

7. $4x + 1 = 9$ 8. $5x + 2 = 12$

9. $6x - 2 = 10$ 10. $7x - 3 = 4$

11. $2x - 15 = 11$ 12. $3x - 4 = 14$

13. $4x + 2 = -14$ 14. $5x + 5 = -10$

15. $14 = 9x - 13$ 16. $25 = 8x - 15$

17. $12x + 17 = 65$ 18. $11x + 19 = 41$

19. $8x - 23 = 31$ 20. $6x - 33 = 29$

----

21. $14 - 4x = -28$ 22. $18 - 6x = -44$

23. $8 = 25 - 3x$ 24. $10 = 27 - 2x$

25. $-73 = 24x + 31$ 26. $-48 = 36x + 42$

27. $18x - 4.8 = 6$ 28. $15x - 7.5 = 8$

🖩 29. $2.5x - 3.8 = -7.9$ 🖩 30. $3.75x + 0.125 = -0.125$

SET II

1. $5x = 35$ 2. $24 = 6x$

3. $12x = 36$ 4. $3x + 2 = 14$

5. $7x - 4 = 10$ 6. $8x - 12 = 12$

7. $4x + 11 = -13$ 8. $16 = 5x - 14$

9. $11x + 19 = 63$ 10. $12x - 17 = 13$

11. $19 - 10x = -26$ 12. $27 = 32 - 15x$

13. $-67 = 18x + 29$ 🖩 14. $3.6x - 7.4 = -11.5$

🖩 15. $2.86x + 5.09 = -8.2$

Solving Equations by Multiplying Both Sides by the Same Signed Number

If we multiply both sides of an equation by the same signed number, the resulting products must be equal.

Example 1. $4 = 4$
$2(4) = 2(4)$ Multiplying both sides by 2.
$8 = 8$ The resulting products are equal.

Example 2. $\dfrac{x}{3} = 5$

$3\left(\dfrac{x}{3}\right) = 3(5)$ Multiplying both sides by 3.

$\cancel{3}\left(\dfrac{x}{\cancel{3}}\right) = 3(5)$

$x = 15$ Solution

Check: $\dfrac{x}{3} = 5$

$\dfrac{15}{3} = 5$

$5 = 5$

Example 3. $-8 = \dfrac{x}{6}$ Remove 6 by multiplying both sides by 6.

$6(-8) = \cancel{6}\left(\dfrac{x}{\cancel{6}}\right)$

$-48 = x$ Solution

Check: $-8 = \dfrac{x}{6}$

$-8 = \dfrac{-48}{6}$

$-8 = -8$

Example 4. $\dfrac{2x}{3} = 4$ Remove 3 by multiplying both sides by 3.

$\cancel{3}\left(\dfrac{2x}{\cancel{3}}\right) = 3(4)$ Multiplying both sides by 3.

$2x = 12$ Remove 2 by dividing both sides by 2.

$\dfrac{\cancel{2}x}{\cancel{2}} = \dfrac{12}{2}$ Dividing both sides by 2.

$x = 6$ Solution

Check: $\dfrac{2x}{3} = 4$

$\dfrac{2(6)}{3} = 4$

$\dfrac{12}{3} = 4$

$4 = 4$

Example 5. Solve: $4 = \dfrac{2x}{5} - 6$

Solution:

$$4 = \frac{2x}{5} - 6$$

$$\begin{array}{rl} +6 & \quad +\ 6 \\ \hline 10 = & \dfrac{2x}{5} \end{array}$$

$$5(10) = \cancel{5}\left(\frac{2x}{\cancel{5}}\right)$$

$$50 = 2x$$

$$\frac{50}{2} = \frac{\cancel{2}x}{\cancel{2}}$$

$$25 = x \qquad \text{Solution}$$

Check: $4 = \dfrac{2x}{5} - 6$

$$4 = \frac{2(25)}{5} - 6$$

$$4 = \frac{50}{5} - 6$$

$$4 = 10 - 6$$

$$4 = 4$$

In Example 5, three numbers (6, 5, and 2) had to be removed from the same side as the unknown letter. When more than one number must be removed, use the following procedure.

TO SOLVE AN EQUATION USING ADDITION, DIVISION, AND MULTIPLICATION

All numbers on the same side as the unknown letter must be removed.

1. First, remove those numbers being added or subtracted.

2. Multiply both sides by the signed number the letter is divided by.

3. Divide both sides by the signed number the letter is multiplied by.

Example 6. Solve: $\dfrac{3x}{4} + 2 = 11$

Solution: The numbers 2, 4, and 3 must be removed from the side with the x.

1. Since the 2 is added, it is removed first.

$$\begin{array}{rl} \dfrac{3x}{4} + 2 = & 11 \\ -\ 2 & \quad -\ 2 \\ \hline \dfrac{3x}{4} = & 9 \end{array}$$

2. Since the letter is divided by 4, we multiply both sides by 4.

$$\frac{3x}{4} = 9$$

$$\cancel{4}\left(\frac{3x}{\cancel{4}}\right) = 4(9)$$

$$3x = 36$$

3. Since the letter is multiplied by 3, we divide both sides by 3.

$$\frac{\cancel{3}x}{\cancel{3}} = \frac{36}{3}$$

$$x = 12 \qquad \text{Solution}$$

<u>Check</u>:
$$\frac{3x}{4} + 2 = 11$$

$$\frac{3(\overset{3}{\cancel{12}})}{\underset{1}{\cancel{4}}} + 2 = 11$$

$$9 + 2 = 11$$

$$11 = 11$$

Equations of the type shown in Examples 5 and 6 may also be solved by a method given in Section 908.

<u>CHANGING SIGNS IN AN EQUATION</u>. Multiplying both sides of an equation by -1 is equivalent to changing the sign of every term in the equation. For example consider the equation $5 - x = 7$:

<u>Changing every sign</u>	<u>Multiplying both sides by -1.</u>
$5 - x = 7$	$5 - x = 7$
$-5 + x = -7$	$(-1)(5 - x) = (-1)7$
⌞ Same equation ────────→	$-5 + x = -7$

<u>Example 7</u>. Changing every sign in an equation does not change the solution.

$5 - x = 7$	$5 - x = 7$
$\underline{-5 \qquad\qquad -5}$	$-5 + x = -7$ Changed every
$-x = 2$	$\underline{+5 \qquad\qquad +5}$ sign
$\dfrac{-x}{-1} = \dfrac{2}{-1}$	$x = -2$
$x = -2$ ←── Same solution ──────→	

```
┌─────────────────────────────────────────────────────┐
│                                                       │
│  IN SOLVING AN EQUATION                               │
│                                                       │
│  Changing the sign of every term will not change the  │
│  solution.                                            │
│                                                       │
└─────────────────────────────────────────────────────┘
```

<u>Example 8</u>. Changing every sign in an equation.

(a) If $-x = 3$
     then $x = -3$ The sign of every term was changed.

(b) If $-x - 8 = -4$
     then $x + 8 = 4$

All the equations solved so far could have been solved by using one or more of the following rules:

```
┌─────────────────────────────────────────────────────┐
│                                                       │
│  IN SOLVING EQUATIONS                                 │
│                                                       │
│   1.  Addition Rule:  The same number may be added to │
│       both sides.                                     │
│                                                       │
│   2.  Subtraction Rule:*  The same number may be sub- │
│       tracted from both sides.                        │
│                                                       │
│   3.  Multiplication Rule:  Both sides may be multiplied│
│       by the same number.                             │
│                                                       │
│   4.  Division Rule:  Both sides may be divided by the │
│       same number (not zero).                         │
│                                                       │
└─────────────────────────────────────────────────────┘
```

*Any subtraction can be considered an addition (Sec. 104).

<u>EXERCISES 404</u>. Solve and check the following equations.

SET I

1. $\dfrac{x}{3} = 4$ 2. $\dfrac{x}{5} = 3$ 3. $\dfrac{x}{5} = -2$

4. $\dfrac{x}{6} = -4$ 5. $4 - \dfrac{x}{7} = 0$ 6. $3 - \dfrac{x}{8} = 0$

7. $-13 = \dfrac{x}{9}$ 8. $-15 = \dfrac{x}{8}$ 9. $\dfrac{x}{10} = 3.14$

10. $\dfrac{x}{5} = 7.8$ 11. $\dfrac{x}{4} + 6 = 9$ 12. $\dfrac{x}{5} + 3 = 8$

13. $\dfrac{x}{10} - 5 = 13$ 14. $\dfrac{x}{20} - 4 = 12$ 15. $-14 = \dfrac{x}{6} - 7$

16. $-22 = \dfrac{x}{8} - 11$

----

17. $7 = \dfrac{2x}{5} + 3$ 18. $9 = \dfrac{3x}{4} + 6$ 19. $4 - \dfrac{7x}{5} = 11$

20. $3 - \dfrac{2x}{9} = 13$ 21. $-24 + \dfrac{5x}{8} = 41$

22. $-16 + \dfrac{9x}{4} = 29$ 23. $41 = 25 - \dfrac{4x}{5}$

24. $54 = 14 - \dfrac{8x}{7}$

<u>SET II</u>

1. $\dfrac{x}{7} = 3$ 2. $\dfrac{x}{4} = -5$ 3. $6 - \dfrac{x}{3} = 0$

4. $-12 = \dfrac{x}{6}$ 5. $\dfrac{x}{8} = 12.5$ 6. $\dfrac{x}{3} + 5 = 7$

7. $\dfrac{x}{10} - 4 = 11$ 8. $-16 = \dfrac{x}{7} - 9$ 9. $8 = \dfrac{3x}{5} + 4$

10. $6 - \dfrac{4x}{5} = 12$ 11. $-19 + \dfrac{7x}{4} = 23$

12. $38 = 14 - \dfrac{6x}{11}$

405 Solving Equations in Which Simplification of Algebraic Expressions Is Necessary

<u>EQUATIONS IN WHICH THE UNKNOWN APPEARS ON BOTH SIDES</u>. All the equations discussed in this chapter up till now have had the unknown letter on only one side of the equation.

TO SOLVE AN EQUATION IN WHICH THE UNKNOWN
APPEARS ON BOTH SIDES

1st Combine like terms on each side of the equation
(if there are any).

2nd Remove from one side the *term* containing the unknown
by adding the negative of that term to both sides.

3rd Solve the resulting equation by the method given in
the preceding section (Sec. 402).

<u>Example 1</u>.   Solve: $6x - 15 = -23 + 2x$

1. We first remove *the entire term 2x* from the right side.

$$6x - 15 = -23 + 2x$$

$$\underline{-2x} \qquad \underline{\quad - 2x} \qquad \text{Subtracting } 2x \text{ from both sides.}$$

$$4x - 15 = -23$$

2. The numbers 4 and -15 must be removed from the side containing the x (-15 first, 4 second).

$$4x - 15 = -23$$

$$\underline{ +15 \quad +15}$$

$$4x = -8 \qquad \text{Adding 15 to both sides.}$$

$$\frac{4x}{4} = \frac{-8}{4} \qquad \text{Dividing both sides by 4}$$

$$x = -2$$

Check for $x = -2$:
$$6x - 15 = -23 + 2x$$
$$6(-2) - 15 \overset{?}{=} -23 + 2(-2)$$
$$-12 - 15 \overset{?}{=} -23 - 4$$
$$-27 = -27$$

The same answer is obtained whether the x-term is removed from the left side or the right side. We now solve the previous example (Example 1) by removing the x-term from the *left* side.

$$6x - 15 = -23 + 2x$$

$$\underline{-6x -6x}$$

$$-15 = -23 - 4x$$

$$\underline{+23 \quad +23 }$$

$$8 = -4x$$

$$\frac{8}{-4} = \frac{-4x}{-4} \qquad \text{Dividing both sides by -4.}$$

$$-2 = x \qquad \text{Same answer.}$$

<u>Example 2.</u> Solve: $4x - 5 - x = 13 - 2x - 3$

<u>Solution:</u>

$$4x - 5 - x = 13 - 2x - 3 \qquad \text{First combine like terms on each}$$
$$3x - 5 = 10 - 2x \qquad\qquad\qquad \text{side.}$$

$$\underline{+2x +2x} \qquad \text{Add } \underline{2x} \text{ to both sides so that an } x\text{-}$$
$$5x - 5 = 10 \qquad\qquad\qquad \text{term remains on only one side.}$$

$$\underline{+5 \quad +5}$$
$$5x = 15 \qquad\qquad\qquad \text{Divide both sides by 5.}$$

$$x = 3$$

Check for $x = 3$:
$$4x - 5 - x = 13 - 2x - 3$$
$$4(3) - 5 - (3) = 13 - 2(3) - 3$$
$$12 - 5 - 3 = 13 - 6 - 3$$
$$4 = 4$$

<u>EXERCISES 405A.</u> Solve the following equations.

<u>SET I</u>

1. $3x + 5 = 14$ 2. $5x + 4 = 19$

3. $9x - 7 = 20$

4. $8x - 9 = 47$

5. $2x - 7 = x$

6. $5x - 8 = x$

7. $5x = 3x - 4$

8. $7x = 4x - 9$

9. $9 - 2x = x$

10. $8 - 5x = 3x$

11. $3x - 4 = 2x + 5$

12. $5x - 6 = 3x + 6$

13. $6x + 7 = 3 + 8x$

14. $4x + 28 = 7 + x$

15. $7x - 8 = 8 - 9x$

16. $5x - 7 = 7 - 9x$

----

17. $3x - 7 - x = 15 - 2x - 6$

18. $5x - 2 - x = 4 - 3x - 27$

19. $8x - 13 + 3x = 12 + 5x - 7$

20. $9x - 16 + 6x = 11 + 4x - 5$

21. $7 - 9x - 12 = 3x + 5 - 8x$

22. $13 - 11x - 17 = 5x + 4 - 10x$

🖩 23. $7.84 - 1.15x = 2.45$ 🖩 24. $6.09 - 3.75x = 5.45x$

SET II

1. $4x + 7 = 19$

2. $8x - 9 = 23$

3. $3x - 10 = x$

4. $6x = 2x - 8$

5. $12 - 5x = x$

6. $5x - 7 = 4x + 6$

7. $8x + 5 = 14 + 11x$

8. $9x - 13 = 13 - 4x$

9. $6x - 2 - x = 21 - 3x - 7$

10. $4x + 14 + 2x = 12 - 3x - 8$

11. $16 - 7x - 4 = 5x + 6 - 4x$

🖩 12. $8.42 - 2.35x = 1.25x$

EQUATIONS CONTAINING GROUPING SYMBOLS. When grouping symbols appear in an equation, those grouping symbols must be removed first. Then solve the resulting equation by the methods discussed in the previous sections.

All methods discussed so far for solving equations are combined in the following box.

TO SOLVE AN EQUATION

1. Remove grouping symbols.

2. Combine like terms on each side of the equation.

3. If the unknown letter appears on both sides of the equation, remove from one side the term containing the unknown letter by adding the negative of that term to both sides.

4. Remove all numbers that appear on the same side as the unknown.

   First, remove those numbers being added or subtracted.

   Second, multiply both sides by the signed number the unknown letter is divided by.

   Third, divide both sides by the coefficient of the unknown letter.

Check the solution in the *original* equation.

Example 1. Solve: $10x - 2(3 + 4x) = 7 - (x - 2)$

Solution:

$$10x - 2(3 + 4x) = 7 - (x - 2)$$

$10x - 6 - 8x = 7 - x + 2$	Removing grouping symbols.
$2x - 6 = 9 - x$	Combining like terms on each side.
$\underline{+ x \qquad\qquad + x}$	To get the x-term on only one side.
$3x - 6 = 9$	
$\underline{+ 6 \quad + 6}$	
$3x \quad\quad = 15$	Divide both sides by 3.
$x = 5$	

Check for $x = 5$:

$$10x - 2(3 + 4x) = 7 - (x - 2)$$
$$10(5) - 2(3 + 4 \cdot 5) = 7 - (5 - 2)$$
$$10(5) - 2(3 + 20) = 7 - (3)$$
$$10(5) - 2(23) = 7 - 3$$
$$50 - 46 = 4$$
$$4 = 4$$

Example 2. Solve: $7y - 3(2y - 5) = 6(2 + 3y) - 31$

Solution:

$$7y - 3(2y - 5) = 6(2 + 3y) - 31$$

$7y - 6y + 15 = 12 + 18y - 31$	Removing grouping symbols.

$$y + 15 = 18y - 19$$

Combining like terms on each side.

$$\underline{-y \qquad\quad -y}$$

To get the y-term on only one side.

$$15 = 17y - 19$$
$$\underline{+ 19 \qquad\quad + 19}$$
$$34 = 17y$$

Divide both sides by 17.

$$2 = y$$

Example 3. Solve: $5(2 - 3x) - 4 = 5x + [-(2x - 10) + 8]$

Solution:

$$
\begin{aligned}
5(2 - 3x) - 4 &= 5x + [-(2x - 10) + 8] \\
10 - 15x - 4 &= 5x + [-2x + 10 + 8] \\
10 - 15x - 4 &= 5x + [-2x + 18] \\
10 - 15x - 4 &= 5x - 2x + 18
\end{aligned}
$$

Removing grouping symbols.

$$-15x + 6 = 3x + 18$$

Combining like terms on both sides.
To get the x-term on only one side.

$$\underline{+ 15x \qquad\quad + 15x}$$
$$6 = 18x + 18$$
$$\underline{- 18 \qquad\quad - 18}$$
$$-12 = 18x$$
$$\frac{-12}{18} = \frac{18x}{18}$$
$$-\frac{2}{3} = x$$

EXERCISES 405B. Solve the following equations.

SET I

1. $5x - 3(2 + 3x) = 6$
2. $7x - 2(5 + 4x) = 8$

3. $6x + 2(3 - 8x) = -14$
4. $4x + 5(4 - 5x) = -22$

5. $7x + 5 = 3(3x + 5)$
6. $8x + 6 = 2(7x + 9)$

7. $9 - 4x = 5(9 - 8x)$
8. $10 - 7x = 4(11 - 6x)$

9. $3y - 2(2y - 7) = 2(3 + y) - 4$

10. $4a - 3(5a - 14) = 5(7 + a) - 9$

11. $6(3 - 4x) + 12 = 10x - 2(5 - 3x)$

12. $7(2 - 5x) + 27 = 18x - 3(8 - 4x)$

13. $2(3x - 6) - 3(5x + 4) = 5(7x - 8)$

14. $4(7z - 9) - 7(4z + 3) = 6(9z - 10)$

15. $6(5 - 4h) = 3(4h - 2) - 7(6 + 8h)$

16. $5(3 - 2k) = 8(3k - 4) - 4(1 + 7k)$

17. $2[3 - 5(x - 4)] = 10 - 5x$

18. $3[2 - 4(x - 7)] = 26 - 8x$

19. $3[2h - 6] = 2\{2(3 - h) - 5\}$

20. $6(3h - 5) = 3\{4(1 - h) - 7\}$

----

21. $5(3 - 2x) - 10 = 4x + [-(2x - 5) + 15]$

22. $4(2 - 6x) - 6 = 8x + [-(3x - 11) + 20]$

23. $9 - 3(2x - 7) - 9x = 5x - 2[6x - (4 - x) - 20]$

24. $14 - 2(7 - 4x) - 4x = 8x - 3[2x - (5 - x) - 30]$

25. $-2\{5 - [6 - 3(4 - x)] - 2x\} = 13 - [-(2x - 1)]$

26. $-3\{10 - [7 - 5(4 - x) - 8]\} = 11 - [-(5x - 4)]$

27. $5.073x - 2.937(8.622 + 7.153x) = 6.208$

28. $21.35 - 27.06x = 34.19(19.22 - 37.81x)$

29. $8.23x - 4.07(6.75x - 5.59) = 3.84(9.18 - x) - 2.67$

30. $11.28(15.93x - 24.66) - 35.42(29.05 - 41.84x)$
    $= 22.41(32.56x - 16.29)$

SET II

1. $4x - 5(3 + 2x) = 3$ 2. $8x + 3(4 - 5x) = -16$

3. $9x + 12 = 2(4x + 5)$ 4. $10 - 6x = 4(8 - 7x)$

5. $2y - 3(4y - 8) = 2(5 + y) - 10$

6. $5(6 - 3a) + 18 = -9a - 3(4 - 2a)$

7. $3(2z - 6) - 2(6z + 4) = 5(z + 8)$

8. $7(3 - 5h) = 4(3h - 2) - 6(7 + 9h)$

9. $3[2 - 4(k - 6)] = 12 - 6k$

10. $4[2x - 5] = 3\{6(7 - x) - 12\}$

11. $20 = 18 - \{-2[3z - 2(z - 1)]\}$

12. $12 = -\{-3[4z - 2(z - 2)]\}$

13. $6(2 - 3y) - 5 = 5y + [-(2y - 7) + 14]$

14. $11 - 2(3k - 5) - 8k = 4k - 2[3k - (6 - k) - 15]$

15. $7.209x - 4.395(6.281 + 9.154x) = 8.013$

16. $21.82(39.51x - 62.46) - 24.53(50.29 - 48.14x)$
    $= 14.28(65.23x - 92.61)$

Conditional Equations, Identities, and Equations with No Solution

There are different kinds of equations. In this section, we discuss three types of equations: conditional equations, identical equations, and equations with no solution.

<u>CONDITIONAL EQUATIONS</u>.   Consider the equation $x + 1 = 3$.

If $x = 5$, then	$x + 1 = 3$	
becomes	$5 + 1 = 3$???	
But we know that	$6 \neq 3$	
If $x = -1$, then	$x + 1 = 3$	
becomes	$-1 + 1 = 3$???	
But we know that	$0 \neq 3$	

However, if $x = 2$, then $x + 1 = 3$
    becomes $2 + 1 = 3$
    and $3 = 3$

The two sides of $x + 1 = 3$ are not always equal. The *condition* $x = 2$ must exist for the two sides of $x + 1 = 3$ to be equal. A *conditional equation* is an equation whose two sides are equal only when certain numbers (called *solutions*) are substituted for the letter. All equations given in this chapter so far are conditional equations.

<u>IDENTITIES</u>.   An *identity* (or *identical equation*) is an equation whose two sides are equal no matter what permissible number (Sec. 901) is substituted for the letter. Therefore, an identity has an endless number of solutions because any real number will make its two sides equal.

<u>Example 1</u>.   The equation $2(5x - 7) = 10x - 14$ is an identity
    because $10x - 14 = 10x - 14$

The two sides of the equation $10x - 14 = 10x - 14$ are identical.

<u>Example 2</u>.   The equation $4(3x - 5) - 2x = 2(5x + 1) - 22$
    is an identity because $12x - 20 - 2x = 10x + 2 - 22$
                            $10x - 20 = 10x - 20$
The two sides of the equation $10x - 20 = 10x - 20$ are identical.

<u>NOT ALL EQUATIONS HAVE A SOLUTION</u>.   A solution of an equation is a number that, when put in place of the letter, makes the two sides of the equation equal. For some equations no such number can be found. In these cases we say that the equation has no solution.

<u>Example 3</u>.   Solve $x + 1 = x + 2$

<u>Solution</u>: $x + 1 = x + 2$
            $-x$ $-x$ Trying to get the x-term on one side.
              $1 \neq 2$ The two sides are unequal.

In this case we say that *the equation has no solution* because no number substituted for x will make the two sides of the equation equal.

Note that $x + 1 \neq x + 2$, because *unequal* numbers have been added to the same number x; so these sums cannot be equal.

The same method is used to solve all three types of equations mentioned in this section. We discover which of the three types of equation we have only after the solution is carried out.

WHEN SOLVING AN EQUATION THAT HAS
ONLY ONE UNKNOWN

1. Attempt to solve the equation (by the method given in Sec. 405).

2. There are three possible results:

    (a) <u>Conditional Equation</u>: If a *single solution* is obtained, the equation is a conditional equation.

    (b) <u>Identity</u>: If the two sides of the equation *simplify to the same expression,* the equation is an identity.

    (c) <u>No solution</u>: If the two sides of the equation *simplify to unequal expressions,* the equation has no solution.

<u>Example 4.</u> Solve: $4x - 2(3 - x) = 12$

$$4x - 6 + 2x = 12$$
$$6x = 18$$
$$x = 3 \quad \text{Conditional equation} \\ \text{(Single solution)}$$

<u>Example 5.</u> Solve: $4x - 2(3 + 2x) = -6$

$$4x - 6 - 4x = -6$$
$$-6 = -6 \quad \text{Identity} \\ \text{(Both sides the same)}$$

<u>Example 6.</u> Solve: $4x - 2(3 + 2x) = 8$

$$4x - 6 - 4x = 8$$
$$-6 \neq 8 \quad \text{No solution} \\ \text{(Sides unequal)}$$

<u>EXERCISES 406.</u> Identify each of the following equations as either a conditional equation, an identity, or an equation with no solution. Find the solution of each conditional equation.

SET I

1. $x + 3 = 8$ 2. $4 - x = 6$

3. $2x + 5 = 7 + 2x$ 4. $10 - 5y = 8 - 5y$

5. $6 + 4x = 4x + 6$ 6. $7x + 12 = 12 + 7x$

7. $5x - 2(4 - x) = 6$ 8. $8x - 3(5 - x) = 7$

9. $6x - 3(5 + 2x) = -15$ 10. $4x - 2(6 + 2x) = -12$

11. $4x - 2(6 + 2x) = -15$ 12. $6x - 3(5 + 2x) = -12$

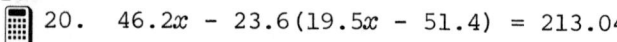

13. $7(2 - 5x) - 32 = 10x - 3(6 + 15x)$

14. $6(3 - 4x) + 10 = 8x - 3(2 - 3x)$

15. $2(2x - 5) - 3(4 - x) = 7x - 20$

16. $3(x - 4) - 5(6 - x) = 2(4x - 21)$

17. $2[3 - 4(5 - x)] = 2(3x - 11)$

18. $3[5 - 2(7 - x)] = 6(x - 7)$

19. $460.2x - 23.6(19.5x - 51.4) = 1213.04$

20. $46.2x - 23.6(19.5x - 51.4) = 213.04$

SET II

1. $7 - x = 11$ 2. $6y - 8 = 3 + 6y$

3. $15 + 8a = 8a + 15$ 4. $10 = 8x - 2(5 + 4x)$

5. $7h - 3(5 - h) = 10$ 6. $2(7k + 9) - 18 = 14k$

7. $9(3 + 4x) - 17 = 14x + 2(6 + 11x)$

8. $3(2y - 7) - 2(5 - y) = 8y - 31$

9. $4(5x - 9) = 3[2 - 4(6 - x)]$

10. $460.2x - 23.6(19.5x - 51.4) = 213.04$

Chapter Summary

Parts of an Equation (Sec. 401)

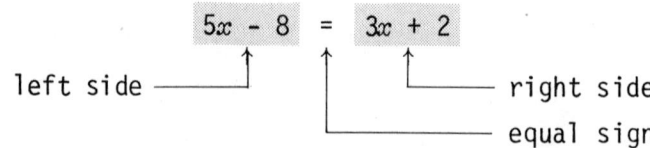

$$5x - 8 = 3x + 2$$

left side ──────── ↑   ↑   ↑ ──── right side
                              └──── equal sign

The equal sign (=) in an equation means that the number represented by the left side *is the same* as the number represented by the right side.

Solution of an Equation (Sec. 402). A *solution* of an equation is a number that, when put in place of the letter, makes the two sides of the equation equal.

Conditional Equations (Sec. 406). A *conditional equation* is an equation whose two sides are equal only when certain numbers (called *solutions*) are substituted for the letter.

Identities (Sec. 406). An *identity* (or *identical equation*) is an equation whose two sides are equal no matter what permissible number is substituted for the letter.

Equations with No Solution (Sec. 406). An equation has *no solution* when there is no number which can be put in place of the letter that will make the two sides of the equation equal.

In Solving Equations (Sec. 404)

1. *Addition Rule*: The same number may be added to both sides.
2. *Subtraction Rule*: The same number may be subtracted from both sides.
3. *Multiplication Rule*: Both sides may be multiplied by the same number.
4. *Division Rule*: Both sides may be divided by the same number (not zero).

To Solve an Equation (Sec. 406)

1. Remove grouping symbols.
2. Combine like terms on each side of the equation.
3. Attempt to solve the resulting equation by the methods of Secs. 402, 403, 404, and 405.
4. There are three possible results:
   (a) *A conditional equation*: if a solution is obtained in Step 3.
   (b) *An identity*: if the two sides of the equation obtained in Step 3 are identical.
   (c) *No solution*: if the two sides of the equation obtained in Step 3 are unequal numbers.

To Check the Solution of an Equation (Sec. 402)

1. Replace the unknown letter in the given equation by the number obtained as a solution.
2. Perform the indicated operations on both sides of the equal sign.
3. If the resulting number on each side of the equal sign is the same, the solution is correct.

REVIEW EXERCISES 407. In the following equations, find the solution of each conditional equation, and check your answers. Identify the equations that are identities and those that have no solution.

SET I

1. $3x - 5 = 4$ 2. $4x - 6 = 10$

3. $17 - 5x = 2$ 4. $22 - 8x = 6$

5. $2 = 20 - 9x$ 6. $3 = 33 - 10x$

7. $2x + 1 = 2x + 7$ 8. $5x - 3 = 5x + 4$

9. $7.5 = \dfrac{A}{10}$ 10. $1.6 = \dfrac{B}{10}$

11. $\dfrac{C}{7} - 15 = 13$ 12. $\dfrac{D}{9} - 12 = 8$

13. $7 - 2(M - 4) = 5$ 14. $6 - 4(N - 3) = 2$

15. $10 - 4(2 - 3x) = 2 + 12x$

16. $20 - 3(4 - 5x) = 8 + 15x$

17. $6R - 8 = 6(2 - 3R)$ 18. $7P - 15 = 7(3 - 2P)$

19. $56T - 18 = 7(8T - 4)$ 20. $65 - 77S = 11(5 - 7S)$

----

21. $15(4 - 5V) = 16(4 - 6V) + 10$

22. $12(4W - 5) = 9(7W - 8) - 13$

23. $9 - 3(x - 2) = 3(5 - x)$ 24. $10 - 5(2x - 3) = 5(5 - 2x)$

25. $5x - 7(4 - 2x) + 8 = 10 - 9(11 - x)$

26. $18 - 6(5x - 4) - 13x = 11(12 - 3x) - 7$

27. $2[-7y - 3(5 - 4y) + 10] = 10y - 12$

28. $5[-13z - 8(4 - 2z) + 20] = 15z - 17$

29. $4[-24 - 6(3x - 5) + 22x] = 0$

30. $3[-53 - 7(4x - 9) + 18x] = 0$

SET II

1. $6 = 7x - 8$ 2. $12 - 6x = -12$

3. $3 = 18 - 5x$ 4. $5 - 3x = 9 - 3x$

5. $\dfrac{x}{4} = 8.6$ 6. $-27 = \dfrac{z}{6} - 18$

7. $-9 - 3(N - 8) = 30$ 8. $19 - 5(3 - 2x) = 4 + 10x$

9. $12R - 9 = 8(3 - 4R)$ 10. $42H + 12 = 6(7H - 2)$

11. $11(3 - 4V) = 8(5 - 6V) + 17$

12. $4 - 5(x - 7) = 10(4 - x)$

13. $25 - 2[4(x - 2) - 12x + 4] = 16x + 33$

14. $15 - 5[2(8x - 4) - 14x + 8] = 25$

15. $2\{3[2(5 - V) + 4V] - 20\} = 0$

CUMULATIVE REVIEW EXERCISES: CHAPTERS 1-3

In Exercises 1-4, evaluate each expression.

1. $\dfrac{-7}{0}$ 2. $\sqrt{8^2 + 6^2}$

3. $7\sqrt{16} - 5(-4)$ 4. $25 - \{-16 - [(11 - 7) - 8]\}$

In Exercises 5 and 6, evaluate each formula using the values of the letters given with the formula.

5. $V = \dfrac{4}{3}\pi R^3$ $\pi \doteq 3.14$, $R = 9$

6. $S = P(1 + i)^n$ $P = 3000$, $i = 0.10$, $n = 2$

In Exercises 7-10, simplify each algebraic expression.

7. $15x - [9y - (7x - 10y)]$ 8. $5(2a - 3b) - 6(4a + 7b)$

9. $x(2x^2 - 5x + 12) - 6(3x^2 + 2x - 5)$

10. $4hk(3hk - hk^2) - hk^2(2h - hk)$

Chapter Four Diagnostic Test

Name_____

_____

The purpose of this test is to see how well you understand solving simple equations. We recommend that you work this diagnostic test *before* your instructor tests you on this chapter. Allow yourself about fifty minutes to do this test.

Complete solutions for all the problems on this test, together with section references, are given in the Answer Section. We suggest that you study the sections referred to for the problems you do incorrectly.

Solve each of the following equations. If the equation is an identity, write "identity." If the equation has no solution, write "no solution."

1. $x - 3 = 7$

    (1)_____

2. $10 = x + 4$

    (2)_____

3. Show your check on this problem:
    $3x + 2 = 14$

    (3)_____

4. $15 - 2x = 7$

    (4)_____

5. $\frac{x}{4} = 3.8$

    (5)_____

6. $-5 = \frac{x}{7}$

    (6)_____

7. $\frac{x}{5} - 3 = 2$

    (7)_____

8. $100 - \dfrac{10x}{7} = -50$

(8) _____

9. $4x + 5 = 17 - 2x$

(9) _____

10. $3z - 21 + 5z = 4 - 6z + 17$

(10) _____

11. Show your check on this problem:
$6k - 3(4 - 5k) = 9$

(11) _____

12. $6x - 2(3x - 5) = 10$

(12) _____

13. $2m - 4(3m - 2) = 5(6 + m) - 7$

(13) _____

14. $2(3x + 5) = 14 + 3(2x - 1)$

(14) _____

15. $3[7 - 6(y - 2)] = -3 + 2y$

(15) _____

_____

FIVE
Word Problems

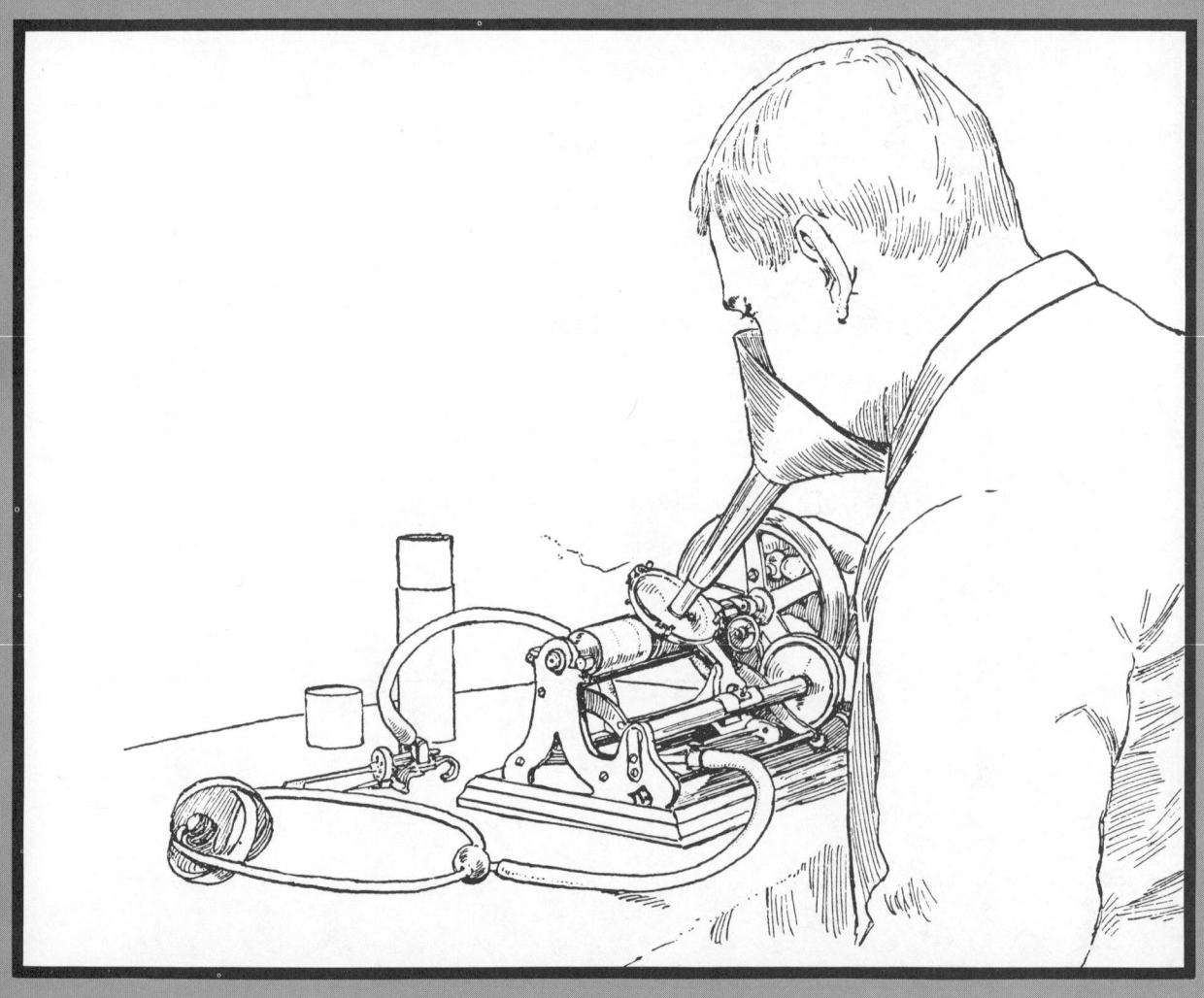

The main reason for studying algebra is to equip oneself with the tools necessary to solve problems. Most problems are expressed in words. In this chapter we show how to change the words of a written problem into an equation. That equation can then be solved by the methods learned in Chapter 4.

501 Changing Word Expressions into Algebraic Expressions

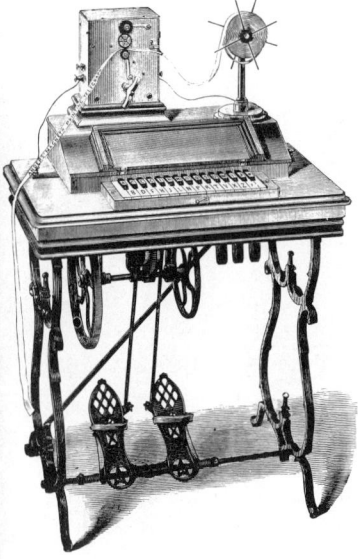

It is helpful in solving word problems to break them up into smaller expressions. In this section we show how you can change these small *word* expressions into *algebraic* expressions.

Example 1. Change the word expression "the sum of A and B" into an algebraic expression.

Solution: $A + B$

Example 2. Change the word expression "the product of L and W" into an algebraic expression.

Solution: LW

Example 3. Change "two more than C" into an algebraic expression.

Solution: $C + 2$

Example 4. Change "three times the square of x, less ten" into an algebraic expression.

Solution: $3x^2 - 10$

Example 5. Change "five decreased by the quotient of S by T" into an algebraic expression.

Solution: $5 - \dfrac{S}{T}$

Example 6. Change "the product of w and z is twenty" into an algebraic expression.

Solution: $wz = 20$

EXERCISES 501A. Change each of the following word expressions into an algebraic expression.

SET I

1. The sum of x and ten
2. A added to B
3. Five less than A
4. B diminished by C
5. The product of six and z
6. A multiplied by B
7. Subtract the product of U and V from x.
8. Subtract x from the product of P and Q.
9. C less D
10. A less 10

11. The product of five and the square of x
12. The product of ten and the cube of x

----

13. The square of the sum of A and B
14. The square of the quotient of A divided by B
15. The sum of x and seven, divided by y
16. T divided by the sum of x and nine
17. The product of x and the difference, six less than y
18. The sum of x and forty is w.

SET II

1. Ten added to x 2. x diminished by 4
3. The quotient of A by the sum of C and ten
4. The quotient of the sum of A and C by B
5. Twice F less fifteen
6. Twice the sum of x and y
7. Three times x less five times y.
8. Ten times x decreased by ten times y.
9. The sum of x and y is twenty.
10. The product of seven and the difference, x less than y.

REPRESENTING WORD EXPRESSIONS CONTAINING UNKNOWN NUMBERS. Word expressions may contain unknown numbers. To change such a word expression into an algebraic expression, each unknown number must first be represented in terms of the same letter.

TO CHANGE A WORD EXPRESSION INTO AN ALGEBRAIC EXPRESSION

1. Identify which number or numbers are unknown.

2. Represent one of the unknown numbers by a letter. Express any other unknown number in terms of the same letter.

3. Change the word expression into an algebraic expression using the letter representations in place of the unknown numbers.

Example 7. Change the word expression "twice Albert's salary" into an algebraic expression.

1. Albert's salary is the unknown number.
2. Let S represent Albert's salary.
3. Then $2S$ is the algebraic expression for "twice Albert's salary."

Example 8. Change the word expression "the cost of five stamps" into an algebraic expression.

    1. The cost of one stamp is the unknown number.
    2. Let c represent the cost of one stamp.
    3. Then $5c$ is the algebraic expression for "the cost of five stamps." Since one stamp costs c cents, then 5 stamps will cost 5 times c cents = $5c$.

Example 9. In the word expression "Mary is ten years older than Nancy," represent both unknown numbers in terms of the same letter.

First Solution:

    1. There are two unknown numbers in this expression: Mary's age and Nancy's age.
    2. Let N represent Nancy's age.

Then $N + 10$ represents Mary's age, because Mary is 10 years older than Nancy.

Second Solution:

    1. There are two unknown numbers in this expression: Mary's age and Nancy's age.
    2. Let M represent Mary's age.

Than $M - 10$ represents Nancy's age, because Nancy is 10 years younger than Mary.

Example 10. In the word expression "The sum of two numbers is ten," represent both unknown numbers in terms of the same letter.

    1. There are two unknown numbers.
    2. Let x = one of the unknown numbers
       Then $\underline{10 - x}$ = the other unknown number

       Sum = 10   Notice that the two numbers add up to 10.

EXERCISES 501B. In the following exercises: (a) *If there is only one unknown number*, represent it by a letter and then change the word expression into an algebraic expression. (b) *If there is more than one unknown number*, represent each number in terms of the same letter.

SET I

1. Fred's salary plus seventy-five dollars
2. Jaime's salary less forty-two dollars
3. Two less than the number of children in Mr. Moore's family
4. Two more players were added to Jerry's team
5. Four times Joyce's age
6. One-fourth of Rene's age

7. Twenty times the cost of a record increased by eighty-nine cents
8. Seventeen cents less than five times the cost of a ballpoint pen
9. One-fifth the cost of a hamburger
10. The length of the building divided by eight
11. Five times the speed of the car plus one hundred miles per hour
12. Twice the speed of a car diminished by forty miles per hour
13. Ten less than five times the square of an unknown number
14. Eight more than four times the cube of an unknown number
15. The length of a rectangle is twelve centimeters more than its width.
16. The altitude of a triangle is seven centimeters less than its base.
17. Take the quotient of seven by an unknown number away from fifty.
18. Add the quotient of an unknown number by nine to fifteen.

----

19. Eleven feet more than twice the length of a rectangle
20. One inch less than the diameter of a circle
21. The combined weight of Walter and Carlos is 320 lb.
22. The combined weight of Teresa and Lucy is 224 lb.
23. 2.2 times the weight in kilograms
24. 0.62 times the distance in kilometres
25. The sum of eight and an unknown number is divided by the square of that unknown number.
26. The sum of the square of an unknown number and eleven is divided by the unknown number.
27. The sum of thirty-two and nine-fifths the Celsius temperature.
28. Five-ninths times the result of subtracting thirty-two from the Fahrenheit temperature.

SET II

1. The sum of two numbers is sixty.
2. Henry is five years younger than his brother.
3. Mrs. Lopez is twenty-one years older than her daughter.
4. One-half the sum of seven and an unknown number
5. Eight added to the sum of ten and an unknown number
6. The sum of two numbers is -22.
7. The speed of the train divided by six
8. The distance to San Francisco divided by seven
9. Tom has $139 more than Linda.
10. Twice the result of subtracting an unknown number from five
11. The square of the result of subtracting twelve from an unknown number
12. Pete has $53 less than Ann.

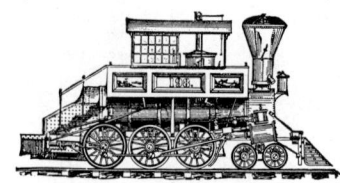

Changing Word Problems into Equations

In this section we show how to change the words of a written problem into an equation.

Example 1. Fifteen plus twice an unknown number is thirty-seven.

Solution:

Fifteen	plus	twice an unknown number	is	thirty-seven .
15	+	2x	=	37

Equation: $15 + 2x = 37$

We broke the word problem into small pieces, then represented each piece by an algebraic expression. This formed the equation. We summarize this method as follows:

TO CHANGE A WORD PROBLEM INTO AN EQUATION

1. Represent the unknown number by x (Sec. 501).

2. Break the word problem into small pieces.

3. Represent each piece by an algebraic expression (Sec. 501).

4. Arrange the algebraic expressions into an equation.

Example 2. Three times an unknown number is equal to twelve increased by the unknown number.

Solution:

Three	times	an unknown number	is equal to	twelve	increased by	the unknown number
3	·	x	=	12	+	x

$$3x = 12 + x$$

Example 3. One-third of an unknown number is seven.

Solution:

| One-third | of | an unknown number | is | seven. |

$$\frac{1}{3} \cdot \quad x \quad = \quad 7$$

$$\frac{1}{3}x = 7$$

Example 4. Twice the sum of six and an unknown number is equal to twenty.

Solution:

| Twice | the sum of six and an unknown number | is | twenty. |

$$2 \cdot \quad (6 + x) \quad = \quad 20$$

$$2(6 + x) = 20$$

Example 5. When three times an unknown number is subtracted from thirteen and the result is divided by nine, the quotient is four times the unknown number.

Solution:

| When three times an unknown number is subtracted from thirteen and the result is divided by nine, | the quotient is | four times the unknown number. |

$$\frac{13 - 3x}{9} \quad = \quad 4x$$

$$\frac{13 - 3x}{9} = 4x$$

EXERCISES 502. Write the equation for each of the following word problems. Do not solve the equations at this time.

SET I

1. Thirteen more than twice an unknown number is twenty-five.
2. Twenty-five more than three times an unknown number is thirty-four.
3. Five times an unknown number, decreased by eight, is twenty-two.
4. Four times an unknown number, decreased by five, is fifteen.
5. Seven minus an unknown number is equal to the unknown number plus one.
6. Six plus an unknown number is equal to twelve decreased by the unknown number.
7. One-fifth of an unknown number is four.
8. An unknown number divided by twelve equals six.

9. When four is subtracted from one-half of an unknown number, the result is six.
10. When five is subtracted from one-third of an unknown number, the result is four.
11. Twice the sum of five and an unknown number is equal to twenty-six.
12. Four times the sum of nine and an unknown number is equal to eighteen.

----

13. When the sum of an unknown number and itself is multiplied by three, the result is twenty-four.
14. Five times the sum of an unknown number and itself is forty.
15. When the sum of six and twice an unknown number is divided by two, the result is seven.
16. When the sum of eight and an unknown number is divided by three, the result is four.
17. When the sum of two and eight times an unknown number is divided by seven, that quotient equals the unknown number.
18. When the sum of nine and five times an unknown number is divided by twenty, the quotient is the unknown number.
19. When one is subtracted from nineteen times an unknown number and the result is divided by eighteen, the quotient equals twice the unknown number.
20. When fifteen times an unknown number is subtracted from eight and the result is divided by thirteen, the quotient is four times the unknown number.

SET II

1. Fifteen more than twice an unknown number is twenty-seven.
2. Four times an unknown number, decreased by nine, is nineteen.
3. When seven is added to an unknown number, the result is twice that unknown number.
4. When a number is decreased by five, the difference is half of the number.
5. When three times an unknown number is subtracted from twenty, the result is the unknown number.
6. Three times the result of subtracting an unknown number from eight is twelve.
7. When the sum of an unknown number and itself is multiplied by four, the result is fifty-six.
8. When the sum of four and twice an unknown number is divided by two, the result is five.
9. When the sum of three and five times an unknown number is divided by six, that quotient equals the unknown number.
10. When six is subtracted from five times an unknown number, the result is the same as when four is added to three times the unknown number.

Solving Word Problems

In the last section we showed how to change the words of a written problem into an equation. In this section we show the complete solution of the word problem.

Example 1. Seven increased by three times an unknown number is thirteen. What is the unknown number?

Solution:

Seven	increased by	three times	an unknown number	is	thirteen .
7	+	3 ·	x	=	13

$$7 + 3x = 13$$
$$3x = 6 \quad \text{Subtracting 7 from both sides.}$$
$$x = 2 \quad \text{Dividing both sides by 3.}$$

Check:

Seven	increased by	three times	an unknown number	is	thirteen .
7	+	3 ·	(2)	=	13

$$7 + 3(2) = 13 \quad \text{The unknown number was}$$
$$7 + 6 = 13 \quad \text{replaced by 2.}$$
$$13 = 13$$

Note. To check a word problem, the solution must be checked in the word statement. The reason for checking in the word statement is that an error may have been made in writing the equation that would not be discovered if you substitute the solution in the equation.

TO SOLVE A WORD PROBLEM

1. Represent the unknown number by x.

2. Break the word problem into small pieces.

3. Represent each piece by an algebraic expression.

4. Arrange the algebraic expressions into an equation.

5. Solve the equation.

6. Check the solution in the word statement.

Example 2. Four times an unknown number is equal to twice the sum of five and that unknown number. Find the unknown number.

Solution:

Four times	an unknown number	is equal to	twice the sum of five and that unknown number.
4 ·	x	=	2 · (5 + x)

$$4x = 2(5 + x)$$

$4x = 2(5 + x)$

$4x = 10 + 2x$ Using the Distributive Rule.

$2x = 10$ Subtracting $2x$ from both sides.

$x = 5$ Dividing both sides by 2.

Check: Checking the solution in the word statement is left to the student.

Example 3. When seven is subtracted from one-half of an unknown number, the result is eleven. What is the unknown number?

Solution:

When

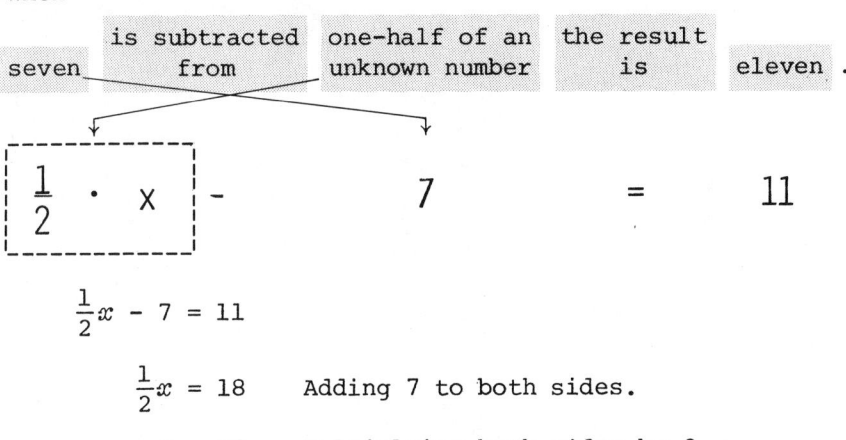

seven	is subtracted from	one-half of an unknown number	the result is	eleven .
		$\frac{1}{2}$ · x		
	7	=		11

$\frac{1}{2}x - 7 = 11$

$\frac{1}{2}x = 18$ Adding 7 to both sides.

$x = 36$ Multiplying both sides by 2.

EXERCISES 503. Solve each of the following word problems for the unknown number. Check each solution in the word statement.

SET I

1. When twice an unknown number is added to thirteen, the sum is twenty-five.
2. When twenty-five is added to three times an unknown number, the sum is thirty-four.
3. Five times an unknown number, decreased by eight, is twenty-two.
4. Four times an unknown number, decreased by five, is fifteen.
5. Seven minus an unknown number is equal to the unknown number plus one.
6. Six plus an unknown number is equal to twelve decreased by the unknown number.

7. When four is subtracted from one-half of an unknown number, the result is six.
8. When five is subtracted from one-third of an unknown number, the result is four.
9. Twice the sum of five and an unknown number is equal to twenty-six.
10. Four times the sum of nine and an unknown number is equal to twenty.

----

11. When twice the sum of four and an unknown number is added to the unknown number, the result is the same as when ten is added to the unknown number.
12. When six is subtracted from five times an unknown number, the result is the same as when four is added to three times the unknown number.
13. Three times the sum of eight and twice an unknown number is equal to four times the sum of three times the unknown number and eight.
14. Five times the sum of four and six times an unknown number is equal to four times the sum of twice the unknown number and ten.
15. When three times the sum of four and an unknown number is subtracted from ten times the unknown number, the result is equal to five times the sum of nine and twice the unknown number.
16. When twice the sum of five and an unknown number is subtracted from five times the sum of six and twice the unknown number, the result is equal to zero.
17. When 5.75 times the sum of 6.94 and an unknown number is subtracted from 8.66 times the unknown number, the result is equal to 4.69 times the sum of 8.55 and 3.48 times the unknown number.
18. When 8.23 is subtracted from 4.85 times an unknown number, the result is the same as when 12.62 is added to 5.49 times the unknown number.

SET II

1. When seven is added to an unknown number, the result is twice that unknown number.
2. When three times an unknown number is subtracted from twenty, the result is the unknown number.
3. One-fifth of an unknown number is four.
4. An unknown number divided by twelve equals six.
5. When an unknown number is subtracted from twelve, the difference is one-third of the number.
6. Five times the sum of an unknown number and itself is forty.
7. Twice the result of subtracting an unknown number from five is eight.
8. If the sum of an unknown number and twelve is subtracted from four times the unknown number, the result is the unknown number less four.
9. When 3.48 times the sum of 9.06 and an unknown number is subtracted from 5.37 times the unknown number, the result is equal to 4.65 times the sum of 2.83 and 8.34 times the unknown number.

Money Problems

In this section we discuss another type of word problem commonly referred to as "coin problems." Not all problems in this section deal with coins, but the method of solving them is essentially the same.

GETTING READY TO SOLVE COIN PROBLEMS. The main idea used in solving problems of this type is:

$$\begin{pmatrix} \text{The Total Value} \\ \text{of One Kind} \\ \text{of Item} \end{pmatrix} = \begin{pmatrix} \text{The Value} \\ \text{of One of} \\ \text{Those Items} \end{pmatrix} \cdot \begin{pmatrix} \text{The Number} \\ \text{of} \\ \text{Those Items} \end{pmatrix}$$

Example 1. If you have 8 nickels,

the total amount of money = 8(5) = 40¢

value of one nickel
number of nickels

Example 2. If you have 7 quarters,

the total amount of money = 7(25) = 175¢ = $1.75

value of one quarter
number of quarters

Example 3. If you have x dimes,

the total amount of money = x(10) = $10x$¢

value of one dime
number of dimes

Example 4. If you have y 15-cent candy bars,

the total amount of money = y(15) = $15y$¢

value of one candy bar
number of candy bars

When more than one kind of item occurs in the same problem, add the total values of each kind of item.

Example 5. If you have 2 adult movie tickets costing $1.75 each and 4 children's tickets costing 90¢ each,

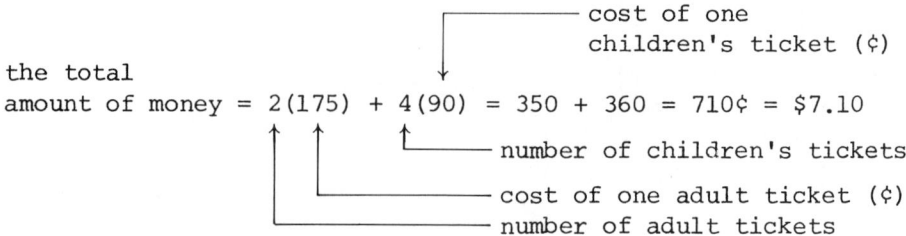

the total
amount of money = 2(175) + 4(90) = 350 + 360 = 710¢ = $7.10

Example 6. If you have x 10-cent stamps and y 12-cent stamps,

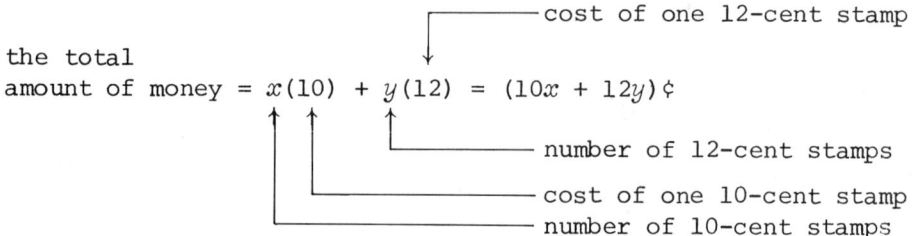

the total
amount of money = $x(10) + y(12) = (10x + 12y)$¢

EXERCISES 504A. In each of the following exercises, express the total amount either as a number or as an algebraic expression.

SET I

1. If you have 7 nickels, what amount of money is this?
2. If you have 11 quarters, what amount of money is this?
3. If you have nine 50-cent pieces, what amount of money is this?
4. If you have 12 dimes, what amount of money is this?
5. If you have x quarters, what amount of money is this?
6. If you have y nickels, what amount of money is this?
7. Find the total cost of 7 adult and 5 children's tickets if adult tickets are $1.50 each and children's are 75¢ each.
8. If adult tickets are $2.50 and children's tickets are $1.25 each, what will 4 adult and 9 children's tickets cost?
9. If adult tickets are $3.50 and children's tickets are $1.90 each, what will x adult and y children's tickets cost?
10. Find the total cost of x adult and y children's tickets if adult tickets are $2.75 each and children's tickets cost $1.50 each.

----

11. Find the total cost of x 25-cent stamps and y 6-cent stamps.
12. Find the total cost of x 4-cent stamps and y 2-cent stamps.
13. What is the total cost of x pounds of cashew nuts costing $1.19 a pound and y pounds of peanuts costing 85¢ a pound?
14. What is the total cost of x pounds of chocolates costing $1.95 a pound and y pounds of hard candy costing $1.25 a pound?

1. If you have nine nickels, what amount of money is this?
2. If you have 11 dimes, what amount of money is this?
3. If you have x 50-cent coins, what amount of money is this?
4. If adult tickets cost $3.50 each and children's tickets cost $1.50 each, what will 5 adult and 3 children's tickets cost?
5. Find the total cost of x adult and y children's tickets if adult tickets are $4.50 each and children's tickets are $2.25 each.
6. Find the total cost of x 13-cent stamps and y 15-cent stamps.

SOLVING MONEY PROBLEMS

Example 7. Doris has 17 coins in her purse that have a total value of $1.15. If they are only nickels and dimes, how many of each are there?

Solution: There are two unknown numbers: the number of nickels and the number of dimes.

Let D = number of dimes

then, $17 - D$ = number of nickels

Each dime is worth 10¢; therefore, D dimes are worth $10D$¢. Each nickel is worth 5¢; therefore, $(17 - D)$ nickels are worth $5(17 - D)$¢.

amount of money in dimes	+	amount of money in nickels	= 115¢
10D	+	5(17 - D)	= 115

$$10D + 5(17 - D) = 115$$
$$10D + 85 - 5D = 115$$
$$5D = 30$$
$$D = 6 \text{ dimes}$$
$$17 - D = 17 - 6 = 11 \text{ nickels}$$

Check: 6 dimes = 6(10) = 60¢
                11 nickels = 11(5) = $\underline{55¢}$
                                    115¢ = $1.15

Example 8. Dianne has $3.20 in nickels, dimes, and quarters. If there are 7 more dimes than quarters and 3 times as many nickels as quarters, how many of each kind of coin does she have?

Solution: Let Q = number of quarters

then, $Q + 7$ = number of dimes   Because there are 7 more dimes than quarters.

and $3Q$ = number of nickels   Because there are 3 times as many nickels as quarters.

Q quarters are worth $25Q$¢.
$(Q + 7)$ dimes are worth $10(Q + 7)$¢.
$3Q$ nickels are worth $5(3Q)$¢.

value of quarters + value of dimes + value of nickels = 320¢

$$25Q \quad + \quad 10(Q + 7) \quad + \quad 5(3Q) \quad = 320$$

$$25Q + 10(Q + 7) + 5(3Q) = 320$$
$$25Q + 10Q + 70 + 15Q = 320$$
$$50Q = 250$$
$$Q = 5 \text{ quarters}$$
$$Q + 7 = 5 + 7 = 12 \text{ dimes}$$
$$3Q = 3(5) = 15 \text{ nickels}$$

Check:
$$5 \text{ quarters} = 5(25) = 125¢$$
$$12 \text{ dimes} = 12(10) = 120¢$$
$$15 \text{ nickels} = 15(5) = \underline{75¢}$$
$$320¢ = \$3.20$$

EXERCISES 504B

SET I

1. Bill has 13 coins in his pocket that have a total value of 95¢. If these coins consist of nickels and dimes, how many of each kind are there?

2. Miko has 11 coins that have a total value of 85¢. If the coins are only nickels and dimes, how many of each kind are there?

3. Jennifer has 12 coins that have a total value of $2.20. The coins are nickels and quarters. How many of each kind of coin are there?

4. Brian has 18 coins consisting of nickels and quarters. If the total value of the coins is $2.50, how many of each kind of coin does he have?

5. Derek has $4.00 in nickels, dimes, and quarters. If there are 4 more quarters than nickels and 3 times as many dimes as nickels, how many of each kind of coin does he have?

6. Staci has $5.50 in nickels, dimes, and quarters. If there are 7 more dimes than nickels and twice as many quarters as dimes, how many of each kind of coin does she have?

7. Michael has $2.25 in nickels, dimes, and quarters. If there are 3 fewer dimes than quarters and as many nickels as the sum of the dimes and quarters, how many of each kind of coin does he have?

8. Muriel has $2.57 in dimes, nickels, and pennies. If there are 5 fewer pennies than nickels and as many dimes as the sum of the nickels and pennies, how many of each kind of coin does she have?

----

9. The total receipts for a concert were $6600 for the 1080 tickets sold. They sold orchestra seats for $7 each, box seats for $10 each, and balcony seats for $4 each. If there were 5 times as many balcony seats as box seats sold, how many of each kind were sold?

10. The total receipts for a football game were $360,800. General admission tickets cost $5 each, reserved seat tickets $8 each, and box seat tickets $10 each. If there were twice as many general admission as reserved seat tickets sold and four times as many reserved as box seat tickets sold, how many of each kind were sold?

11. Christy spent $3.80 for 60 stamps. She bought only 2-cent, 10-cent, and 12-cent stamps. If there were twice as many 10-cent stamps as 12-cent stamps, how many of each kind did she buy?

12. Mark spent $9.80 for 100 stamps. He bought only 6-cent, 8-cent, and 12-cent stamps. If there were three times as many 6-cent stamps as 8-cent stamps, how many of each kind did he buy?

SET II

1. Don spent $2.36 for 22 stamps. If he bought only 10-cent stamps and 12-cent stamps, how many of each kind did he buy?

2. Several families went to a movie together. They spent $10.60 for 8 tickets. If adult tickets cost $1.95 and children's tickets cost 95¢, how many of each kind of ticket was bought?

3. A class received $233 for selling 200 tickets to the school play. If student tickets cost $1 each and nonstudent tickets cost $2 each, how many nonstudents attended the play?

4. A 10-pound mixture of almonds and walnuts costs $7.20. If walnuts cost 69¢ a pound and almonds 79¢ a pound, how many pounds of each kind are there?

5. A dealer makes up a 100-pound mixture of Colombian coffee costing 85¢ per pound and Brazilian coffee costing 75¢ per pound. How many pounds of each kind must he use in order for the mixture to cost 78¢ per pound?

6. A dealer makes up a 50-pound mixture of cashews and peanuts. If the cashews cost 80¢ a pound and the peanuts cost 65¢ a pound, how many pounds of each kind of nut must he use in order for the mixture to cost 74¢ a pound?

Ratio Problems

Ratio is another word for fraction, so in algebra fractions are often called *ratio*nal numbers.

The ratio of a to b is written $\frac{a}{b}$ or $a : b$.

The ratio of b to a is written $\frac{b}{a}$ or $b : a$.

We call a and b the *terms* of the ratio.

The terms of a ratio can be any kind of number, the only restriction being that the denominator cannot be zero.

The key to solving ratio problems is to use the given ratio to help represent the unknown numbers.

TO REPRESENT THE UNKNOWNS
IN A RATIO PROBLEM

1. Multiply each term of the ratio by x.

2. The resulting products are used to represent the unknowns.

Example 1. In an algebra class there are 13 men and 17 women.

(a) The ratio of men to women is $\dfrac{13}{17}$.

(b) The ratio of women to men is $\dfrac{17}{13}$.

There are three different meanings we can give to an expression such as $\dfrac{3}{4}$.

1. 3 of the 4 equal parts a unit has been divided into (fraction meaning)
2. $3 \div 4$ (division meaning)
3. The ratio of 3 to 4 (ratio meaning)

The meaning chosen depends upon how the expression is used. The ratio meaning is used when *comparing* two numbers by division.
Following are some typical examples using ratios.

Example 2. Two numbers are in the ratio 3 to 5. Their sum is 32. Find the numbers.

$3 \ : \ 5$ The ratio

$3x \ : \ 5x$ Multiplied each term of the ratio by x.

     The resulting products represent the unknowns.

Let $5x$ = larger number

Let $3x$ = smaller number

Their sum is 32

$$3x + 5x = 32$$

$$8x = 32$$

$$x = 4$$

$3x = 3(4) = 12$ Smaller number

$5x = 5(4) = \underline{20}$ Larger number

               32   Check

Perimeter. *The* **perimeter** *of a geometric figure is the sum of the lengths of all its sides. The word perimeter means "the measure around a figure."*

<u>Example 3.</u> The length and width of a rectangle are in the ratio of 7 to 5. The perimeter is 72. Find the length and width.

<u>Solution:</u>

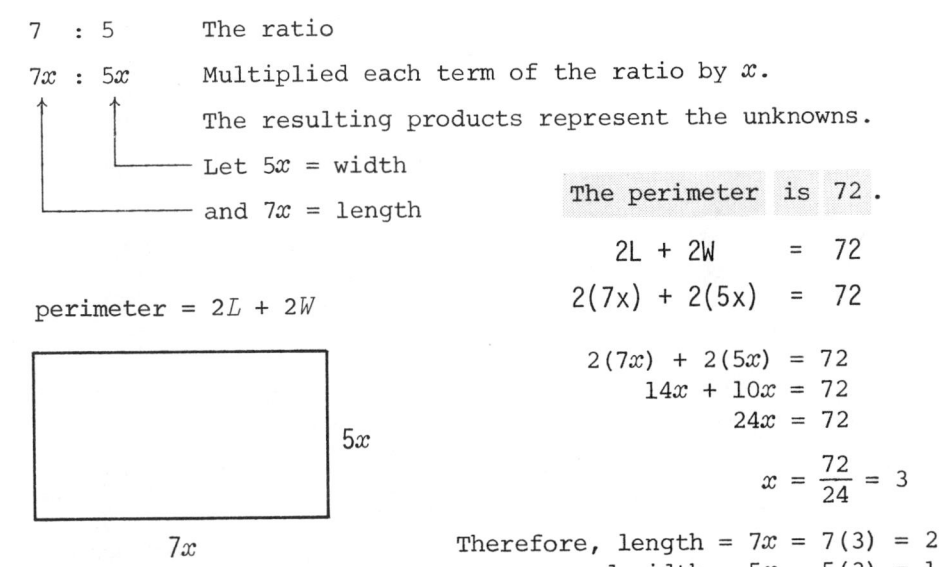

7 : 5   The ratio

7x : 5x Multiplied each term of the ratio by x.

The resulting products represent the unknowns.

Let 5x = width
and 7x = length

perimeter = 2L + 2W

The perimeter is 72.

$$2L + 2W = 72$$
$$2(7x) + 2(5x) = 72$$

$$2(7x) + 2(5x) = 72$$
$$14x + 10x = 72$$
$$24x = 72$$
$$x = \frac{72}{24} = 3$$

Therefore, length = 7x = 7(3) = 21
and width = 5x = 5(3) = 15

<u>Example 4.</u> The three sides of a triangle are in the ratio 2:3:4. The perimeter is 63. Find the three sides.

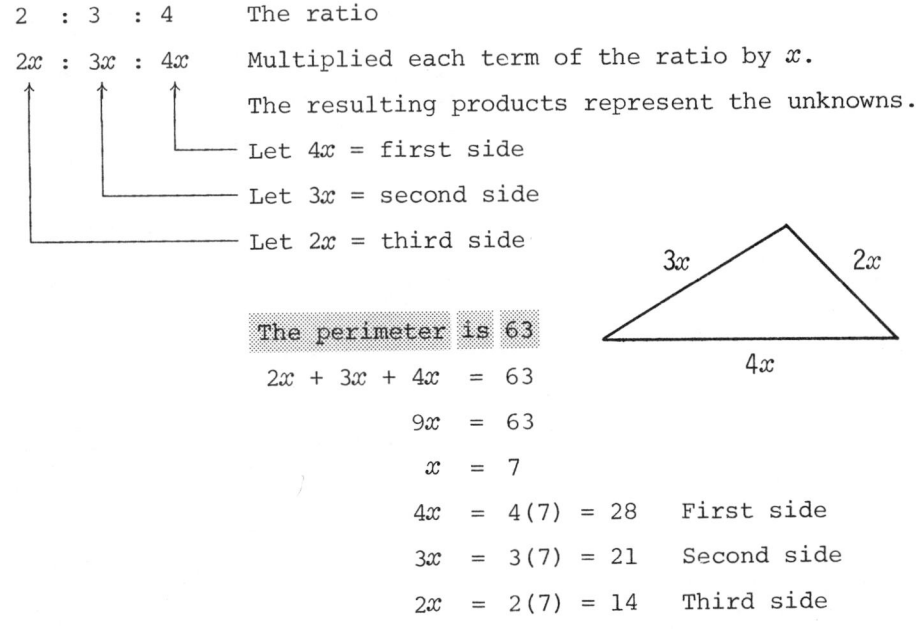

2 : 3 : 4   The ratio

2x : 3x : 4x Multiplied each term of the ratio by x.

The resulting products represent the unknowns.

Let 4x = first side
Let 3x = second side
Let 2x = third side

The perimeter is 63

$$2x + 3x + 4x = 63$$
$$9x = 63$$
$$x = 7$$

4x = 4(7) = 28   First side
3x = 3(7) = 21   Second side
2x = 2(7) = 14   Third side

Example 5. Sixty-six hours of a student's week are spent in
study, in class, and in work. The times spent in these
activities are in the ratio 4 : 2 : 5. How many hours are
spent in each activity?

<u>Solution</u>:

4 : 2 : 4   The ratio

$4x$: $2x$: $5x$ Multiplied each term of the ratio by x.

The resulting products represent the unknowns.

Let $5x$ = hours spent at work

$2x$ = hours spent in class

and $4x$ = hours spent in study

| 66 hours | of student's week | are spent in | study , class , and | work . |

66   =   4x + 2x + 5x

$66 = 4x + 2x + 5x$
$66 = 11x$
$6 = x$

$4x = 4(6) = 24$ Study hours
$2x = 2(6) = 12$ Class hours
$5x = 5(6) = \underline{30}$ Work hours
                    66   Check

EXERCISES 505

<u>SET I</u>

1. Two numbers are in the ratio of 3 to 4. Their sum is
    35. Find the numbers.
2. Two numbers are in the ratio of 7 to 3. Their sum
    is 130. Find the numbers.
3. The length and width of a rectangle are in the ratio
    of 9 to 4. The perimeter is 78. Find the length and
    width.
4. The length and width of a rectangle are in the ratio
    7 : 2. The perimeter is 72. Find the length and width.
5. The amounts Beverly spend for food, rent, and clothing
    are in the ratio 4 : 5 : 1. She spends an average of
    $300 a month for these items. What can she expect to
    spend for these items each year?
6. Frank spends $4725 for tuition, housing, and food
    each school year. The amounts spent for these three
    items are in the ratio 4 : 1 : 2. How much does he
    spend for each item?
7. Divide 88 into two parts whose ratio is 6 to 5.
8. Divide 99 into two parts whose ratio is 2 to 7.

----

9. The three sides of a triangle are in the ratio 4 : 5 : 6.
    The perimeter is 90. Find the three sides.
10. The three sides of a triangle are in the ratio 5 : 6 : 7.
    The perimeter is 72. Find the three sides.

11. An uncle divided $27,000 among his three nephews in the ratio 2 : 3 : 4. How much did each receive?

12. A pension fund of $150,000 is invested in stocks, bonds, and real estate in the ratio 5 : 1 : 4. How much is invested in each?

13. When mixing the concrete for his patio floor, Mr. Mora used a cement-sand-gravel ratio of 1 : $2\frac{1}{2}$: 4. If he used 5 cubic yards of gravel, how much sand and cement were used?

14. In one week's time a restaurant served 865 dinners. For every 5 dinners served, 3 of them were seafood dinners. How many seafood dinners were served during the week?

SET II

1. Two numbers are in the ratio of 3 to 5. Their sum is 40. Find the numbers.

2. The length and width of a rectangle are in the ratio of 7 to 4. The perimeter is 88. Find the length and width.

3. The amounts Joan spends for food, rent, and clothing are in the ratio of 5 : 6 : 1. She spends an average of $360 a month for these items. What can she expect to spend for each of these items in a year?

4. A farmer plants 162 acres of corn and soy beans in the ratio of 5 to 4. How many acres of each does he plant?

5. A man cuts a 65-inch board into two parts whose ratio is 9 : 4. Find the length of the pieces.

6. The gold solder used in a crafts class has gold, silver, and copper in the ratio 5 : 3 : 2. How much gold is there in 30 grams of this solder?

7. A civil service office tries to employ people with no discrimination because of age. If the ratio of people over 40 to those under 40 is 3 : 4, how many out of 259 people hired would have to be over 40?

8. Fast Eddie's Pro Shop sells 4 types of bowling balls: Type A, B, C, and D. Sales of the balls totaled $3,600.00 for the year. If the balls sold in ratios of 3 : 2 : 1 : 4, how much of the sales, in dollars, can be attributed to each type of ball?

506

Proportion Problems

<u>MEANING OF A PROPORTION.</u> A *proportion* is a statement that two ratios are equal.

Common notation for a proportion:

$$\frac{a}{b} = \frac{c}{d}$$ Read: "*a* is to *b* as *c* is to *d*."
                or: "*a* over *b* equals *c* over *d*."

Another notation for a proportion:

$$a : b :: c : d$$ Read: "*a* is to *b* as *c* is to *d*."

The *terms* of a proportion:

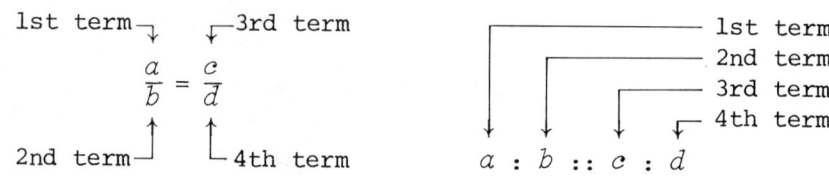

The *means and extremes* of a proportion:

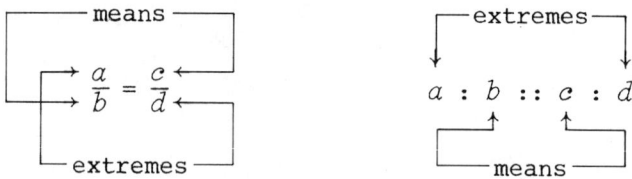

The means of this proportion are "b" and "c."

The extremes of this proportion are "a" and "d."

Example 1. In the proportion $\frac{x}{3} = \frac{5}{15}$, read: "$x$ is to 3 as 5 is to 15,"

the first term is x,   the second term is 3,
the third term is 5,   the fourth term is 15,
the means are 3 and 5, the extremes are x and 15.

PRODUCT OF MEANS EQUALS PRODUCT OF EXTREMES. In any proportion, *the product of the means equals the product of the extremes.*

In the proportion $\frac{2}{3} = \frac{4}{6}$,

$$\underbrace{3 \times 4}_{\text{Product of means}} = \underbrace{2 \times 6}_{\text{Product of extremes}}$$

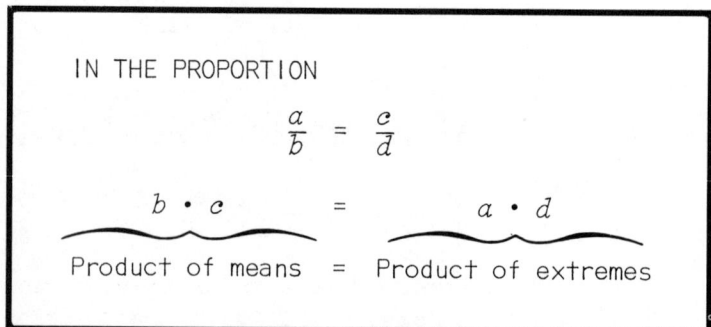

This is sometimes called the *cross-multiplication rule.* This rule can be justified by multiplying both sides of the proportion by bd.

$$\frac{a}{b} = \frac{c}{d}$$

$$\cancel{bd}\left(\frac{a}{\cancel{b}}\right) = b\cancel{d}\left(\frac{c}{\cancel{d}}\right)$$

$$da = bc$$

or
$$ad = bc$$

Cross-multiplication makes it possible to see if two ratios are equal. If the product of the means equals the product of the extremes, then the ratios form a proportion. If the product of the means does not equal the product of the extremes, then the ratios do not form a proportion.

Example 2. Do the given ratios form a proportion?

(a) $\frac{5}{12}$, $\frac{3}{7}$.   No, because $5 \cdot 7 \neq 12 \cdot 3$
$$35 \neq 36$$

They *do not* form a proportion.

(b) $\frac{16}{6}$, $\frac{8}{3}$.   Yes, because $16 \cdot 3 = 6 \cdot 8$
$$48 = 48$$

They *do* form a proportion.

SOLVING A PROPORTION. Solving a proportion means finding the value of the unknown letter that makes the two ratios of the proportion equal.

When three of the four terms of a proportion are known, it is always possible to find the value of the unknown term.

TO SOLVE A PROPORTION

1. Set the product of the means equal to the product of the extremes.

2. Solve the resulting equation for the unknown.

To Check Your Solution

1. Replace the unknown letter in the proportion by the value you obtained for it.

2. Cross-multiply, and verify that the cross-products are equal.

Example 3. In the proportion $\frac{2}{3} = \frac{x}{51}$, the third term is unknown and is represented by the letter x. Since the product of the means equals the product of the extremes,

$$\frac{2}{3} = \frac{x}{51}$$

$$3 \cdot x = 2 \cdot 51$$

$$3 \cdot x = 102$$

The "=" sign tells us that $3 \cdot x$ and 102 are the same number. Therefore, if $3 \cdot x$ and 102 are both divided by 3, the resulting numbers will be equal. That is,

$$\frac{\overset{1}{\cancel{3}} \cdot x}{\underset{1}{\cancel{3}}} = \frac{\overset{34}{\cancel{102}}}{\underset{1}{\cancel{3}}}$$

$$x = 34$$

Check: In the original proportion, $\frac{2}{3} = \frac{x}{51}$, replace x by 34. Then,

$$\frac{2}{3} = \frac{34}{51}$$

$$3 \cdot 34 = 2 \cdot 51$$

$$102 = 102$$

Example 4. Solve $\frac{x}{25} = \frac{18}{15}$ for x.

Solution: $\qquad \frac{x}{25} = \frac{18}{15}$

$\qquad 15 \cdot x = 18 \cdot 25 \qquad$ Product of extremes
$\qquad\qquad\qquad\qquad\qquad$ = product of means.

$\qquad 15 \cdot x = 450$

$$\frac{\overset{1}{\cancel{15}} \cdot x}{\underset{1}{\cancel{15}}} = \frac{\overset{30}{\cancel{450}}}{\underset{1}{\cancel{15}}} \qquad \text{Dividing both products by the coefficient of the unknown.}$$

$\qquad\qquad x = 30$

Check: $\qquad \frac{30}{25} = \frac{18}{15} \qquad x$ was replaced by 30.

$\qquad 30 \cdot 15 = 25 \cdot 18$

$\qquad\quad 450 = 450$

Often the work in solving a proportion can be simplified by reducing a ratio to its lowest terms. We use this procedure to simplify the solution of Example 4.

$$\frac{x}{25} = \frac{18}{15}$$

$$\frac{x}{25} = \frac{6}{5} \qquad \text{Since } \frac{18}{15} = \frac{6}{5} \text{ when reduced to}$$
$$\text{lowest terms.}$$

$$5 \cdot x = 25 \cdot 6$$

$$\frac{\cancel{5} \cdot x}{\cancel{5}} = \frac{\overset{5}{\cancel{25}} \cdot 6}{\cancel{5}}$$

$$x = 30$$

<u>Example 5.</u>   Solve $\dfrac{8}{14} = \dfrac{16}{x}$ for x.

<u>Solution:</u>

$$\left(\text{reducing } \frac{8}{14} \text{ to } \frac{4}{7} \right) \longrightarrow \frac{4}{7} = \frac{16}{x}$$

$$4 \cdot x = 7 \cdot 16$$

$$\frac{\cancel{4} \cdot x}{\cancel{4}} = \frac{7 \cdot \overset{4}{\cancel{16}}}{\cancel{4}}$$

$$x = 28$$

<u>Check:</u>
$$\frac{8}{14} = \frac{16}{28} \longleftarrow \text{ in place of } x$$

$$\frac{4}{7} = \frac{4}{7} \qquad \begin{array}{l}\text{Obtained by reducing} \\ \text{both ratios to} \\ \text{lowest terms.}\end{array}$$

<u>Example 6.</u>   Solve $\dfrac{x + 1}{x - 2} = \dfrac{7}{4}$

<u>Solution:</u> $\dfrac{x + 1}{x - 2} = \dfrac{7}{4}$ <u>Check:</u> $\dfrac{x + 1}{x - 2} = \dfrac{7}{4}$

$$4(x + 1) = 7(x - 2) \qquad\qquad \frac{6 + 1}{6 - 2} = \frac{7}{4}$$

$$4x + 4 = 7x - 14 \qquad\qquad\qquad \frac{7}{4} = \frac{7}{4}$$

$$18 = 3x$$

$$6 = x$$

EXERCISES 506A

<u>SET I</u>

In Exercises 1—6, do the ratios form a proportion?

1. $\dfrac{3}{5}$, $\dfrac{6}{10}$ 2. $\dfrac{6}{4}$, $\dfrac{3}{2}$ 3. $\dfrac{2}{3}$, $\dfrac{5}{7}$

4. $\dfrac{3}{7}$, $\dfrac{4}{9}$ 5. $\dfrac{6}{9}$, $\dfrac{4}{6}$ 6. $\dfrac{12}{9}$, $\dfrac{4}{3}$

7. In the proportion $\frac{8}{14} = \frac{16}{x}$, find the following:

    (a) the first term   (b) the second term
    (c) the third term   (d) the fourth term
    (e) the means   (f) the extremes

8. In the proportion $\frac{3}{5} = \frac{x}{20}$, find the following:

    (a) the first term   (b) the second term
    (c) the third term   (d) the fourth term
    (e) the means   (f) the extremes

In Exercises 9—24, solve for x.

9. $\dfrac{x}{4} = \dfrac{2}{3}$ 10. $\dfrac{x}{5} = \dfrac{6}{4}$ 11. $\dfrac{8}{x} = \dfrac{4}{5}$

12. $\dfrac{10}{x} = \dfrac{15}{4}$ 13. $\dfrac{4}{7} = \dfrac{x}{21}$ 14. $\dfrac{15}{12} = \dfrac{x}{9}$

15. $\dfrac{100}{x} = \dfrac{40}{30}$

----

16. $\dfrac{144}{36} = \dfrac{96}{x}$ 17. $\dfrac{x}{100} = \dfrac{75}{125}$ 18. $\dfrac{24}{98} = \dfrac{x}{147}$

19. $\dfrac{x + 1}{x - 1} = \dfrac{3}{2}$ 20. $\dfrac{x + 1}{5} = \dfrac{x - 1}{3}$

21. $\dfrac{2x + 7}{9} = \dfrac{2x + 3}{5}$ 22. $\dfrac{2x + 7}{3x + 10} = \dfrac{3}{4}$

23. $\dfrac{5x - 10}{10} = \dfrac{3x - 5}{7}$ 24. $\dfrac{8x - 2}{3x + 4} = \dfrac{3}{2}$

🖩 25. $\dfrac{2.78x - 8.91}{14.73x + 22.85} = \dfrac{35.64}{57.26}$ 🖩 26. $\dfrac{23.8x - 91.6}{35.4x + 42.5} = \dfrac{73.1}{58.2}$

SET II

In Exercises 1—4, do the ratios form a proportion?

1. $\dfrac{21}{17}$, $\dfrac{19}{15}$ 2. $\dfrac{16}{35}$, $\dfrac{17}{37}$

3. $\dfrac{12}{18}$, $\dfrac{28}{42}$ 4. $\dfrac{40}{100}$, $\dfrac{22}{55}$

5. In the proportion $\frac{5}{6} = \frac{15}{x}$, find the following:

    (a) the first term   (b) the second term
    (c) the third term   (d) the fourth term
    (e) the means   (f) the extremes

In Exercises 6—14, solve for x.

6. $\dfrac{4}{13} = \dfrac{16}{x}$ 7. $\dfrac{28}{18} = \dfrac{14}{x}$ 8. $\dfrac{x}{18} = \dfrac{24}{30}$

9. $\dfrac{26}{x} = \dfrac{39}{14}$ 10. $\dfrac{15}{22} = \dfrac{x}{33}$ 11. $\dfrac{x}{21} = \dfrac{80}{42}$

12. $\dfrac{55}{x} = \dfrac{35}{28}$ 13. $\dfrac{44}{77} = \dfrac{x}{14}$ 14. $\dfrac{2x + 5}{3} = \dfrac{3x - 1}{2}$

15. $\dfrac{43.4}{53.2x - 37.5} = \dfrac{82.6}{68.3x + 29.7}$

PROPORTIONS WHOSE TERMS ARE NOT WHOLE NUMBERS. The terms of a proportion can be any kind of number, the only restriction being that the denominator in either ratio cannot be zero (Sec. 109).

Example 7. Solve for P: $\dfrac{P}{3} = \dfrac{\frac{5}{6}}{5}$

Solution: $\dfrac{P}{3} = \dfrac{\frac{5}{6}}{5}$

$$5 \cdot P = \dfrac{\overset{1}{\cancel{3}}}{1} \cdot \dfrac{5}{\underset{2}{\cancel{6}}}$$

$$5 \cdot P = \dfrac{5}{2}$$

$$\dfrac{\cancel{5} \cdot P}{\cancel{5}} = \dfrac{\frac{5}{2}}{5}$$

$$P = \dfrac{5}{2} \div 5 = \dfrac{\overset{1}{\cancel{5}}}{2} \cdot \dfrac{1}{\underset{1}{\cancel{5}}} = \dfrac{1}{2}$$

Example 8. Solve for x: $\dfrac{3\frac{1}{2}}{5\frac{1}{4}} = \dfrac{x}{4}$

Solution: $\dfrac{3\frac{1}{2}}{5\frac{1}{4}} = \dfrac{x}{4}$

$$5\frac{1}{4} \cdot x = 3\frac{1}{2} \cdot 4$$

$$\dfrac{21}{4} \cdot x = \dfrac{7}{\underset{1}{\cancel{2}}} \cdot \dfrac{\overset{2}{\cancel{4}}}{1} = 14$$

$$\dfrac{\frac{\cancel{21}}{4} \cdot x}{\frac{\cancel{21}}{4}} = \dfrac{14}{\frac{21}{4}}$$

$$x = 14 \div \dfrac{21}{4}$$

$$x = \dfrac{\overset{2}{\cancel{14}}}{1} \cdot \dfrac{4}{\underset{3}{\cancel{21}}} = \dfrac{8}{3} = 2\frac{2}{3}$$

Example 9. Solve for B: $\dfrac{0.24}{2.7} = \dfrac{4}{B}$

Solution:

$$\frac{0.24}{2.7} = \frac{4}{B}$$

$$\frac{\overset{4}{\cancel{24}}}{\underset{45}{\cancel{270}}} = \frac{4}{B}$$

First multiply numerator and denominator by 100 to eliminate both decimals; then reduce.

$$\frac{4}{45} = \frac{4}{B}$$

$$45 \cdot 4 = 4 \cdot B$$

$$\frac{45 \cdot \cancel{4}}{\cancel{4}} = \frac{\cancel{4} \cdot B}{\cancel{4}}$$

$$45 = B$$

EXERCISES 506B

SET I

1. $\dfrac{\frac{3}{4}}{6} = \dfrac{P}{16}$ 2. $\dfrac{\frac{2}{5}}{4} = \dfrac{P}{25}$ 3. $\dfrac{A}{9} = \dfrac{3\frac{1}{3}}{5}$

4. $\dfrac{A}{8} = \dfrac{2\frac{1}{4}}{18}$ 5. $\dfrac{7.7}{B} = \dfrac{3.5}{5}$ 6. $\dfrac{6.8}{B} = \dfrac{17}{57.4}$

7. $\dfrac{P}{100} = \dfrac{\frac{3}{2}}{15}$ 8. $\dfrac{P}{100} = \dfrac{\frac{7}{5}}{35}$

----

9. $\dfrac{12\frac{1}{2}}{100} = \dfrac{A}{48}$ 10. $\dfrac{16\frac{2}{3}}{100} = \dfrac{9}{B}$ 11. $\dfrac{2.54}{1} = \dfrac{X}{7.5}$

12. $\dfrac{12.5}{W} = \dfrac{7.8}{16}$ Round off to 2 decimal places.

SET II

1. $\dfrac{\frac{2}{3}}{6} = \dfrac{P}{9}$ 2. $\dfrac{A}{16} = \dfrac{2\frac{1}{2}}{10}$ 3. $\dfrac{P}{100} = \dfrac{\frac{3}{4}}{15}$

4. $\dfrac{P}{100} = \dfrac{12\frac{1}{2}}{50}$ 5. $\dfrac{6\frac{1}{4}}{100} = \dfrac{1}{B}$ 6. $\dfrac{43.6}{x} = \dfrac{20.8}{65.3}$

SOLVING WORD PROBLEMS THAT LEAD TO PROPORTIONS

1. Represent the unknown quantity by a letter.

2. Be sure to put the units next to the numbers when writing the proportion.

3. Be sure the same units occupy corresponding positions in the two ratios of the proportion.

<table>
<tr><td colspan="2">Correct Arrangements</td><td colspan="2">Incorrect Arrangements</td></tr>
<tr><td>$\dfrac{\text{miles}}{\text{hours}} = \dfrac{\text{miles}}{\text{hours}}$</td><td></td><td>$\dfrac{\text{dollars}}{\text{weeks}} = \dfrac{\text{weeks}}{\text{dollars}}$</td><td></td></tr>
<tr><td>$\dfrac{\text{hours}}{\text{miles}} = \dfrac{\text{hours}}{\text{miles}}$</td><td></td><td>$\dfrac{\text{dollars}}{\text{weeks}} = \dfrac{\text{dollars}}{\text{days}}$</td><td></td></tr>
<tr><td>$\dfrac{\text{miles}}{\text{miles}} = \dfrac{\text{hours}}{\text{hours}}$</td><td></td><td></td><td></td></tr>
</table>

4. Once the numbers have been correctly entered in the proportion by using the units as a guide, drop the units when cross-multiplying to solve for the unknown.

Example 10. A man used 10 gallons of gas on a 180-mile trip. How many gallons of gas can he expect to use on a 300-mile trip?

Solution: A man used 10 gallons of gas on a 180-mile trip.   How many gallons of gas can he expect to use on a 300-mile trip?

$$\frac{10 \text{ gallons}}{180 \text{ miles}} = \frac{x \text{ gallons}}{300 \text{ miles}}$$

Note. The ratios used on each side have gallons in the numerator and miles in the denominator.

Therefore,

$$180x = 300 \cdot 10$$

$$x = \frac{\overset{50}{\cancel{300}} \cdot \cancel{10}}{\underset{3}{\cancel{180}}} = \frac{50}{3} = 16\frac{2}{3} \text{ gallons}$$

Example 11. A market is selling four cans of beets for 53 cents. How much will 12 cans cost at the same rate?

Solution:

> A market is selling four cans of beets for 53 cents

> How much will 12 cans cost at the same rate?

$$\frac{4 \text{ cans}}{53 \text{ cents}} = \frac{12 \text{ cans}}{x \text{ cents}}$$

$$4 \cdot x = 12(53)$$

$$x = \frac{\overset{3}{\cancel{12}}(53)}{\cancel{4}} = 159 \text{ cents}$$

$$= \$1.59$$

Example 12. A baseball team wins seven of its first 12 games. How many would you expect it to win out of its first 36 games if the team continues to play with the same degree of success?

Solution:

> A baseball team wins 7 of its first 12 games.

> How many would you expect it to win out of its first 36 games?

$$\frac{7 \text{ wins}}{12 \text{ games}} = \frac{x \text{ wins}}{36 \text{ games}}$$

$$7 \cdot 36 = 12 \cdot x$$

$$\frac{7 \cdot \overset{3}{\cancel{36}}}{\cancel{12}} = \frac{\cancel{12} \cdot x}{\cancel{12}}$$

$$21 = x$$

Therefore, the team could expect to win 21 out of its first 36 games.

Example 13. There are 25 men in a college class containing 38 students. Assuming this is typical of all classes, how many of the college's 7500 students would be men?

Solution:

> There are 25 men in a college class of 38 students.

> Assuming this as a typical class, how many of the college's 7500 students would be men?

$$\frac{25 \text{ men}}{38 \text{ students}} = \frac{x \text{ men}}{7500 \text{ students}}$$

$$38 \cdot x = 25(7500)$$

$$\frac{\cancel{38} \cdot x}{\cancel{38}} = \frac{25(\overset{3750}{\cancel{7500}})}{\underset{19}{\cancel{38}}}$$

$$x = \frac{25(3750)}{19} = \frac{93,750}{19} \doteq 4934 \text{ men}$$

Example 14. At a soda fountain 8 quarts of ice cream were used to make 100 milk shakes. How many quarts are needed to make 550 milk shakes?

Solution: 8 quarts of ice cream were used to make 100 milk shakes. | How many quarts are needed to make 550 milk shakes?

$$\frac{8 \text{ quarts}}{100 \text{ milk shakes}} = \frac{x \text{ quarts}}{550 \text{ milk shakes}}$$

$$100 \cdot x = 8(550)$$

$$\frac{\cancel{100} \cdot x}{\cancel{100}} = \frac{8(55\cancel{0})}{10\cancel{0}}$$

$$x = \frac{8(\overset{11}{\cancel{55}})}{\underset{2}{\cancel{10}}} = \frac{\overset{4}{\cancel{8}}(11)}{\cancel{2}}$$

$$x = 4(11) = 44 \text{ quarts}$$

Example 15. If a 6-foot man casts a $4\frac{1}{2}$-foot shadow, how tall is a tree that casts a 30-foot shadow?

Solution:

A six-foot man casts a $4\frac{1}{2}$-foot shadow. | How tall is a tree that casts a 30-foot shadow?

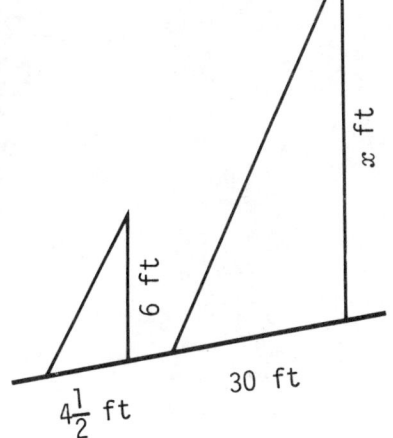

$$\frac{6 \text{ feet high (man)}}{4\frac{1}{2} \text{ feet high (shadow)}} = \frac{x \text{ feet high (tree)}}{30 \text{ feet high (shadow)}}$$

$$\frac{6}{4\frac{1}{2}} = \frac{x}{30}$$

$$4\frac{1}{2} \cdot x = 6 \cdot 30$$

$$\frac{9}{2} \cdot x = 180$$

$$\frac{\frac{\cancel{9}}{\cancel{2}} \cdot x}{\frac{9}{2}} = \frac{180}{\frac{9}{2}}$$

$$x = \frac{180}{1} \div \frac{9}{2} = \frac{\overset{20}{\cancel{180}}}{1} \cdot \frac{2}{\underset{1}{\cancel{9}}}$$

$$x = 40 \text{ feet}$$

SET I

1. A painter uses about 3 gallons of paint in doing 2 rooms. How many gallons would he need to paint 20 rooms?

2. A person drives 600 miles in $1\frac{1}{2}$ days. How long would it take to drive 3000 miles?

3. A 6-foot man has a 4-foot shadow when a tree casts a 20-foot shadow. How tall is the tree?

4. Seven men finish 10 houses in a month. How many houses could 35 men finish in the same time?

5. The scale in an architectural drawing is 1 inch equals 8 feet. What are the dimensions of a room that measures $2\frac{1}{2}$ by 3 inches on the drawing?

6. The property tax on a $15,000 home is $450. What would be the tax on a $25,000 home?

7. An investment of $3000 earned $180 for a year. How much would have to be invested to earn $540 in the same time?

8. A store has a bargain price of 85¢ for three jars of grape jelly. How many jars could someone buy for $5.95?

----

9. The ratio of a woman's weight on earth compared to her weight on the moon is 6 : 1. How much would a 150-pound woman weigh on the moon?

10. The ratio of a man's weight on Mars compared to his weight on earth is 2 : 5. How much would a 196-pound man weigh on Mars?

11. The ratio of the weight of lead to the weight of an equal volume of aluminum is 21 : 5. If an aluminum bar weighs 150 pounds, what would a lead bar of the same size weigh?

12. The ratio of the weight of platinum to the weight of an equal volume of copper is 12 : 5. If a platinum bar weighs 18 pounds, what would a copper bar of the same size weigh?

13. On the first $6\frac{1}{2}$ hours of their shift, a fire crew built 26 chains of fire line. How much fire line can they build in the remainder of a 10-hour day if they work at the same pace?

14. The IRS informed a local businessman that for every $5000.00 worth of sales he made, his tax would increase by $75.00. If the man's sales totaled $125,000.00 for the year, how much was his tax?

15. A meat packer paid a cattle producer $3,420.00 for 9 steers. Assuming all of the animals are of the same approximate weight, how much will the producer receive for 16 steers?

16. A hog producer fed 1,320 hogs until they reached a marketing weight of 100 kg each. He received a check for their sale amounting to $59,400.00. How much did the producer receive per hog? What was the price paid for the hogs per kg of live weight?

1. An apartment house manager spent 22 hours painting 3 apartments. How long can he expect to take painting the remaining 15 apartments?

2. Ralph drove 420 miles in $\frac{3}{4}$ of a day. About how far can he drive in $2\frac{1}{2}$ days?

3. Amalia noticed that her shadow was 4 feet long when that of a 16-foot flagpole was 12 feet long. What is her height in feet and inches?

4. A crew of 10 men take a week to overhaul 25 trucks in a fleet of 100 trucks. How many men would it take to complete the fleet overhaul in one week?

5. A car burns $2\frac{1}{2}$ quarts of oil on a 1800-mile trip. How many quarts of oil can the owner expect to use on a 12,000 mile trip?

6. Fifteen defective axles were found in 100,000 cars of a particular model. How many defective axles would you expect to find in the 2 million cars made of that same model?

7. Mr. Sanders has 300 Leghorn hens and needs 22.86 cm of roosting space per hen. How many meters of roosting space does he need?

8. The Forest Service must determine how many acres will be needed to make an addition of 22 campsites. If the existing 24 acre campground accommodates 55 campsites, how many additional acres will they need?

Percent Problems

THE MEANING OF PERCENT. Percent means hundredths. For example, 5% of a quantity is $\frac{5}{100}$ of that quantity. Consider a 5-gallon paint can containing 2 gallons of paint. We can say, "The can is $\frac{2}{5}$ full." But you have learned that $\frac{2}{5} = \frac{2 \cdot 20}{5 \cdot 20} = \frac{40}{100}$, so we can also say, "The can is $\frac{40}{100}$ full." The decimal

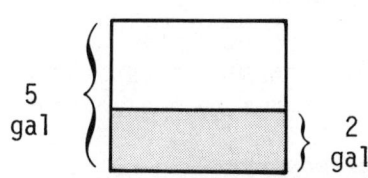

representation for $\frac{40}{100}$ is 0.40. Since $\frac{40}{100}$ is 40 per hundred, we can say, "40 *per cent*." (*Cent*um means 100 in Latin.) The can is 40 percent full. 40 percent is also written 40%.

THE PERCENT PROPORTION. We described the amount of paint in the can in three different ways.

1. The can is $\frac{2}{5}$ full.

2. The can is 0.40 (40 hundredths) full.

3. The can is 40 percent full.

We have talked about three quantities:

1. 40 *percent* (P)
2. 5, which represents the *whole thing*, and is called the *base* (B)
3. 2, which is called the *amount* (A)

These three numbers are related by the proportion:

$$\frac{2}{5} = \frac{40}{100}$$

This proportion is called "*the percent proportion.*"

THE PERCENT PROPORTION

$$\frac{A}{B} = \frac{P}{100}$$

where A = Amount, B = Base, P = Percent

In Sec. 506 you learned how to solve a proportion for an unknown term.

Example 1. Suppose we want to find P in the above example, where A = 2 and B = 5.

Solution: $\dfrac{A}{B} = \dfrac{P}{100}$ The percent proportion.

$\dfrac{2}{5} = \dfrac{P}{100}$ Here we replaced A with 2 and B with 5.

Then, $5 \cdot P = 2 \cdot 100$

$$\frac{\overset{1}{\cancel{5}} \cdot P}{\underset{1}{\cancel{5}}} = \frac{\overset{40}{\cancel{200}}}{\underset{1}{\cancel{5}}}$$ (See Sec. 505.)

$P = 40$

IDENTIFYING THE NUMBERS IN A PERCENT PROBLEM. There are three unknown terms in the percent proportion. They are:

1. The amount A
2. The base B
3. The percent P

In Example 1, we showed how to solve the percent proportion for one of the three terms when the other two terms are known. In every percent problem, two numbers must be given. We must be able to identify which of the three terms the given numbers represent. The easiest term to identify is the percent (P). "P" is the number written with the word "percent," or the symbol (%).

Example 2.   Identifying P.

(a)   What number is (8 percent) of 40?
P

(b)   16 is (40%) of what number?
P

(c)   15 is (what percent) of 60?
P

We next identify the base (B). "B" is the number that represents 100 percent, and usually follows the words "percent of."

Example 3.   Identifying B.

(a)   What number is 8 *percent of* (40) ?
B

(b)   16 is 40% *of* (what number) ?
B

(c)   15 is what *percent of* (60) ?
B

"A" is the remaining number after P and B have been identified. "A" is the *amount*.

Example 4.   Identifying A.

(a)   *What number* is (8 percent) of (40) ?
P B

This must be A, because it is the remaining number after P and B have been identified.

(b)   *16* is (40%) of (what number) ?
P B

This must be A, because it is the remaining number after P and B have been identified.

(c)   *15* is (what percent) of (60) ?
P B

This must be A.

TO IDENTIFY THE NUMBERS IN A PERCENT PROBLEM

1. P is the number followed by the word "percent" (or %).

2. B is the number that follows the words "percent of."

3. A is the number left after P and B have been identified.

Example 5. Identifying all three terms in percent problems.

(a) (What number) is (175%) of (80) ?
         A   P   B

(b) (35) is (what percent) of (105) ?
   A   P   B

(c) (400) is (200%) of (what number) ?
   A   P   B

THE THREE TYPES OF PERCENT PROBLEMS. Since there are only three letters in the percent proportion,

$$\frac{A}{B} = \frac{P}{100}$$

there can be only three kinds of percent problems.

THE THREE TYPES OF PERCENT PROBLEMS

Type I: Solving for A

in $\frac{A}{B} = \frac{P}{100}$ when B and P are known.

Type II: Solving for P

in $\frac{A}{B} = \frac{P}{100}$ when A and B are known.

Type III: Solving for B

in $\frac{A}{B} = \frac{P}{100}$ when A and P are known.

TYPE I PERCENT PROBLEM SOLUTION. Solving for A.

Example 6. What is 12% of 85?

Solution: (What) is (12%) of (85) ?
       A   P   B

$$\frac{A}{B} = \frac{P}{100}$$

$$\frac{A}{85} = \frac{12}{100}$$

$$\frac{A}{85} = \frac{\overset{3}{\cancel{12}}}{\underset{25}{\cancel{100}}}$$

$$25 \cdot A = 85 \cdot 3$$

$$\frac{\cancel{25} \cdot A}{\cancel{25}} = \frac{255}{25}$$

$$A = 10.2$$

Therefore, 10.2 is 12% of 85.

Alternate Solution: $A = 12\%$ of 85

$$= .12 \times 85$$

$12\% = \dfrac{12}{100} = .12$ ————————— "of" means "to multiply" in problems of this type.

$$A = 10.2$$

TYPE II PERCENT PROBLEM SOLUTION.   Solving for P.

Example 7.   5 is what percent of 20?

Solution: $\boxed{\begin{array}{c}5\\A\end{array}}$ is $\boxed{\begin{array}{c}\text{what percent}\\P\end{array}}$ of $\boxed{\begin{array}{c}20\\B\end{array}}$?

$$\frac{A}{B} = \frac{P}{100}$$

$$\frac{5}{20} = \frac{P}{100} \qquad \text{Reduce } \frac{\overset{1}{\cancel{5}}}{\underset{4}{\cancel{20}}} = \frac{1}{4}$$

$$\frac{1}{4} = \frac{P}{100}$$

$$4 \cdot P = 100$$

$$P = 25$$

Therefore, 5 is 25% of 20.

TYPE III PERCENT PROBLEM SOLUTION.   Solving for B.

Example 8.   In an examination a student worked 15 problems correctly. This was 75% of the problems. Find the total number of problems on the examination.

Solution: In this problem we are saying:

$\boxed{\begin{array}{c}75\%\\P\end{array}}$ of $\boxed{\begin{array}{c}\text{some number}\\B\end{array}}$ is $\boxed{\begin{array}{c}15\\A\end{array}}$.

$$\frac{A}{B} = \frac{P}{100}$$

$$\frac{15}{B} = \frac{75}{100} \qquad \text{Reduce } \frac{\overset{3}{\cancel{75}}}{\underset{4}{\cancel{100}}} = \frac{3}{4}$$

$$\frac{15}{B} = \frac{3}{4}$$

$$3 \cdot B = 4 \cdot 15$$

$$B = \frac{60}{3} = 20$$

Therefore, 20 problems were on the examination.

Example 9. Mr. Delgado, a salesman, makes a 6% commission on all items he sells. One week he made $390. What were his gross sales for the week?

Solution: In this problem we are saying:

$$\boxed{\begin{matrix}6\%\\P\end{matrix}}\ \text{of}\ \boxed{\begin{matrix}\text{some number}\\B\end{matrix}}\ \text{is}\ \boxed{\begin{matrix}\$390\\A\end{matrix}}$$

$$\frac{A}{B} = \frac{P}{100}$$

$$\frac{390}{B} = \frac{6}{100} \qquad \text{Reduce}\ \frac{\overset{3}{\cancel{6}}}{\underset{50}{\cancel{100}}} = \frac{3}{50}$$

$$\frac{390}{B} = \frac{3}{50}$$

$$3 \cdot B = 50 \cdot 390$$

$$\frac{\cancel{3} \cdot B}{\cancel{3}} = \frac{\overset{6500}{\cancel{19,500}}}{\cancel{3}}$$

$$B = \$6500$$

Therefore, his gross sales for the week were $6500.

MARKUP. In a business that buys and sells merchandise, the merchandise must be sold at a price high enough to return to the merchant (1) the price paid for the goods; (2) the expenses, salaries, rents, taxes, etc.; and (3) a reasonable profit. To accomplish this, the cost of each item must be *marked up* before it is sold. We use markup based on cost. Selling price, cost, and markup are related by the following formula:

$$\text{Selling price} = \text{Cost} + \text{Markup}$$
$$S \quad\ \ = \ \ C \ + \ \ M$$

Example 10. If a business pays $75 for an item, what is the selling price of the item if it is marked up 40%?

Solution: $\boxed{\begin{matrix}\text{Markup}\\A\end{matrix}} = \boxed{\begin{matrix}40\%\\P\end{matrix}}\ \text{of}\ \boxed{\begin{matrix}\text{cost}\\B\end{matrix}}$

$$\frac{A}{B} = \frac{P}{100} \qquad\qquad A = \text{markup}$$
$$ \qquad\qquad\qquad\qquad B = \text{cost ($75)}$$
$$\frac{A}{75} = \frac{\overset{2}{\cancel{40}}}{\underset{5}{\cancel{100}}} \qquad\qquad P = 40\%$$

$$5A = 2(75) = 150$$

$$\frac{5A}{5} = \frac{150}{5}$$

$$A = 30 \qquad \text{(markup)}$$

$$\text{Selling price} = \text{cost} + \text{markup}$$
$$= \ \ 75 \ + \ \ 30 \ \ = \$105$$

<u>EXERCISES 507</u>. Solve the following percent problems.

SET I

1. 15 is 30% of what number?
2. 16 is 20% of what number?
3. 115 is what percent of 250?
4. 330 is what percent of 225?
5. What is 25% of 40?
6. What is 45% of 65?
7. 15% of what number is 127.5?
8. 32% of what number is 256?
9. What percent of 8 is 17?
10. What percent of 6 is 12?
11. 63% of 48 is what number?
12. 87% of 49 is what number?
13. 750 is 125% of what number?
14. 325 is 130% of what number?
15. 23 is what percent of 16?
16. 57 is what percent of 23?
17. What is 200% of 12?
18. What is 300% of 9?
19. 15% of a number is 37.5. What is the number?
20. What is 27% of $135?

----

21. 42 is $66\frac{2}{3}$% of what number?

22. 36 is $16\frac{2}{3}$% of what number?

23. A team wins 80% of its games. If it wins 68 games, how many games has it played?

24. Seventy percent of the 46,000 burglaries in a city were committed by persons that had previously been convicted at least 3 times for the same crime. If all of these criminals had been kept in jail, how many burglaries could have been prevented?

25. In a class of 42 students, 7 students received a grade of B. What percent of the class received a grade of B?

26. John's weekly gross pay is $110, but 23% of his check is withheld. How much is withheld?

27. Fifty-four out of 210 civil service applicants pass their exams. What percent of the applicants passes?

28. A 4200-pound automobile contains 462 pounds of rubber. What percent of the car's total weight is rubber?

29. A merchant pays $125 for an item. What is the selling price of this item if it is marked up 35% of the cost?

30. A suit costing a merchant $72 is marked up 20%. What is its selling price?

31. 5.85% of a person's salary is withheld for social security. How much is deducted from Leon's $460 salary for social security?

32. Every quarter an employer must send 11.7% of the total amount earned by his employees to the collector of internal revenue. If the employees' earnings are $178,475 for a quarter, how much must he send to the collector of internal revenue? (Round off your answer to the nearest cent.)

33. A truckload of 15 steers and 18 heifers was hauled to market. The average weights of the steers and heifers were 1027 lbs and 956 lbs respectively. Due to weight loss during shipment a 3% deduction is made from the total live weight and the seller is paid on this reduced weight. If the producer received 84 cents per pound for the steers and 78 cents per pound for the heifers, how much was his check from the buyer?

34. A timber company paid $632,000 for 1.27 million board feet of timber in the Mt. Hood National Forest. The timber had been appraised at $456,000. What percent of the appraised value was the amount that the company paid above the appraised value?

SET II

1. 24 is 40% of what number?
2. 650 is what percent of 325?
3. What is 55% of 82?
4. 23% of what number is 13.11?
5. What percent of 12 is 18?
6. 91% of 64 is what number?
7. 335 is 134% of what number?
8. 39 is what percent of 27? (Round off your answer to one decimal place.)
9. What is 400% of 19?
10. There are 43 grams of sulfuric acid in 500 grams of solution. Find the percent of acid in the solution.
11. A camera costing a merchant $244 is marked up 30%. What is its selling price?
12. A team wins 105 games. This is 70% of the games played. How many games were played?
13. Rosie's weekly salary is $225. If her deductions amount to $63, what percent of her salary is take-home pay?
14. 500 grams of a solution contain 27 grams of a drug. Find the percent of drug strength.
15. Mary is interested in renting an apartment which rents for $225 per month. She cannot afford to spend more than 40% of her total monthly income which is $500 per month. Can Mary afford the apartment?
16. Ten years ago Joe put $300 into the bank and forgot about it. Today Joe's bank account is worth $625. What percent of its worth today is due to the interest alone?
17. The largest meteorite found in the United States was discovered in a forest near Willamette, Oregon, in 1902. This 13.5 ton meteorite is about 91 percent iron and 8.3 percent nickel. How much iron and nickel does this meteorite contain?
18. The largest meteorite found in the world was discovered in southwest Africa. This 60.2 meteorite is about 81 percent iron and 17.5 percent nickel. How much iron and nickel does this meteorite contain?

Variation Problems

A *variation* is an equation that relates one variable to one or more other variables by means of multiplication, division, or both.

Subscripts. x_1 ← This small number written below and to the right of the letter is used to indicate a particular value of that letter. It is called a *subscript*.

x_1 is read "x sub one."

x_2 ← A different subscript indicates a different value of that letter.

x_2 is read "x sub two."

Example 1.   Examples of subscripted variables.

(a) y_1 and y_2 are different values of y.

y_1 is read "y sub one."

y_2 is read "y sub two."

(b) P_1 and P_2 are different values of P.

(c) D_1 and D_2 are different values of D.

We use subscripts in the discussion of variation in this section.

Subscripts also make it possible to indicate *corresponding values* of variables. For example, x_1 and y_1 are a pair of corresponding variables. *Condition 1* lists all corresponding values of the variables with the subscript 1. *Condition 2* lists all corresponding values of the variables with the subscript 2.

DIRECT VARIATION.   Direct variation is a type of variation relating one variable to another by the formula

$$y = kx$$

$\uparrow$———— constant of proportionality

Condition 1 $\begin{cases} \text{If} \quad x = x_1 \\ \text{and } y = y_1 \end{cases}$ then $y_1 = kx_1$ (1) | Equation (1) results from substituting x_1 and y_1 into the formula $y = kx$.

Equation (1)

Condition 2 $\begin{cases} \text{If} \quad x = x_2 \\ \text{and } y = y_2 \end{cases}$ then $y_2 = kx_2$ (2) | Equation (2) results from substituting x_2 and y_2 into the formula $y = kx$.

Equation (2)

Dividing Equation (1) by Equation (2) we have $\dfrac{y_1}{y_2} = \dfrac{Kx_1}{Kx_2} = \dfrac{x_1}{x_2}$.

Therefore, $\dfrac{y_1}{y_2} = \dfrac{x_1}{x_2}$ This proportion is called the *related proportion* for direct variation.

Note that in *direct* variation the subscripts of the letters in *both* ratios are in the *same* order.

These ideas about direct variation can be summarized as follows:

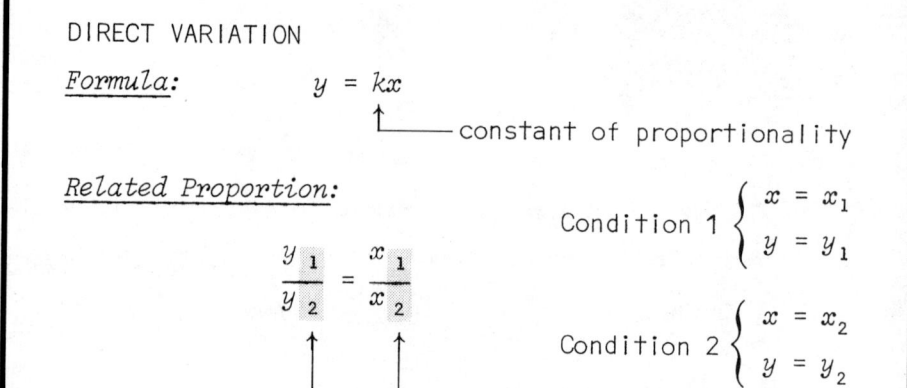

DIRECT VARIATION

Formula: $y = kx$

—— constant of proportionality

Related Proportion:

$$\frac{y_1}{y_2} = \frac{x_1}{x_2}$$

Condition 1 $\begin{cases} x = x_1 \\ y = y_1 \end{cases}$

Condition 2 $\begin{cases} x = x_2 \\ y = y_2 \end{cases}$

—— subscripts in *same* order

__Example 2.__ y varies directly with x according to the formula $y = kx$. If $y = 10$ when $x = 2$, find y when $x = 3$.

__Solution:__

Condition 1 $\begin{cases} x_1 = 2 \\ y_1 = 10 \end{cases}$ Condition 2 $\begin{cases} x_2 = 3 \\ y_2 = ? \end{cases}$

$\dfrac{y_1}{y_2} = \dfrac{x_1}{x_2}$ The related proportion for direct variation.

$\dfrac{10}{y_2} = \dfrac{2}{3}$ Substituting the given values in the related proportion.

$2y_2 = 10(3)$ Product of means equals product of extremes.

$y_2 = \dfrac{10(3)}{2} = 15$

__Example 3.__ The circumference C of a circle varies directly with the diameter D according to the formula $C = \pi D$. If $C = 12.56$ when $D = 4$, find C when $D = 7$.

__Solution:__

Condition 1 $\begin{cases} D_1 = 4 \\ C_1 = 12.56 \end{cases}$ Condition 2 $\begin{cases} D_2 = 7 \\ C_2 = ? \end{cases}$

$$\frac{C_1}{C_2} = \frac{D_1}{D_2}$$

The related proportion for direct variation.

$$\frac{12.56}{C} = \frac{4}{7}$$

Substituting the given values in the related proportion.

$$4C_2 = 12.56(7)$$

Product of means = product of extremes

$$C_2 = \frac{12.56(7)}{4} = 21.98$$

If the formula of the variation is $y = kx$, we say that "y varies directly with x." If the formula of the variation is $y = kx^2$, we say that "y varies directly with x^2." In this case

$$\text{Condition 1} \left\{ \begin{array}{l} \text{If} \quad x = x_1 \\ \text{and } y = y_1 \end{array} \right\} \text{then } y_1 = kx_1^2 \qquad (1)$$

$$\text{Condition 2} \left\{ \begin{array}{l} \text{If} \quad x = x_2 \\ \text{and } y = y_2 \end{array} \right\} \text{then } y_2 = kx_2^2 \qquad (2)$$

Dividing Equation (1) by Equation (2) we have $\dfrac{y_1}{y_2} = \dfrac{\cancel{k}x_1^2}{\cancel{k}x_2^2} = \dfrac{x_1^2}{x_2^2}$

Therefore, the related proportion for this type of direct variation is

$$\frac{y_1}{y_2} = \frac{x_1^2}{x_2^2}$$

Note that *when a letter appears to the second power in the variation formula, it also appears to the second power in the related proportion.*

<u>Example 4.</u> y varies directly with x^2 according to the formula $y = kx^2$. If $y = 20$ when $x = 2$, find y when $x = 6$.

<u>Solution:</u> $\text{Condition 1} \left\{ \begin{array}{l} x_1 = 2 \\ y_1 = 20 \end{array} \right. \qquad \text{Condition 2} \left\{ \begin{array}{l} x_2 = 6 \\ y_2 = ? \end{array} \right.$

$$\frac{y_1}{y_2} = \frac{x_1^2}{x_2^2}$$

The related proportion.

$$\frac{20}{y_2} = \frac{2^2}{6^2} = \frac{4}{36} = \frac{1}{9}$$

$$1(y_2) = 20(9)$$

Product of means = product of extremes.

$$y_2 = 180$$

SET I

1. y varies directly with x according to the formula $y = kx$. If $y = -14$ when $x = -2$, find y when $x = 4$.

2. y varies directly with x according to the formula $y = kx$. If $y = 6$ when $x = -2$, find y when $x = 10$.

3. y varies directly with x. If $y = -9$ when $x = -3$, find x when $y = -12$.

4. y varies directly with x. If $y = -6$ when $x = 3$, find x when $y = -18$.

5. y varies directly with x^2 according to the formula $y = kx^2$. If $y = -20$ when $x = -2$, find y when $x = 5$.

6. y varies directly with x^2 according to the formula $y = kx^2$. If $y = 90$ when $x = -3$, find y when $x = 10$.

----

7. The amount (s) a spring is stretched varies directly with the force (F) applied according to the formula $s = kF$. If a 5-pound force stretches a spring 3 inches, how far will a 2-pound force stretch it?

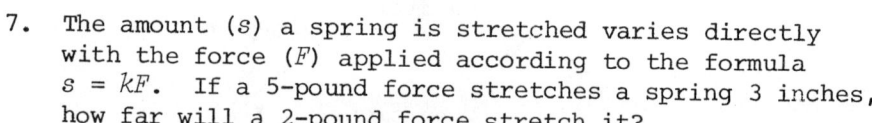

8. The pressure (p) in water varies directly with the depth (d). This relation is expressed by the formula $p = kd$. If the pressure at a depth of 100 feet is 43.3 pounds per square inch (neglecting atmospheric pressure), find the pressure at a depth of 60 feet.

9. The distance (s) an object falls (in a vacuum) varies directly with the square of the time (t) it takes to fall according to the formula $s = kt^2$. If an object falls 64 feet in 2 seconds, how far will it fall in 3 seconds?

10. The air resistance (R) on a car varies directly with the square of the car's velocity (v) according to the formula $R = kv^2$. If the air resistance is 400 pounds at 60 miles per hour, find the air resistance at 90 miles per hour.

SET II

1. y varies directly with x according to the formula $y = kx$. If $y = -28$ when $x = 2$, find y when $x = -3$.

2. y varies directly with x. If $y = -6$ when $x = -\frac{1}{3}$, find x when $y = 9$.

3. y varies directly with x^2 according to the formula $y = kx^2$. If $y = -12$ when $x = -2$, find y when $x = -5$.

4. Stella's weekly salary (S) varies directly with the number of hours (h) she works during the week. If she made $116.40 for working 24 hours, how many hours would she have to work to earn $169.75?

5. The resistance (R) of a boat moving through water varies directly with the square of its speed (S). If its resistance is 50 pounds at a speed of 10 knots, what is the resistance at 20 knots?

6. In a business, the revenue (R) is directly proportional to the number of items sold (n), if the price (p) is fixed. If the revenue is $12,000 when 800 items are

sold, how many items must be sold for the revenue to be $15,000?

INVERSE VARIATION. Inverse variation is a type of variation relating one variable to another by the formula

$$y = \frac{k}{x} \longleftarrow \text{constant of proportionality}$$

Condition 1 If $x = x_1$
and $y = y_1$ $\Big\}$ then $y_1 = \frac{k}{x_1}$

Equation (1)

Equation (1) results from substituting x_1 and y_1 in the formula $y = \frac{k}{x}$.

Condition 2 If $x = x_2$
and $y = y_2$ $\Big\}$ then $y_2 = \frac{k}{x_2}$

Equation (2)

Equation (2) results from substituting x_2 and y_2 in the formula $y = \frac{k}{x}$.

Dividing Equation (1) by Equation (2) we have

$$\frac{y_1}{y_2} = \frac{\frac{k}{x_1}}{\frac{k}{x_2}} = \frac{k}{x_1} \cdot \frac{x_2}{k} = \frac{x_2}{x_1}$$

Therefore, $\dfrac{y_1}{y_2} = \dfrac{x_2}{x_1}$ This proportion is called the related proportion for inverse variation.

Note that in inverse variation the subscripts of the letters in the two ratios are in *opposite* order.

These ideas about inverse variation can be summarized as follows:

INVERSE VARIATION

Formula:

$$y = \frac{k}{x} \qquad \text{constant of proportionality} \qquad xy = k$$

or

Related Proportion:

$$\frac{y_1}{y_2} = \frac{x_2}{x_1}$$

Condition 1 $\begin{cases} x = x_1 \\ y = y_1 \end{cases}$

Condition 2 $\begin{cases} x = x_2 \\ y = y_2 \end{cases}$

subscripts in *opposite* order

Example 5. y varies inversely with x according to the formula $y = \dfrac{k}{x}$. If $y = 6$ when $x = 2$, find y when $x = 3$.

Solution:

Condition 1 $\begin{cases} x_1 = 2 \\ y_1 = 6 \end{cases}$ Condition 2 $\begin{cases} x_2 = 3 \\ y_2 = \,? \end{cases}$

$\dfrac{y_1}{y_2} = \dfrac{x_2}{x_1}$ The related proportion for inverse variation.

$\dfrac{6}{y_2} = \dfrac{3}{2}$ Substituting the given values in the related proportion.

$3y_2 = 6(2)$ Product of means = product of extremes.

$y_2 = \dfrac{6(2)}{3} = 4$

Example 6. The pressure P varies inversely with the volume V according to the formula $PV = k$. If $P = 30$ when $V = 500$, find P when $V = 200$.

Solution:

Condition 1 $\begin{cases} P_1 = 30 \\ V_1 = 500 \end{cases}$ Condition 2 $\begin{cases} P_2 = \,? \\ V_2 = 200 \end{cases}$

$\dfrac{P_1}{P_2} = \dfrac{V_2}{V_1}$ The related proportion for inverse variation.

$\dfrac{30}{P_2} = \dfrac{200}{500} = \dfrac{2}{5}$ Substituting the given values and reducing the fraction.

$2P_2 = 30(5)$ Product of means = product of extremes.

$P_2 = \dfrac{30(5)}{2} = 75$

If the formula of the variation is $y = \dfrac{k}{x^2}$, we say "y varies inversely with x^2." In this case, the related proportion becomes

$\dfrac{y_1}{y_2} = \dfrac{x_2^2}{x_1^2}$ Note that the letter x always appears to the second power in the proportion because x appears to the second power in the formula for the variation.

Example 7. y varies inversely with x^2 according to the formula $y = \dfrac{k}{x^2}$. If $y = -3$ when $x = 4$, find y when $x = -6$.

Solution:

Condition 1 $\begin{cases} x_1 = 4 \\ y_1 = -3 \end{cases}$ Condition 2 $\begin{cases} x_2 = -6 \\ y_2 = \,? \end{cases}$

$\dfrac{y_1}{y_2} = \dfrac{x_2^2}{x_1^2}$ The related proportion.

$$\frac{-3}{y_2} = \frac{(-6)^2}{(4)^2} = \frac{36}{16} = \frac{9}{4}$$

$$9y_2 = (-3)(4) \qquad\qquad \text{Product of means = product of extremes.}$$

$$y_2 = \frac{(\overset{-1}{\cancel{-3}})(4)}{\underset{3}{\cancel{9}}} = -\frac{4}{3}$$

EXERCISES 508B

SET I

1. y varies inversely with x according to the formula $y = \frac{k}{x}$. If $y = 3$ when $x = 5$, find y when $x = -10$.

2. y varies inversely with x according to the formula $y = \frac{k}{x}$. If $y = 2$ when $x = -3$, find y when $x = \frac{1}{2}$.

3. y varies inversely with x. If $y = 3$ when $x = -2$, find x when $y = -1$.

4. y varies inversely with x. If $y = -\frac{1}{2}$ when $x = 16$, find x when $y = -2$.

5. F varies inversely with d^2 according to the formula $F = \frac{k}{d^2}$. If $F = 3$ when $d = -4$, find F when $d = 8$.

6. C varies inversely with v^2 according to the formula $C = \frac{54}{v^2}$. If $C = 6$ when $v = -3$, find C when $v = 6$.

----

7. The volume (V) of a gas (at constant temperature) varies inversely with its pressure (P) according to the formula $V = \frac{k}{P}$ (Boyle's Law). If the volume is 1600 cc at a pressure of 250 mm of mercury, find the volume at a pressure of 400 mm of mercury.

8. The weight (W) of an object varies inversely with the square of the distance (d) separating that object from the center of the earth according to the formula $W = \frac{k}{d^2}$. If a man at the surface of the earth weighs 160 pounds, find his weight at an altitude of 8000 miles. (Hint: At the surface of the earth the man is 4000 miles from the earth's center. Therefore, at an altitude of 8000 miles, he is 12,000 miles from the earth's center.)

9. The sound intensity (I) (loudness) varies inversely with the square of the distance (d) from the source according to the formula $I = \frac{k}{d^2}$. If a pneumatic drill has a sound intensity of 75 decibels at 50 feet, find its sound intensity at 150 feet.

10. The intensity (I) of light received from a light source varies inversely with the square of the distance (d) from the source according to the formula $I = \frac{k}{d^2}$. If the light

intensity is 15 candelas at a distance of 10 feet from the light source, what is the light intensity at a distance of 15 feet?

SET II

1. y varies inversely with x according to the formula $y = \dfrac{k}{x}$. If $y = -4$ when $x = -5$, find y when $x = 10$.

2. y varies inversely with x. If $y = -3$ when $x = 8$, find x when $y = 6$.

3. L varies inversely with r^2 according to the formula $L = \dfrac{k}{r^2}$. If $L = 16$ when $r = -3$, find L when $r = 4$.

4. The pressure (P) of a gas (at constant temperature) varies inversely with its volume (V) according to the formula $P = \dfrac{k}{V}$. If the pressure is 15 pounds per square inch when the volume is 350 cubic inches, find the pressure when the volume is 70 cubic inches.

5. The gravitational attraction (F) between two bodies varies inversely with the square of the distance (d) separating them. If the attraction measures 36.5 when the distance is 3.92 cm, find the attraction when the distance is 81.7 cm.

6. The electrical resistance of a wire varies inversely with the square of its diameter. If the resistance of a wire having a diameter of 0.0201 of an inch is 3.85 ohms, find the resistance of a wire of the same length and material having a diameter of 0.0315 of an inch.

Chapter Summary

Method for Solving Word Problems (Secs. 501, 502, 503)

1. To solve a word problem, first read the problem very carefully to determine what is unknown. What is being asked for? *Don't* try to solve the problem at this time.

2. Represent one unknown number by a letter. Then go back and read the problem again to see how you can represent any other unknown numbers in terms of that same letter.

3. Now that every unknown number has been represented in terms of a letter, there is nothing left in the word problem that cannot be represented by algebraic symbols.

4. Next, go back and reread the entire word problem, breaking it up into small pieces that can be represented by algebraic expressions.

5. After each of the pieces has been written as an algebraic expression, fit them together into an equation.

6. Solve the equation for the unknown letter by the methods learned in Chapter 4.

7. Check the solution in the *word* statement.

The Key to Solving Ratio Problems (Sec. 505). First multiply each
term of the ratio by x. Then use the resulting products to
represent the unknowns.

To Solve a Proportion (Sec. 506). First set the product of the
means equal to the product of the extremes. Then solve the
resulting equation for the unknown.

To Solve Word Problems that Lead to Proportions (Sec. 506).

1. Represent the unknown quantity by a letter.

2. Write the appropriate unit of measure next to each number
   in your proportion.

3. Use the units as a guide to place the numbers in your
   proportion. The same units must occupy corresponding
   positions in the two ratios.

4. Once the numbers have been correctly entered in your proportion, cross-multiply and solve for the unknown.

To Solve a Percent Problem (Sec. 507).

1. Identify the given numbers as A, B or P.

   P is the number followed by the word "percent."   (or %)

   B is the number that follows the words "percent of."

   A is the number left after P and B have been identified.

2. Substitute the given numbers in the Percent Proportion:

$$\frac{A}{B} = \frac{P}{100}$$

3. Solve the Percent Proportion for the unknown.

To Solve a Variation Problem (Sec. 508).

Each variation problem has three given numbers and one unknown.

1. Identify a pair of corresponding values out of the three
   numbers given in the variation problem. Call these values
   Condition 1.

2. The third given number, together with the unknown variable,
   make up the corresponding pair that we call Condition 2.

3. Substitute the two pairs of corresponding values into the
   related proportion.

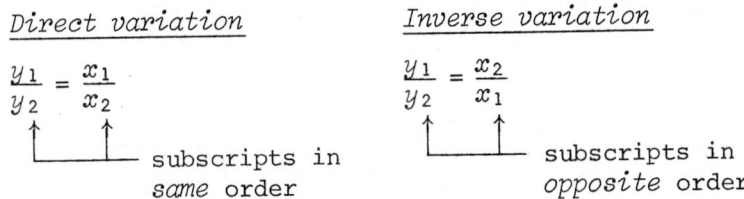

Direct variation

$$\frac{y_1}{y_2} = \frac{x_1}{x_2}$$

subscripts in _same_ order

Inverse variation

$$\frac{y_1}{y_2} = \frac{x_2}{x_1}$$

subscripts in _opposite_ order

4. Solve the related proportion for the unknown variable.

REVIEW EXERCISES 509

SET I

1. Two numbers are in the ratio of 6 to 7. Their sum is 52. Find the numbers.
2. Two numbers are in the ratio of 11 to 9. Their sum is 160. Find the numbers.
3. What is 35% of $275?
4. What is 245% of $450?
5. 77.5 is 31% of what number?
6. 366 is 150% of what number?
7. 7 is what percent of 8?
8. 6 is what percent of 16?
9. The rent of a $180-a-month apartment was raised $4\frac{1}{2}\%$. Find the new rent.
10. The rent on a $90-a-month apartment is raised $2\frac{1}{2}\%$. Find the new rent.
11. The three sides of a triangle are in the ratio of $3 : 4 : 5$. The perimeter is 108. Find the three sides of the triangle.
12. Solder used for soldering zinc is composed of lead and tin in the ratio $3 : 5$. How many ounces of each are present in 24 ounces of solder?
13. y varies directly with x according to the formula $y = kx$. If $y = -6$ when $x = 2$, find y when $x = 4$.
14. y varies inversely with x according to the formula $y = \frac{k}{x}$. If $y = -6$ when $x = 2$, find y when $x = -3$.
15. y varies inversely with x^2 according to the formula $y = \frac{k}{x^2}$. If $y = 2$ when $x = -3$, find y when $x = 2$.
16. y varies directly with x^2 according to the formula $y = kx^2$. If $y = 16$ when $x = 2$, find y when $x = 3$.

In Exercises 17 and 18, solve the proportion.

17. $\dfrac{P}{100} = \dfrac{7\frac{1}{2}}{45}$

18. $\dfrac{8\frac{1}{3}}{100} = \dfrac{24}{B}$

----

19. Leona has 15 coins having a total value of $1.75. If these coins are nickels and quarters, how many of each kind are there?
20. Raul has 22 coins having a total value of $5.00. If these coins are dimes and 50-cent pieces, how many of each kind are there?
21. Roger bought $2.10 worth of stamps. He bought only 2-cent, 10-cent, and 12-cent stamps. If there were twice as many 12-cent stamps as 10-cent stamps and twice as many 2-cent stamps as 12-cent stamps, how many of each did he buy?
22. Sandra bought $2.60 worth of stamps. She bought only 1-cent, 2-cent, and 8-cent stamps. If there were twice as many 8-cent stamps as 2-cent stamps and four times as many 1-cent stamps as 8-cent stamps, how many of each did she buy?

23. The total receipts for a concert were $11,250. They sold $12 box seats, $8 orchestra seats, and $5 balcony seats. If they sold 300 more balcony seats than box seats and twice as many orchestra seats as balcony seats, how many of each did they sell?

24. The total receipts for a football game were $164,000. General admission tickets cost $5 each, reserved seat tickets $8, and box seat tickets $10. If they sold 4500 more reserved seats than box seats and four times as many general admissions as reserved seats, how many of each did they sell?

25. An affirmative action committee demands that 24% of the 1800 entering freshmen be minority students. How many more than the actual 256 minority freshmen entering would satisfy the committee?

26. Sergio gets a $696 raise on his $11,600 yearly salary. There is a 9% rate of inflation for the year. How much more (or less) should his raise have been in order for him to keep up with the inflation?

27. A disc jockey plays folk, rock, country-western, and Latino records in the ratio of 2 : 5 : 3 : 4. If he played 126 records in a week, how many of each type were included?

28. A TV station tries to divide its programs in travel, drama, comedy, wildlife, and game shows in the ratio of 2 : 6 : 4 : 1 : 3. If there were 240 such programs aired during the week, how many of each kind were there?

SET II

1. A man cuts a 5-foot board into two parts whose ratio is 1 : 3. Find the length (in inches) of the pieces.

2. What is 175% of $350?

3. 93 is what percent of 124?

4. 62.4 is 26% of what number?

5. 45 is what percent of 300?

6. Find $7\frac{3}{4}$% of $500.

7. The evening enrollment at a certain college is 6% less than the day enrollment. If the day enrollment is 2450, find the evening enrollment.

8. Mr. Edmonson's new contract calls for a 12% raise in salary. His present salary is $11,250. What will his new salary be?

9. Alice has 60 coins having a total value of $13.35. The coins are dimes, quarters, and 50-cent pieces. If there are four times as many dimes as quarters, how many coins of each kind does she have?

10. y varies directly with x according to the formula $y = kx$. If $y = 5$ when $x = -1$, find y when $x = 6$.

11. y varies inversely with x^2 according to the formula $y = \frac{k}{x^2}$. If $y = 1$ when $x = 2$, find y when $x = 4$.

12. A 100-pound mixture of two different grades of coffee costs $72.50. If grade A costs 90¢ a pound and grade B costs 65¢ a pound, how many pounds of each grade were used?

13. 500 grams of a solution contain 75 grams of a drug. Find the percent of drug.
14. A particular meteorite weighing 30 pounds is composed of nickel and iron in the ratio of 1 : 9. How many pounds of each element are present in the meteorite?
15. Gloria thinks that 40% of the 50 teachers at her school should be women. The school board decides to increase the number of women teachers at her school from 16 to 22 (without changing the total number). Will this satisfy Gloria?

CUMULATIVE REVIEW EXERCISES: CHAPTERS 1-4

In Exercises 1-3, evaluate each expression.

1. $\dfrac{0}{0}$

2. $3\sqrt{36} - 4^2(-5)$

3. $46 - 2\{4 - [3(5 - 8) - 10]\}$

In Exercises 4 and 5, evaluate each formula using the values of the letters given with the formula.

4. $A = \dfrac{h}{2}(b + B)$ $h = 5, \; b = 7, \; B = 11$

5. $S = 4\pi R^2$ $\pi \doteq 3.14, \; R = 5$

In Exercises 6-10, solve each equation.

6. $32 - 4x = 15$

7. $-11 = \dfrac{x}{3}$

8. $5w - 12 + 7w = 6 - 8w - 3$

9. $4(2y - 5) = 16 + 3(6y - 2)$

10. $6z - 22 = 2[8 - 4(5z - 1)]$

Chapter Five Diagnostic Test

Name_____

_____

The purpose of this test is to see how well you understand solving word problems. We recommend that you work this diagnostic test *before* your instructor tests you on this chapter. Allow yourself about one hour to do this test.

   Complete solutions for all the problems on this test, together with section references, are given in the Answer Section. We suggest that you study the sections referred to for the problems you do incorrectly.

---

1. 28 is 42% of what number?   (Round off your answer to the nearest unit.)

(1) _____

---

2. Bill worked 17 problems correctly on a test having 20 problems. Find his percent score.

(2) _____

---

3. A dealer agrees to sell transistor radios costing him $12.50 at a markup of only 5%. What is the selling price?

(3) _____

---

4. When 16 is added to three times an unknown number, the sum is 37. Find the unknown number.

_____
Equation used to solve problem

(4) Unknown number_____

---

5. Mrs. Gomez put 48 pints of strawberries and cherries into her freezer. If the ratio of strawberries to cherries is 3 to 5, how many pints of each did she freeze?

_____
Equation used to solve problem

(5)_____pints of cherries

_____pints of strawberries

---

6. Cheryl has 25 coins in her purse that have a total value of $1.65. If these coins consist of nickels and dimes, how many of each kind are there?

_____
Equation used to solve problem

(6)_____nickels, _____dimes

_____

7. When 4 is subtracted from five times an unknown number, the result is the same as when 6 is added to three times the unknown number. Find the unknown number.

_____
Equation used to solve problem

(7) Unknown number_____

_____

8. A 6-foot man has a $3\frac{1}{2}$-foot shadow when a tree casts a 21-foot shadow. Find the height of the tree.

(8)_____

_____

9. y varies inversely with x according to the formula $y = \dfrac{k}{x}$. If $y = 3$ when $x = -4$, find y when $x = \dfrac{4}{5}$.

(9)_____

_____

10. The pressure (p) in water varies directly with the depth (d). This relation is expressed by the formula $p = kd$. If the pressure at a depth of 40 feet is 17.32 pounds per square inch (neglecting atmospheric pressure), find the pressure at a depth of 70 feet.

(10)_____

_____

In this chapter we discuss the rules of exponents that will be used throughout the remainder of the book.

Positive Exponents

We first discuss examples in which the exponents are positive integers. The first rule of exponents was introduced in Sec. 302.

MULTIPLYING POWERS HAVING THE SAME BASE

$$x^a \cdot x^b = x^{a+b} \qquad \textit{Rule 1}$$

Example 1. Using Rule 1

(a) $x^7 \cdot x^5 = x^{7+5} = x^{12}$

(b) $w^{11} \cdot w^7 = w^{11+7} = w^{18}$

(c) $x \cdot x^2 = x^{1+2} = x^3$

    $\uparrow\!\!\!-\!\!-x = x^1$ When no exponent is written, the exponent is understood to be 1.

(d) $x^3 \cdot x^7 \cdot x^4 = x^{3+7+4} = x^{14}$

(e) $10^7 \cdot 10^5 = 10^{7+5} = 10^{12} = \underbrace{1,000,000,000,000}_{}$

                                             12 zeros

(f) $2 \cdot 2^3 \cdot 2^2 = 2^{1+3+2} = 2^6 = 64$

(g) $2^a \cdot 2^b = 2^{a+b}$

(h) $x^3 \cdot y^2$ Notice: *The rule does not apply* because the bases are different.

Consider the expression $(x^4)^2$.

$$(x^4)^2 = (x^4)(x^4) = x^4 \cdot x^4 = x^{4+4} = x^{2 \cdot 4} = x^{4 \cdot 2} = x^8$$

Note that $(x^4)^2 = x^{4 \cdot 2}$. In this case the exponents are multiplied. This leads to the rule:

POWER OF A POWER

$$(x^a)^b = x^{ab} \qquad \textit{Rule 2}$$

Example 2. Using Rule 2

(a) $(x^5)^4 = x^{5 \cdot 4} = x^{20}$

(b) $(x)^4 = (x^1)^4 = x^{1 \cdot 4} = x^4$

(c) $(y^4)^3 = y^{4 \cdot 3} = y^{12}$

(d) $(10^6)^2 = 10^{6 \cdot 2} = 10^{12} = \underbrace{1,000,000,000,000}_{12 \text{ zeros}}$

(e) $(2^a)^b = 2^{a \cdot b} = 2^{ab}$

Consider the expression $\dfrac{x^5}{x^3}$.

$$\frac{x^5}{x^3} = \frac{xxxxx}{xxx} = \frac{xxx \cdot xx}{xxx \cdot 1} = \boxed{\frac{xxx}{xxx}} \cdot \frac{xx}{1} = 1 \cdot \frac{xx}{1} = xx = x^2$$

The value of this fraction is 1 (for $x \neq 0$).

Note that $\dfrac{x^5}{x^3} = x^{5-3} = x^2$. In this case, three of the factors of the denominator canceled with three of the five factors of the numerator, leaving $5 - 3 = 2$ factors of x. This leads to the rule:

DIVIDING POWERS HAVING THE SAME BASE

$$\frac{x^a}{x^b} = x^{a-b}, \quad x \neq 0 \qquad \textit{Rule 3}$$

<u>Note</u>. When using Rule 3, the exponent in the denominator is subtracted from the exponent in the numerator.

<u>Example 3.</u> Using Rule 3

(a) $\dfrac{x^6}{x^2} = x^{6-2} = x^4$

(b) $\dfrac{r^{12}}{r^5} = r^{12-5} = r^7$

(c) $\dfrac{y^3}{y} = \dfrac{y^3}{y^1} = y^{3-1} = y^2$

(d) $\dfrac{10^7}{10^3} = 10^{7-3} = 10^4 = \underbrace{10,000}_{4 \text{ zeros}}$

(e) $\dfrac{x^5}{y^2}$ Rule 3 does not apply when the bases are different.

(f) $\dfrac{8x^3}{2x} = \dfrac{\overset{4}{\cancel{8}}}{\underset{1}{\cancel{2}}} \cdot \dfrac{x^3}{x} = 4 \cdot x^2 = 4x^2$

(g) $\dfrac{6a^3b^4}{9ab^2} = \dfrac{\overset{2}{\cancel{6}}}{\underset{3}{\cancel{9}}} \cdot \dfrac{a^3}{a} \cdot \dfrac{b^4}{b^2} = \dfrac{2}{3} \cdot \dfrac{a^2}{1} \cdot \dfrac{b^2}{1} = \dfrac{2a^2b^2}{3}$

(h) $\dfrac{2^a}{2^b} = 2^{a-b}$

(i) $\dfrac{x^5 - y^3}{x^2}$ The expression is usually left in this form.

The expression could be changed as follows:

$$\frac{x^5 - y^3}{x^2} = \frac{x^5}{x^2} - \frac{y^3}{x^2} = x^3 - \frac{y^3}{x^2}$$

Expressions of this form are discussed in Secs. 705 and 902.

A word of caution. We show examples of a common mistake students make in division.

	<u>Correct method</u>	<u>Incorrect method</u>
(a)	$\dfrac{2 + 6}{2} = \dfrac{8}{2} = 4$	$\dfrac{\cancel{2} + 6}{\cancel{2}} \neq \dfrac{1 + 6}{1} = 7$
(b)	$\dfrac{x^2 + y}{x^2} = \dfrac{x^2}{x^2} + \dfrac{y}{x^2}$	$\dfrac{\cancel{x^2} + y}{\cancel{x^2}} \neq 1 + y$
	$\qquad\quad = 1 + \dfrac{y}{x^2}$	

This expression is usually left in the form $\dfrac{x^2 + y}{x^2}$.

<u>Why $x \neq 0$ in Rule 3</u>. When writing Rule 3, we added the restriction $x \neq 0$. Consider the example $\dfrac{0^5}{0^2}$. By Rule 3,

$\dfrac{0^5}{0^2} = 0^{5-2} = 0^3 = 0$. However, $\dfrac{0^5}{0^2} = \dfrac{0 \cdot 0 \cdot 0 \cdot 0 \cdot 0}{0 \cdot 0} = \dfrac{0}{0}$, which

cannot be determined (Sec. 109). For this reason, x cannot be zero in Rule 3.

In this book, unless otherwise noted, none of the letters has a value that makes a denominator zero.

When Rule 3 was used, we were careful to choose the exponent in the numerator larger than the exponent in the *denominator*, so that the quotient always had a positive exponent. *When the exponent in the denominator is larger than the exponent in the numerator*, the quotient has a negative exponent. Negative exponents are discussed in the next section.

<u>EXERCISES 601</u>. Use the rules of exponents to simplify each of the following expressions.

SET I

1. $x^5 \cdot x^8$ 2. $H^3 \cdot H^4$ 3. $(y^2)^5$ 4. $(N^3)^4$

5. $\dfrac{x^7}{x^2}$ 6. $\dfrac{y^8}{y^6}$ 7. $a \cdot a^4$ 8. $B^7 \cdot B$

9. $(x^4)^7$ 10. $(v^3)^8$ 11. $\dfrac{a^5}{a}$ 12. $\dfrac{b^7}{b}$

13. $\dfrac{z^5}{z^4}$ 14. $\dfrac{x^8}{x^7}$ 15. $10^2 \cdot 10^5$

16. $5^3 \cdot 5^2$ 17. $(10^2)^3$ 18. $(10^7)^2$

19. $\dfrac{10^{11}}{10}$ 20. $\dfrac{5^6}{5}$ 21. $x^2 y^3$

22. $a^4 b$ 23. $\dfrac{6x^2}{2x}$ 24. $\dfrac{9y^3}{3y}$

----

25. $\dfrac{a^3}{b^2}$ 26. $\dfrac{x^5}{y^3}$ 27. $\dfrac{10x^4}{5x^3}$

28. $\dfrac{15y^5}{9y^2}$ 29. $\dfrac{12h^4 k^3}{8h^2 k}$ 30. $\dfrac{16a^5 b^3}{12ab^2}$

31. $3^2 \cdot 5^3$ 32. $2^4 \cdot 3^2$ 33. $2 \cdot 2^3 \cdot 2^2$

34. $3 \cdot 3^2 \cdot 3^3$ 35. $x \cdot x^3 \cdot x^4$ 36. $y \cdot y^5 \cdot y^3$

37. $x^2 y^3 x^5$ 38. $z^3 z^4 w^2$

39. $a\,b^3 a^5$ 40. $x^8 y x^4$

41. $5^{2a} \cdot 5^{4a}$ 42. $6^x \cdot 6^{2x}$ 43. $\dfrac{x^{5a}}{x^{3a}}$

44. $\dfrac{M^{6x}}{M^{2x}}$ 45. $\dfrac{a^4 - b^3}{a^2}$ 46. $\dfrac{x^6 + y^4}{y^2}$

SET II

1. $y^2 \cdot y^4$ 2. $(x^3)^2$ 3. $\dfrac{a^6}{a^4}$ 4. $x^5 \cdot x$

5. $(z^2)^4$ 6. $\dfrac{b^4}{b}$ 7. $\dfrac{y^5}{y^3}$ 8. $10^3 \cdot 10^2$

9. $(5^4)^2$ 10. $\dfrac{2^3}{2^2}$ 11. hk^2 12. $\dfrac{12x^3}{10x}$

13. $\dfrac{m^4}{n^2}$ 14. $\dfrac{18z^6}{10z^4}$ 15. $\dfrac{25a^3 b^4}{15ab^3}$

16. $10^{3a} \cdot 10^{5a}$ 17. $\dfrac{H^{4n}}{H^{3n}}$ 18. $\dfrac{x^3 - y^2}{x^2}$

19. $4^2 \cdot 2^3$ 20. $2^2 \cdot 2 \cdot 2^4$ 21. $z \cdot z^2 \cdot z^5$

22. $a^2 b^4 a^3$

Negative and Zero Exponents

<u>NEGATIVE EXPONENTS.</u> Rule 3 leads to the introduction of negative
and zero exponents.

Consider the expression $\dfrac{x^3}{x^5}$.

$$\dfrac{x^3}{x^5} = \dfrac{xxx}{xxxxx} = \dfrac{xxx \cdot 1}{xxx \cdot xx} = \dfrac{xxx}{xxx} \cdot \dfrac{1}{xx} = 1 \cdot \dfrac{1}{xx} = \dfrac{1}{x^2}$$

↑—— The value of this
fraction is 1.

However, if we use Rule 3,

$$\dfrac{x^3}{x^5} = x^{3-5} = x^{-2}$$

Therefore,
$$x^{-2} = \dfrac{1}{x^2}$$

This leads to the rule

NEGATIVE EXPONENT

$$x^{-n} = \dfrac{1}{x^n}, \qquad x \neq 0 \qquad\qquad Rule\ 4$$

When using Rule 4, the exponent n can be either positive or negative.

Example 1. Using Rule 4 starting with a negative exponent.

(a) $x^{-5} = \dfrac{1}{x^5}$

(b) $a^{-3} = \dfrac{1}{a^3}$

(c) $10^{-4} = \dfrac{1}{10^4}$

Example 2. Using Rule 4 starting with a positive exponent.

(a) $x^4 = \dfrac{1}{x^{-4}}$ $\qquad\qquad$ (b) $w^{11} = \dfrac{1}{w^{-11}}$

It is also true that $x^n = \dfrac{1}{x^{-n}}$

because $\dfrac{1}{x^{-n}} = 1 \div x^{-n} = 1 \div \dfrac{1}{x^n} = \dfrac{1}{1} \cdot \dfrac{x^n}{1} = x^n$

Example 3. Using Rule 4 reading from right to left.

(a) $\dfrac{1}{x^{-4}} = x^4$

(b) $\dfrac{1}{w^{-2}} = w^2$

(c) $\dfrac{1}{y^3} = y^{-3}$

Examples 1, 2, and 3 lead to the following rule:

A <u>factor</u> can be moved either from the numerator to the denominator or from the denominator to the numerator simply by changing the sign of its exponent.

Note: This does not change the sign of the *expression*.

<u>Example 4</u>. Moving a factor from the numerator to the denominator of a fraction by changing the sign of its exponent.

(a) $a^{-3}b^4 = \dfrac{a^{-3}}{1} \cdot \dfrac{b^4}{1} = \dfrac{1}{a^3} \cdot \dfrac{b^4}{1} = \dfrac{b^4}{a^3}$

The factor a^{-3} was moved from the numerator to the denominator by changing the sign of its exponent.

(b) $y^{-4}w^5z^{-2} = \dfrac{y^{-4}}{1} \cdot \dfrac{w^5}{1} \cdot \dfrac{z^{-2}}{1} = \dfrac{1}{y^4} \cdot \dfrac{w^5}{1} \cdot \dfrac{1}{z^2} = \dfrac{w^5}{y^4z^2}$

These steps need not be written. We use them in these examples to show you why this method works.

(c) $\dfrac{x^{-2}}{y} = \dfrac{x^{-2}}{1} \cdot \dfrac{1}{y} = \dfrac{1}{x^2} \cdot \dfrac{1}{y} = \dfrac{1}{x^2y}$

<u>Example 5</u>. Moving a factor from the denominator to the numerator of a fraction by changing the sign of its exponent.

(a) $\dfrac{h^5}{k^{-4}} = \dfrac{h^5}{1} \cdot \dfrac{1}{k^{-4}} = \dfrac{h^5}{1} \cdot \dfrac{k^4}{1} = h^5k^4$

(b) $\dfrac{a^3}{b^2} = \dfrac{a^3}{1} \cdot \dfrac{1}{b^2} = \dfrac{a^3}{1} \cdot \dfrac{b^{-2}}{1} = a^3b^{-2}$

(c) $\dfrac{z^3}{x} = \dfrac{z^3}{1} \cdot \dfrac{1}{x} = \dfrac{z^3}{1} \cdot \dfrac{x^{-1}}{1} = z^3x^{-1}$

<u>Example 6</u>. Writing expressions with only positive exponents.

(a) $x^4y^{-3}z^{-6} = \dfrac{x^4}{1} \cdot \dfrac{y^{-3}}{1} \cdot \dfrac{z^{-6}}{1} = \dfrac{x^4}{1} \cdot \dfrac{1}{y^3} \cdot \dfrac{1}{z^6} = \dfrac{x^4}{y^3z^6}$

(b) $\dfrac{a^{-2}b^4}{c^5d^{-3}} = \dfrac{a^{-2}}{1} \cdot \dfrac{b^4}{1} \cdot \dfrac{1}{c^5} \cdot \dfrac{1}{d^{-3}} = \dfrac{1}{a^2} \cdot \dfrac{b^4}{1} \cdot \dfrac{1}{c^5} \cdot \dfrac{d^3}{1} = \dfrac{b^4d^3}{a^2c^5}$

(c) $\dfrac{e^2f}{g^{-1}} = \dfrac{e^2}{1} \cdot \dfrac{f^1}{1} \cdot \dfrac{1}{g^{-1}} = \dfrac{e^2}{1} \cdot \dfrac{f^1}{1} \cdot \dfrac{g^1}{1} = e^2fg$

Example 7. Writing expressions without fractions, using negative exponents if necessary.

(a) $\dfrac{m^5}{n^2} = \dfrac{m^5}{1} \cdot \dfrac{1}{n^2} = \dfrac{m^5}{1} \cdot \dfrac{n^{-2}}{1} = m^5 n^{-2}$

(b) $\dfrac{y^3}{z^{-2}} = \dfrac{y^3}{1} \cdot \dfrac{1}{z^{-2}} = \dfrac{y^3}{1} \cdot \dfrac{z^2}{1} = y^3 z^2$

(c) $\dfrac{a}{bc^2} = \dfrac{a^1}{1} \cdot \dfrac{1}{b^1} \cdot \dfrac{1}{c^2} = \dfrac{a^1}{1} \cdot \dfrac{b^{-1}}{1} \cdot \dfrac{c^{-2}}{1} = ab^{-1}c^{-2}$

A word of caution. An expression that is *not* a factor *cannot* be moved from the numerator to the denominator of a fraction simply by changing the sign of its exponent.

$$\dfrac{a^{-2} + b^5}{c^4} = \dfrac{\dfrac{1}{a^2} + b^5}{c^4}$$

a^{-2} *cannot* be moved to the denominator because it is not a *factor* of the numerator. (The + sign indicates that a^{-2} is a term rather than a factor of the numerator.)

Expressions of this kind will be simplified in Sec. 907.

Why $x \neq 0$ in Rule 4. When writing Rule 4, we added the restriction $x \neq 0$. Consider the example, 0^{-3}.

$$0^{-3} = \dfrac{1}{0^3} = \dfrac{1}{0 \cdot 0 \cdot 0} = \dfrac{1}{0} ,$$ which is not a number (Sec. 109).

For this reason x cannot be zero in Rule 4.

ZERO EXPONENTS. In using Rule 3 when the exponent of the numerator is larger than that of the denominator, the answer has a *positive* exponent. When the exponent of the denominator is larger than that of the numerator, the answer has a *negative* exponent. Now we consider the case where the exponents of the numerator and denominator are the same.

$$\dfrac{x^4}{x^4} = \dfrac{xxxx}{xxxx} = 1$$ Because a number divided by itself is 1

and $\dfrac{x^4}{x^4} = x^{4-4} = x^0$ Using Rule 3

Therefore we define

> ZERO EXPONENT
>
> $x^0 = 1, \quad x \neq 0$ *Rule 5*

Example 8. Showing zero as an exponent.

(a) $a^0 = 1$ Provided $a \neq 0$.

(b) $H^0 = 1$ Provided $H \neq 0$.

(c) $10^0 = 1$

(d) $5^0 = 1$

(e) $6x^0 = 6 \cdot 1 = 6$ Provided $x \neq 0$. The 0 exponent applies only to x.

Why $x \neq 0$ in Rule 5. When writing Rule 5, we added the restriction $x \neq 0$. Consider the example, $\frac{0^2}{0^2}$.

$$\frac{0^2}{0^2} = 0^{2-2} = 0^0. \qquad \text{But } \frac{0^2}{0^2} = \frac{0 \cdot 0}{0 \cdot 0} = \frac{0}{0}, \text{ which cannot be determined (Sec. 109).}$$

USING THE RULES OF EXPONENTS WITH POSITIVE, NEGATIVE, AND ZERO EXPONENTS. The rules for positive exponents already discussed in Sec. 601 also apply to expressions having negative and zero exponents.

Example 9. Applying the rules of exponents.

(a) $a^4 \cdot a^{-3} = a^{4+(-3)} = a^1 = a$ Rule 1

(b) $x^{-5} \cdot x^2 = x^{-5+2} = x^{-3} = \frac{1}{x^3}$ Rules 1 and 4

(c) $(y^{-2})^{-1} = y^{(-2)(-1)} = y^2$ Rule 2

(d) $(x^2)^{-4} = x^{2(-4)} = x^{-8} = \frac{1}{x^8}$ Rules 2 and 4

(e) $\frac{y^{-2}}{y^{-6}} = y^{(-2)-(-6)} = y^{-2+6} = y^4$ Rule 3

(f) $\frac{z^{-4}}{z^{-2}} = z^{(-4)-(-2)} = z^{-4+2} = z^{-2} = \frac{1}{z^2}$ Rules 3 and 4

(g) $h^3 h^0 h^{-2} = h^{3+0+(-2)} = h^1 = h$ Rules 1 and 5

An expression such as $\frac{x^3}{x^5}$ can be simplified in two ways:

$$\frac{x^3}{x^5} = x^{3-5} = x^{-2} = \frac{1}{x^2}$$

$or \quad \frac{x^3}{x^5} = \frac{1}{x^5 \cdot x^{-3}} = \frac{1}{x^{5-3}} = \frac{1}{x^2} \quad$ Moved factor x^3 to denominator and changed sign of its exponent.

Example 10. Simplifying fractions using the rules of exponents. Write results using only positive exponents.

(a) $\frac{12x^{-2}}{4x^{-3}} = \frac{\overset{3}{\cancel{12}}}{\underset{1}{\cancel{4}}} \cdot \frac{x^{-2}}{x^{-3}} = \frac{3}{1} \cdot \frac{x^{-2-(-3)}}{1} = 3x$

(b) $\dfrac{5a^4b^{-3}}{10a^{-2}b^{-4}} = \dfrac{\overset{1}{\cancel{5}}}{\underset{2}{\cancel{10}}} \cdot \dfrac{a^4}{a^{-2}} \cdot \dfrac{b^{-3}}{b^{-4}} = \dfrac{1}{2} \cdot a^{4-(-2)}b^{-3-(-4)} = \dfrac{a^6b}{2}$

(c) $\dfrac{9xy^{-3}}{15x^3y^{-4}} = \dfrac{\overset{3}{\cancel{9}}}{\underset{5}{\cancel{15}}} \cdot \dfrac{x}{x^3} \cdot \dfrac{y^{-3}}{y^{-4}} = \dfrac{3}{5} \cdot \dfrac{x^{1-3}}{1} \cdot \dfrac{y^{-3-(-4)}}{1}$

$$= \dfrac{3}{5} \cdot \dfrac{x^{-2}}{1} \cdot \dfrac{y}{1} = \dfrac{3}{5} \cdot \dfrac{1}{x^2} \cdot \dfrac{y}{1} = \dfrac{3y}{5x^2}$$

EVALUATING EXPRESSIONS HAVING NUMERICAL BASES

Example 11.

After applying the rules of exponents, it is customary to evaluate the power of a number.

(a) $10^3 \cdot 10^2 = 10^5 = 10 \cdot 10 \cdot 10 \cdot 10 \cdot 10 = \overbrace{100,000}^{5\ zeros}$

(b) $10^{-2} = \dfrac{1}{10^2} = \dfrac{1}{10 \cdot 10} = \dfrac{1}{\underbrace{100}_{2\ zeros}}$

(c) $(2^3)^{-1} = 2^{-3} = \dfrac{1}{2^3} = \dfrac{1}{2 \cdot 2 \cdot 2} = \dfrac{1}{8}$

(d) $\dfrac{5^0}{5^2} = \dfrac{1}{5 \cdot 5} = \dfrac{1}{25}$

A word of caution. A common mistake students make is shown by the following examples:

Correct method	*Incorrect method*
(a) $2^3 \cdot 2^2 = 2^{3+2}$	$2^3 \cdot 2^2 \neq (2 \cdot 2)^{3+2} = 4^5$
$\qquad = 2^5 = 32$	$\qquad = 1024$
(b) $10^2 \cdot 10 = 10^{2+1}$	$10^2 \cdot 10 \neq (10 \cdot 10)^{2+1} = 100^3$
$\qquad = 10^3 = 1000$	$\qquad = 1,000,000$

In words: When multiplying powers of the same base, add the exponents; do *not* multiply the bases as well.

SIMPLIFIED FORM OF EXPRESSIONS THAT HAVE EXPONENTS

An expression with exponents is considered simplified when each different base appears only once, and its exponent is a single integer.

Example 12. Simplifying expressions that have exponents.

(a) $x^2 \cdot x^7 = x^9$ (b) $\dfrac{x^5y^2}{x^3y} = x^2y$ (c) $(x^2)^3 = x^6$

(d) $\dfrac{x^5y^2}{x^4y} = \dfrac{xy^2}{y}$ This expression is not considered to be completely simplified because the base y appears twice.

Continue the simplification.

$$\frac{xy^2}{y} = xy \qquad \text{The expression is now completely simplified.}$$

EXERCISES 602

In Exercises 1—28, simplify each expression. Write answers using only positive exponents.

1. x^{-4}

2. y^{-7}

3. $\frac{1}{a^{-4}}$

4. $\frac{1}{b^{-5}}$

5. $r^{-4}st^{-2}$

6. $r^{-5}s^{-3}t$

7. $x^{-2}y^3$

8. x^3y^{-2}

9. $\frac{h^2}{k^{-4}}$

10. $\frac{m^3}{n^{-2}}$

11. $\frac{x^{-4}}{y}$

12. $\frac{a^{-5}}{b}$

13. $ab^{-2}c^0$

14. $x^{-3}y^0z$

15. $x^{-3} \cdot x^4$

16. $y^6 \cdot y^{-2}$

17. $10^3 \cdot 10^{-2}$

18. $2^{-3} \cdot 2^2$

19. $(x^2)^{-4}$

20. $(z^3)^{-2}$

21. $(a^{-2})^3$

22. $(b^{-5})^2$

23. $\frac{y^{-2}}{y^5}$

24. $\frac{z^{-2}}{z^2}$

25. $\frac{10^2}{10^{-5}}$

26. $\frac{2^3}{2^{-2}}$

27. $x^4x^0x^{-3}$

28. $y^{-2}y^0y^5$

In Exercises 29—34, write each expression without fractions, using negative exponents if necessary.

29. $\frac{1}{x^{+2}}$

30. $\frac{1}{y^3}$

31. $\frac{h}{k}$

32. $\frac{m}{n}$

33. $\frac{x^2}{yz^5}$

34. $\frac{a^3}{b^2c}$

In Exercises 35—46, evaluate each expression.

35. $10^4 \cdot 10^{-2}$

36. $3^{-2} \cdot 3^3$

37. 10^{-4}

38. 2^{-3}

39. $5^0 \cdot 7^2$

40. $4^3 \cdot 2^0$

41. $\frac{10^0}{10^2}$

42. $\frac{5^2}{5^0}$

----

43. $\frac{10^{-3} \cdot 10^2}{10^5}$

44. $\frac{2^3 \cdot 2^{-4}}{2^2}$

45. $(10^2)^{-1}$

46. $(2^{-3})^2$

In Exercises 47—66, simplify each expression. Write answers using only positive exponents.

47. $\dfrac{a^3b^0}{c^{-2}}$ 48. $\dfrac{d^0e^2}{f^{-3}}$ 49. $\dfrac{p^4r^{-1}}{t^{-2}}$

50. $\dfrac{u^5v^{-2}}{w^{-3}}$ 51. $\dfrac{8x^{-3}}{12x}$ 52. $\dfrac{15y^{-2}}{10y}$

53. $\dfrac{20h^{-2}}{35h^{-4}}$ 54. $\dfrac{35k^{-1}}{28k^{-4}}$ 55. $\dfrac{7x^{-3}y}{14y^{-2}}$

56. $\dfrac{24m^{-4}p}{16m^{-2}}$ 57. $\dfrac{15m^0n^{-2}}{5\,m^{-3}n^4}$ 58. $\dfrac{14x^0y^{-3}}{12x^{-2}y^{-4}}$

59. $x^{3m}\cdot x^{-m}$ 60. $y^{-2n}\cdot y^{5n}$ 61. $(x^{3b})^{-2}$

62. $(y^{2a})^{-3}$ 63. $\dfrac{x^{2a}}{x^{-5a}}$ 64. $\dfrac{a^{3x}}{a^{-5x}}$

65. $\dfrac{x+y^{-1}}{y}$ 66. $\dfrac{a^{-1}-b}{b}$

SET II

In Exercises 1—14, simplify each expression. Write answers using only positive exponents.

1. a^{-3} 2. $\dfrac{1}{x^{-2}}$ 3. $r^{-2}st^{-4}$

4. $h^{-3}k^5$ 5. $\dfrac{x}{y^{-3}}$ 6. $\dfrac{a^{-2}}{b}$

7. mn^0p^{-4} 8. $x^{-2}\cdot x^5$ 9. $10^{-4}\cdot 10^3$

10. $(n^4)^{-1}$ 11. $(z^{-3})^2$ 12. $\dfrac{y^{-1}}{y^4}$

13. $\dfrac{10^3}{10^{-2}}$ 14. $p^2p^0p^{-3}$

In Exercises 15—17, write each expression without fractions, using negative exponents if necessary.

15. $\dfrac{1}{c^4}$ 16. $\dfrac{x}{y}$ 17. $\dfrac{h^4}{kt^3}$

In Exercises 18—23, evaluate each expression.

18. $2^{-3}\cdot 2^5$ 19. 10^{-6} 20. $3^0\cdot 5^2$

21. $\dfrac{10^0}{10^{-2}}$ 22. $\dfrac{10^{-2}\cdot 10^3}{10^4}$ 23. $(2^{-4})^2$

In Exercises 24 — 33, simplify each expression. Write answers using only positive signs in the exponents.

24. $\dfrac{x^0 y^2}{z^{-5}}$ 25. $\dfrac{u^{-1} v^2}{w^{-3}}$ 26. $\dfrac{16h^{-2}}{10h}$

27. $\dfrac{24m^{-1}}{18m^{-3}}$ 28. $\dfrac{22a^{-1}b}{33b^{-3}}$ 29. $\dfrac{18w^0 z^{-4}}{16w^{-2} z^2}$

30. $x^{2n} \cdot x^{-n}$ 31. $(k^{-2c})^2$ 32. $\dfrac{y^{4n}}{y^{-3n}}$

33. $\dfrac{b^{-1} - c}{c}$

General Rule of Exponents

Rules 1 through 5 of exponents can be combined into the following general rule:

GENERAL RULE OF EXPONENTS

$$\left(\frac{x^a y^b}{z^c}\right)^n = \frac{x^{an} y^{bn}}{z^{cn}} \qquad \textit{Rule 6}$$

None of the letters can have a value that makes the denominator zero.

In applying Rule 6, notice:

1. x, y, and z are *factors* of the expression within the parentheses. They are *not* separated by + or − signs.
2. The exponent of each factor within the parentheses is multiplied by the exponent outside the parentheses.

Example 1. In the following examples, none of the factors appearing in any denominator is zero.

(a) $\left(\dfrac{x^2 y^5}{z^3}\right)^4 = \dfrac{x^{2 \cdot 4} y^{5 \cdot 4}}{z^{3 \cdot 4}} = \dfrac{x^8 y^{20}}{z^{12}}$

(b) $(x^3 y^{-1})^5 = x^{3 \cdot 5} y^{(-1)5} = x^{15} y^{-5} = \dfrac{x^{15}}{y^5}$

The same rules of exponents apply to *numerical* bases as well as literal bases.

(c) $\left(\dfrac{2a^{-3} b^2}{c^5}\right)^3 = \dfrac{2^{1 \cdot 3} a^{(-3)3} b^{2 \cdot 3}}{c^{5 \cdot 3}} = \dfrac{2^3 a^{-9} b^6}{c^{15}} = \dfrac{8b^6}{a^9 c^{15}}$

(d) $\left(\dfrac{3^2 c^{-4}}{d^3}\right)^{-1} = \dfrac{3^{2(-1)} c^{(-4)(-1)}}{d^{3(-1)}} = \dfrac{3^{-2} c^4}{d^{-3}} = \dfrac{c^4 d^3}{3^2} = \dfrac{c^4 d^3}{9}$

(e) $\left(\dfrac{3^{-7} x^{10}}{y^{-4}}\right)^0 = 1$

(f) $\left(\dfrac{x^5 y^4}{x^3 y^7}\right)^2 = (x^2 y^{-3})^2 = x^4 y^{-6} = \dfrac{x^4}{y^6}$

Simplify the expression within the parentheses first whenever possible.

(g) $(5^0 h^{-2})^{-3} = (1 h^{-2})^{-3} = (h^{-2})^{-3} = h^6$

(h) $\left(\dfrac{10^{-2} \cdot 10^5}{10^4}\right)^3 = \left(\dfrac{10^3}{10^4}\right)^3 = (10^{-1})^3 = 10^{-3} = \dfrac{1}{10^3}$

This exponent applies only to the symbol immediately preceding it, 5.

(i) $\dfrac{-5^2}{(-5)^2} = \dfrac{-25}{25} = -1$

This exponent applies only to the symbol immediately preceding it, (-5).

Compare (j) and (k) and note the difference when negative values are raised to an even or an odd power.

(j) $\dfrac{-2^3}{(-2)^3} = \dfrac{-8}{-8} = 1$ (k) $\dfrac{-2^4}{(-2)^4} = \dfrac{-16}{16} = -1$

(l) $(x^2 + y^3)^4$ Rule 2 or Rule 6 *cannot* be used here because the + sign means that x^2 and y^3 are *not* factors; they are *terms* of the expression being raised to the fourth power.

A word of caution. An exponent applies only to the symbol immediately preceding it. For example:

(a) Find the value of $3x^2$ if $x = 4$.

$$3x^2 = 3(4)^2 = 3(16) = 48$$

(b) $2x^3 \neq (2x)^3 = 2^3 x^3$

The exponent 3 applies to *both* 2 and x.
The exponent 3 applies *only* to x.

(c) Find the value of $-x^2$ when $x = 3$.

Correct method	*Incorrect method*
$-x^2 = -(3)^2 = -9$	$-x^2 = -(3^2) \neq 9$

The exponent 2 applies *only* to x.

<u>EXERCISES 603.</u> Simplify each expression, then write the
answer using only positive exponents.

<u>SET I</u>

1. $3(-2)^3$ 2. $2(-3)^2$ 3. $(2 \cdot 3)^2$

4. $(3 \cdot 4)^2$ 5. $\dfrac{(-4)^2}{-4^2}$ 6. $\dfrac{-3^2}{(-3)^2}$

7. $(a^2b^3)^2$ 8. $(x^4y^5)^3$ 9. $(2z^3)^2$

10. $(3w^2)^3$ 11. $(m^{-2}n)^4$ 12. $(p^{-3}r)^5$

13. $(x^{-2}y^3)^{-4}$ 14. $(w^{-3}z^4)^{-2}$ 15. $\left(\dfrac{xy^4}{z^2}\right)^2$

16. $\left(\dfrac{a^3b}{c^2}\right)^3$ 17. $\left(\dfrac{M^{-2}}{N^3}\right)^4$ 18. $\left(\dfrac{R^5}{S^{-4}}\right)^3$

19. $\left(\dfrac{a^2b^{-4}}{b^{-5}}\right)^2$ 20. $\left(\dfrac{x^{-2}y^2}{x^{-3}}\right)^3$ 21. $\left(\dfrac{10^2 \cdot 10^{-1}}{10^{-2}}\right)^2$

22. $\left(\dfrac{10^{-3} \cdot 10^2}{10^{-2}}\right)^3$

----

23. $\left(\dfrac{mn^{-1}}{m^3}\right)^{-2}$ 24. $\left(\dfrac{ab^{-2}}{a^2}\right)^{-3}$ 25. $\left(\dfrac{x^4}{x^{-1}y^{-2}}\right)^{-1}$

26. $\left(\dfrac{x^3}{x^{-2}y^{-4}}\right)^{-1}$ 27. $\left(\dfrac{8s^{-3}}{4st^2}\right)^{-2}$ 28. $\left(\dfrac{10u^{-4}}{5uv^3}\right)^{-2}$

29. $(10^0k^{-4})^{-2}$ 30. $(6^0z^{-5})^{-2}$ 31. $(x^3 + y^4)^5$

32. $(a^5 - b^2)^6$ 33. $\left(\dfrac{r^7s^8}{r^9s^6}\right)^0$ 34. $\left(\dfrac{t^5u^6}{t^8u^7}\right)^0$

35. $\left(\dfrac{6m^{-4}p}{8m^{-2}}\right)^{-1}$ 36. $\left(\dfrac{10x^{-6}y}{12x^{-4}}\right)^{-1}$

<u>SET II</u>

1. $5(-2)^4$ 2. $(3 \cdot 5)^2$ 3. $\dfrac{-5^2}{(-5)^2}$

4. $(h^3k^4)^2$ 5. $(5a^3)^2$ 6. $(m^{-3}n)^3$

7. $(w^2z^{-4})^3$ 8. $\left(\dfrac{x^3y}{z^2}\right)^2$ 9. $\left(\dfrac{R^4}{S^{-2}}\right)^3$

10. $\left(\dfrac{a^{-3}b^2}{a^{-4}}\right)^3$ 11. $\left(\dfrac{10 \cdot 10^{-2}}{10^{-3}}\right)^3$ 12. $\left(\dfrac{m^{-1}n^3}{m}\right)^{-2}$

13. $\left(\dfrac{x^2}{x^{-3}y^{-2}}\right)^{-1}$ 14. $\left(\dfrac{9u^{-3}}{12uv^2}\right)^{-2}$ 15. $(2^0h^2)^{-3}$

16. $\left(\dfrac{5t^{-1}u^2}{t^4u^{-3}}\right)^0$ 17. $\left(\dfrac{18yz^{-3}}{15z^{-2}}\right)^{-1}$ 18. $(e^4 - f^2)^3$

604

Chapter Summary

> THE RULES OF EXPONENTS
>
> 1. $x^a x^b = x^{a+b}$ (Sec. 601)
>
> 2. $(x^a)^b = x^{ab}$ (Sec. 601)
>
> 3. $\dfrac{x^a}{x^b} = x^{a-b}$, $x \neq 0$ (Sec. 601)
>
> 4. $x^{-n} = \dfrac{1}{x^n}$, $x \neq 0$ (Sec. 602)
>
> 5. $x^0 = 1$, $x \neq 0$ (Sec. 602)
>
> 6. $\left(\dfrac{x^a y^b}{z^c}\right)^n = \dfrac{x^{an} y^{bn}}{z^{cn}}$, $z \neq 0$ (Sec. 603)

Simplified Form of Expressions Having Exponents (Sec. 603).
An expression having exponents is considered simplified
when each different base appears only once, and its
exponent is a single integer.

REVIEW EXERCISES 604

SET I

In Exercises 1—40, simplify each expression. Write the
answers using only positive exponents.

1. $x^4 \cdot x^7$ 2. $y^3 \cdot y^5$ 3. $a^5 \cdot a^{-3}$

4. $b^4 \cdot b^{-2}$ 5. $c^{-5} \cdot d^0$ 6. $e^0 \cdot f^{-6}$

7. $\dfrac{p^5}{p^2}$ 8. $\dfrac{r^7}{r^5}$ 9. $\dfrac{x^{-4}}{x^5}$

10. $\dfrac{z^{-3}}{z^4}$ 11. $\dfrac{m^0}{m^{-3}}$ 12. $\dfrac{n^{-6}}{n^0}$

13. $\dfrac{10^6}{10^2}$ 14. $\dfrac{10^5}{10^3}$ 15. $\dfrac{10^4}{10^{-3}}$

16. $\dfrac{10^7}{10^{-2}}$ 17. $(x^2)^5$ 18. $(y^3)^4$

19. $(p^{-3})^5$ 20. $(r^{-2})^7$ 21. $(m^{-4})^{-2}$

22. $(n^{-5})^{-3}$ 23. $(h^0)^{-4}$ 24. $(k^{-7})^0$

25. $(x^2 y^3)^4$ 26. $(w^3 z^4)^2$ 27. $(p^{-1} r^3)^{-2}$

28. $(s^4 t^{-1})^{-3}$ 　　　　 29. $(2a^3)^4$ 　　　　 30. $(3b^2)^3$

31. $(-2x^4)^2$ 　　　　 32. $(-5y^3)^2$ 　　　　 33. $(-4b^{-2})^3$

34. $(-5a^{-4})^3$ 　　　　 35. $(-10)^{-1}$ 　　　　 36. $(-10)^{-3}$

37. $\left(\dfrac{x^2 y^3}{z^4}\right)^5$ 　　　　 38. $\left(\dfrac{x^6 y^2}{z^5}\right)^4$ 　　　　 39. $\left(\dfrac{x^{-3}}{y^0 z^2}\right)^{-4}$

40. $\left(\dfrac{a^{-4}}{b^3 c^0}\right)^{-5}$

In Exercises 41—44, write each expression without fractions. Use negative exponents if necessary.

41. $\dfrac{x^2}{y^3}$ 　　　　 42. $\dfrac{a^3}{b^2}$ 　　　　 43. $\dfrac{m^2}{n^{-3}}$

44. $\dfrac{w^3}{z^{-5}}$

In Exercises 45—56, evaluate each expression.

45. 4^{-2} 　　　　 46. 3^{-3} 　　　　 47. $(10^{-1})^3$

48. $(10^{-2})^2$ 　　　　 49. $\dfrac{2^0}{2^{-3}}$ 　　　　 50. $\dfrac{5^{-2}}{5^0}$

----

51. $8^0 \cdot 10^{-2}$ 　　　　 52. $4^0 \cdot 3^2$ 　　　　 53. $\dfrac{(-8)^2}{-8^2}$

54. $\dfrac{(-7)^2}{-7^2}$ 　　　　 55. $\left(\dfrac{10^{-3} \cdot 10}{10^{-2}}\right)^5$ 　　　　 56. $\left(\dfrac{10^{-4}}{10^{-5} \cdot 10}\right)^7$

In Exercises 57—74, simplify each expression. Write answers using only positive exponents.

57. $\left(\dfrac{u^{-5}}{v^2 w^{-4}}\right)^3$ 　　　　 58. $\left(\dfrac{r^{-6}}{s^5 t^{-3}}\right)^4$ 　　　　 59. $(5a^3 b^{-4})^{-2}$

60. $(3c^{-3} d^5)^{-4}$ 　　　　 61. $\left(\dfrac{4h^2}{i j^{-2}}\right)^{-3}$ 　　　　 62. $\left(\dfrac{5k^2}{mn^{-1}}\right)^2$

63. $\left(\dfrac{x^{10} y^5}{x^5 y}\right)^3$ 　　　　 64. $\left(\dfrac{a^5 b^6}{ab^3}\right)^4$ 　　　　 65. $\left(\dfrac{6x^{-5} y^8}{3x^2 y^{-4}}\right)^0$

66. $\left(\dfrac{15r^{-8} s^4}{5r^4 s^{-2}}\right)^0$ 　　　　 67. $(a^2 + b^3)^3$ 　　　　 68. $(m^4 - n^5)^4$

69. $x^{3d} \cdot x^d$ 　　　　 70. $y^{3e} \cdot y^e$ 　　　　 71. $(x^{4a})^{-2}$

72. $(y^{3b})^{-3}$ 　　　　 73. $\dfrac{6^{2x}}{6^{-x}}$ 　　　　 74. $\dfrac{5^{3a}}{5^{-a}}$

In Exercises 75 and 76, write each expression without fractions. Use negative exponents if necessary.

75. $\dfrac{a^{-3}b^2}{10c^{-4}}$

76. $\dfrac{u^{-4}v^3}{10^2w^{-5}}$

SET II

In Exercises 1—20, simplify each expression. Write answers using only positive exponents.

1. $z^2 \cdot z^5$

2. $x^{-3} \cdot x^4$

3. $a^0 \cdot b^{-2}$

4. $\dfrac{y^6}{y^2}$

5. $\dfrac{x^{-2}}{x^2}$

6. $\dfrac{h^0}{h^{-4}}$

7. $\dfrac{10^4}{10}$

8. $\dfrac{10^2}{10^{-3}}$

9. $(e^3)^2$

10. $(m^{-2})^4$

11. $(u^{-3})^{-2}$

12. $(k^{-5})^0$

13. $(w^2z^4)^2$

14. $(m^{-1}n^2)^{-3}$

15. $(2v^4)^2$

16. $(-4x^3)^2$

17. $(-2t^{-3})^2$

18. $(-10)^{-2}$

19. $\left(\dfrac{2x^3}{y^2}\right)^2$

20. $\left(\dfrac{a^{-2}}{5^0b}\right)^{-3}$

In Exercises 21—23, write each expression without fractions. Use negative exponents if necessary.

21. $\dfrac{z}{y^{-2}}$

22. $\dfrac{h^2}{k^2}$

23. $\dfrac{u^{-3}v^2}{5^2w}$

In Exercises 24—29, evaluate each expression.

24. 5^{-2}

25. $(2^{-3})^2$

26. $\dfrac{10^{-2}}{10^0}$

27. $2^4 \cdot 3^0$

28. $\dfrac{(-5)^2}{-5^2}$

29. $\left(\dfrac{10^{-2} \cdot 10}{10^{-5}}\right)^{-1}$

In Exercises 30—39, simplify each expression. Write answers using only positive exponents.

30. $\left(\dfrac{r^{-3}}{s^2t^{-2}}\right)^2$

31. $(2c^{-4}d^2)^{-2}$

32. $\left(\dfrac{3p}{m^2n^{-1}}\right)^{-3}$

33. $\left(\dfrac{x^8y}{x^5}\right)^2$

34. $\left(\dfrac{a^2b}{a^{-3}b^4}\right)^{-2}$

35. $\left(\dfrac{18x^{-3}y}{15x^2y^{-2}}\right)^0$

36. $(x^2 - y^3)^4$

37. $m^{3x} \cdot m^{-x}$

38. $(z^{2n})^{-3}$

39. $\dfrac{10^{3x}}{10^{-x}}$

CUMULATIVE REVIEW EXERCISES: CHAPTERS 1-5

1. In the formula $F = \frac{9}{5}C + 32$, find the value of F when $C = -20$.

In Exercises 2 and 3, evaluate each expression.

2. $16 \div 2 \cdot 4 - 9\sqrt{25}$

3. $5[11 - 2(6 - 9)] - 4(13 - 5)$

4. Simplify: $2x(3x^2 + 6x + 8) - 4(3x^2 + 5x - 6)$

5. The three sides of a triangle are in the ratio 3 : 5 : 7. The perimeter is 75. Find the three sides.

6. Susan worked 22 problems correctly on a Math test having 25 problems. Find her percent score.

7. A business pays $125 for an item. What is the selling price of the item if it is marked up 40%?

8. Several families went to a movie together. They spent $16.25 for 9 tickets. If adult tickets cost $2.50 and children's tickets cost $1.25, how many of each kind of ticket was bought?

9. A girl 5-feet tall has a 4-foot shadow when a tree casts a 24-foot shadow. How tall is the tree?

10. The distance (s) an object falls (in a vacuum) varies directly with the square of the time (t) it takes to fall, according to the formula $s = kt^2$. If an object falls 96 feet in 3 seconds, how far will it fall in 5 seconds?

Chapter Six Diagnostic Test

Name_____

_____

The purpose of this test is to see how well you understand the rules of exponents. We recommend that you work this diagnostic test *before* your instructor tests you on this chapter. Allow yourself about forty minutes to do this test.

Complete solutions for all the problems on this test, together with section references, are given in the Answer Section. We suggest that you study the sections referred to for the problems you do incorrectly.

Simplify each expression. Write your answers using only positive exponents.

1. $x^3 \cdot x^4$

    (1)_____

2. $(x^2)^3$

    (2)_____

3. $\dfrac{x^5}{x^2}$

    (3)_____

4. x^{-4}

    (4)_____

5. $x^2 y^{-3}$

    (5)_____

6. $\dfrac{a^{-3}}{b}$

    (6)_____

7. $\dfrac{x^{5a}}{x^{3a}}$

    (7)_____

8. $(4^{3x})^0$

    (8)_____

9. $(x^2 y^4)^3$

    (9)_____

10. $(a^{-3}b)^2$

    (10)_____

11. $\left(\dfrac{p^3}{q^2}\right)^2$

    (11)_____

12. $\left(\dfrac{m^2}{n}\right)^0$

    (12)_____

13. $\left(\dfrac{x}{y^2}\right)^{-3}$

    (13)_____

14. $\left(\dfrac{4x^{-2}}{2x^{-3}}\right)^{-1}$

    (14)_____

Write each expression without fractions, using negative exponents if necessary.

15. $\dfrac{1}{x^{-2}}$

(15) _____

16. $\dfrac{a^3}{b}$

(16) _____

17. $\dfrac{h^{-2}}{k^{-3}h^{-4}}$

(17) _____

_____

Evaluate each expression.

18. $2^3 \cdot 2^2$

(18) _____

19. $10^{-4} \cdot 10^2$

(19) _____

20. 5^{-2}

(20) _____

21. $(2^{-3})^2$

(21) _____

22. $(4^{-2})^{-1}$

(22) _____

23. $\dfrac{10^{-3}}{10^{-4}}$

(23) _____

24. $\dfrac{-3^2}{(-3)^2}$

(24) _____

25. $(5^0)^2$

(25) _____

_____

SEVEN
Polynomials

In this chapter we look in detail at a particular type of algebraic expression called a *polynomial*. Polynomials have the same importance in algebra that whole numbers have in arithmetic. Most of the work in arithmetic involves operations with whole numbers. In the same way, most of the work in algebra involves operations with polynomials.

Much of the work with polynomials has already been done in previous chapters. In this chapter we will review and extend concepts already discussed.

Basic Definitions

Some of the definitions learned in Chapter 3 are needed here. They are:

TERMS. The + and - signs in an algebraic expression break it into smaller pieces called *terms*. Each + and - sign is part of the term that follows it. *Exception*: An expression within grouping symbols is considered as a single piece, even though it may contain + and - signs. See Example 1(c), 1(d), and Example 2.

Example 1. Identifying terms in an algebraic expression.

(a) In the algebraic expression $3x^2y - 5xy^3 + 7xy$,

The - and + signs separate the algebraic expression into three terms.

The minus sign is part of the second term

$$\boxed{3x^2y} + \boxed{-5xy^3} + \boxed{7xy}$$

first term   second term   third term

(b) In the algebraic expression $3x^2 - 9x(2y + 5z)$,

$$\boxed{3x^2} + \boxed{-9x(2y + 5z)}$$

first term   second term

(c) In the algebraic expression $\frac{2 - x}{xy} + 5(2x^2 - y)$,

$$\boxed{\frac{2 - x}{xy}} + \boxed{5(2x^2 - y)}$$

first term   second term

Example 2. The number of terms in an algebraic expression.

(a) $3 + 2x - 1$ has three terms.

(b) $3 + (2x - 1)$ has two terms.

(c) $(3 + 2x - 1)$ has one term.

Literal refers to letters.

Numerical refers to numbers.

Like Terms. Terms having identical literal parts are called *like terms*.

Unlike Terms. Terms having different literal parts are called *unlike terms*.

COEFFICIENTS. The *coefficient* of one factor in a term is the product of all the other factors in that term.

Numerical Coefficient. A *numerical coefficient* is a coefficient that is a number.

VARIABLES. A *variable* is something that changes in value. It is represented by a letter.

We can now define a polynomial.

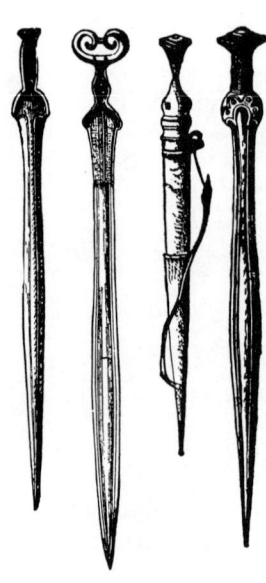

POLYNOMIALS. *A polynomial in x* is an algebraic expression having only terms of the form ax^n, where a is any real number and n is a positive integer (or zero).

Example 3. Examples of polynomials.

(a) $3x$ A polynomial of one term is called a *monomial*.

(b) $4x^4 - 2x^2$ A polynomial of two unlike terms is called a *binomial*.

(c) $7x^2 - 5x + 2$ A polynomial of three unlike terms is called a *trinomial*.

(d) $x^3 + 3x^2 + 3x + 1$ We will not use special names for polynomials of more than three terms.

(e) 5 This is a polynomial of one term (monomial) because its only term has the form $5x^0 = 5 \cdot 1 = 5$.

(f) $6z^3 - 3z + 1$ Polynomials can be in any letter. This is a polynomial in z.

Example 4. Examples of expressions that are not polynomials.

(a) $4x^{-2}$ This expression is *not* a polynomial because the exponent -2 is not a positive integer (or zero).

(b) $\dfrac{2}{x - 5}$ This is *not* a polynomial because the term does not have the form ax^n.

Polynomials often have terms containing more than one variable.

A polynomial in x and y is an algebraic expression having only terms of the form ax^ny^m, where a is any real number and n, m are positive integers (or zero).

Example 5. Polynomials in two letters.

(a) $5x^2y$ Monomial

(b) $-3xy^3 + 2x^2y$ Binomial

(c) $4x^2y^2 - 7xy + 6$ Trinomial

(d) $x^3y^2 \; - 2x \; + 3y^2 \; - 1$

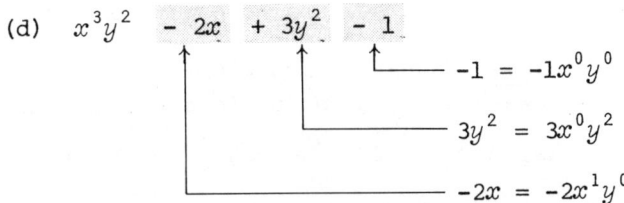

$-1 = -1x^0y^0$

$3y^2 = 3x^0y^2$

$-2x = -2x^1y^0$

(e) $7uv^4 - 5u^2v + 2u$ Polynomials can be in any variables. This is a polynomial in u and v.

DEGREE OF POLYNOMIALS. The *degree of a term* in a polynomial is the sum of the exponents of its variables.

Example 6. Finding the degree of a *term*.

(a) $5x^3$ 3rd degree

(b) $6x^2y$ 3rd degree because $6x^2y = 6x^2y^1$ $2 + 1 = 3$

(c) 14 0 degree because $14 = 14x^0$

(d) $-2u^3vw^2$ 6th degree because $-2u^3vw^2 = -2u^3v^1w^2$

                       $3 + 1 + 2 = 6$

The *degree of a polynomial* is the same as that of its highest-degree term (provided like terms have been combined).

Example 7. Finding the degree of a *polynomial*.

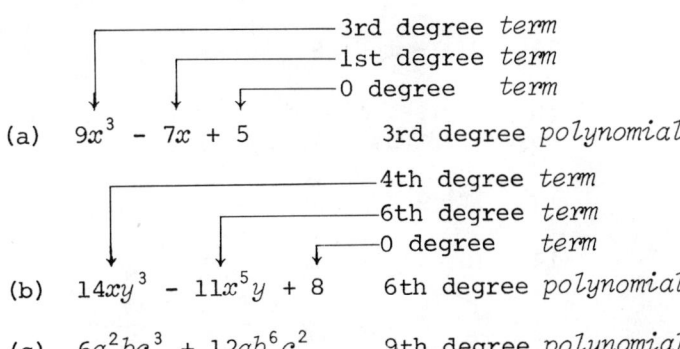

3rd degree *term*
1st degree *term*
0 degree *term*

(a) $9x^3 - 7x + 5$ 3rd degree *polynomial*

4th degree *term*
6th degree *term*
0 degree *term*

(b) $14xy^3 - 11x^5y + 8$ 6th degree *polynomial*

(c) $6a^2bc^3 + 12ab^6c^2$ 9th degree *polynomial*

<u>DESCENDING POWERS</u>. Polynomials are usually written in *descending powers* of one of the letters. For example:

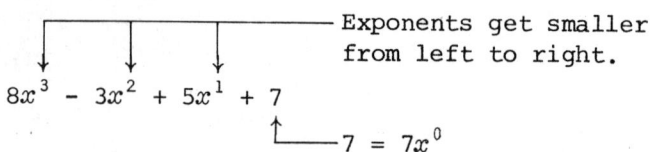

Exponents get smaller from left to right.

$$8x^3 - 3x^2 + 5x^1 + 7$$

$$7 = 7x^0$$

<u>Example 8</u>. Arrange $5 - 2x^2 + 4x$ in descending powers of x.

<u>Solution</u>: $-2x^2 + 4x + 5$

When a polynomial has more than one letter, it can be arranged in descending powers of any one of its letters.

<u>Example 9</u>. Arrange $3x^3y - 5xy + 2x^2y^2 - 10$: (a) in descending powers of x, then (b) in descending powers of y.

(a) $3x^3y + 2x^2y^2 - 5xy - 10$ Arranged in descending powers of x

(b) $2x^2y^2 + 3x^3y - 5xy - 10$ Arranged in descending powers of y

Since y is the same power in both terms, the higher-degree term is written first.

EXERCISES 701

SET I

In Exercises 1-6, find (a) the number of terms, and (b) the number of different variables in each expression.

1. $3x^2y + 5x + 7$

2. $5u^3v + u + 8$

3. $\dfrac{3}{x + y}$

4. $\dfrac{x}{y + z}$

5. $[6 - (u + v)] + 5$

6. $5 - \{4 - (a - b)\}$

In Exercises 7-12, if the expression is a polynomial, find (a) the degree of the polynomial, and (b) the degree of the second term.

7. $2x^2 + 3x$

8. $5y^3 + 4y$

9. $x^3y^3 - 3x^2y + 3xy^2 - y^3$

10. $8m^3 - 12m^2n + 6mn^2 - n^3$

11. $3x^4 - xy + 5$

12. $5x^3 - xy + 2$

In Exercises 13 and 14, write each polynomial in descending powers of the indicated letter.

13. $7x^3 - 4x - 5 + 8x^5$ Powers of x.

14. $10 - 3y^5 + 4y^2 - 2y^3$ Powers of y.

In Exercises 15 and 16, find (a) the number of terms, and
(b) the number of different variables in each expression.

15. $7x^2y^3 + 3yz^2 + xz + 10$ 16. $8RS^2 + 4R^2T^3 + ST$

In Exercises 17-20, if the expression is a polynomial, find
(a) the degree of the polynomial, and (b) the degree of the
second term.

17. $x^{-2} + 5x^{-1} + 4$ 18. $y^{-3} + y^{-2} + 6$

19. $5x^2 - xy + 3$ 20. $6x^3 - xy + 2$

In Exercises 21 and 22, write each polynomial in descending
powers of the indicated letter.

21. $8xy^2 + xy^3 - 4x^2y$ Powers of y.

22. $3x^3y + x^4y^2 - 3xy^3$ Powers of x.

SET II

In Exercises 1 and 2, find (a) the number of terms, and (b)
the number of different variables in each expression.

1. $7x + (x + 2)^2$ 2. 10

In Exercises 3-6, if the expression is a polynomial, find
(a) the degree of the polynomial, and (b) the degree of the
second term.

3. $7uv + 8$ 4. $2x^3 - xy + 5$

5. $\dfrac{1}{2x^2 - 5x}$ 6. $8xyz^2 + 3x^2y - z^3$

In Exercises 7—9, write each polynomial in descending powers
of the indicated letter.

7. $17a - 15a^3 + a^{10} - 4a^5$ Powers of a.

8. $3x^2y + 8x^3 + y^3 - xy^5$ Powers of y.

9. $5st - 9rs^2t - rt^2 - 3rs$ Powers of r.

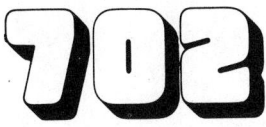

Addition of Polynomials

Polynomials can be added horizontally by combining like
terms as was done in Sec. 306.

<u>Example 1.</u> Adding polynomials.

(a) $\quad (3x^2 + 5x - 4) + (2x + 5) + (x^3 - 4x^2 + x)$

$= 3x^2 + 5x - 4 + 2x + 5 + x^3 - 4x^2 + x$

$= x^3 - x^2 + 8x + 1$

(b) $\quad (5x^3y^2 - 3x^2y^2 + 4xy^3) + (4x^2y^2 - 2xy^2)$

$$+ (-7x^3y^2 + 6xy^2 - 3xy^3)$$

$= 5x^3y^2 - 3x^2y^2 + 4xy^3 + 4x^2y^2 - 2xy^2 - 7x^3y^2 + 6xy^2 - 3xy^3$

$= -2x^3y^2 + x^2y^2 + xy^3 + 4xy^2$

Most addition of polynomials will be done horizontally as already shown. However, in a few cases it is convenient to use *vertical addition*. See Sec. 704 Multiplication of Polynomials.

<u>Example 2.</u> Add $(3x^2 + 2x - 1)$, $(2x + 5)$, and $(4x^3 + 7x^2 - 6)$ vertically.

<u>Solution:</u>

$$
\begin{array}{r}
3x^2 + 2x - 1 \\
2x + 5 \\
4x^3 + 7x^2 \quad - 6 \\
\hline
4x^3 + 10x^2 + 4x - 2
\end{array}
$$

Example 3. Add $(8x^2y - 3xy^2 + xy - 2)$, $(4xy^2 - 7xy)$, and

$(-5x^2y + 9)$ vertically.

Solution:

$$\begin{array}{r} 8x^2y - 3xy^2 + xy - 2 \\ 4xy^2 - 7xy \\ \underline{-5x^2y \qquad\qquad + 9} \\ 3x^2y + xy^2 - 6xy + 7 \end{array}$$

EXERCISES 702. Add the polynomials.

SET I

1. $(2m^2 - m + 4) + (3m^2 + m - 5)$

2. $(5n^2 + 8n - 7) + (6n^2 - 6n + 10)$

3. $(2x^3 - 4) + (4x^2 + 8x) + (-9x + 7)$

4. $(5 + 8z^2) + (4 - 7z) + (z^2 + 7z)$

5. $(6a - 5a^2 + 6) + (4a^2 + 6 - 3a)$

6. $(2b + 7b^2 - 5) + (4b^2 - 2b + 8)$

7. $\begin{array}{r} 17a^3 \qquad + 4a - 9 \\ \underline{8a^2 - 6a + 9} \end{array}$ 8. $\begin{array}{r} - b^3 + 5b^2 - 8 \\ \underline{-20b^4 + 2b^3 \qquad\quad + 7} \end{array}$

9. $(7 - 8v^3 + 9v^2 + 4v) + (9v^3 - 8v^2 + 4v + 6)$

10. $(15 - 10w + w^2 - 3w^3) + (18 + 4w^3 + 7w^2 + 10w)$

11. $\begin{array}{r} 14x^2y^3 - 11xy^2 + 8xy \\ -9x^2y^3 + 6xy^2 - 3xy \\ \underline{7x^2y^3 - 4xy^2 - 5xy} \end{array}$ 12. $\begin{array}{r} 12a^2b - 8ab^2 + 6ab \\ -7a^2b + 11ab^2 - 3ab \\ \underline{4a^2b - ab^2 - 13ab} \end{array}$

13. $(3x^4 + 2x^3 - 5) + (2x^4 + 4x^3 + 8)$

14. $(2y^3 - 3y^2 + 4) + (7y^3 + 5y^2 - 5)$

----

15. $(7m^8 - 4m^4) + (4m^4 + m^5) + (8m^8 - m^5)$

16. $(8h - 4h^6) + (5h^7 + 3h^6) + (9h - 5h^7)$

17. $(6r^3t + 14r^2t - 11) + (19 - 8r^2t + r^3t) + (8 - 6r^2t)$

18. $(13m^2n^2 + 4mn + 23) + (17 + 4mn - 9m^2n^2) + (-29 - 8mn)$

19. $\begin{array}{r} 4m^3n^3 \qquad\qquad - 10mn \\ - 10m^2n^2 - 15mn \\ \underline{5m^3n^3 - 8m^2n^2 + 20mn} \end{array}$ 20. $\begin{array}{r} 14h^2k^2 - 9hk^2 \\ -19h^2k^2 - 17hk^2 + 23hk \\ \underline{- 6hk^2 - 14hk} \end{array}$

21. $(16x^2y + 4xy) + (5x^2y - 6xy) + (4xy - 5x^2y)$

22. $(3xy^2 - 5xy) + (10xy - 3xy^2) + (8 + y^3)$

23. $(7.239x^2 - 4.028x + 6.205) + (-2.846x^2 + 8.096x + 5.307)$

24. $(29.62x^2 + 35.78x - 19.80) + (7.908x^2 - 29.63x - 32.84)$

1. $(2x^2 - 3x + 1) + (4x^2 + 5x - 3)$

2. $(4n^2 - 5n - 2) + (3n^2 + 7n + 4)$

3. $(5x^2y - 4x + 3y^2) + (-yx^2 + 6x - y^2)$

4. $(2x^2 - 11x + 4) + (15x - 12) + (5x^3 - 7x^2 - 4x)$

5. $(13m^2n^2 - 4mn - 23) + (17 + 4mn - 9m^2n^2) + (-29 + 8mn)$

6. $4x^3 + 7x^2 - 5x + 4$ 7. $3y^4 - 2y^3 + 4y + 10$

     $\underline{2x^3 - 5x^2 + 5x - 6}$ $-5y^4 + 2y^3 + 4y - 6$

                                       $\underline{7y^4 \qquad\quad - 6y - 8}$

8. $(7x^2y + 4xy^2 - 5) + (8xy^2 - 7x^2y + xy)$

9. $(5yz^2 + 8yz + z) + (-7yz + 8 - 5yz^2)$

10. $(3x^4 + 2x^3 - 5x^2 + 2x - 7) + (2x^4 - 2x^3 - 2x - 8)$

11. $(5x^3 - 3x^4 + 2x^5 - 6) + (2x^2 + 6 + 3x^4 - 2x^5)$

12. $(5.416x - 34.54x^2 + 7.806) + (51.75x^2 - 1.644x - 9.444)$

Subtraction of Polynomials

We subtract polynomials the same way we subtract signed numbers. This means: We change the signs in the polynomial being subtracted, then add the resulting polynomials.

TO SUBTRACT POLYNOMIALS HORIZONTALLY

1. Change the sign of *each* term in the polynomial being subtracted.

2. Add the *resulting* terms horizontally (Sec. 702).

Example 1.   Subtracting polynomials

This is the polynomial being subtracted

(a) $(-4x^3 + 8x^2 - 2x - 3) - (4x^3 - 7x^2 + 6x + 5)$

    $= \underline{-4x^3} + \underline{8x^2} - \underline{2x} - \underline{3} - \underline{4x^3} + \underline{7x^2} - \underline{6x} - \underline{5}$

    $= -8x^3 + 15x^2 - 8x - 8$

(b)   Subtract $(-4x^2y + 10xy^2 + 9xy - 7)$ from

                              $(11x^2y - 8xy^2 + 7xy + 2)$.

             This is the polynomial being subtracted

Solution: $(11x^2y - 8xy^2 + 7xy + 2) - (-4x^2y + 10xy^2 + 9xy - 7)$

$$= \underline{11x^2y} - \underline{8xy^2} + \underline{7xy} + \underline{2} + \underline{4x^2y} - \underline{10xy^2} - \underline{9xy} + \underline{7}$$

$$= 15x^2y - 18xy^2 - 2xy + 9$$

(c) Subtract $(2x^2 - 5x + 3)$ from the sum of

$(8x^2 - 6x - 1)$ and $(4x^2 + 7x - 9)$.

Solution: $(8x^2 - 6x - 1) + (4x^2 + 7x - 9) - (2x^2 - 5x + 3)$

$$= \underline{8x^2} - \underline{6x} - \underline{1} + \underline{4x^2} + \underline{7x} - \underline{9} - \underline{2x^2} + \underline{5x} - \underline{3}$$

$$= 10x^2 + 6x - 13$$

(d) $(x^2 + 5) - [(x^2 - 3) + (2x^2 - 1)]$

Solution: $= (x^2 + 5) - [(x^2 - 3) + (2x^2 - 1)]$

$= (x^2 + 5) - [x^2 - 3 + 2x^2 - 1]$ Removing inner-most ( ).

$= (x^2 + 5) - [3x^2 - 4]$ Combining like terms inside [ ].

$= x^2 + 5 - 3x^2 + 4$ Removing grouping symbols.

$= -2x^2 + 9$ Combining like terms.

Most subtraction of polynomials will be done horizontally as already shown, but in a few cases it is convenient to use *vertical subtraction*. See Sec. 705, Division of Polynomials.

TO SUBTRACT POLYNOMIALS VERTICALLY

1. Write the polynomial being subtracted *under* the polynomial it is being subtracted from. Write like terms in the same vertical line.

2. *Mentally* change the sign of each term in the polynomial being subtracted.

3. Find the sum of the *resulting* terms in each vertical line by adding their numerical coefficients.

In vertical subtraction, the problem could be rewritten changing all the signs in the polynomial being subtracted. Then the two polynomials could be added. However it is convenient to only *mentally* change the signs in the polynomial being subtracted, so that the problem does not have to be rewritten.

Example 2. Subtract $(3x^2 - 5x + 2)$ from $(2x^2 + 3x - 6)$ vertically.

Solution:
$$2x^2 + 3x - 6$$
$$+3x^2 - 5x + 2$$
$$\overline{-x^2 + 8x - 8}$$

Mentally change the sign of each term in the polynomial being subtracted, then *add* the resulting terms in each vertical line.

Example 3. Subtract $(4x^2y^2 + 7x^2y - 2xy + 9)$ from
$(6x^2y^2 - 2x^2y + 5xy + 8)$ vertically.

Solution:

$$
\begin{array}{r}
6x^2y^2 - 2x^2y + 5xy + 8 \\
+4x^2y^2 + 7x^2y - 2xy + 9 \\
\hline
2x^2y^2 - 9x^2y + 7xy - 1
\end{array}
$$

— *Mentally* change the sign of each term in the polynomial being subtracted, then *add* the resulting terms in each vertical line.

Example 4. Subtract $(3x^2 - 2x - 7)$ from $(x^3 - 2x - 5)$ vertically.

Solution:

$$
\begin{array}{r}
x^3 \qquad - 2x - 5 \\
+ 3x^2 - 2x - 7 \\
\hline
x^3 - 3x^2 \qquad + 2
\end{array}
$$

EXERCISES 703. Work the following subtraction exercises.

SET I

1. $(3x^2 + 4x - 10) - (5x^2 - 3x + 7)$
2. $(2a^2 - 3a + 9) - (3a^2 + 4a - 5)$
3. $(8b^2 + 2b - 14) - (-5b^2 + 4b + 8)$
4. $(11c^2 - 4c + 7) - (-8c^2 - 9c + 6)$
5. $(4a^2 + 6 - 3a) - (5a + 3a^2 - 4)$
6. $(8 + 3b^2 - 7b) - (2b + b^2 - 9)$

In Exercises 7 and 8 subtract the lower polynomial from the upper polynomial vertically.

7. $\begin{array}{l} 15x^3 - 4x^2 \qquad + 12 \\ \underline{8x^3 \qquad\qquad + 9x - 5} \end{array}$ 8. $\begin{array}{l} \qquad - 14y^2 + 6y - 24 \\ \underline{7y^3 + 14y^2 - 13y} \end{array}$

9. $(7x^2y^2 - 3x^2y + xy + 7) - (3x^2y^2 + 7x^2y - 5xy + 4)$
10. $(4x^2y^2 + x^2y - 5xy - 4) - (5x^2y^2 - 3x^2y + 9)$
11. $(x^2 + 4) - [(x^2 - 5) - (3x^2 + 1)]$
12. $(3x^2 - 2) - [(4 - x^2) - (2x^2 - 1)]$

----

13. Subtract $(2x^2 - 4x + 3)$ from the sum of
    $(5x^2 - 2x + 1)$ and $(-4x^2 + 6x - 8)$.
14. Subtract $(6y^2 + 3y - 4)$ from the sum of
    $(-2y^2 + y - 9)$ and $(8y^2 - 2y + 5)$.
15. Subtract $(10a^3 - 8a + 12)$ from the sum of
    $(11a^2 + 9a - 14)$ and $(-6a^3 + 17a)$.
16. Subtract $(15b^3 - 17b^2 + 6)$ from the sum of
    $(14b^2 - 8b - 11)$ and $(-9b^3 + 12b)$.
17. Subtract the sum of $(x^3y + 3xy^2 - 4)$ and $(2x^3y - xy^2 + 5)$
    from the sum of $(5 + xy^2 + x^3y)$ and $(-6 - 3xy^2 + 4x^3y)$.

18. Subtract the sum of $(2m^2n - 4mn^2 + 6)$ and $(-3m^2n + 5mn^2 - 4)$ from the sum of $(5 + m^2n - mn^2)$ and $(3 + 4m^2n + 2mn^2)$.

19. $(12.62x^2 - 8.905x - 16.08) - (7.625x^2 + 11.94x - 18.54)$

20. $(23.56x^2 + 17.42x - 5.846) - (14.76x^2 - 13.09x + 17.62)$

SET II

1. $(5z + 7) - (7z^2 - 8)$

2. $(y^2 - 3y + 12) - (8y^3 - 3y)$

3. $(-5m - 4) - (3m^2 + 10)$

4. $(-3z^2 - z + 9) - (9 - z + z^2)$

5. $(3y^2z - 4x^2y^2 + 5) - (5x^2y^2 - 4y^2z)$

6. Subtract the lower polynomial from the upper polynomial vertically.

$$5z^3 \qquad\quad - 7z + 8$$
$$\underline{8z^3 - 10z^2 + 7z}$$

7. Subtract $(-3m^2n^2 + 2mn - 7)$ from the sum of $(6m^2n^2 - 8mn + 9)$ and $(-10m^2n^2 + 18mn - 11)$.

8. Subtract $(-9u^2v + 8uv^2 - 16)$ from the sum of $(7u^2v - 5uv^2 + 14)$ and $(11u^2v + 17uv^2 - 13)$.

9. Given the polynomials $(2x^2 - 5x - 7)$, $(-4x^2 + 8x - 3)$, and $(6x^2 - 2x + 1)$. Subtract the sum of the first two from the sum of the last two.

10. Given the polynomials $(8y^2 + 10y - 9)$, $(13y^2 - 11y + 6)$, and $(-2y^2 - 16y + 4)$. Subtract the sum of the first two from the sum of the last two.

11. $(x^2 - 3xy + 4) - [x^2 - 3xy - (6 + x^2)]$

12. $(5.886x^2 - 3.009x + 7.966) - [4.961x^2 - 54.51x$
    $- (7.864 - 1.394x^2)]$

Multiplication of Polynomials

MULTIPLICATION OF A POLYNOMIAL BY A MONOMIAL. The basis of multiplication of polynomials is the distributive rule and its extensions. For practice, rework Exercises 304.

$$a(b + c + \cdots) = ab + ac + \cdots$$
$$(b + c + \cdots)a = ba + ca + \cdots$$

The Distributive Rule has already been used to multiply a polynomial by a monomial.

TO MULTIPLY A POLYNOMIAL BY A MONOMIAL

Multiply *each* term in the polynomial by the monomial, then add the results.

Example 1. Multiplying a polynomial by a monomial.

(a) $3x^2(2x + 7) = (3x^2)(2x) + (3x^2)(7) = 6x^3 + 21x^2$

(b) $-5x(3x^2 - 2x + 6) = (-5x)(3x^2) + (-5x)(-2x) + (-5x)(6)$

$\qquad\qquad\qquad\qquad = \quad -15x^3 \quad + \quad 10x^2 \quad - \quad 30x$

(c) $2a^2b(3b^3c - 4ab^2 - 6c^3)$

$\quad = (2a^2b)(3b^3c) + (2a^2b)(-4ab^2) + (2a^2b)(-6c^3)$

$\quad = \quad 6a^2b^4c \qquad - \qquad 8a^3b^3 \qquad - \quad 12a^2bc^3$

(d) $(2a^3bc^2 - 3ac + b^3)(-5ab^2)$

$\quad = (2a^3bc^2)(-5ab^2) + (-3ac)(-5ab^2) + (b^3)(-5ab^2)$

$\quad = \quad -10a^4b^3c^2 \qquad + \qquad 15a^2b^2c \qquad - \qquad 5ab^5$

EXERCISES 704A. Find the following products. (For more
    practice on problems of this type, refer to Exercises 304.)

SET I

1. $2x(3x^2 + 7)$ 2. $3y(4y^3 - 2)$

3. $(5a^2 - b^2)(2a)$ 4. $(7c^2 - d^2)(3c)$

5. $-3z^2(5z^3 - 4z^2 + 2z - 8)$

6. $-4m^3(2m^3 - 3m^2 + m - 5)$

7. $(-3x^2y + xy^2 - 4y^3)(-2xy)$

8. $(-4xy^2 - x^2y + 3x^3)(-3xy)$

----

9. $(-10x^8y - x^4y^5 + 5xy)(2x^2yz)$

10. $(8x^{10}y^4 - 3x^8y^3 - 2xy)(5xy^2z^2)$

11. $(8a^2b^3c - 3ab^2 - 4bc^3)(-3a^2b^3c^4)$

12. $(9x^2yz^3 - 2xy^3 - 3yz^4)(-2xy^2z^3)$

13. $5xy^2z(15x^{10}z^8 - 10y^5z^4 - 2xz^3)$

14. $3ab^2c(10a^{12}b - 5b^{10}c^4 - 3a^4c)$

15. $5.732x(2.508x^2 - 7.37)$

16. $82.05a^2(-52.6a + 16.9)$

SET II

1. $3m(4m^3 - 5)$ 2. $(4x^2 + 3)(-2x)$

3. $-4y^2(2y^3 - 3y^2 + 4)$

4. $(3xy^2 - 5x^2y + 4)(-2x^2y)$

5. $(a^3 - 3a^2b + 3ab^2 - b^3)(5a^2b)$

6. $(m^3 - 3m^2p + 3mp^2 - p^3)(-4mp^2)$

7. $2x^2y(3x^3 + 4y^2 - 6z^2)$

8. $3ab^2(4a^3 + 2b^2 - 5c^2)$

9. $5jk^3(-2j^5k + 4k^5 - jm)$

10. $6r^2t^4(6r^4t^5 - 2t^7 - 3r^2k)$

🖩 11. $3.806x(5.66x - 3.405)$

PRODUCT OF A POLYNOMIAL AND A POLYNOMIAL. Consider the product
$(x + 2)(x - 5)$. By the Distributive Rule, this is equal
to $(x + 2)(x) + (x + 2)(-5)$. This means that the first polynomial $(x + 2)$ must be multiplied by *each term* of the second
polynomial and the results added.

$(x + 2)(x - 5)$	Using the Distributive
$= (x + 2)(x) + (x + 2)(-5)$	Rule.
$= (x)(x) + (2)(x) + (x)(-5) + (2)(-5)$	Using the Distributive
$= x^2 + \underline{2x} - \underline{5x} - 10$	Rule again.
$= x^2 - 3x - 10$	Combining like terms.

When the two polynomials being multipled are simple,
the above procedure may be used (Examples 2 and 8).

Example 2.　　$(y - 4)(y + 3)$

$= (y - 4)(y) + (y - 4)(3)$	Distributive Rule.
$= y^2 - 4y + 3y - 12$	Distributive Rule.
$= y^2 - y - 12$	Combining like terms.

*When the polynomials being multiplied are more compli-
cated,* the multiplication can be conveniently arranged as
follows in Examples 3-7.

Example 3.　　$(2x^2 - 5x)(3x + 7)$

$$
\begin{array}{r}
2x^2 - 5x \\
3x + 7 \\
\hline
14x^2 - 35x \\
6x^3 - 15x^2 \\
\hline
6x^3 - x^2 - 35x
\end{array}
$$

$14x^2 - 35x = (2x^2 - 5x)7$

$6x^3 - 15x^2 \longleftarrow = (2x^2 - 5x)3x$

Notice that the second line is moved
one place to the left so we have like
terms in the same vertical line.

It helps to compare this procedure with the one used in
arithmetic for multiplying whole numbers.

$$
\begin{array}{r}
56 \\
23 \\
\hline
168 \\
112 \\
\hline
1288
\end{array}
$$

Product of 56 and 3.

Product of 56 and 2.

Notice that the second line in this
arithmetic example is also moved one
place to the left.

Example 4. $(3a^2b - 6ab^2)(2ab - 5)$

$$
\begin{array}{r}
3a^2b - 6ab^2 \\
\underline{2ab - 5} \\
- 15a^2b + 30ab^2
\end{array}
$$

$6a^3b^2 - 12a^2b^3$ ⟵———————————— Notice that the second line
———————————————————— is moved over far enough so
$6a^3b^2 - 12a^2b^3 - 15a^2b + 30ab^2$ only like terms are in the
same vertical line.

Example 5. $(7x^3 - 3x^2 + 2x - 4)(5x + 2)$

$$
\begin{array}{r}
7x^3 - 3x^2 + 2x - 4 \\
\underline{5x + 2}
\end{array}
$$

The higher degree poly-
nomial is placed above the
other, as in arithmetic.

$$
\begin{array}{r}
14x^3 - 6x^2 + 4x - 8 \\
\underline{35x^4 - 15x^3 + 10x^2 - 20x} \\
35x^4 - x^3 + 4x^2 - 16x - 8
\end{array}
$$

Example 6. $(2m - 4m^3 + 2m^4 - 5 - 3m^2)(2 + m^2 - 3m)$

$$
\begin{array}{r}
2m^4 - 4m^3 - 3m^2 + 2m - 5 \\
\underline{m^2 - 3m + 2}
\end{array}
\Big\}
$$

Multiplication
is simplified by
first arranging
the polynomials
in descending
powers of m.

$$
\begin{array}{r}
4m^4 - 8m^3 - 6m^2 + 4m - 10 \\
- 6m^5 + 12m^4 + 9m^3 - 6m^2 + 15m \\
\underline{2m^6 - 4m^5 - 3m^4 + 2m^3 - 5m^2} \\
2m^6 - 10m^5 + 13m^4 + 3m^3 - 17m^2 + 19m - 10
\end{array}
$$

Example 7. $(a^2 + 3a + 9)(a - 3)$

$$
\begin{array}{r}
a^2 + 3a + 9 \\
\underline{a - 3} \\
- 3a^2 - 9a - 27 \\
\underline{a^3 + 3a^2 + 9a} \\
a^3 \qquad\qquad - 27
\end{array}
$$

POWERS OF POLYNOMIALS. Since raising to a power is repeated
multiplication, we now have a method for finding powers of
polynomials.

Example 8. $(2x + 3)^2 = (2x + 3)(2x + 3)$

$(2x + 3)(2x + 3)$

$= (2x + 3)(2x) + (2x + 3)(3)$ Distributive Rule.

$= 4x^2 + 6x + 6x + 9$ Distributive Rule.

$= 4x^2 + 12x + 9$ Combining like terms.

Example 9.　　$(a - b)^3 = \underbrace{(a - b)(a - b)}\underbrace{(a - b)}$

First find　　then multiply
$(a - b)^2$,　　by $(a - b)$

$$
\begin{array}{r}
a - b \\
a - b \\
\hline
- ab + b^2 \\
a^2 - ab \\
\hline
a^2 - 2ab + b^2
\end{array}
$$

$$
\begin{array}{r}
a^2 - 2ab + b^2 \\
a - b \\
\hline
- a^2b + 2ab^2 - b^3 \\
a^3 - 2a^2b + ab^2 \\
\hline
a^3 - 3a^2b + 3ab^2 - b^3
\end{array}
$$

EXERCISES 704B.　Find the following products.

SET I

1.　$(x + 3)(x - 2)$　　　　　　2.　$(a - 4)(a + 3)$

3.　$(2y + 5)(y - 4)$　　　　　4.　$(3z - 2)(z + 5)$

5.　$(2x^2 - 5)(x + 2)$　　　　6.　$(3y^2 - 2)(y - 2)$

7.　$(x + y)(a - b)$　　　　　　8.　$(x - y)(a + b)$

9.　$(z + 4)(z^2 - 4z + 16)$　　10.　$(a - 5)(a^2 + 5a + 25)$

11.　$(4 - 3z^3 + z^2 - 5z)(4 - z)$

12.　$(3 + 2v^2 - v^3 + 4v)(2 - v)$

13.　$(x + 4)^2$　　　　　　　　14.　$(x - 5)^2$

15.　$(x + y)^2(x - y)^2$　　　　16.　$(x - 2)^2(x + 2)^2$

17.　$(x + 2)^3$　　　　　　　　18.　$(x + 3)^3$

19.　$[(x + y)(x^2 - xy + y^2)][(x - y)(x^2 + xy + y^2)]$

20.　$[(a - 1)(a^2 + a + 1)][(a + 1)(a^2 - a + 1)]$

SET II

1.　$(a + 2)(a - 5)$　　　　　　2.　$(x - 4)(x + 7)$

3.　$(3m^2 + 2n)(m - n)$　　　　4.　$(7m^2 - 3n)(m - n)$

5.　$(x + 3x^3 + 4)(5 - x)$　　　6.　$(7 + 2x^3 + 3x)(4 - x)$

7.　$(4 + a^4 + 3a^2 - 2a)(a + 3)$

8.　$(z^2 - 3z - 4)^2$　　　　　9.　$(2w - 3)^3$

10.　$[(y + 2)(y^2 - 2y + 4)][(y - 2)(y^2 + 2y + 4)]$

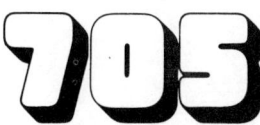

Division of Polynomials

DIVISION OF A POLYNOMIAL BY A MONOMIAL.　Consider the example:

$$\frac{4x^3 - 6x^2}{2x} = \frac{1}{2x} \cdot \frac{4x^3 - 6x^2}{1} = \frac{1}{2x}(4x^3 - 6x^2)$$

$$= \left(\frac{1}{2x}\right)(4x^3) + \left(\frac{1}{2x}\right)(-6x^2) \qquad \text{By the Distributive Rule.}$$

$$= \frac{4x^3}{2x} \qquad + \qquad \frac{-6x^2}{2x} \qquad \text{Dividing each term of the polynomial by the monomial.}$$

$$= 2x^2 \qquad - \qquad 3x$$

TO DIVIDE A POLYNOMIAL BY A MONOMIAL

Divide *each* term in the polynomial by the monomial, then add the results.

Example 1. Dividing a polynomial by a monomial.

(a) $\dfrac{6 + 8}{2} = \dfrac{6}{2} + \dfrac{8}{2} = 3 + 4 = 7$

(b) $\dfrac{4x + 2}{2} = \dfrac{4x}{2} + \dfrac{2}{2} = 2x + 1$

(c) $\dfrac{9x^3 - 6x^2 + 12x}{3x} = \dfrac{9x^3}{3x} + \dfrac{-6x^2}{3x} + \dfrac{12x}{3x} = 3x^2 - 2x + 4$

(d) $\dfrac{4x^2 - 8x + 16}{-4x} = \dfrac{4x^2}{-4x} + \dfrac{-8x}{-4x} + \dfrac{16}{-4x} = -x + 2 - \dfrac{4}{x}$

(e) $\dfrac{15x^2y + 20y^2z - 10xz^2}{5xyz} = \dfrac{15x^2y}{5xyz} + \dfrac{20y^2z}{5xyz} + \dfrac{-10xz^2}{5xyz}$

$$= \dfrac{3x}{z} + \dfrac{4y}{x} - \dfrac{2z}{y}$$

(f) $\dfrac{4a^2bc^2 - 6ab^2c^2 + 12bc}{-6abc} = \dfrac{4a^2bc^2}{-6abc} + \dfrac{-6ab^2c^2}{-6abc} + \dfrac{12bc}{-6abc}$

$$= -\dfrac{2}{3}ac + bc - \dfrac{2}{a}$$

EXERCISES 705A. Perform the indicated divisions.

SET I

1. $\dfrac{3x + 6}{3}$　　　　　　　2. $\dfrac{10x + 15}{5}$

3. $\dfrac{4 + 8x}{4}$　　　　　　　4. $\dfrac{5 - 10x}{5}$

5. $\dfrac{6x - 8y}{2}$　　　　　　　6. $\dfrac{5x - 10y}{5}$

7. $\dfrac{2x^2 + 3x}{x}$

8. $\dfrac{4y^2 - 3y}{y}$

9. $\dfrac{15x^3 - 5x^2}{5x^2}$

10. $\dfrac{12y^4 - 6y^2}{6y^2}$

11. $\dfrac{3a^2b - ab}{ab}$

12. $\dfrac{5mn^2 - mn}{mn}$

----

13. $\dfrac{5x^3 - 4x^2 + 10}{-5x^2}$

14. $\dfrac{7y^3 - 5y^2 + 14}{-7y^2}$

15. $\dfrac{-15x^2y^2z^2 - 30xyz}{-5xyz}$

16. $\dfrac{-24a^2b^2c^2 - 16abc}{-8abc}$

17. $\dfrac{13x^3y^2 - 26xy^3 + 39xy}{13x^2y^2}$

18. $\dfrac{21m^2n^3 - 35m^3n^2 - 14mn}{7m^2n^2}$

🖩 19. $\dfrac{42.63x^5 - 72.48x^3 + 18.45x}{9.07x}$

🖩 20. $\dfrac{9.843x^4 + 11.24x^2 - 8.255x}{5.09x}$

SET II

1. $\dfrac{4x - 6}{2}$

2. $\dfrac{5x - 15y}{5}$

3. $\dfrac{3x^2 - 6x}{3x}$

4. $\dfrac{6ab^2 - ab}{ab}$

5. $\dfrac{11a^2b^2 - 33ab}{-11ab}$

6. $\dfrac{26m^2n^2 - 13mn}{-13mn}$

7. $\dfrac{6m^2n^2 - 3mn}{6mn}$

8. $\dfrac{4u^2v^2 - 2uv}{4uv}$

9. $\dfrac{8a^3b^2c - 4a^2bc - 10ac}{4abc}$

🖩 10. $\dfrac{7.418x^3 - 3.155x^2 + 7.444x}{1.964x}$

DIVISION OF A POLYNOMIAL BY A POLYNOMIAL. The method used to
divide a polynomial by a polynomial is like long division of
whole numbers in arithmetic. It is based on the fact that
division is repeated subtraction.

Example 2. $966 \div 23$

First term in quotient $= \dfrac{\text{first term of dividend}}{\text{first term of divisor}} = \dfrac{9}{2} = 4^+.$

$$
\begin{array}{r}
4\ 2 \\
2\ 3\ \overline{\smash{)}\ 9\ 6\ 6} \\
\underline{9\ 2} \\
4\ 6 \\
\underline{4\ 6} \\
0
\end{array}
$$

Subtracting $4 \cdot 23 = 92.$

Subtracting $2 \cdot 23 = 46.$

Second term in quotient $= \dfrac{4}{2} = 2.$

Example 3. $(x^2 - 3x - 10) \div (x + 2)$

First term in quotient $= \dfrac{\text{first term of dividend}}{\text{first term of divisor}} = \dfrac{x^2}{x} = x.$

Second term in quotient $= \dfrac{-5x}{x} = -5.$

$$
\begin{array}{r}
x\ -\ 5 \\
x + 2\ \overline{\smash{)}\ x^2\ -\ 3x\ -\ 10} \\
\underline{x^2\ +\ 2x} \\
-\ 5x\ -\ 10 \\
\underline{-\ 5x\ -\ 10} \\
0
\end{array}
$$

Subtracting $x(x + 2) = x^2 + 2x.$

Subtracting $(-5)(x + 2) = -5x - 10.$

Example 4. $(6x^2 + x - 10) \div (2x + 3)$

$$
\begin{array}{r}
3x\ -\ 4 \\
2x + 3\ \overline{\smash{)}\ 6x^2\ +\ \ x\ -\ 10} \\
\underline{6x^2\ +\ 9x} \\
-\ 8x\ -\ 10 \\
\underline{-\ 8x\ -\ 12} \\
2
\end{array}
$$

R 2 *or* $3x - 4 + \dfrac{2}{2x + 3}$

Remainder

Example 5. $(27x - 19x^2 + 6x^3 + 10) \div (5 - 3x)$

   The terms of the dividend and divisor should be arranged in *descending powers* of the variable *before* beginning the division.

$$
\begin{array}{r}
-\ 2x^2\ +\ 3x\ -\ 4 \\
-3x + 5\ \overline{\smash{)}\ 6x^3\ -\ 19x^2\ +\ 27x\ +\ 10} \\
\underline{6x^3\ -\ 10x^2} \\
-\ 9x^2\ +\ 27x \\
\underline{-\ 9x^2\ +\ 15x} \\
12x\ +\ 10 \\
\underline{12x\ -\ 20} \\
30
\end{array}
$$

R 30 *or*

$-2x^2 + 3x - 4 + \dfrac{30}{-3x + 5}$

Example 6. $(17ab^2 + 12a^3 - 10b^3 - 11a^2b) \div (3a - 2b)$

Arrange the terms of the dividend and divisor in descending powers of a before beginning the division.

$$
\begin{array}{r}
4a^2 \;-\; ab \;+\; 5b^2 \\
3a - 2b\;\overline{\big)\;12a^3 - 11a^2b + 17ab^2 - 10b^3} \\
\underline{12a^3 - 8a^2b} \\
-3a^2b + 17ab^2 \\
\underline{-3a^2b + 2ab^2} \\
15ab^2 - 10b^3 \\
\underline{15ab^2 - 10b^3} \\
0
\end{array}
$$

Example 7. $(x^3 - 1) \div (x - 1)$

$$
\begin{array}{r}
x^2 + x + 1 \\
x - 1\;\overline{\big)\;x^3 + 0x^2 + 0x - 1} \\
\underline{x^3 - x^2} \\
x^2 - 0x \\
\underline{x^2 - x} \\
x - 1 \\
\underline{x - 1} \\
0
\end{array}
$$

It is helpful to leave space for missing powers by using zeros in this way.

Example 8. $(2x^4 + x^3 - 8x^2 - 5x - 2) \div (x^2 - x - 2)$

When the divisor is a polynomial of more than two terms, exactly the same procedure is used.

$$
\begin{array}{r}
2x^2 + 3x - 1 \quad \text{R} -4 \\
x^2 - x - 2\;\overline{\big)\;2x^4 + x^3 - 8x^2 - 5x - 2} \\
\underline{2x^4 - 2x^3 - 4x^2} \\
3x^3 - 4x^2 - 5x \\
\underline{3x^3 - 3x^2 - 6x} \\
-x^2 + x - 2 \\
\underline{-x^2 + x + 2} \\
-\,4
\end{array}
$$

EXERCISES 705B. Perform the indicated divisions.

SET I

1. $(x^2 + 5x + 6) \div (x + 2)$ 2. $(x^2 + 5x + 6) \div (x + 3)$

3. $(x^2 - x - 12) \div (x - 4)$ 4. $(x^2 - x - 12) \div (x + 3)$

5. $(6x^2 + 5x - 6) \div (3x - 2)$

6. $(20x^2 + 13x - 15) \div (5x - 3)$

7. $(15v^2 + 19v + 10) \div (5v - 7)$

8. $(15v^2 + 19v - 4) \div (3v + 8)$

----

9. $(8x - 4x^3 + 10) \div (2 - x)$

10. $(12x - 15 - x^3) \div (3 - x)$

11. $(6a^2 + 5ab + b^2) \div (2a + 3b)$

12. $(6a^2 + 5ab - b^2) \div (3a - 2b)$

13. $(a^3 - 8) \div (a - 2)$

14. $(c^3 - 27) \div (c - 3)$

15. $(x^4 + 2x^3 - x^2 - 2x + 4) \div (x^2 + x - 1)$

16. $(x^4 - 2x^3 + 3x^2 - 2x + 7) \div (x^2 - x + 1)$

SET II

1. $(x^2 + x - 12) \div (x - 3)$　　2. $(x^2 + x - 12) \div (x + 4)$

3. $(6m^2 - m - 30) \div (2m - 5)$

4. $(6m^2 - m + 30) \div (3m + 7)$

5. $(10x^2 - 3x^3 + 100) \div (5 - x)$

6. $(8a^2 - 2ab - b^2) \div (2a - b)$

7. $(6z^3 - 13z^2 - 4z + 15) \div (3z - 5)$

8. $(6x^2 + 5xy - 6y^2) \div (3x - 2y)$

9. $(15u^2 + 4uv - 4v^2) \div (5u - 2v)$

10. $(x^4 - x^3 - 5x^2 + 3x + 6) \div (x^2 - 2x - 1)$

Chapter Summary

Terms (Sec. 701). The + and - signs in an algebraic expression break it into smaller pieces called *terms*. Each + and - sign is part of the term that follows it. *Exception*: An expression within grouping symbols is considered as a single piece, even though it may contain + and - signs.

Polynomials (Sec. 701). A *polynomial in x* is an algebraic expression having only terms of the form ax^n, where a is any real number and n is a positive integer (or zero). A *polynomial in x and y* is an algebraic expression having only terms of the form $ax^n y^m$, where a is any real number and n, m are positive integers (or zero).

　　A *monomial* is a polynomial of one term.
　　A *binomial* is a polynomial of two unlike terms.
　　A *trinomial* is a polynomial of three unlike terms.

Degree of Polynomials (Sec. 701). The *degree of a term* in a polynomial is the sum of the exponents of its variables. The *degree of a polynomial* is the same as that of its highest-degree term (provided like terms have been combined).

To Add Polynomials, add *like* terms (Sec. 702).

To Subtract Polynomials, change the sign of each term in
the polynomial being subtracted, then add the resulting
like terms (Sec. 703).

To Multiply a Polynomial by a Monomial, multiply *each* term in
the polynomial by the monomial, then add the results
(Sec. 704).

To Multiply a Polynomial by a Polynomial, multiply the first
polynomial by *each term* of the second polynomial, then
add the results (Sec. 704).

To Divide a Polynomial by a Monomial, divide *each* term in
the polynomial by the monomial, then add the results
(Sec. 705).

To Divide a Polynomial by a Polynomial, see Sec. 705 for the method.

REVIEW EXERCISES 706

SET I

In Exercises 1 and 2, find (a) the number of terms, and
(b) the number of different variables in each expression.

1. $2xy^2z + 5$ 2. $10 - xyz^2$

In Exercises 3—6, if the expression is a polynomial, find
(a) the degree of the polynomial, and (b) the degree of the
first term.

3. $5xy^2 + 3x$ 4. $4u - 2u^2v^2$

5. $5u^2 + \dfrac{3}{u + v}$ 6. $4x^3 - \dfrac{7}{x + y}$

In Exercises 7 and 8, write each polynomial in descending
powers of the indicated letter.

7. $3x^4 - 6 + 7x^2 + x$ Powers of x.

8. $x^3 + 3x^2y + y^3 + 3xy^2$ Powers of y.

In Exercises 9-31, perform the indicated operations and
simplify the results.

9. $(5x^2y + 3xy^2 - 4y^3) + (2xy^2 + 4y^3 + 3x^2y)$

10. $(7ab^2 + 3a^3 - 5) + (6a^3 + 10 - 10ab^2)$

11. $(5x^2y + 3xy^2 - 4 + y^2) - (8 - 4x^2y + 2xy^2 - y^2)$

12. $(8a + 5a^2b - 3 + 6ab^2) - (5 + 4a - 3ab^2 + a^2b)$

13. $(7a^2 - 3ab + 5 - b^2) - (6 - 3a^2 + 2ab + 2b^2)$

14. $(-8 - 17y^2 + 12y^3 + 16y) + (24y - 18y^3 + 14 - 19y^2)$

15. $\dfrac{8x + 2}{2}$

16. $\dfrac{14 - 7y}{7}$

17. $5m^2n(3m - 4mn^2)$

18. $(5x^2y - 3y)(-4xy^2)$

19. $(x - 5)(x + 7)$

20. $(x - 2)(x^2 + 2x + 4)$

----

21. $(2a - 4)(3a + 5)$

22. $(3b + 2)(5b - 1)$

23. $(a + b + 4)^2$

24. $(3 + x + y)^2$

25. $\dfrac{3x^2y - 6xy^2}{3xy}$

26. $\dfrac{-15a^2b^3 + 4ab^2 - 10ab}{-5ab}$

27. $(6x^2 - 9x + 10) \div (2x - 3)$

28. $(10a^2 + 23ab - 5b^2) \div (5a - b)$

29. $(4 - 9y^2) \div (3y + 2)$

30. $(2a^4 - a^3 + a^2 + a - 3) \div (2a^2 - a + 3)$

31. $(2m^2 - 5) - [(7 - m^2) - (4m^2 - 3)]$

32. Subtract $(5x^2 - 9x + 6)$ from the sum of $(2x - 8 - 7x^2)$ and $(12 - 2x^2 + 11x)$.

▦ 33. $(26.8x^2 - 17.5x) - (83.2 - 65.9x) + (68.1 - 53.6x^2)$

▦ 34. $5.47x(2.93 - 7.08x) + \dfrac{6.42x^3 - 8.15x^2}{1.73x}$ (Round numbers in answer to one decimal place.)

SET II

In Exercises 1 and 2, find (a) the number of terms, and (b) the number of different variables in each expression.

1. $4xyz^2 + x + y$

2. $8 - 5xy^3$

In Exercises 3 and 4, if the expression is a polynomial, find (a) the degree of the polynomial, and (b) the degree of the first term.

3. $7x^2y - 2x$

4. $3x + \dfrac{4}{x}$

In Exercises 5 and 6, write each polynomial in descending powers of the indicated letter.

5. $5 - 3y^3 + y$ Powers of y.

6. $5 - a^2b^3 + a^3b^2 + ab$ Powers of a.

In Exercises 7-18, perform the indicated operations and simplify the results.

7. $(13x - 6x^3 + 14 - 15x^2) + (-17 - 23x^2 + 4x^3 + 11x)$

8. $(6x^3y - 4x^2y^2 + xy + 5) - (-4x^2y^2 + 3xy + 7 + 6x^3y)$

9. $5x^2y(3xy^3 + 4x - 2z)$

10. $3ab^2(5a^2b + 3a - 2c)$

11. $(z + 3)(z^2 - 3z + 9)$

12. $(z + 3)(z - 5)$

13. $\dfrac{5mn^2 - 10m^2n^3}{5mn^2}$

14. $\dfrac{-12x^2y^2 + 4xy^3 - 3xy^2}{-3xy^2}$

15. $(20a^2 - 7a + 5) \div (4a - 3)$

16. $(4x^2 - 1) \div (2x + 1)$

17. $(15x^2 - 29xy - 14y^2) \div (3x - 7y)$

18. $(3x^4 - 2x^3 + 2x^2 + 2x - 5) \div (3x^2 - 2x + .5)$

19. $45.2x(92.3 - 87.1x) - \dfrac{34.8x^2 - 67.4x^3}{15.6x}$ (Round numbers in answer to one decimal place.)

CUMULATIVE REVIEW EXERCISES: CHAPTERS 1-6

1. Evaluate the expression $-5^2 \cdot 4 - 15 \div 3\sqrt{25}$.

2. Solve the equation $5(x - 6) + 2(3 - 4x) = 6 - (2x + 8)$.

3. Evaluate the formula using the values of the letters given with the formula.

   $A = P(1 + i)^n$ $P = 500, i = 0.01, n = 2$

In Exercises 4-8, simplify each expression and write your answers using only positive exponents.

4. $\dfrac{10^2 \cdot 10^0}{10^{-3}}$

5. $\dfrac{x^{3c}}{x^c}$

6. $(2a^2b^{-1})^3$

7. $\left(\dfrac{6y^{-1}}{3y^3}\right)^2$

8. $\left(\dfrac{12x^3}{4x^5}\right)^{-2}$

9. When twice the sum of 11 and an unknown number is subtracted from 6 times the sum of 8 and twice the unknown number, the result is 6. What is the unknown number?

10. In a quality control experiment, 3 defective items were found out of a lot of 36 items chosen at random. What percent of the items were good? (Round answer to nearest percent.)

Chapter Seven Diagnostic Test

Name_____

_____

The purpose of this test is to see how well you understand the operations with polynomials. We recommend that you work this diagnostic test *before* your instructor tests you on this chapter. Allow yourself about thirty minutes to do this test.

Complete solutions for all the problems on this test, together with section references, are given in the Answer Section. We suggest that you study the sections referred to for the problems you do incorrectly.

---

1. In the polynomial $x^2 - 4xy^2 + 5$, find:

   (a) the degree of the first term   (1a)_____

   (b) the degree of the polynomial   (1b)_____

   (c) the numerical coefficient
      of the second term   (1c)_____

---

2. Add: $-5x^3 + 2x^2 \qquad\quad - 5$
$$7x^3 \qquad\quad + 5x - 8$$
$$3x^2 - 6x + 10$$

                             (2)_____

---

3. Add: $(3xy^2 - 4xy) + (12xy - 3xy^2) + (4xy + x^3)$

                             (3)_____

---

4. Subtract $(10 - z + 2z^2)$ from $(-4z^2 - 5z + 10)$

                             (4)_____

Find the following products.

5. $-2ab(5a^2 - 3ab^2 + 4b)$

(5)_____

6. $(2x - 5)(3x + 4)$

(6)_____

7. $(2y - 3)^2$

(7)_____

8. $(w - 3)(w^2 + 3w + 9)$

(8)_____

_____

Perform the following divisions.

9. $\dfrac{6x^3 - 4x^2 + 8x}{2x}$

(9)_____

10. $(10x^2 + x - 5) \div (2x - 1)$

(10)_____

_____

EIGHT
Factoring and
Special Products

Prime Factorization of Positive Integers

PRODUCTS AND POSITIVE FACTORS. We know that $2 \cdot 3 = 6$. There are two ways of looking at this fact. We can think of starting with with the $2 \cdot 3$ and *finding the product* 6. Or we can start with the 6 and ask ourselves what positive integers multiplied together will give us 6, then think of $2 \cdot 3$. When we do this we are *finding the factors of* 6, or more simply, *factoring* 6.

Finding the product of 2 and 3:

$$2 \cdot 3 = 6$$
product

Starting with $2 \cdot 3$ and *finding the product* 6.

Factoring 6:

$$6 = 2 \cdot 3$$
factors

Starting with 6 and *finding the factors* 2 and 3.

In this last case, 2 and 3 are called *factors* (or *divisors*) of 6. But since $6 = 1 \cdot 6$, 1 and 6 are also factors of 6. Therefore, 6 has four positive factors: 1, 2, 3, and 6.

Example 1. Products and factors of positive integers.

(a) Finding the product
$$\begin{cases} 2 \cdot 4 = 8. & \text{Therefore, 8 is the product of 2 and 4.} \\ 1 \cdot 8 = 8. & \text{Therefore, 8 is the product of 1 and 8.} \end{cases}$$

Factoring
$$\begin{cases} 8 = 2 \cdot 4, & \text{2 and 4 are factors of 8.} \\ 8 = 1 \cdot 8, & \text{1 and 8 are factors of 8.} \end{cases}$$

Therefore, the factors of 8 are 1, 2, 4, and 8.

(b) The factors (or divisors) of 12 are 1, 2, 3, 4, 6, and 12,

because $\begin{cases} 1 \cdot 12 = 12 \\ 2 \cdot 6 = 12 \\ 3 \cdot 4 = 12 \end{cases}$

(c) The factors (or divisors) of 36 are 1, 2, 3, 4, 6, 9, 12, 18, and 36,

because $\begin{cases} 1 \cdot 36 = 36 \\ 2 \cdot 18 = 36 \\ 3 \cdot 12 = 36 \\ 4 \cdot 9 = 36 \\ 6 \cdot 6 = 36 \end{cases}$

PRIME AND COMPOSITE NUMBERS. A *prime number* is a positive
integer greater than 1 that can be exactly divided only by
itself and 1. A prime number has *no* factors other than
itself and 1.

A *composite number* is a positive integer that can be
exactly divided by some integer other than itself and 1.
A composite number has factors other than itself and 1.

Example 2. Prime and composite numbers.

(a) 9 is a composite number because $3 \cdot 3 = 9$, so that
9 has a factor other than itself or 1.

(b) 17 is a prime number because 1 and 17 are the only
integral factors of 17.

(c) 45 is a composite number because it has factors
3, 5, 9, and 15 other than 1 and 45.

(d) 31 is a prime number because 1 and 31 are the only
integral factors of 31.

PRIME FACTORIZATION OF POSITIVE INTEGERS. The *prime factorization*
of a positive integer is the indicated product of all its
factors that are themselves prime numbers. For example,

$$18 = 2 \cdot 9 \brace 18 = 3 \cdot 6$$ These are *not prime* factorizations because
9 and 6 are not prime numbers

$$18 = 2 \cdot 9 = 2 \cdot 3 \cdot 3 = 2 \cdot 3^2 \brace 18 = 3 \cdot 6 = 3 \cdot 2 \cdot 3 = 2 \cdot 3^2$$ These *are prime* factorizations
because all the factors are
prime numbers

Note that the two ways we factored 18 led to the *same*
prime factorization $(2 \cdot 3^2)$. The prime factorization of
any positive integer (greater than 1) is unique.

METHOD FOR FINDING THE PRIME FACTORIZATION. A partial list of
prime numbers is: 2, 3, 5, 7, 11, 13, 17, 19, 23, 29, ...
The smallest prime is 2; the next smallest is 3; the next
smallest is 5; and so on.

Note: The only even prime number is 2. All other even numbers
are composite numbers with 2 among their factors. ■
The work of finding the prime factorization of a number can
be conveniently arranged as shown in Example 3.

Example 3. Finding the prime factorization of a positive integer.

(a) Find the prime factorization of 24.

To find the prime factorization of 24, first try to divide
24 by the smallest prime, 2. Two does divide 24 and gives
a quotient of 12. Next try to divide 12 by the smallest
prime, 2. Two does divide 12 and gives a quotient of 6.
Next try to divide 6 by the smallest prime, 2. Two does
divide 6 and gives a quotient of 3. This process ends
here because the final quotient 3 is itself a prime.

$$\begin{array}{r|r} 2 & 24 \\ \hline 2 & 12 \\ \hline 2 & 6 \\ \hline & 3 \end{array}$$

The prime factorization is the product of these numbers ⟶

Therefore, $24 = 2 \cdot 2 \cdot 2 \cdot 3 = 2^3 \cdot 3$, where $2^3 \cdot 3$ is the prime factorization of 24.

(b) Find the prime factorization of 30.

$$\begin{array}{r|r} 2 & 30 \\ \hline 3 & 15 \\ \hline & 5 \end{array}$$

Prime factorization of $30 = 2 \cdot 3 \cdot 5$.

(c) Find the prime factorization of 20.

$$\begin{array}{r|r} 2 & 20 \\ \hline 2 & 10 \\ \hline & 5 \end{array}$$

Prime factorization of $20 = 2 \cdot 2 \cdot 5$

$= 2^2 \cdot 5$.

(d) Find the prime factorization of 36.

$$\begin{array}{r|r} 2 & 36 \\ \hline 2 & 18 \\ \hline 3 & 9 \\ \hline & 3 \end{array}$$

Prime factorization of $36 = 2 \cdot 2 \cdot 3 \cdot 3$

$= 2^2 \cdot 3^2$.

(e) Find the prime factorization of 315.

$$\begin{array}{r|r} 3 & 315 \\ \hline 3 & 105 \\ \hline 5 & 35 \\ \hline & 7 \end{array}$$

Prime factorization of $315 = 3 \cdot 3 \cdot 5 \cdot 7$

$= 3^2 \cdot 5 \cdot 7$.

When trying to find a prime factor of a number, no prime whose square is greater than that number need be tried (Example 4).

Example 4. Find the prime factorization of 97.

⎡── primes in order of size
↓

2 does not divide 97.

3 does not divide 97.

5 does not divide 97.

7 does not divide 97.

11 is not possible because $11^2 = 121$, which is greater than 97.

Therefore 97 is prime.

TESTS FOR DIVISIBILITY. When finding the prime factorization, use the following rules to tell if a number is divisible by the primes 2, 3, or 5. We have listed only those rules that will be most useful.

Divisibility by 2. A number is divisible by 2 if its last digit is 0, 2, 4, 6, 8.

   Examples: 1②; 3 0⓪; 2 0 3④; 5 7⑧ are

            divisible by 2.

Divisibility by 3. A number is divisible by 3 if the sum of its digits is divisible by 3.

   Examples: 210 is divisible by 3 because 2 + 1 + 0 = 3
             is divisible by 3.

             5162 is not divisible by 3 because
             5 + 1 + 6 + 2 = 14, which is not divisible
             by 3.

Divisibility by 5. A number is divisible by 5 if its last digit is 0 or 5.

   Examples: 2 5⓪ and 7 5⑤ are both divisible by 5.

             1 1 2⑦ is not.

We have not included tests of divisibility by larger primes because the tests are usually longer than the actual trial division.

EXERCISES 801

SET I

In Exercises 1—16, find all the positive integral factors of each of the numbers.

1.	4	2.	9	3.	10	4.	14
5.	15	6.	16	7.	18	8.	20
9.	21	10.	22	11.	27	12.	28
13.	33	14.	34	15.	44	16.	45

In Exercises 17—32, state whether each of the numbers is prime or composite. To justify your answer, give the set of all positive integral factors for each number.

17.	5	18.	8	19.	13	20.	15
21.	12	22.	11	23.	21	24.	23
25.	55	26.	41	27.	49	28.	31
29.	51	30.	42	31.	111	32.	101

In Exercises 33—48, find the prime factorization of each number.

33.	14	34.	15	35.	21	36.	22

37. 26	38. 27	39. 29	40. 31
41. 32	42. 33	43. 34	44. 35
45. 84	46. 75	47. 144	48. 180

SET II

In Exercises 1—8, find all the positive integral factors of each number.

1. 6	2. 20	3. 24	4. 26
5. 30	6. 32	7. 38	8. 46

In Exercises 9—16, state whether each of the numbers is prime or composite. To justify your answer, give the set of all positive integral factors for each number.

9. 17	10. 14	11. 18	12. 19
13. 61	14. 63	15. 81	16. 73

In Exercises 17—24, find the prime factorization of each number.

17. 16	18. 18	19. 28	20. 30
21. 65	22. 78	23. 120	24. 112

Greatest Common Factor (GCF)

The greatest common factor (GCF) of two integers is the greatest integer that is a factor of both integers.

Example 1. Find the GCF of 12 and 16

$$12 \qquad 16$$
$$\underbrace{2 \cdot 2} \cdot 3 \qquad \underbrace{2 \cdot 2} \cdot 2 \cdot 2$$

The greatest factor common to both 12 and 16 is $2 \cdot 2 = 4$

Therefore the GCF of 12 and 16 is 4.

We can also find the GCF of terms in an algebraic expression.

Example 2. Find the GCF for the terms of $6y^3 - 21y$

$$6y^3 - 21y = 2 \cdot \underbrace{3 \cdot y} \cdot y \cdot y - 7 \cdot \underbrace{3 \cdot y}$$

Prime factorization of terms

GCF = $3y$

GCF AND POLYNOMIAL FACTOR

Example 3. Finding the GCF and polynomial factor.

(a) $2(x - 5) = 2x - 10$ By the Distributive Rule.

Therefore, 2 and $x - 5$ are factors of $2x - 10$

GCF ⟶↑   ↑⟶ polynomial factor

(b) $3y(2y^2 - 7) = 6y^3 - 21y$ By the Distributive Rule.

Therefore, $3y$ and $2y^2 - 7$ are factors of $6y^3 - 21y$.

GCF ⟶↑   ↑⟶ polynomial factor

(c) $5z(3z^2 + 2z - 1) = 15z^3 + 10z^2 - 5z$

Therefore, $5z$ and $3z^2 + 2z - 1$ are factors of
$$15z^3 + 10z^2 - 5z.$$

GCF ⟶↑   ↑⟶ polynomial factor

    In these examples we started with the factors and found the product. We will now consider how to find the factors when starting with the product. This process of finding the factors when the product is already known is called *factoring*.

Finding the Product   (Distributive Rule)

⟶

$2(x - 5) = 2x - 10$

⟵

Finding the Factors

TO FIND THE GREATEST COMMON FACTOR (GCF)

1. Write the *prime* factors of each term. Repeated factors should be expressed as powers.

2. Write each different prime factor that is common to all terms.

3. Raise each prime factor (selected in Step 2) to the *lowest* power it occurs anywhere in the expression.

4. The greatest common factor is the product of all powers found in Step 3.

TO FIND THE POLYNOMIAL FACTOR

5. Divide the expression being factored by the greatest common factor found in Step 4.

Check. Find the product of the greatest common factor and the polynomial factor by using the distributive rule.

Example 4. Factor the expression $6x + 4$.

Solution: $6x + 4 = \boxed{2} \cdot 3x + \boxed{2} \cdot 2$ Prime factorization of numerical coefficients 6 and 4.

— 2 is the GCF

$6x + 4 = 2(3x + 2)$

— This term is $\frac{4}{2} = 2$

— This term is $\frac{6x}{2} = 3x$

Therefore the factors of $6x + 4$ are 2 and $(3x + 2)$. So that

$6x + 4 = 2\ (3x + 2)$

GCF ⌐   ⌐ polynomial factor

Check. $2(3x + 2) = 2(3x) + 2(2) = 6x + 4$

Example 5. Factor $15x^3 + 9x$

Finding the GCF.

Step 1: $15x^3 + 9x = 3 \cdot 5x^3 + 3^2 x$
         Each term in prime factored form

Steps
2 & 3:
$\begin{cases} 3 \text{ is common to both terms} \\ 3^1 \text{ is the } \textit{lowest} \text{ power of 3 that occurs in any term} \\ \\ x \text{ is common to both terms} \\ x^1 \text{ is the } \textit{lowest} \text{ power of } x \text{ that occurs in any term} \end{cases}$

Step 4: GCF $= 3^1 x^1 = 3x.$

Finding the Polynomial Factor

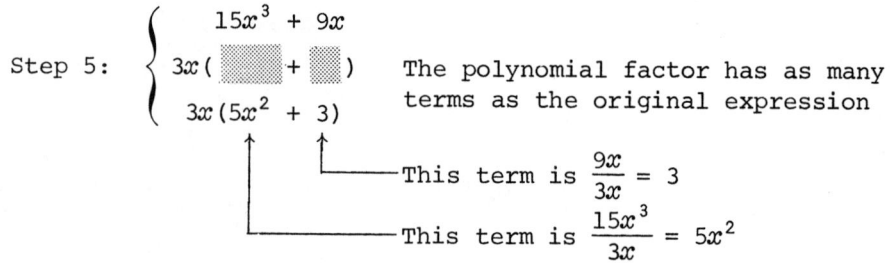

Step 5:
$\begin{cases} 15x^3 + 9x \\ 3x (\quad + \quad) \\ 3x(5x^2 + 3) \end{cases}$ The polynomial factor has as many terms as the original expression

This term is $\dfrac{9x}{3x} = 3$

This term is $\dfrac{15x^3}{3x} = 5x^2$

Therefore the factors of $15x^3 + 9x$ are $3x$ and $(5x^2 + 3)$. So
that $15x^3 + 9x = 3x(5x^2 + 3)$
                              GCF ⎯⎯| |⎯Polynomial factor

Check. $3x(5x^2 + 3) = (3x)(5x^2) + (3x)(3) = 15x^3 + 9x$

We summarize using the GCF in factoring in the following box.

FACTORING A POLYNOMIAL THAT HAS A GREATEST
COMMON FACTOR (GCF)

1. Find the GCF

2. Write the
    polynomial to
    be factored
    here

3. Write the term that ⎯⎯| |⎯Write the term
    the GCF must be   that the GCF
    multiplied by to   must be multi-
    give the 1st term   plied by to
    of the polynomial   give the 2nd
    being factored.   term of the
                                     polynomial
                                     being factored.

4. Check by multiplying the GCF and the polynomial
    factor by using the distributive rule.

Example 6.   Factor $2x^4 + 4x^3 - 8x^2$.

    Solution: $2x^4 + 4x^3 - 8x^2$

$$= 2^1 x^4 + 2^2 x^3 - 2^3 x^2$$ Numerical coefficients written in prime factored form.

2^1 is the *lowest* power of 2 that occurs in any term.
x^2 is the *lowest* power of x that occurs in any term.

GCF $= 2^1 x^2 = 2x^2$.

The polynomial factor $= \dfrac{2x^4}{2x^2} + \dfrac{4x^3}{2x^2} - \dfrac{8x^2}{2x^2} = x^2 + 2x - 4$.

Therefore, $2x^4 + 4x^3 - 8x^2 = $ $2x^2 \; (x^2 + 2x - 4)$.

                          GCF ⟶   ⟵ polynomial factor

Example 7.   Factor $6a^3 b^3 - 8a^2 b^2 + 10a^3 b$.

    Solution: $6a^3 b^3 - 8a^2 b^2 + 10a^3 b$

$$= 2 \cdot 3a^3 b^3 - 2^3 a^2 b^2 + 2 \cdot 5a^3 b^1$$

GCF $= 2^1 \cdot a^2 \cdot b^1 = 2a^2 b$.

The polynomial factor $= \dfrac{6a^3 b^3}{2a^2 b} - \dfrac{8a^2 b^2}{2a^2 b} + \dfrac{10a^3 b}{2a^2 b}$

$$= 3ab^2 - 4b + 5a.$$

Therefore, $6a^3 b^3 - 8a^2 b^2 + 10a^3 b = 2a^2 b(3ab^2 - 4b + 5a)$.

Example 8.   Factor $3xy - 6y^2 - 3y$.

    Solution: $3xy - 6y^2 - 3y$

$$= 1 \cdot 3xy - 2 \cdot 3y^2 - 1 \cdot 3y$$

GCF $= 3 \cdot y = 3y$.

The polynomial factor $= \dfrac{3xy}{3y} - \dfrac{6y^2}{3y} - \dfrac{3y}{3y}$

$$= x - 2y - 1.$$

Therefore, $3xy - 6y^2 - 3y = 3y(x - 2y - 1)$.

EXERCISES 802

SET I

In Exercises 1—4, find the products by inspection.

1. $2(x + 4)$ 2. $3(x + 3)$

3. $5(a - 2)$ 4. $7(b - 2)$

In Exercises 5—22, factor each expression.

5. $2x + 8$ 6. $3x + 9$ 7. $5a - 10$

8. $7b - 14$ 9. $6y - 3$ 10. $15z - 5$

11. $9x^2 + 3x$ 12. $8y^2 - 4y$ 13. $10a^3 - 25a^2$

14. $27b^2 - 18b^4$ 15. $21w^2 - 20z^2$ 16. $15x^3 - 16y^3$

17. $2a^2b + 4ab^2$ 18. $3mn^2 + 6m^2n^2$

19. $12c^3d^2 - 18c^2d^3$ 20. $15ab^3 - 45a^2b^4$

21. $4x^3 - 12x - 24x^2$ 22. $18y - 6y^2 - 30y^3$

In Exercises 23—26, find the products by inspection.

23. $3a(2a^2 - 5a + 4)$ 24. $5b(3b^2 + 2b - 6)$

25. $6x^2(3x^3 - 7x + 1)$ 26. $4y^2(5y^4 + 3y^2 - 1)$

In Exercises 27—38, factor each expression.

27. $24a^4 + 8a^2 - 40$ 28. $45b^3 - 15b^4 - 30$

29. $-14x^8y^9 + 42x^5y^4 - 28xy^3$

30. $-21u^7v^8 - 63uv^5 + 35u^2v^5$

31. $15h^2k - 8hk^2 + 9st$

32. $10uv^3 + 5u^2v - 4wz$

33. $-44a^{14}b^7 - 33a^{10}b^5 + 22a^{11}b^4$

34. $-26e^8f^6 + 13e^{10}f^8 - 39e^{12}f^5$

35. $18u^{10}v^5 + 24 - 14u^{10}v^6$

36. $30a^3b^4 - 15 + 45a^8b^7$

37. $18x^3y^4 - 12y^2z^3 - 48x^4y^3$

38. $32m^5n^7 - 24m^8p^9 - 40m^3n^6$

SET II

In Exercises 1—4, find the products by inspection.

1. $6(h + 3)$ 2. $4(2k - 1)$

3. $4x(3x^2 - 7x + 2)$ 4. $10z^2(2z^3 - 3z + 1)$

In Exercises 5—19, factor each expression.

5. $6h + 18$ 6. $8k - 4$

7. $10x + 25$ 8. $4y - 12y^2$

9. $14a^2 - 21a^3$ 10. $9w^2 + 16z^2$

11. $12x^2y + 9xy^2$ 12. $15a^2b^3 - 12ab^2$

13. $16z - 8z^3 - 12z^2$ 14. $12x^3 - 28x^2 + 8x$

15. $20z^5 - 30z^3 + 10z^2$ 16. $12h^2k - 18hk^2 - 35mp$

17. $30e^3f + 18 - 12ef^2$ 18. $10m^2n - 21mn^3 - 13mn$

19. $-16u^3v^2 + 24uv^3 - 40v^4w^2$

Factoring the Difference of Two Squares

Each type of factoring depends upon a particular *special product*. GCF factoring is based on products found by using the Distributive Rule. The kind of factoring discussed in this section depends upon the special product $(a + b)(a - b)$.

$$(a + b)(a - b) = (a + b)a + (a + b)(-b) \quad \text{Distributive Rule}$$
$$= a^2 + ba - ab - b^2$$
$$= a^2 - b^2$$

This useful product can be summarized as follows:

THE PRODUCT OF THE SUM AND DIFFERENCE OF TWO TERMS

Is equal to the square of the first term minus the square of the second term:

$$(a + b)(a - b) = a^2 - b^2$$

Example 1

(a) $(x + 2)(x - 2) = (x)^2 - (2)^2 = x^2 - 4$

Therefore, $x^2 - 4$ factors into $(x + 2)(x - 2)$.

(b) $(2x + 3y)(2x - 3y) = (2x)^2 - (3y)^2 = 4x^2 - 9y^2$

Therefore, $4x^2 - 9y^2$ factors into $(2x + 3y)(2x - 3y)$.

(c) $(10x^2 + 7y^3)(10x^2 - 7y^3) = (10x^2)^2 - (7y^3)^2 = 100x^4 - 49y^6$

Therefore, $100x^4 - 49y^6 = (10x^2 + 7y^3)(10x^2 - 7y^3)$.

(d) $(5a^3b^2 + 6cd^4)(5a^3b^2 - 6cd^4) = (5a^3b^2)^2 - (6cd^4)^2$
$$= 25a^6b^4 - 36c^2d^8$$

Therefore,
$$25a^6b^4 - 36c^2d^8 = (5a^3b^2 + 6cd^4)(5a^3b^2 - 6cd^4).$$

EXERCISES 803A. Find the following products by inspection.

SET I

1. $(x + 3)(x - 3)$ 2. $(z + 4)(z - 4)$

3. $(w - 6)(w + 6)$ 4. $(y - 5)(y + 5)$

5. $(5a + 4)(5a - 4)$ 6. $(6a - 5)(6a + 5)$

7. $(2u + 5v)(2u - 5v)$ 8. $(3m - 7n)(3m + 7n)$

9. $(4b - 9c)(4b + 9c)$ 10. $(7a - 8b)(7a + 8b)$

----

11. $(2x^2 - 9)(2x^2 + 9)$ 12. $(10y^2 - 3)(10y^2 + 3)$

13. $(1 + 8z^3)(1 - 8z^3)$ 14. $(9v^4 - 1)(9v^4 + 1)$

15. $(5xy + z)(5xy - z)$ 16. $(10ab + c)(10ab - c)$

17. $(7mn + 2rs)(7mn - 2rs)$ 18. $(8hk + 5ef)(8hk - 5ef)$

SET II

1. $(h - 7)(h + 7)$ 2. $(u + 9)(u - 9)$

3. $(3m + 5)(3m - 5)$ 4. $(2x - 3y)(2x + 3y)$

5. $(6a - 7b)(6a + 7b)$ 6. $(4h^2 - 5)(4h^2 + 5)$

7. $(1 + 9k^3)(1 - 9k^3)$ 8. $(4w + 3xy)(4w - 3xy)$

9. $(5uv - 8ef)(5uv + 8ef)$

PRINCIPAL SQUARE ROOT OF A TERM

When factoring the difference of two squares, we must find the principal square root of each term. The principal square root of a number is its positive square root.

In this section we assume that all letters represent positive numbers. This makes it possible to identify the principal (or positive) square root in each case.

Example 2. Find the principal square root of each term.

(a) $\sqrt{16} = 4$ because $(4)^2 = 16$

(b) $\sqrt{25x^2} = 5x$ because $(5x)^2 = 25x^2$

(c) $\sqrt{100a^4b^6} = 10a^2b^3$ because $(10a^2b^3)^2 = 100a^4b^6$

TO FIND THE PRINCIPAL SQUARE ROOT OF A TERM

1. The square root of the numerical coefficient is found by inspection.

2. The square root of each literal factor is found by dividing its exponent by 2.

Example 3. Use the information given in the preceding box to find the principal square root for each of the following terms.

(a) $\sqrt{36e^8f^4} = 6e^{8/2}f^{4/2} = 6e^4f^2$

(b) $\sqrt{9x^{10}y^6} = 3x^{10/2}y^{6/2} = 3x^5y^3$

Following is a short table of the squares of numbers that you can use in getting the square roots of numerical coefficients by inspection.

Number	Square of number		Number	Square of number
0	0		9	81
1	1		10	100
2	4		11	121
3	9		12	144
4	16		13	169
5	25		14	196
6	36		15	225
7	49		16	256
8	64			

EXERCISES 803B.   Find the principal square roots by inspection.

SET I

1. $\sqrt{64}$ 2. $\sqrt{81}$ 3. $\sqrt{4x^2}$

4. $\sqrt{9y^2}$ 5. $\sqrt{100a^8}$ 6. $\sqrt{49b^6}$

7. $\sqrt{m^4n^2}$ 8. $\sqrt{u^{10}v^6}$ 9. $\sqrt{x^{10}y^4}$

10. $\sqrt{x^{12}y^8}$

----

11. $\sqrt{25a^4b^2}$ 12. $\sqrt{100b^4c^2}$ 13. $\sqrt{36e^8f^2}$

14. $\sqrt{81h^{12}k^{14}}$ 15. $\sqrt{100a^{10}y^2}$ 16. $\sqrt{121a^{24}b^4}$

17. $\sqrt{9a^4b^2c^6}$ 18. $\sqrt{144x^8y^2z^6}$

SET II

1. $\sqrt{49}$ 2. $\sqrt{16z^2}$ 3. $\sqrt{64a^6}$

4. $\sqrt{x^2y^6}$ 5. $\sqrt{h^8k^4}$ 6. $\sqrt{81m^6n^8}$

7. $\sqrt{144u^{12}v^8}$ 8. $\sqrt{121c^{10}d^6}$ 9. $\sqrt{25r^6s^8t^4}$

FACTORING THE DIFFERENCE OF TWO SQUARES

Factoring $a^2 - b^2$ depends on the product $(a + b)(a - b) = a^2 - b^2$.

Finding Product

$$(a + b)(a - b) = a^2 - b^2$$

Finding Factors

Therefore, $a^2 - b^2$ *factors into* $(a + b)(a - b)$.

TO FACTOR THE DIFFERENCE OF TWO SQUARES $(a^2 - b^2)$

1. Make the following blank form for the factors:

$$(\quad + \quad)(\quad - \quad)$$

One factor has +, the other has -.

2. Put the principal square root of the *first* term here.

$$(\quad + \quad)(\quad - \quad)$$

Put the principal square root of the *second* term here.

The factors of the difference of two squares are:

$$a^2 - b^2 = (a + b)(a - b)$$

Example 4.   Factor $x^2 - 4$.

Solution: Step 1. $x^2 - 4 = (\quad + \quad)(\quad - \quad)$

$\sqrt{x^2}$

Step 2. $= (x + 2)(x - 2)$

$\sqrt{4}$

Example 5.   Factor $25y^4 - 9z^2$.

Solution: Step 1. $25y^4 - 9z^2 = (\quad + \quad)(\quad - \quad)$

$\sqrt{9z^2}$

Step 2. $= (5y^2 + 3z)(5y^2 - 3z)$

$\sqrt{25y^4}$

Example 6.   Factor $49a^6b^2 - 81c^4d^8$.

Solution: Step 1. $49a^6b^2 - 81c^4d^8 = (\quad + \quad)(\quad - \quad)$

$\sqrt{81c^4d^8}$

Step 2. $= (\ 7a^3b\ +\ 9c^2d^4\ )(\ 7a^3b\ -\ 9c^2d^4\ )$

$\sqrt{49a^6b^2}$

EXERCISES 803C.   Factor each of the following expressions.

SET I

1. $m^2 - n^2$ 2. $u^2 - v^2$ 3. $x^2 - 9$

4. $x^2 - 25$ 5. $a^2 - 1$ 6. $1 - b^2$

7. $4c^2 - 1$ 8. $16d^2 - 1$ 9. $16x^2 - 9y^2$

10. $25a^2 - 4b^2$ 11. $9h^2 - 10k^2$ 12. $16e^2 - 15f^2$

13. $49u^4 - 36v^4$ 14. $81m^6 - 100n^4$

15. $x^6 - a^4$ 16. $b^2 - y^6$

----

17. $a^2b^2 - c^2d^2$ 18. $m^2n^2 - r^2s^2$ 19. $49 - 25w^2z^2$

20. $36 - 25u^2v^2$ 21. $4h^4k^4 - 1$ 22. $9x^4y^4 - 1$

23. $81a^4b^6 - 16m^2n^8$ 24. $49c^8d^4 - 100e^6f^2$

SET II

1. $h^2 - k^2$ 2. $36 - m^2$ 3. $x^2 - 1$

4. $1 - 25a^2$ 5. $9w^2 - 49z^2$ 6. $16x^2 - 11y^2$

7. $49m^4 - 64n^2$ 8. $e^6 - 4$ 9. $r^2s^2 - t^2u^2$

10. $81 - 49u^2v^2$ 11. $9 - 16a^4b^4$

12. $144w^4x^6 - 121y^8z^2$

804

Factoring Trinomials

THE PRODUCT OF TWO BINOMIALS.   In the preceding section, when we
multiplied two binomials, we got a binomial.

$$(a + b)(a - b) = a^2 - b^2$$

In general, however, when two binomials are multiplied, we
get a trinomial.

$(x + 2)(x + 3) = x(x + 3) + 2(x + 3)$ Distributive rule

$= x^2 + 3x + 2x + 6$

$= x^2 + 5x + 6$

product of two   trinomial
binomials

The product $(x + 2)(x + 3)$ can also be found by the following method.

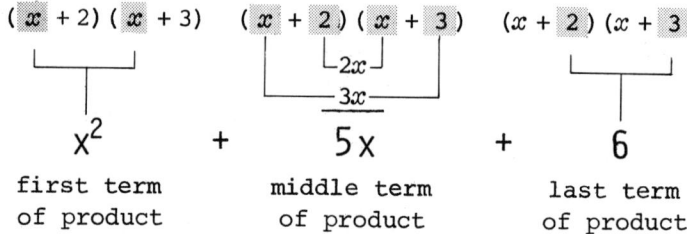

$$x^2 \qquad + \qquad 5x \qquad + \qquad 6$$

first term   middle term   last term
of product   of product   of product

We call the products that are added to give the middle term, the inner and outer products

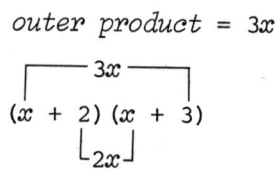

$$outer\ product = 3x$$

$$inner\ product = 2x$$

TO MULTIPLY TWO BINOMIALS

1. <u>The first term of the product</u> is the *product* of the first terms of the binomials.

2. <u>The middle term of the product</u> is the *sum* of the inner and outer products.

3. <u>The last term of the product</u> is the *product* of the last terms of the binomials.

<u>Example 1</u>. $(3x + 2)(4x - 5) = 12x^2 - 7x - 10$

$$12x^2 \qquad\qquad - 7x \qquad\qquad - 10$$

<u>Example 2</u>. $(5x - 4y)(6x + 7y) = 30x^2 + 11xy - 28y^2$

$$30x^2 \qquad\qquad + 11xy \qquad\qquad - 28y^2$$

The procedure can be shortened as in the next example.

Example 3.

$$(3x - 8y)(4x - 5y)$$

$$12x^2 \quad - \quad 47xy \quad + \quad 40y^2$$

Practice this procedure until you can find the three terms of the product without having to write anything down.

THE SQUARE OF A BINOMIAL. A binomial can be squared by multiplying it by itself.

Example 4.

(a) $(a + b)^2 = (a + b)(a + b) = a^2 + 2ab + b^2$

$$a^2 + 2ab + b^2$$

(b) $(a - b)^2 = (a - b)(a - b) = a^2 - 2ab + b^2$

$$a^2 - 2ab + b^2$$

The two special products shown in Example 4 occur so often that they are worth remembering.

TO SQUARE A BINOMIAL

1. The first term of the product is *the square of the first term* of the binomial.

2. The middle term of the product is *twice the product* of the two terms of the binomial.

3. The last term of the product is the *square of the last term* of the binomial.

$$(a + b)^2 = a^2 + 2ab + b^2$$
$$(a - b)^2 = a^2 - 2ab + b^2$$

Example 5. Finding the square of a binomial by using the formulas given in the preceding box.

(a) $(m + n)^2 = (m)^2 + 2(m)(n) + (n)^2 = m^2 + 2mn + n^2$

(b) $(a - 3)^2 = (a)^2 + 2(a)(-3) + (-3)^2 = a^2 - 6a + 9$

(c) $(2x - 5)^2 = (2x)^2 + 2(2x)(-5) + (-5)^2 = 4x^2 - 20x + 25$

Another way to find the formula for the square of a binomial is shown in Fig. 804.

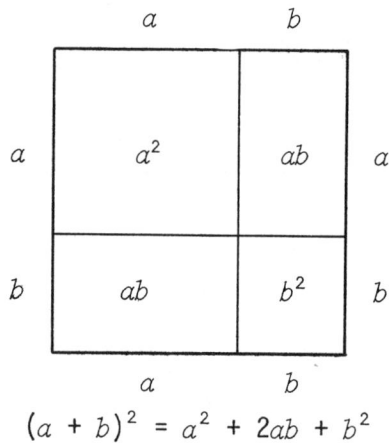

Each area written on the figure is found by multiplying its length by its width.

$$(a + b)^2 = a^2 + 2ab + b^2$$

Figure 804

A word of caution. Students remember that

$$(ab)^2 = a^2b^2$$ from using the rules for exponents.

⸺ Here a and b are *factors*.

They try to apply this rule of exponents to the expression $(a + b)^2$. But

$(a + b)^2$ cannot be found simply by squaring a and b.

⸺ Here a and b are *terms*.

Correct Method   Incorrect Method

$(a + b)^2 = (a + b)(a + b)$ $(a + b)^2 \neq a^2 + b^2$

$\quad\quad = a^2 + \boxed{2ab} + b^2$

⸺ This is the term that students sometimes leave out.

EXERCISES 804A. Find the following products by inspection.

SET I

1. $(x + 1)(x + 4)$ 2. $(x + 3)(x + 1)$

3. $(a + 5)(a + 2)$ 4. $(a + 7)(a + 1)$

5. $(m - 4)(m + 2)$ 6. $(n - 3)(n + 7)$

7. $(y + 8)(y - 9)$ 8. $(z - 3)(z + 10)$

9. $(x + 3)^2$ 10. $(x + 5)^2$

11. $(b - 4)^2$ 12. $(b - 6)^2$

----

13. $(2a + 5b)(a + b)$ 14. $(3c + 2d)(c + d)$

15. $(4x - y)(2x + 7y)$ 16. $(3x - 2y)(4x + 5y)$

17. $(7x - 10y)(7x - 10y)$ 18. $(4u - 9v)(4u - 9v)$

19. $(3x + 4)^2$ 20. $(2x + 5)^2$

21. $(4c - 3d)(4c + 3d)$ 22. $(5e + 2f)(5e - 2f)$

SET II

1. $(x + 2)(x + 3)$ 2. $(m + 3)(m + 5)$

3. $(h - 6)(h + 3)$ 4. $(w + 7)(w - 8)$

5. $(a + 4)^2$ 6. $(y - 5)^2$

7. $(3x + 4)(2x - 5)$ 8. $(2y + 5)(4y - 3)$

9. $(2x - 3y)(2x + 3y)$ 10. $(11x + 10y)(3x - 4y)$

11. $(10x - 7y)(8x + 9y)$ 12. $(5m - 2n)^2$

FACTORING A TRINOMIAL WHOSE LEADING COEFFICIENT IS 1

The leading coefficient of a polynomial is the numerical coefficient of its *highest*-degree term.

Example 6. Finding the leading coefficient.

(a) The leading coefficient of $x^2 - 2x + 8$ is 1.

(b) The leading coefficient of $2x^2 - 3x + 5$ is 2.

(c) The leading coefficient of $2y + 5y^2 - 7$ is 5. Because 5 is the coefficient of the highest degree term, $5y^2$.

(d) The leading coefficient of $28a^2 - 13ab - 6b^2$ is 28. Because this polynomial in two letters is arranged in descending powers of the letter a.

The easiest type of trinomial to factor is one having a leading coefficient of 1. Consider the product $(x + 2)(x + 5)$.

$$(x + 2)(x + 5) = x^2 + 7x + 10$$

Therefore, $x^2 + 7x + 10$ factors into $(x + 2)$ $(x + 5)$.

Notice

$$x^2 = x \cdot x$$

$$x^2 = \sqrt{x^2} \cdot \sqrt{x^2}$$

When the leading coefficient is 1, *the first term in each binomial factor is the square root of the first term of the trinomial.*

Example 7

$$(a) \quad x^2 + 6x + 8 = (x \qquad)(x \qquad)$$

$$(b) \quad z^2 - z - 6 = (z \qquad)(z \qquad)$$

$$(c) \quad m^2 + 7m + 12 = (m \qquad)(m \qquad)$$

We continue the discussion of the product $(x + 2)(x + 5)$.

$$(x + 2)(x + 5) = x^2 + 7x + 10$$

Therefore, $x^2 + 7x + 10$ factors into $(x + 2)(x + 5)$.

Notice $10 = 2 \cdot 5$

This shows that *the last terms of the binomial factors must be factors of the last term of the trinomial.*

$$(x + 2)(x + 5)$$
$$+2x$$
$$+5x$$
$$x^2 + 7x + 10$$

When we multiply the binomials, notice that *the sum of the inner and outer products must equal the middle term of the trinomial.*

We can consider this relationship in another way.

$$x^2 + 7x + 10 = (x + 2)(x + 5)$$
$$+7 = +2 + +5$$

When the leading coefficient is 1, *the sum of the last terms of the binomials equals the middle term of the tri-nomial.*

Example 8. *All terms of the trinomial positive.*

All pairs of factors of the last term of the trinomial.

$$(a) \quad x^2 + 7x + 6 = (x + 1)(x + 6)$$
$$+7 = +1 + +6$$

$$6 = 1 \cdot 6$$
$$= 2 \cdot 3$$

$$(b) \quad x^2 + 5x + 6 = (x + 2)(x + 3)$$
$$+5 = +2 + +3$$

$$6 = 1 \cdot 6$$
$$= 2 \cdot 3$$

$$(c) \quad z^2 + 8z + 12 = (z + 2)(z + 6)$$
$$+8 = +2 + +6$$

$$12 = 1 \cdot 12$$
$$= 2 \cdot 6$$
$$= 3 \cdot 4$$

(d) $y^2 + 7y + 12 = (y + 3)(y + 4)$ $12 = 1 \cdot 12$

$+7 = +3 + +4$ $= 2 \cdot 6$

$= 3 \cdot 4$

(e) $x^2 + 5xy + 6y^2 = (x + 3y)(x + 2y)$ $6 = 1 \cdot 6$

$+5 = +3 + 2$ $= 2 \cdot 3$

Example 9. *Middle term negative, first and last terms positive.*

(a) $x^2 - 7x + 6 = (x - 1)(x - 6)$ $6 = 1 \cdot 6$

$-7 = -1 + -6$ $= 2 \cdot 3$

(b) $x^2 - 5x + 6 = (x - 2)(x - 3)$ $6 = 1 \cdot 6$

$-5 = -2 + -3$ $= 2 \cdot 3$

(c) $m^2 - 6m + 8 = (m - 2)(m - 4)$ $8 = 1 \cdot 8$

$-6 = -2 + -4$ $= 2 \cdot 4$

(d) $k^2 - 16k + 15 = (k - 1)(k - 15)$ $15 = 1 \cdot 15$

$-16 = -1 + -15$ $= 3 \cdot 5$

(e) $a^2 - 9ab + 20b^2 = (a - 4b)(a - 5b)$ $20 = 1 \cdot 20$

$= 2 \cdot 10$

$-9 = -4 + -5$ $= 4 \cdot 5$

Example 10. *First and middle terms positive, last term negative.*

All pairs of factors of the last term of the trinomial.

(a) $x^2 + 5x - 6 = (x - 1)(x + 6)$ $6 = 1 \cdot 6$

$+5 = -1 + +6$ $= 2 \cdot 3$

(b) $x^2 + 1x - 6 = (x - 2)(x + 3)$ $6 = 1 \cdot 6$

$+1 = -2 + +3$ $= 2 \cdot 3$

(c) $x^2 + 8x - 20 = (x - 2)(x + 10)$ $20 = 1 \cdot 20$

$+8 = -2 + +10$ $= 2 \cdot 10$

$= 4 \cdot 5$

(d) $h^2 + 2hk - 15k^2 = (h - 3k)(h + 5k)$ $15 = 1 \cdot 15$

$+2 = -3 + +5$ $= 3 \cdot 5$

Example 11. *First term positive, middle and last terms negative.*

(a) $x^2 - 1x - 6 = (x + 2)(x - 3)$ $6 = 1 \cdot 6$

$-1 = +2 + -3$ $= 2 \cdot 3$

(b) $x^2 - 7x - 30 = (x + 3)(x - 10)$ $30 = 1 \cdot 30$

     $= 2 \cdot 15$

$-7 = +3 + -10$ $= 3 \cdot 10$

     $= 5 \cdot 6$

(c) $h^2 - 49h - 50 = (h + 1)(h - 50)$ $50 = 1 \cdot 50$

     $= 2 \cdot 25$

$-49 = +1 + -50$ $= 5 \cdot 10$

(d) $a^2 - 3ab - 10b^2 = (a + 2b)(a - 5b)$ $10 = 1 \cdot 10$

$-3 = +2 + -5$ $= 2 \cdot 5$

The method of factoring a trinomial having a leading coefficient of 1 is summarized as follows:

TO FACTOR A TRINOMIAL WHOSE LEADING COEFFICIENT IS 1

1. The first term of each binomial factor is the square root of the first term of the trinomial (Example 7).

2. List all pairs of factors of the numerical coefficient of the last term of the trinomial.

3. Select the pair of factors so that the sum of the last terms of the binomials equals the middle term of the trinomial (Examples 8—11).

When you become more familiar with factoring: If there are not many pairs of factors for the last coefficient, you can mentally check each pair. Only write down the pair that works.

EXERCISES 804B. Factor each of the following expressions.

SET I

1. $x^2 + 6x + 8$ 2. $x^2 + 9x + 8$

3. $x^2 + 5x + 4$ 4. $x^2 + 4x + 4$

5. $k^2 + 7k + 6$ 6. $k^2 + 5k + 6$

7. $u^2 + 7u + 10$ 8. $u^2 + 11u + 10$

9. $y^2 - 2y + 8$ 10. $y^2 - 7y + 8$

11. $b^2 - 9b + 14$ 12. $b^2 - 15b + 14$

13. $z^2 - 9z + 20$ 14. $z^2 - 12z + 20$

15. $x^2 - 11x + 18$ 16. $x^2 - 9x + 18$

17. $x^2 + 9x - 10$ 18. $y^2 - 3y - 10$

19. $z^2 - z - 6$ 20. $m^2 + 5m - 6$

----

21. $t^2 + 11t - 30$ 22. $m^2 - 17m - 30$

23. $u^4 + 12u^2 - 64$ 24. $v^4 - 30v^2 - 64$

25. $16 - 8v + v^2$ 26. $16 - 10v + v^2$

27. $b^2 - 11bd - 60d^2$ 28. $c^2 + 17cx - 60x^2$

29. $r^2 - 13rs - 48s^2$ 30. $s^2 + 22st - 48t^2$

SET II

1. $m^2 + 7m + 12$ 2. $h^2 + 11h + 18$

3. $a^2 + 10a + 16$ 4. $k^2 + 10k + 24$

5. $x^2 - 7x + 12$ 6. $n^2 - 9n + 18$

7. $z^2 - 8z + 16$ 8. $n^2 + 13n - 14$

9. $w^2 + 2w - 24$ 10. $r^2 - 9r - 20$

11. $n^2 - 10n - 24$ 12. $36 - 15y + y^2$

13. $v^4 - 18v^2 + 45$ 14. $p^2 - 9pt - 52t^2$

15. $w^2 - 8wz - 48z^2$

FACTORING A TRINOMIAL WHOSE LEADING COEFFICIENT IS GREATER THAN 1

Example 12.   Factor $2x^2 + 5x + 3$.

The signs in the trinomial are both +. Therefore, the signs in both binomial factors must be positive.

$$(\quad + \quad)(\quad + \quad)$$

Each first term of the binomial factors must contain an x in order to give the x^2 in the first term of the trinomial $2x^2$.

$$(x \quad + \quad)(x \quad + \quad)$$

The product of the first terms of the binomial factors must be $2x^2$. Therefore, we have

$$(1x \quad + \quad)(2x \quad + \quad)$$

The product of the last terms of the binomial factors must be 3.   Therefore, we could have

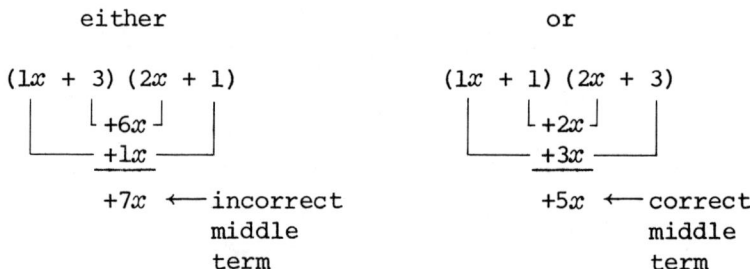

The sum of the inner and outer products must equal the middle term of the trinomial. We found the correct pair by trial.   Therefore, $2x^2 + 5x + 3$ factors into $(x + 1)(2x + 3)$.

<u>Example 13.</u>   Factor $5x^2 + 13x + 6$.

Make a blank outline and fill in all the obvious information.

$5x^2 + 13x + 6$

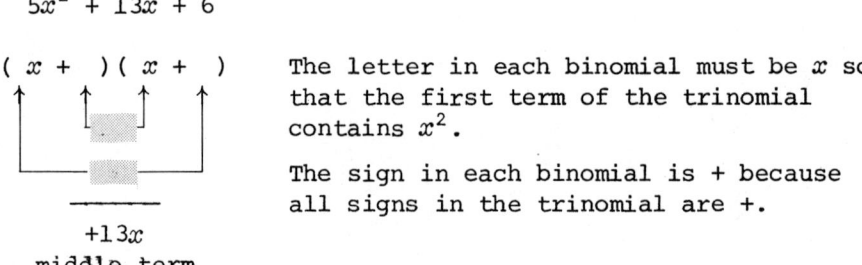

The letter in each binomial must be x so that the first term of the trinomial contains x^2.

The sign in each binomial is + because all signs in the trinomial are +.

Next, list all pairs of factors of the first coefficient and the last term of the trinomial.

Factors of the first coefficient.

$5 = 1 \cdot 5$

Factors of the last term.

$6 = 1 \cdot 6$
$ = 2 \cdot 3$

$5x^2 + 12x + 6$

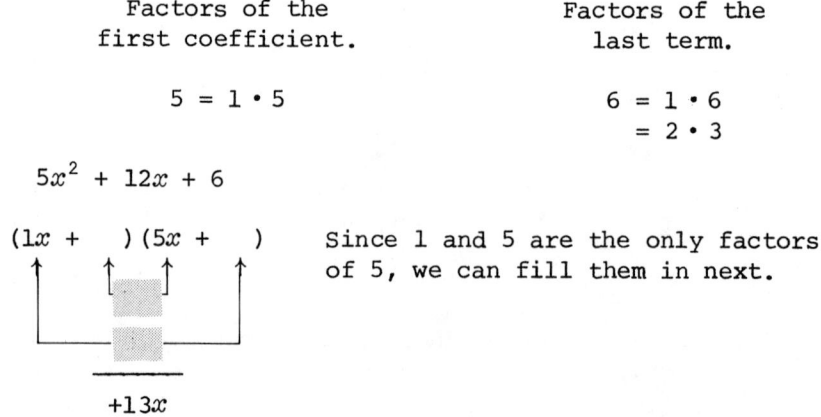

Since 1 and 5 are the only factors of 5, we can fill them in next.

Now we must select the correct pair of factors of the last term, 6, so that the sum of the inner and outer products is $13x$. We find the correct pair by trial.

$$(1x + 2)(5x + 3) \qquad\qquad 6 = 1 \cdot 6$$

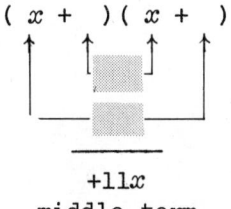

$$= \boxed{2 \cdot 3}$$

$+10x$

$+ 3x$

$+13x$

Therefore, $5x^2 + 13x + 6$ factors into $(x + 2)(5x + 3)$

Example 14. Factor $2x^2 + 11x + 15$.

Make a blank outline and fill in all obvious information.

$$(\ x + \ )(\ x + \ )$$

$+11x$
middle term

List all pairs of factors for the coefficients of the first and last terms of the trinomial; then select the pairs that give the correct middle term, $11x$.

$$2 = \boxed{1 \cdot 2} \qquad (1x + 3)(2x + 5) \qquad 15 = 1 \cdot 15$$

$$= \boxed{3 \cdot 5}$$

$+ 6x$

$+ 5x$

$+11x$

Therefore, $2x^2 + 11x + 15$ factors into $(x + 3)(2x + 5)$.

Example 15. Factor $4z^2 - 11z + 7$.

Make a blank outline.

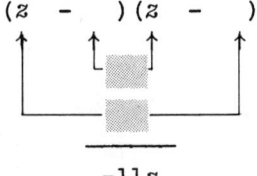

$$(z - \ )(z - \ )$$

$-11z$

Since the last term is + and the middle term is -, the signs in both binomials must be -.

Select the correct pairs of factors by trial.

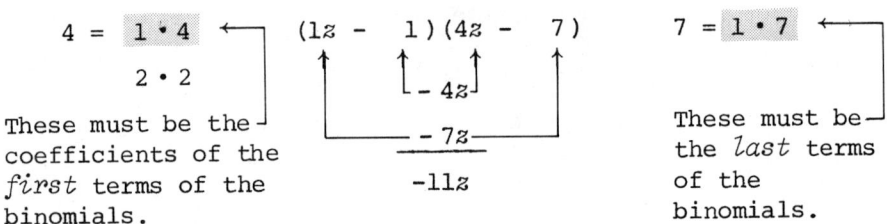

$4 = \boxed{1 \cdot 4}$
$ 2 \cdot 2$

$(1z - 1)(4z - 7)$

$7 = \boxed{1 \cdot 7}$

These must be the coefficients of the *first* terms of the binomials.

These must be the *last* terms of the binomials.

Therefore, $4z^2 - 11z + 7 = (z - 1)(4z - 7)$.

Example 16.   Factor $6x^2 - 19x + 15$.

Make a blank outline.

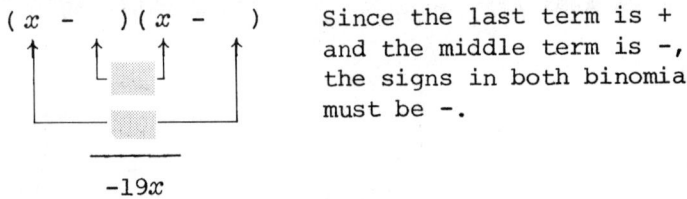

$(x -)(x -)$

$-19x$

Since the last term is + and the middle term is -, the signs in both binomials must be -.

Select correct pairs of factors by trial.

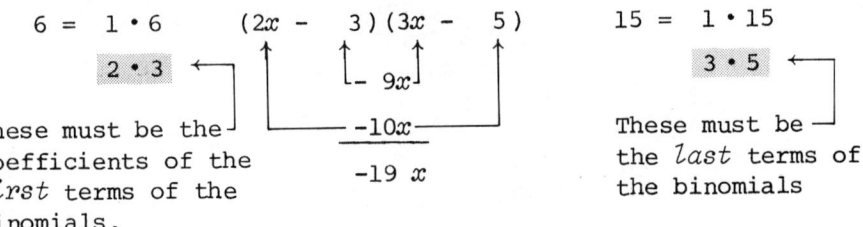

$6 = 1 \cdot 6$
$ \boxed{2 \cdot 3}$

$(2x - 3)(3x - 5)$

$15 = 1 \cdot 15$
$ \boxed{3 \cdot 5}$

These must be the coefficients of the *first* terms of the binomials.

These must be the *last* terms of the binomials

Therefore, $6x^2 - 19x + 15 = (2x - 3)(3x - 5)$.

Example 17.   Factor $3m^2 - 2m - 8$.

$(m -)(m +)$

$-2m$

Since the last term is -, the signs in the binomials must be unlike.

$3 = \boxed{1 \cdot 3}$

$(m - 2)(3m + 4)$

$8 = 1 \cdot 8$
$ \boxed{2 \cdot 4}$

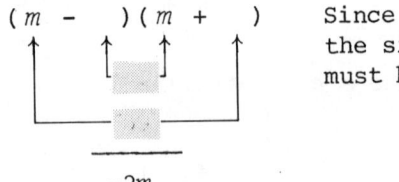

$-2m$

Therefore, $3m^2 - 2m - 8 = (m - 2)(3m + 4)$.

<u>Example 18.</u> Factor $4u^2 + 5u - 6$.

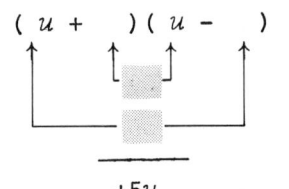

(u +   )(u -   )   Since the last term is $-$,
                              the signs in the binomials
                              must be unlike.

$+5u$

$4 = \boxed{1 \cdot 4}$ $(1u +   2)(4u -   3)$ $6 = 1 \cdot 6$

$\quad = 2 \cdot 2$ $\qquad\qquad +8u$ $\qquad\qquad = \boxed{2 \cdot 3}$

$\qquad\qquad -3u$

$+5u$

Therefore, $4u^2 + 5u - 6 = (u + 2)(4u - 3)$.

<u>Example 19.</u> Factor $12a^2 + 7ab - 10b^2$.

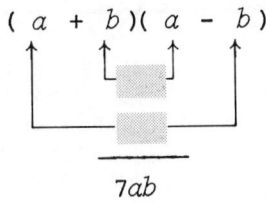

(a + b)(a - b)   Since the last term is $-$,
                              the signs in the binomials
                              must be unlike.

$7ab$

$12 = 1 \cdot 12$ $(4a +   5b)(3a -   2b)$ $10 = 1 \cdot 10$

$\quad = 2 \cdot 6$ $\qquad\qquad +15ab$ $\qquad\qquad = \boxed{2 \cdot 5}$

$\quad = \boxed{3 \cdot 4}$ $\qquad\qquad - 8ab$

$7ab$

Therefore, $12a^2 + 7ab - 10b^2 = (4a + 5b)(3a - 2b)$.

Sometimes the first term is a constant and the last term is
the one with the letter. When this is the case, we proceed
in almost the same way.

<u>Example 20</u>

(a) Factor $8 - 6x + x^2$.

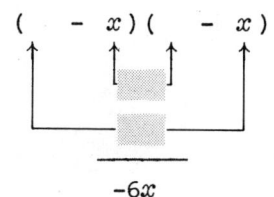

(- x)(- x)

$-6x$

$8 = 1 \cdot 8$ $(2 -   1x)(4 -   1x)$ $1 = \boxed{1 \cdot 1}$

$\quad = \boxed{2 \cdot 4}$ $\qquad\qquad -4x$

$\qquad\qquad -2x$

$-6x$

Therefore, $8 - 6x + x^2 = (2 - x)(4 - x)$.

(b) Factor $3 - 2x - 5x^2$.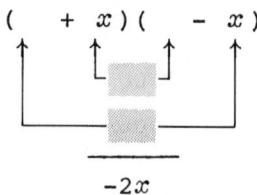

$$3 = \boxed{1 \cdot 3} \qquad (1 + 1x)(3 - 5x) \qquad 5 = \boxed{1 \cdot 5}$$

Therefore, $3 - 2x - 5x^2 = (1 + x)(3 - 5x)$.

The method of factoring a trinomial having a leading coefficient greater than 1 is summarized as follows:

TO FACTOR A TRINOMIAL WHOSE LEADING COEFFICIENT IS GREATER THAN 1

1. Make a blank outline and fill in all obvious information (Examples 13—17).

2. List all pairs of factors for the coefficients of the first term *and* the last term of the trinomial.

3. Select the correct pairs of factors so that the sum of the inner and outer products equals the middle term of the trinomial.

4. Check your factoring by multiplying the binomial factors to see if their product is the correct trinomial.

EXERCISES 804C. Factor each of the following expressions.

SET I

1. $3x^2 + 7x + 2$ 2. $3x^2 + 5x + 2$

3. $5x^2 + 7x + 2$ 4. $5x^2 + 11x + 2$

5. $4x^2 + 7x + 3$ 6. $4x^2 + 13x + 3$

7. $5x^2 + 20x + 4$ 8. $5x^2 + 11x + 4$

9. $5a^2 - 16a + 3$ 10. $5m^2 - 8m + 3$

11. $3b^2 - 22b + 7$ 12. $3u^2 - 10u + 7$

13. $5z^2 - 36z + 7$ 14. $5z^2 - 12z + 7$

15. $3n^2 + 14n - 5$ 16. $3n^2 - 2n - 5$

17. $5k^2 - 34k - 7$ 18. $5k^2 + 2k - 7$

----

19. $7x^2 + 23xy + 6y^2$ 20. $7a^2 + 43ab + 6b^2$

21. $7h^2 - 11hk + 4k^2$ 22. $7h^2 - 16hk + 4k^2$

23. $3t^2 + 9tz - 6z^2$ 24. $3w^2 - 11wx - 6x^2$

25. $6 - 17v + 5v^2$ 26. $6 - 11v + 5v^2$

27. $6e^4 - 7e^2 - 20$ 28. $10f^4 - 29f^2 - 21$

SET II

1. $3y^2 + 16y + 5$ 2. $2z^2 + 9z + 7$

3. $4a^2 + 9a + 5$ 4. $3b^2 + b + 4$

5. $7m^2 - 10m + 3$ 6. $5h^2 - 8h + 3$

7. $35k^2 - 12k + 1$ 8. $3e^2 - 20e - 7$

9. $7x^2 + 2x - 5$ 10. $3a^2 + 8ab + 5b^2$

11. $4m^2 - 16mn + 7n^2$ 12. $6s^2 - 17st - 5t^2$

13. $12 - 17u - 5u^2$ 14. $8v^4 - 14v^2 - 15$

Factoring by Grouping

Sometimes it is possible to factor an expression by rearranging its terms into smaller groups. Then finding the GCF *of each group*. The GCF does not have to be a monomial.

TO FACTOR AN EXPRESSION OF FOUR TERMS BY GROUPING

1. Arrange the four terms into two groups of two terms each. Each group of two terms must have a GCF.

2. Factor each group by using its GCF.

3. Factor the two-term expression resulting from Step 2 if the two terms have a GCF.

Example 1. Factor $ax + ay + bx + by$.

GCF = a ⌐   ⌐GCF = b

Solution: $ax + ay$ + $bx + by$

$= a(x + y) + b(x + y)$ ($x + y$) is the GCF of these 2 terms

$= (x + y)(a + b)$

this term is $\dfrac{b(x + y)}{(x + y)} = b$

this term is $\dfrac{a(x + y)}{(x + y)} = a$

Therefore, $ax + ay + bx + by = (x + y)(a + b)$.

DIFFERENT WAYS OF GROUPING. It is sometimes possible to group terms differently and still be able to factor the expression. The same factors are obtained no matter what grouping is used.

Example 2. Factor $ab - b + a - 1$

One Grouping

$ab - b$ + $a - 1$

$= b(a - 1) + 1(a - 1)$

$= (a - 1)(b + 1)$

A Different Grouping

$ab + a$ - $b - 1$

$= a(b + 1) - 1(b + 1)$

$= (b + 1)(a - 1)$

————— Same factors —————

Therefore $ab - b + a - 1 = (a - 1)(b + 1) = (b + 1)(a - 1)$.

Example 3. Factor $2x^2 - 6xy + 3x - 9y$.

Solution:

GCF = $2x$ ———   ┌─── GCF = 3

$2x^2 - 6xy$ + $3x - 9y$

$= 2x(x - 3y) + 3(x - 3y)$ $(x - 3y)$

                                is the GCF

$= (x - 3y)(2x + 3)$

Therefore, $2x^2 - 6xy + 3x - 9y = (x - 3y)(2x + 3)$.

A Word of Caution. An expression is *not* factored until it has been written as a single term that is a product of factors. To illustrate this, consider Example 1 again.

$ax + ay + bx + by$

$=$ | $a(x + y)$ | + | $b(x + y)$ | This expression is *not* in factored form because it has *two* terms

   First   Second
   term   term

$=$ | $(x + y)(a + b)$ | Factored form of $ax + ay + bx + by$

     Single term

Expressions with more than four terms may also be factored by grouping. However, in this book we only consider factoring expressions of four terms by grouping.

<u>EXERCISES 805.</u> Factor each of the following expressions.

SET I

1. $am + bm + an + bn$ 2. $cu + cv + du + dv$

3. $mx - nx - my + ny$ 4. $ah - ak - bh + bk$

5. $xy + x - y - 1$ 6. $ad - d + a - 1$

7. $3a^2 - 6ab + 2a - 4b$ 8. $2h^2 - 6hk + 5h - 15k$

9. $6e^2 - 2ef - 9e + 3f$ 10. $8m^2 - 4mn - 6m + 3n$

----

11. $h^2 - k^2 + 2h + 2k$ 12. $x^2 - y^2 + 4x + 4y$

13. $x^3 + 3x^2 - 4x + 12$ 14. $a^3 + 5a^2 - 2a + 10$

15. $a^3 - 2a^2 - 4a + 8$ 16. $x^3 - 3x^2 - 9x + 27$

17. $10xy - 15y + 8x - 12$ 18. $35 - 42m - 18mn + 15n$

19. $y(a + b) - x(a + b) + y(c - d) - x(c - d)$

20. $a(2y + 5) - b(2y + 5) + a(x - z) - b(x - z)$

SET II

1. $ax + ay + bx + by$ 2. $hw - kw - hz + kz$

3. $ef + f - e + 1$ 4. $2s^2 - 6st + 5s - 15t$

5. $6a^2 - 3ab - 14a + 7b$ 6. $x^2 - y^2 + 3x - 3y$

7. $z^3 + 5z^2 + 3z + 15$ 8. $u^3 - 3u^2 - 9u + 27$

9. $m(x - 2) - n(x - 2) + m(2 + x) - n(2 + x)$

10. $e(5a - 3) - f(5a - 3) + e(8 - 5a) - f(8 - 5a)$

[Optional] The Master Product Method for Factoring Trinomials

The Master Product method for factoring trinomials makes use of factoring by grouping.

TO FACTOR A TRINOMIAL BY THE MASTER PRODUCT METHOD

Arrange the trinomial in descending powers.

$$ax^2 + bx + c$$

1. Find the Master Product (MP) by multiplying the first and last coefficients of the trinomial being factored (MP = $a \cdot c$)

2. Write the pairs of factors of the Master Product (MP).

3. Choose the pair of factors whose sum is the coefficient of the middle term (b).

4. Rewrite the given trinomial, replacing the middle term by the sum of two terms whose coefficients are the pair of factors found in Step 3.

5. Factor the Step 4 expression by grouping.

Check your factoring by multiplying the binomial factors to see if their product is the given trinomial.

Example 1.   Factor $5x + 2x^2 + 3$ by the Master Product method.
              $2x^2 + 5x + 3$ Arranged in descending powers

Master Product = $(+2)(+3) = +6$

$1 \cdot 6$ Factors of 6   The middle
$2 \cdot 3$ $(+2) + (+3) = 5$ coefficient

$\underbrace{2x^2 + 2x}_{} + \underbrace{3x + 3}_{}$ ⎫ Factoring
$2x(x + 1) + 3(x + 1)$ ⎬ by

Therefore $2x^2 + 5x + 3 = (x + 1)(2x + 3)$ ⎭ grouping

Example 2.   Factor $3m^2 - 2m - 8$ by the Master Product method.

Master Product = $(3)(-8) = -24$

$1 \cdot 24$ ⎫
$2 \cdot 12$ ⎪ Factors of 24
$3 \cdot 8$ ⎬
$4 \cdot 6$ ⎭ $(+4) + (-6) = -2$ Middle coefficient

$\underbrace{3m^2 + 4m}_{} - \underbrace{6m - 8}_{}$ ⎫ Factoring
$m(3m + 4) - 2(3m + 4)$ ⎬ by grouping

Therefore $3m^2 - 2m - 8 = (3m + 4)(m - 2)$ ⎭

Example 3. Factor $12a^2 + 7ab - 10b^2$ by the Master Product method.

Master product = $(12)(-10) = -120$

$$
\left.
\begin{array}{l}
1 \cdot 120 \\
2 \cdot 60 \\
3 \cdot 40 \\
4 \cdot 30 \\
5 \cdot 24 \\
6 \cdot 20 \\
8 \cdot 15
\end{array}
\right\} \text{Factors of 120}
$$

$(-8) + (+15) = +7$ The middle coefficient

$$
\left.
\begin{array}{l}
\underbrace{12a^2 - 8ab} + \underbrace{15ab - 10b^2} \\
4a(3a - 2b) + 5b(3a - 2b)
\end{array}
\right\}
\begin{array}{l}
\text{Factoring} \\
\text{by grouping}
\end{array}
$$

Therefore $12a^2 + 7ab - 10b^2 = (3a - 2b)(4a + 5b)$

Note. The Master Product method of factoring trinomials can also be used with trinomials whose leading coefficient is 1. However, we think the method presented in Section 6-4B is shorter and simpler for trinomials of that type. ■

EXERCISES 806. Factor each expression in Exercises 804C by the Master Product method.

Factoring Completely

Consider the following example:

Example 1. Factor $27x^2 - 12y^2$.

Solution:

$$27x^2 - 12y^2 \qquad \text{3 is the GCF}$$

This factor can be factored again.

$$= 3(9x^2 - 4y^2) \qquad (9x^2 - 4y^2) = (3x + 2y)(3x - 2y)$$
$$= 3(3x + 2y)(3x - 2y)$$

We say that $27x^2 - 12y^2 = 3(3x + 2y)(3x - 2y)$ has been *completely factored*. We will consider an expression to be completely factored if no more factoring can be done (by *any* method we have discussed).

Example 1 illustrates the importance of the statement:

Always remove a common monomial factor first when possible.

```
┌─────────────────────────────────────────────────────────────┐
│                                                               │
│  TO FACTOR AN EXPRESSION COMPLETELY                           │
│                                                               │
│  1.  Look for a greatest common factor first.                 │
│                                                               │
│  2.  Look for a difference of two squares.                    │
│                                                               │
│  3.  Look for a factorable trinomial.                         │
│                                                               │
│  4.  Look for four terms that can be factored by              │
│      grouping.                                                │
│                                                               │
│  5.  Check to see if any factor already obtained              │
│      can be factored again.                                   │
│                                                               │
└─────────────────────────────────────────────────────────────┘
```

<u>Example 2.</u> Factor $3x^3 - 27x + 5x^2 - 45$.

Solution:

$$3x^3 - 27x + 5x^2 - 45 \qquad \text{Factor by grouping}$$

$$3x(x^2 - 9) + 5(x^2 - 9)$$

This factor can be factored again.

$$(x^2 - 9)(3x + 5) \qquad x^2 - 9 = (x + 3)(x - 3)$$

$$(x + 3)(x - 3)(3x + 5)$$

<u>Example 3.</u> Factor $5x^2 + 10x - 40$.

Solution: $\quad 5x^2 + 10x - 40 \qquad$ 5 is the GCF

This factor can be factored again.

$$= 5(x^2 + 2x - 8) \qquad (x^2 + 2x - 8) = (x - 2)(x + 4)$$
$$= 5(x - 2)(x + 4)$$

<u>Example 4.</u> Factor $a^4 - b^4$.

Solution: $\quad a^4 - b^4$

This factor can be factored again.

$$= (a^2 + b^2)(a^2 - b^2) \qquad (a^2 - b^2) = (a + b)(a - b)$$
$$= (a^2 + b^2)(a + b)(a - b)$$

<u>EXERCISES 807.</u> Factor each expression *completely*.

SET I

1. $2x^2 - 8y^2$ 2. $3x^2 - 27y^2$

3. $5a^4 - 20b^2$ 4. $6m^2 - 54n^4$

5. $x^4 - y^4$ 6. $a^4 - 16$

7. $4v^2 + 14v - 8$ 8. $6v^2 - 27v - 15$

9. $8z^2 - 12z - 8$ 10. $18z^2 - 21z - 9$

11. $12x^2 + 10x - 8$ 12. $45x^2 - 6x - 24$
13. $ab^2 - 2ab + a$ 14. $au^2 - 2au + a$

----

15. $x^4 - 81$ 16. $16y^8 - z^4$
17. $a^5b^2 - 4a^3b^4$ 18. $x^2y^4 - 100x^4y^2$
19. $2ax^2 - 8a^3y^2$ 20. $3b^2x^4 - 12b^2y^2$
21. $2u^3 + 2u^2v - 12uv^2$ 22. $3m^3 - 3m^2n - 36mn^2$
23. $8h^3 - 20h^2k + 12hk^2$ 24. $15h^2k - 35hk^2 + 10k^3$
25. $12 + 4x - 3x^2 - x^3$ 26. $45 - 9z - 5z^2 + z^3$
27. $6my - 4nz + 15mz - 5zn$ 28. $10xy + 5mn - 6xy - nm$
29. $6ac - 6bd + 6bc - 6ad$ 30. $10cy - 6cz + 5dy - 3dz$

SET II

1. $3a^2 - 75b^2$ 2. $4h^4 - 36b^2$
3. $m^4 - 1$ 4. $10x^2 + 25x - 15$
5. $10y^2 + 14y - 12$ 6. $30w^2 + 27w - 21$
7. $h^2k - 4hk + 4k$ 8. $81c^4 - 16$
9. $4m^3n^3 - mn^5$ 10. $2t^2r^4 - 18t^4$
11. $5wz^2 + 5w^2z - 10w^3$ 12. $12x^2y - 42xy^2 + 36y^3$
13. $45 + 9b - 5b^2 - b^3$ 14. $8wx + 5xy - 4yz - 11yz$
15. $6ef + 3gf - 12eh - 9gh$

Solving Equations by Factoring

Factoring has many applications. In this section we use
factoring to solve equations.

A *polynomial equation* is a polynomial set equal to zero. The
degree of the equation is the degree of the polynomial.

Polynomial equations with a first-degree term as the highest-degree term are called *first-degree equations*. Polynomial
equations with a second-degree term as the highest-degree term
are called *second-degree* or *quadratic equations*.

Example 1. Polynomial equations.

(a) $5x - 3 = 0$ First-degree equation in one variable

(b) $2x^2 - 4x + 7 = 0$ Second-degree equation in one variable
                (also called *quadratic* equation)

We know from arithmetic that if the product of two numbers
is zero, one or both of the numbers must be zero.

> *If* the product of two factors is zero, *then* one or both of the factors must be zero.
>
> If $a \cdot b = 0$, then $\begin{cases} a = 0 \\ \text{or } b = 0 \\ \text{or both } a \text{ and } b = 0 \end{cases}$

We make use of this fact in solving some polynomial equations.

<u>Example 2</u>. Solve $(x - 1)(x - 2) = 0$.

 <u>Solution</u>: Since $(x - 1)(x - 2) = 0$,
 then $(x - 1) = 0$ or $(x - 2) = 0$.

$$
\begin{array}{ll}
\text{If} \quad x - 1 = 0 & \qquad \text{If} \quad x - 2 = 0 \\
\qquad\quad \underline{+1 \quad +1} & \qquad\qquad\quad \underline{+2 \quad +2} \\
\text{then } x \qquad = 1 & \qquad \text{then } x \qquad = 2
\end{array}
$$

Therefore, 1 and 2 are solutions for the equation $(x - 1)(x - 2) = 0$.

<u>Check for $x = 1$</u>

$(x - 1)(x - 2) = 0$

$(1 - 1)(1 - 2) \overset{?}{=} 0$

$(0)(-1) \overset{?}{=} 0$

$0 = 0$

<u>Check for $x = 2$</u>

$(x - 1)(x - 2) = 0$

$(2 - 1)(2 - 2) \overset{?}{=} 0$

$(1)(0) \overset{?}{=} 0$

$0 = 0$

<u>Example 3</u>. Solve $(2x - 1)(3x + 5) = 0$.

The solution can be conveniently arranged as follows:

<u>Solution</u>: $(2x - 1)(3x + 5) = 0$

$$
\begin{array}{ll}
2x - 1 = 0 & \quad 3x + 5 = 0 \\
\quad \underline{+1 \quad +1} & \qquad \underline{-5 \quad -5} \\
2x \qquad = 1 & \quad 3x \qquad = -5
\end{array}
$$

Dividing both sides by 2.
$$x = \frac{1}{2}$$

$$x = -\frac{5}{3}$$
Dividing both sides by 3.

The method for solving an equation by factoring can be summarized as follows:

```
TO SOLVE AN EQUATION BY FACTORING

1.  Write all nonzero terms on one side of the
    equation by adding the same expression to
    both sides.  Only zero must remain on the
    other side.  Then arrange the polynomial in
    descending powers.

2.  Factor the polynomial.

3.  Set each factor equal to zero, and solve
    for the unknown letter.

4.  Check apparent solutions in the original
    equation.
```

Example 4. Solve $3(x + 2)(x - 1) = 0$.

Solution: $3(x + 2)(x - 1) = 0$

$$
3 \neq 0 \quad \Big| \quad
\begin{array}{rr}
x + 2 = & 0 \\
- 2 & - 2 \\
\hline
x = & -2
\end{array}
\quad \Big| \quad
\begin{array}{rr}
x - 1 = & 0 \\
+ 1 & + 1 \\
\hline
x = & 1
\end{array}
$$

We leave checking these solutions to the student.

The same method can be used *when a product of more than two factors is equal to zero.*

Example 5. Solve $2x(x - 3)(x + 4) = 0$.

Solution: $2x(x - 3)(x + 4) = 0$

$$
\begin{array}{l}
2x = 0 \\
\dfrac{2x}{2} = \dfrac{0}{2} \\
x = 0
\end{array}
\quad \Big| \quad
\begin{array}{rr}
x - 3 = & 0 \\
+ 3 & + 3 \\
\hline
x = & 3
\end{array}
\quad \Big| \quad
\begin{array}{rr}
x + 4 = & 0 \\
- 4 & - 4 \\
\hline
x = & -4
\end{array}
$$

Example 6. Solve $4x^2 - 16x = 0$.

Solution: The polynomial must be factored first.

$$4x^2 - 16x = 0$$

$$4x(x - 4) = 0$$

$$
\begin{array}{l}
4x = 0 \\
\dfrac{4x}{4} = \dfrac{0}{4} \\
x = 0
\end{array}
\quad \Big| \quad
\begin{array}{rr}
x - 4 = & 0 \\
+ 4 & + 4 \\
\hline
x = & 4
\end{array}
$$

<u>Example 7</u>.   Solve $x^2 - x - 6 = 0$.

<u>Solution</u>: $x^2 - x - 6 = 0$

$$(x + 2)(x - 3) = 0$$

$$
\begin{array}{c|c}
x + 2 = \quad 0 & x - 3 = \quad 0 \\
\underline{\; -2 \quad\;\; -2\;} & \underline{\; +3 \quad\;\; +3\;} \\
x \quad = -2 & x \quad = \quad 3
\end{array}
$$

<u>Example 8</u>.   Solve $3x^2 = 4 - x$.

First, add $(-4 + x)$ to both sides so that only zero remains on the right side. Then arrange the terms in descending powers.

Second, factor the polynomial.

<u>Solution</u>: $3x^2 = 4 - x$

$$3x^2 + x - 4 = 0$$

$$(x - 1)(3x + 4) = 0$$

$$
\begin{array}{c|c}
x - 1 = \quad 0 & 3x + 4 = \quad 0 \\
\underline{\; +1 \quad\;\; +1\;} & \underline{\quad\; -4 \quad\;\; -4\;} \\
x \quad = \quad 1 & 3x \quad = \quad -4 \\
 & x = -\dfrac{4}{3}
\end{array}
$$

<u>Example 9</u>.   Solve $\dfrac{x - 1}{x - 3} = \dfrac{12}{x + 1}$.

<u>Solution</u>: $\dfrac{x - 1}{x - 3} = \dfrac{12}{x + 1}$ This is a proportion.

$(x - 1)(x + 1) = 12(x - 3)$ Product of means = product of extremes.

$x^2 - 1 = 12x - 36$ This is a *quadratic* equation because its highest-degree term is second-degree.

$x^2 - 12x + 35 = 0$

$(x - 7)(x - 5) = 0$

$$
\begin{array}{c|c}
x - 7 = \quad 0 & x - 5 = \quad 0 \\
\underline{\; +7 \quad\;\; +7\;} & \underline{\; +5 \quad\;\; +5\;} \\
x \quad = \quad 7 & x \quad = \quad 5
\end{array}
$$

A word of caution. The product must equal *zero*, or no conclusions can be drawn about the factors.
    Suppose $(x - 1)(x - 3) = 8$.

⌐No conclusion can be drawn because the product $\neq 0$

Some common mistakes: Students sometimes think that

One common mistake

if $(x - 1)(x - 3) = \boxed{8}$

then $\begin{array}{rr} x - 1 = & 8 \\ +1 & +1 \\ \hline x = & 9 \end{array}$ | $\begin{array}{rr} x - 3 = & 8 \\ +3 & +3 \\ \hline x = & 11 \end{array}$

This "solution" is incorrect because

if $(x - 1) = 8$

and $(x - 3) = 8$

then $(x - 1)(x - 3)$

$= 8 \cdot 8 = 64 \neq 8.$

Another common mistake

if $(x - 1)(x - 3) = \boxed{8}$

$\begin{array}{rr} x - 1 = & 0 \\ +1 & +1 \\ \hline x = & 1 \end{array}$ | $\begin{array}{rr} x - 3 = & 0 \\ +3 & +3 \\ \hline x = & 3 \end{array}$

This "solution" is incorrect because

if $(x - 1) = 0$

and $(x - 3) = 0$

then $(x - 1)(x - 3)$

$= 0 \cdot 0 = 0 \neq 8.$

The correct solution is:
$$(x - 1)(x - 3) = 8$$
$$x^2 - 4x + 3 = 8$$
$$x^2 - 4x - 5 = 0$$
$$(x - 5)(x + 1) = 0$$

$\begin{array}{rr} x - 5 = & 0 \\ +5 & +5 \\ \hline x = & 5 \end{array}$ | $\begin{array}{rr} x + 1 = & 0 \\ -1 & -1 \\ \hline x = & -1 \end{array}$

∎

EXERCISES 808. Solve each of the following equations.

SET I

1. $(x - 5)(x + 4) = 0$ 2. $(x + 7)(x - 2) = 0$

3. $3x(x - 4) = 0$ 4. $5x(x + 6) = 0$

5. $(x + 10)(2x - 3) = 0$ 6. $(x - 8)(3x + 2) = 0$

7. $x^2 + 9x + 8 = 0$ 8. $x^2 + 6x + 8 = 0$

9. $x^2 - x - 12 = 0$ 10. $x^2 + x - 12 = 0$

11. $x^2 - 18 = 9x$ 12. $x^2 - 20 = 12x$

13. $6x^2 - 10x = 0$ 14. $6y^2 - 21y = 0$

15. $24w = 4w^2$ 16. $20m = 5m^2$

17. $5a^2 = 16a - 3$ 18. $3z^2 = 22z - 7$

19. $3u^2 = 2u + 5$ 20. $5k^2 = 34k + 7$

----

21. $(x - 2)(x - 3) = 2$ 22. $(x - 3)(x - 5) = 3$

23. $x(x - 4) = 12$ 24. $x(x - 2) = 15$

25. $4x(2x - 1)(3x + 7) = 0$ 26. $5x(4x - 3)(7x - 6) = 0$

27. $2x^3 + x^2 = 3x$ 28. $4x^3 = 10x - 18x^2$

29. $2a^3 - 10a^2 = 0$ 30. $4b^3 - 24b^2 = 0$

31. $\dfrac{x + 2}{x + 1} = \dfrac{10}{x + 5}$ 32. $\dfrac{x - 1}{x + 4} = \dfrac{3}{x}$

SET II

1. $(x + 3)(x - 5) = 0$ 2. $2y(y - 7) = 0$

3. $(z - 6)(3z + 2) = 0$ 4. $a^2 + 8a + 12 = 0$

5. $m^2 + 3m - 18 = 0$ 6. $w^2 - 24 = 5w$

7. $5h^2 - 20h = 0$ 8. $12t = 6t^2$

9. $3n^2 = 7n + 6$ 10. $13x + 3 = -4x^2$

11. $(y - 3)(y - 6) = -2$ 12. $u(u - 9) = -14$

13. $2x(3x - 2)(5x + 9) = 0$ 14. $21x^2 + 60x = 18x^3$

15. $3a^3 + 18a = 0$ 16. $\dfrac{2x + 5}{3x} = \dfrac{x}{2x - 5}$

 **Word Problems Solved by Factoring**

NUMBER PROBLEMS

Example 1. The difference of two numbers is 3. Their product is
10. What are the two numbers?

Let $\quad x =$ Smaller number $\Big\}$ Since their difference is 3
then $\;x + 3 =$ Larger number

Their product is 10 $\qquad$ Remember, *it is incorrect* to
$\qquad x(x + 3) \quad\;= 10$ $\qquad$ say that $x = 10$ or $x + 3 =$
$\qquad\qquad x^2 + 3x = 10$ $\qquad$ 10
$\quad x^2 + 3x - 10 = \;\;0$
$\quad (x - 2)(x + 5) = \;\;0$

$x - 2 = 0 \;\big|\; x + 5 = \;\;0$
$\qquad x = 2 \;\big|\qquad x = -5$ $\qquad$ Smaller number
$x + 3 = 5 \;\big|\; x + 3 = -2$ $\qquad$ Larger number

Therefore the numbers 2 and 5 are a solution and the numbers -5
and -2 are another solution.

CONSECUTIVE INTEGER PROBLEMS

Integers that follow one another (without interruption) are
called *consecutive integers*. Consecutive integers can be represented in the following way. If x is any integer, then:

$x, \;\; x + 1$ $\qquad$ represent two consecutive integers
$x - 1, x, x + 1$ $\quad$ represent three consecutive integers
$x - 2, x, x + 2$ $\quad$ represent three consecutive even integers
$\qquad\qquad\qquad$ or represent three consecutive odd integers.

<u>Example 2</u>. Find two consecutive integers whose product is 19 more than their sum.

Let x and $x + 1$ represent the two consecutive integers.
Then $x(x + 1)$ represents their product
and $x + (x + 1)$ represents their sum.

Their product	is	19	more than	their sum
$x(x + 1)$	$=$	19	$+$	$x + (x + 1)$

$$x^2 + x = 19 + 2x + 1$$
$$x^2 - x - 20 = 0$$
$$(x + 4)(x - 5) = 0$$

$x + 4 = 0$	$x - 5 = 0$
$x = -4$	$x = 5$
$x + 1 = -3$	$x + 1 = 6$

There are two answers: the numbers are -4 and -3, or the numbers are 5 and 6.

<u>GEOMETRY PROBLEMS</u>

Following is a collection of facts about geometric figures needed to work the geometry problems in this section.

Rectangle

Area = LW
Perimeter = $2L + 2W$

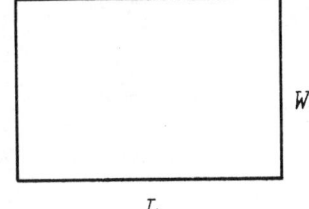

Square

Area = s^2
Perimeter = $4s$

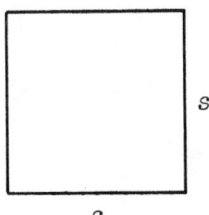

Triangle

Area = $\frac{1}{2}bh$
Perimeter = $a + b + c$

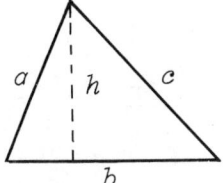

In solving word problems about geometric figures, make a drawing of the figure and write the given information on it.

Example 3.   The length of a rectangle is 2 inches more than
     its width.   The area of the rectangle is 8 square inches.
     What are its dimensions?

Solution: There are two unknown numbers, the width and the
length.

Let w = width $\Big)$ because the length is
then $w + 2$ = length $\Big)$ 2 more than the width.

$$\boxed{\begin{array}{c} \text{Area = 8} \end{array}} \; w$$

$w + 2$

Area of rectangle = $\boxed{\text{width}} \times \boxed{\text{length}}$

$$w(w + 2)$$

The $\boxed{\text{area of the rectangle}}$ is $\boxed{8}$ square inches.

$$w(w + 2) \qquad = 8$$

$$w(w + 2) = 8$$
$$w^2 + 2w = 8$$
$$w^2 + 2w - 8 = 0$$
$$(w - 2)(w + 4) = 0$$

	$w - 2 = 0$	$w + 4 = 0$
width	$w = 2$	$w = -4$
length	$w + 2 = 4$	

-4 is not considered a
solution for this problem
because in this book the
dimensions of the sides of
geometric figures are
always taken as positive
numbers.

Therefore, the rectangle has a width of 2 inches and a length
of 4 inches.

Example 4.   One square has a side 3 feet longer than the side
     of a second square.   If the area of the larger square is
     4 times as great as the area of the smaller square, find the
     length of the side of each square.

Solution:

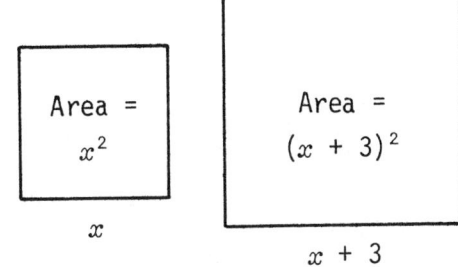

<table>
<tr><td>Area = x^2</td><td>Area = $(x + 3)^2$</td></tr>
</table>

x $x + 3$

| The area of the larger square | is | 4 times as great as | the area of the smaller square. |

$$(x + 3)^2 \quad = \quad 4 \quad \cdot \quad x^2$$

$$(x + 3)^2 = 4x^2$$
$$x^2 + 6x + 9 = 4x^2$$
$$-3x^2 + 6x + 9 = 0$$
$$3x^2 - 6x - 9 = 0$$
$$3(x^2 - 2x - 3) = 0$$
$$3(x - 3)(x + 1) = 0$$

$$x - 3 = 0 \quad | \quad x + 1 = 0$$

small square $x = 3$ $x = -1 \longleftarrow$ -1 cannot be a

large square $x + 3 = 6$ solution of the word statement.

Therefore, the smaller square has a side of 3 feet and the larger square a side of 6 feet.

Example 5. The width of a rectangle is 5 centimeters less than its length. Its area is 10 more (numerically*) than its perimeter. What are the dimensions of the rectangle?

Solution:

*We say that the area is "numerically" ten more than the perimeter because the area is measured in *square centimeters* whereas the perimeter is measured in *centimeters*.

Let L = length;
then, $L - 5$ = width.

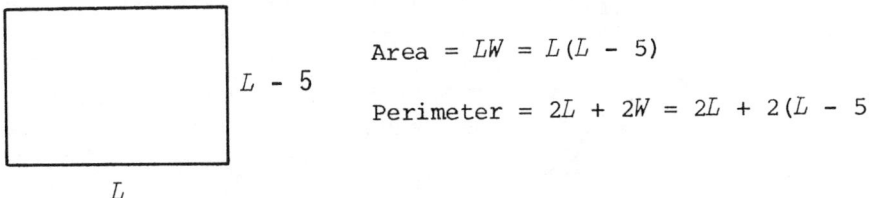

Area = $LW = L(L - 5)$

Perimeter = $2L + 2W = 2L + 2(L - 5)$

L

Its area is 10 more than its perimeter.

$$L(L-5) = 10 + 2L + 2(L-5)$$

$$L(L - 5) = 10 + 2L + 2(L - 5)$$
$$L^2 - 5L = 10 + 2L + 2L - 10$$
$$L^2 - 9L = 0$$
$$L(L - 9) = 0$$

$L = 0$	$L - 9 = 0$	
not a solution	$L = 9$	length
	$L - 5 = 4$	width

Therefore, the rectangle has a length of 9 centimeters and a width of 4 centimeters.

EXERCISES 809. Solve the following word problems.

SET I

1. The difference of two numbers is 5. Their product is 14. Find the numbers.
2. The difference of two numbers is 6. Their product is 27. Find the numbers.
3. The sum of two numbers is 12. Their product is 35. Find the numbers.
4. The sum of two numbers is -4. Their product is -12. Find the numbers.
5. Find two consecutive integers whose product is 11 more than their sum.
6. Find two consecutive integers whose product is 5 more than their sum.
7. Find three consecutive integers such that the product of the first two plus the product of the last two is 8.
8. Find three consecutive integers such that the product of the first two plus the product of the first and third is 14.
9. Find three consecutive even integers such that twice the product of the first two is 16 more than the product of the last two.
10. Find three consecutive odd integers such that twice the product of the last two is 91 more than the product of the first two.
11. The length of a rectangle is 5 feet more than its width. Its area is 84 square feet. What are its dimensions?
12. The width of a rectangle is 3 feet less than its length. Its area is 28 square feet. What are its dimensions?
13. One square has a side 3 centimeters shorter than the side of a second square. The area of the larger square is 4 times as great as the area of the smaller square. Find the length of the side of each square.

14. One square has a side four feet longer than the side of a second square. The area of the larger square is 9 times as great as the area of the smaller square. Find the length of the side of each square.

----

15. The width of a rectangle is 4 yards less than its length. The area is 17 more (numerically) than its perimeter. What are the dimensions of the rectangle?
16. The area of a square is twice its perimeter (numerically). What is the length of its side?
17. The base of a triangle is 3 inches more than its altitude. Its area is 20 square inches. Find the base and altitude.
18. The sum of the base and altitude of a triangle is 15 centimeters. The area of the triangle is 27 square centimeters. Find the base and the altitude.
19. The fourth term of a proportion is 7 more than its first term. Write the proportion if its second term is 3 and its third term is 6.
20. The third term of a proportion is 2 more than its second term. Write the proportion if its first term is 3 and its fourth term is 8.

SET II

1. The difference of two numbers is 12. Their product is 28. Find the numbers.
2. The sum of two numbers is 10. Their product is -24. Find the numbers.
3. Find two consecutive integers whose product is one less than their sum.
4. Find three consecutive integers such that the product of the first two minus the third is 7.
5. Find three consecutive odd integers such that twice the product of the first two is 7 more than the product of the last two.
6. The length of a rectangle is 8 meters more than its width. Its area is 48 square meters. What are its dimensions?
7. One square has a side 2 kilometers shorter than the side of a second square. The area of the larger square is 9 times as great as the area of the smaller square. Find the length of the side of each square.
8. The width of a rectangle is 2 inches less than its length. The area is 4 more (numerically) than its perimeter. What are the dimensions of the rectangle?
9. The base of a triangle is 5 centimeters more than its altitude. Its area is 7 square centimeters. What is the lenth of its altitude?
10. The fourth term of a proportion is 13 more than its first term. Write the proportion if its second term is 3 and its third term is 10.

Chapter Summary

Prime and Composite Numbers (Sec. 801). A *prime number* is a positive integer greater than 1 that can be exactly divided only by itself and 1. A prime number has no factors other than itself and 1.

A *composite number* is a positive integer that can be exactly divided by some integer other than itself and 1. A composite number has factors other than itself and 1.

Prime Factorization of Positive Integers (Sec. 801). The *prime factorization* of a positive integer is the indicated product of all its factors that are themselves prime numbers.

Special Products

$$a(b + c) = ab + ac$$ Distributive Rule (Sec. 802).

$$(a + b)(a - b) = a^2 - b^2$$ Sum and difference of two terms (Sec. 803).

$$\left.\begin{array}{l} (a + b)^2 = a^2 + 2ab + b^2 \\ (a - b)^2 = a^2 - 2ab + b^2 \end{array}\right\}$$ Square of a binomial (Sec. 804).

The greatest common factor (GCF) of two integers is the greatest integer that is a factor of both integers. (Sec. 802)

Methods of Factoring

1. Greatest common factor (GCF) (Section 802)
2. Difference of two squares (Section 803):
   $$a^2 - b^2 = (a + b)(a - b)$$
3. Trinomial $\left\{\begin{array}{l} \text{leading coefficient equal to 1 (Section 804)} \\ \text{leading coefficient greater than 1} \\ \text{(Sections 804, 806)} \end{array}\right.$
4. Grouping (Section 805)

Factoring completely (Sec. 807)

1. Look for a greatest common factor first.
2. Look for a difference of two squares.
3. Look for a factorable trinomial.
4. Look for four terms that can be factored by grouping.
5. Check to see if any factor already obtained can be factored again.

To Solve an Equation by Factoring (Sec. 808)

1. Write all nonzero terms on one side of the equation by adding the same expression to both sides. Only zero must remain on the other side. Then arrange the polynomial in descending powers.
2. Factor the polynomial.

3. Set each factor equal to zero, and solve for the unknown letter.
4. Check apparent solutions in the *original* equation.

REVIEW EXERCISES 810

SET I

In Exercises 1—10, find the prime factorization of each number.

1. 12	2. 20	3. 36	4. 24	5. 31
6. 37	7. 42	8. 44	9. 210	10. 111

In Exercises 11—18, find each of the indicated products by inspection.

11. $(m - 2)(4m + 1)$ 12. $(3u + 1)(5u - 2)$

13. $(c - 2)(5c + 2)$ 14. $(7x + 5)(7x - 5)$

15. $(a - 5)^2$ 16. $(b + 8)^2$

17. $(5x - 4y)(7x - 2y)$ 18. $(6m - 5n)(3m - 4n)$

In Exercises 19—36, factor each expression completely.

19. $8x - 4$ 20. $5 + 15a$

21. $m^2 - 4$ 22. $25 - n^2$

23. $x^2 + 10x + 21$ 24. $y^2 + 10y + 16$

25. $2u^2 + 4u$ 26. $3b - 6b^2$

27. $z^2 - 7z - 18$ 28. $x^2 - 7x - 30$

29. $4x^2 - 25x + 6$ 30. $5c^2 - 22c + 8$

31. $9k^2 - 144$ 32. $100 - 81p^2$

33. $8 - 2a^2$ 34. $2y^2 - 18$

35. $ab + 2b - a - 2$ 36. $mn - 5n - m + 5$

In Exercises 37—48, solve each of the equations.

37. $(x - 5)(x + 3) = 0$ 38. $(y + 4)(y - 7) = 0$

39. $x^2 - 5x - 14 = 0$ 40. $x^2 - 5x - 24 = 0$

41. $m^2 = 18 + 3m$ 42. $n^2 = 20 + 8n$

43. $x^2 - 9 = 0$ 44. $x^2 - 36 = 0$

45. $3z^2 = 12z$ 46. $6y^2 = 10y$

47. $6e^2 = 13e + 5$ 48. $12u^2 = 47u - 45$

In Exercises 49—52, find each indicated product by inspection.

49. $3xy^2(4x^2y^2 - 5xy - 10)$ 50. $5x^2y(2xy^3 - 3x^2y - 4)$

51. $4x(x^2 - y^2)(x^2 + y^2)$ 52. $3a(a^2 + 5b)(a^2 - 5b)$

In Exercises 53—64, factor each expression completely.

53. $15u^2v - 3uv$

54. $21ab^2 - 7ab$

55. $4x^2y - 8xy^2 + 4xy$

56. $5ab^2 - 10a^2b - 5ab$

57. $10x^2 - xy - 24y^2$

58. $28x^2 - 13xy - 6y^2$

59. $15a^2 + 15ab - 30b^2$

60. $27u^2 + 6uv - 33v^2$

61. $6u^3v^2 - 9uv^3 - 12uv$

62. $8x^5y^2 - 12x^2y^4 - 16x^2y^2$

63. $x^2 - y^2 + x - y$

64. $a^2 - b^2 - a + b$

In Exercises 65—70, solve each equation.

65. $2u(u + 6)(u - 2) = 0$

66. $3v(v - 8)(v + 9) = 0$

67. $68x^2 = 30x^3 + 30x$

68. $39y^2 = 18y^3 + 18y$

69. $\dfrac{x - 2}{9} = \dfrac{4}{x + 7}$

70. $\dfrac{x - 2}{2} = \dfrac{16}{x + 2}$

71. The difference of two numbers is 3. Their product is 28. Find the numbers.
72. The difference of two numbers is 3. Their product is 54. Find the numbers.
73. The width of a rectangle is 3 less than its length. Its area is 40. Find the length and width of the rectangle.
74. One side of a square is 6 feet longer than the side of a second square. The area of the larger square is 16 times as great as the area of the smaller square. Find the length of the side of each square.
75. The area of a square is 3 times its perimeter. What is the length of its side?
76. The length of a rectangle is 6 yards more than its width. The area is 12 more (numerically) than its perimeter. Find the dimensions of the rectangle.
77. Find two consecutive integers whose product is one more than their sum.
78. Find two consecutive integers whose product is 19 more than their sum.
79. Find three consecutive integers such that the product of the first two plus the product of the last two is 18.
80. Find three consecutive odd integers such that four times the product of the first two is 3 less than the product of the last two.

SET II

In Exercises 1—5, find the prime factorization of each number.

1. 28   2. 54   3. 43   4. 70   5. 350

In Exercises 6—11, find each indicated product by inspection.

6. $(a + 3)(2a - 5)$

7. $(6b + 5)(6b - 5)$

8. $(h - 6)^2$

9. $(3m - 7n)(4m - 3n)$

10. $2x^2y(5x^2y^2 - 3xy - 7)$

11. $4k(h^2 - 3k)(h^2 + 3k)$

In Exercises 12—26, factor each expression completely.

12. $6 - 30u$

13. $36 - m^2$

14. $x^2 + 9x + 18$

15. $12v^2 - 8v$

16. $z^2 + 2z - 35$

17. $4e^2 - 27e + 18$

18. $64 - 49p^2$

19. $48 - 3a^2$

20. $st - 3t - s + 3$

21. $24hk^2 - 6hk$

22. $3a^2b - 15ab^2 - 3ab$

23. $21u^2 + 13uv - 20v^2$

24. $40x^2 + 10xy - 50y^2$

25. $8m^3n^2 - 14mn^4 - 6mn^2$

26. $w^2 - z^2 - w - z$

In Exercises 27—35, solve each equation.

27. $(x + 8)(x - 6) = 0$

28. $x^2 - x - 20 = 0$

29. $z^2 = 4z + 21$

30. $m^2 - 81 = 0$

31. $5t^2 = 40t$

32. $12m^2 = 10 - 7m$

33. $5h(h - 11)(h + 3) = 0$

34. $30x^3 = 87x^2 + 63x$

35. $\dfrac{3x + 2}{x + 2} = \dfrac{5x - 2}{3x - 2}$

36. The difference of two numbers is 6. Their product is 72. Find the numbers.

37. One side of a square is 8 centimeters longer than the side of a second square. The area of the larger square is 9 times as great as the area of the smaller square. Find the length of the side of each square.

38. The length of a rectangle is 7 yards more than its width. The area is 4 more (numerically) than its perimeter. Find the dimensions of the rectangle.

39. Find two consecutive integers whose product is 10 less than four times their sum.

40. Find three consecutive even integers such that twice the product of the first two is 10 more than the last integer.

CUMULATIVE REVIEW EXERCISES: CHAPTERS 1-7

1. Evaluate $24 \div 2\sqrt{16} - 3^2 \cdot 5$

2. Solve $5(2b - 4) = 8(3b + 5) - 4(9 + 6b)$

3. Evaluate the formula using the values of the letters given with the formula.

$$C = \frac{a}{a + 12} \cdot A \qquad a = 8, \; A = 35$$

In Exercises 4 and 5, simplify each expression and write your answers using only positive exponents.

4. $(3y^{-3}z^2)^{-2}$

5. $\left(\dfrac{15x^2}{10x^3}\right)^3$

6. The owner of a general store has 8600 items in his store, of which 1548 are perishable. What percent of his total stock consists of perishable items?

In Exercises 7-10, perform the indicated operations and simplify.

7. $(2x^2 + 5x - 3) - (-4x^2 + 8x + 10) + (6x^2 + 3x - 8)$

8. $(y - 4)(3y^2 - 2y + 5)$

9. $\dfrac{12a^2 - 3a}{3a}$

10. $(8x^2 - 2x - 17) \div (2x - 3)$

Chapter Eight Diagnostic Test

Name _____

_____

The purpose of this test is to see how well you understand factoring and special products. We recommend that you work this diagnostic test *before* your instructor tests you on this chapter. Allow yourself about one hour to do this test.

Complete solutions for all the problems on this test, together with section references, are given in the Answer Section. We suggest that you study the sections referred to for the problems you do incorrectly.

---

1. State whether each of the following numbers is prime or composite.

   (a) 18   (1a) _____

   (b) 21   (1b) _____

   (c) 31   (1c) _____

---

2. List all the factors of each of the following numbers.

   (a) 6   (2a) _____

   (b) 13   (2b) _____

Find the prime factorization of each of the following numbers.

3. 45   4. 160

   (3) _____   (4) _____

Find the following products by inspection.

5. $(2x - 3)(2x + 3)$

                                      (5) _____

6. $(3y - 5)(4y + 7)$

                                      (6) _____

7. $(4a - 5b)^2$

(7) _____

Factor each of the following expressions completely.

8. $5x + 10$

(8) _____

9. $3x^2 - 6x$

(9) _____

10. $16x^2 - 49y^2$

(10) _____

11. $2z^2 - 8$

(11) _____

12. $z^2 + 6z + 8$

(12) _____

13. $m^2 + m - 6$

(13) _____

14. $5w^2 - 12w + 7$

(14) _____

15. $3v^2 + 14v - 5$

(15) _____

16. $5n - mn - 5 + m$

(16) _____

17. $6h^2k - 8hk^2 + 2k^3$

(17) _____

Solve each of the following equations by factoring.

18. $x^2 - 12x + 20 = 0$

(18) _____

19. $3x^2 = 12x$

(19) _____

20. The length of a rectangle is 3 feet more than its width. Its area is 28 square feet. What are its dimensions?

(20) Length_____

Width_____

NINE
Fractions

In this chapter we define algebraic fractions, how to perform necessary operations with them, and how to solve equations and word problems involving them. A knowledge of the different methods of factoring discussed in Chapter 8 is essential in your work with *algebraic* fractions.

Algebraic Fractions

A simple *algebraic fraction* (also called a "rational expression") is an algebraic expression of the form $\frac{P}{Q}$ where P and Q are polynomials. We call P and Q the *terms* of the fraction. We call P the *numerator* and Q the *denominator* of the fraction.

$$\text{terms of fraction} \left[\begin{array}{c} \text{numerator} \\ \frac{P}{Q} \leftarrow \text{fraction line} \\ \text{denominator (cannot be zero)} \end{array}\right.$$

EXCLUDED VALUES. Any value of the letter (or letters) that makes the denominator Q equal to zero is *excluded* (Sec. 109).

Example 1. Examples of algebraic fractions, some showing excluded value(s) of the letter.

(a) $\frac{x}{3}$ *No* value of x is excluded because no value of x makes the denominator zero.

(b) $\frac{5}{x}$ x cannot be 0.

(c) $\frac{2x - 5}{x - 1}$ x cannot be 1, because that would make the denominator 0.

(d) $\frac{x^2 + 2}{x^2 - 3x - 4} = \frac{x^2 + 2}{(x - 4)(x + 1)}$ x cannot be 4 or -1 because either value makes the denominator zero.

(e) $\frac{2}{3}$ Arithmetic fractions are also algebraic fractions. Here 2 and 3 are polynomials of degree zero.

Note. After this section, whenever a fraction is written, it is understood that the value(s) of the variable(s) that make the denominator zero are excluded. ■

THE THREE SIGNS OF A FRACTION. Every fraction has three signs associated with it.

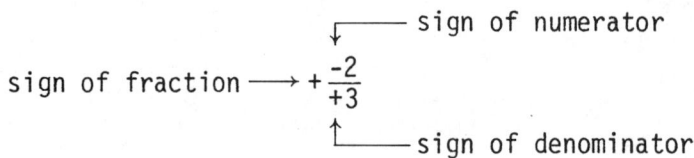

If any two of the three signs of a fraction are changed, the value of the fraction is unchanged.

Fractions obtained in this way are *equivalent fractions*.

This rule of signs is helpful in simplifying some expressions with fractions.

We illustrate the rule given in the box by applying it to the fraction $\frac{8}{4}$.

$$+\frac{+8}{+4} = \begin{cases} +\dfrac{-8}{-4} = +\left(\dfrac{-8}{-4}\right) = +(+2) = 2 \\[2pt] \text{Here we changed sign of numerator and denominator.} \\[6pt] -\dfrac{-8}{+4} = -\left(\dfrac{-8}{+4}\right) = -(-2) = 2 \\[2pt] \text{Here we changed sign of fraction and numerator.} \\[6pt] -\dfrac{+8}{-4} = -\left(\dfrac{+8}{-4}\right) = -(-2) = 2 \\[2pt] \text{Here we changed sign of fraction and denominator.} \end{cases}$$

Example 2. Changing two signs of a fraction to obtain an equivalent fraction

(a) $-\dfrac{-5}{xy} = +\dfrac{+5}{xy} = \dfrac{5}{xy}$

Here we changed sign of fraction and numerator.

(b) $-\dfrac{1}{2 - x} = +\dfrac{1}{-(2 - x)} = \dfrac{1}{-2 + x} = \dfrac{1}{x - 2}$

Here we changed sign of fraction and denominator.

The simplification in Example 2(b) can be explained as follows:

$-(2 - x) = (-1)(2 - x) = -2 + x = x - 2$ Distributive Rule.

This fact is summarized as follows:

> If the sign of a binomial *difference* is changed, the terms of the binomial are interchanged.
>
> sign of binomial difference changed
>
> $-(\,b - a\,) = (\,a - b\,)$
>
> terms interchanged

Example 3. Changing the sign of a binomial difference.

(a) $-(6 - y) = (y - 6) = y - 6$

(b) $-(z - 5) = (5 - z) = 5 - z$

EXERCISES 901

In Exercises 1—6, what value(s) of the variable (if any) must be excluded?

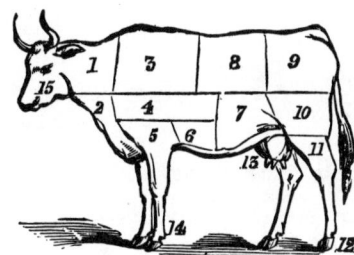

1. $\dfrac{3x + 4}{x - 2}$

2. $\dfrac{5 - 4x}{x + 3}$

3. $\dfrac{x}{10}$

4. $\dfrac{y}{20}$

5. $\dfrac{3 + x}{(x - 1)(x + 2)}$

6. $\dfrac{x - 4}{3x(x - 2)}$

In Exercises 7—14, use the rule about the three signs of a fraction to find the missing term.

7. $-\dfrac{5}{6} = \dfrac{?}{6}$

8. $\dfrac{2}{-x} = \dfrac{?}{x}$

9. $\dfrac{5}{-y} = \dfrac{-5}{?}$

10. $\dfrac{2 - x}{-9} = \dfrac{?}{9}$

11. $\dfrac{7}{5 - x} = \dfrac{?}{x - 5}$

12. $\dfrac{1 - x}{-8} = \dfrac{?}{8}$

----

13. $\dfrac{6 - y}{5} = \dfrac{y - 6}{?}$

14. $-\dfrac{3}{x - 4} = \dfrac{3}{?}$

In Exercises 15—18, what value(s) of the variable (if any) must be excluded?

15. $\dfrac{z}{4}$

16. $\dfrac{x - 1}{3}$

17. $\dfrac{x^2 + 4}{x^2 - x - 2}$

18. $\dfrac{x^2 - 2}{x^2 - 4}$

In Exercises 1—6, what value(s) of the variable (if any) must be excluded?

1. $\dfrac{7}{x}$ 2. $\dfrac{3}{x-4}$ 3. $\dfrac{x+1}{5}$ 4. $\dfrac{6}{x^2-1}$

In Exercises 5—9, use the rule about the three signs of a fraction to find the missing term.

5. $\dfrac{4}{3} = \dfrac{?}{-3}$ 6. $\dfrac{5}{7} = \dfrac{-5}{?}$ 7. $-\dfrac{3}{4} = \dfrac{3}{?}$

8. $\dfrac{1-x}{3-y} = \dfrac{?}{y-3}$ 9. $\dfrac{4-d}{2c-1} = \dfrac{d-4}{?}$

Reducing Fractions to Lowest Terms

We reduce fractions to lowest terms in algebra for the same reason we do in arithmetic: It makes them simpler and easier to work with. After this section, it is understood that *all fractions are to be reduced to lowest terms* (unless otherwise indicated).

<u>In Arithmetic.</u> The reasoning behind reducing fractions is explained by the following example:

$$\frac{6}{8} = \frac{2 \cdot 3}{2 \cdot 4} = \frac{2}{2} \cdot \frac{3}{4} = 1 \cdot \frac{3}{4} = \frac{3}{4}$$

This work is usually shortened by dividing numerator and denominator by the same number.

$$\frac{\overset{3}{\cancel{6}}}{\underset{4}{\cancel{8}}} = \frac{3}{4}$$

This is only possible when the numerator and denominator have a common factor. For the example,

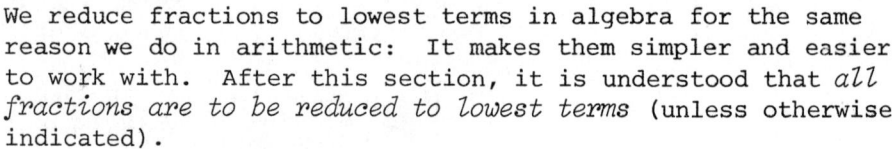

$$\frac{6}{8} = \frac{\boxed{2} \cdot 3}{\boxed{2} \cdot 4} = \frac{\cancel{2} \cdot 3}{\cancel{2} \cdot 4} = \frac{3}{4}$$

2 is a factor of the numerator.

Both numerator and denominator were divided by 2.

2 is a factor of the denominator.

A common error made in reducing fractions is to forget that the number the numerator and denominator are divided by *must* be a *factor* of *both*.

<u>In Algebra.</u> The procedure for reducing fractions in algebra is the same as the method used in arithmetic.

Example 1. Reduce to lowest terms.

(a) $\dfrac{4x^2y}{2xy} = \dfrac{\overset{2}{\cancel{4}}}{\underset{1}{\cancel{2}}} \cdot \dfrac{x^2}{x} \cdot \dfrac{y}{y} = 2 \cdot x \cdot 1 = 2x$

(b) $\dfrac{15ab^2c^3}{6a^4bc^2} = \dfrac{\overset{5}{\cancel{15}}}{\underset{2}{\cancel{6}}} \cdot \dfrac{a}{a^4} \cdot \dfrac{b^2}{b} \cdot \dfrac{c^3}{c^2} = \dfrac{5}{2} \cdot \dfrac{1}{a^3} \cdot \dfrac{b}{1} \cdot \dfrac{c}{1} = \dfrac{5bc}{2a^3}$

(c) $\dfrac{x - 3}{x^2 - 9} = \dfrac{\overset{1}{\cancel{(x - 3)}}}{(x + 3)\underset{1}{\cancel{(x - 3)}}} = \dfrac{1}{x + 3}$

(d) $\dfrac{x^2 - 4x - 5}{x^2 + 5x + 4} = \dfrac{\cancel{(x + 1)}\,(x - 5)}{\cancel{(x + 1)}\,(x + 4)} = \dfrac{x - 5}{x + 4}$

(e) $\dfrac{3x^2 - 5xy - 2y^2}{6x^3y + 2x^2y^2} = \dfrac{(x - 2y)\cancel{(3x + y)}}{2x^2y\cancel{(3x + y)}} = \dfrac{x - 2y}{2x^2y}$

(f) $\dfrac{x - y}{y - x} = \boxed{- \dfrac{x - y}{-(y - x)}} = -\dfrac{\overset{1}{\cancel{(x - y)}}}{\underset{1}{\cancel{(x - y)}}} = -1$

      ⟍_____ Changing sign of fraction
                  and denominator.

                            ┌─ $(-1)(b - a) = (a - b)$ ─┐

(g) $\dfrac{(b - a)(2b + 3a)}{(a - b)(4a - 5b)} = \dfrac{(-1)(b - a)(2b + 3a)}{(-1)(a - b)(4a - 5b)} = \dfrac{(a - b)(2b + 3a)}{(-1)(a - b)(4a - 5b)}$

                                  └─ Changing the sign of both numerator
                                      and denominator is equivalent to
                                      multiplying each by -1

                     $= \dfrac{(2b + 3a)}{(-1)(4a - 5b)} = \dfrac{2b + 3a}{5b - 4a}$

(h) $\dfrac{\overset{1}{\cancel{z}}}{2\underset{1}{\cancel{z}}} = \dfrac{1}{2}$ **Note:** A factor of 1 will always remain in the numerator and denominator after they have been divided by factors common to both. ∎

(i) $\dfrac{x + 3}{x + 6}$ cannot be reduced. $\left\{\begin{array}{l}\text{Neither } x \text{ nor 3 is a}\\ \textit{factor} \text{ of numerator}\\ \text{or denominator.}\end{array}\right.$

        ↓_____ x is *not* a factor of the numerator.

(j) $\dfrac{x + y}{x}$ cannot be reduced.

A Word of Caution. A common error made in reducing fractions is to forget that the number the numerator and denominator are divided by *must* be a *factor* of *both* [see Examples 1(i) and 1(j)].

Error:

$\longrightarrow$ 3 is *not* a factor of the numerator

$$\frac{3 + 2}{3} \neq 2 \quad \textit{Incorrect} \text{ reduction}$$

The above reduction is incorrect because

$$\frac{3 + 2}{3} = \frac{5}{3} \neq 2$$

■

EXERCISES 902. Reduce each fraction to lowest terms.

SET I

1. $\dfrac{9}{12}$

2. $\dfrac{8}{14}$

3. $\dfrac{6ab^2}{3ab}$

4. $\dfrac{10m^2 n}{5mn}$

5. $\dfrac{4x^2 y}{2xy}$

6. $\dfrac{12x^3 y}{4xy}$

7. $\dfrac{5x - 10}{x - 2}$

8. $\dfrac{3x + 12}{x + 4}$

9. $-\dfrac{5x - 6}{6 - 5x}$

10. $\dfrac{4 - 3z}{3z - 4}$

11. $\dfrac{5x^2 + 30x}{10x^2 - 40x}$

12. $\dfrac{4x^3 - 4x^2}{12x^2 - 12x}$

13. $\dfrac{2 + 4}{4}$

14. $\dfrac{3 + 9}{3}$

15. $\dfrac{5 + x}{5}$

16. $\dfrac{x + 8}{8}$

17. $\dfrac{x^2 - 1}{x + 1}$

18. $\dfrac{x^2 - 4}{x - 2}$

----

19. $\dfrac{6x^2 - x - 2}{10x^2 + 3x - 1}$

20. $\dfrac{8x^2 - 10x - 3}{12x^2 + 11x + 2}$

21. $\dfrac{x^2 - y^2}{(x + y)^2}$

22. $\dfrac{a^2 - 9b^2}{(a - 3b)^2}$

23. $\dfrac{2y^2 + xy - 6x^2}{3x^2 + xy - 2y^2}$

24. $\dfrac{10y^2 + 11xy - 6x^2}{4x^2 - 4xy - 15y^2}$

25. $\dfrac{8x^2 - 2y^2}{2ax - ay + 2bx - by}$

26. $\dfrac{3x^2 - 12y^2}{ax + 2by + 2ay + bx}$

27. $\dfrac{(-1)(z - 8)}{8 - z}$

28. $\dfrac{x - 12}{(-1)(12 - x)}$

29. $\dfrac{(-1)(a - 2b)(b - a)}{(2a + b)(a - b)}$

30. $\dfrac{8(n - 2m)}{(-1)(3n + m)(2m - n)}$

1. $\dfrac{12}{16}$

2. $\dfrac{8mn^3}{4n^2}$

3. $\dfrac{9x^2y}{3xy}$

4. $\dfrac{15(x+1)}{3x+3}$

5. $\dfrac{x-1}{x^2-1}$

6. $\dfrac{x-4}{4-x}$

7. $\dfrac{4x^4y^2z}{12x^3yz}$

8. $\dfrac{3x^5yz^2}{18x^4y^2z^2}$

9. $\dfrac{2x-4}{2-x}$

10. $\dfrac{x^2-9}{x^2+5x+6}$

11. $\dfrac{x^2-16}{x^2-x-12}$

12. $\dfrac{x^2+x-20}{x^2+2x-15}$

13. $\dfrac{x^2-11x+30}{x^2-9x+20}$

14. $\dfrac{12a^3b+6a^2b^2}{18a^2b^2+9ab^3}$

15. $\dfrac{15m^2n^2-15mn^3}{10m^2-10mn}$

16. $\dfrac{ax^2-ay^2}{ax+ay+bx+by}$

17. $\dfrac{(-1)(6-w)}{w-6}$

18. $\dfrac{5(x-4y)}{(-1)(3y-2x)(4y-x)}$

903

Multiplication and Division of Fractions

MULTIPLICATION OF FRACTIONS

In Arithmetic

$$\frac{4}{9}\cdot\frac{3}{8}=\frac{\overset{1}{\cancel{4}}\cdot\overset{1}{\cancel{3}}}{\underset{3}{\cancel{9}}\cdot\underset{2}{\cancel{8}}}=\frac{1}{6}$$

In Algebra. We multiply algebraic fractions the same way we multiply fractions in arithmetic.

TO MULTIPLY FRACTIONS

1. Factor the numerator and denominator of the fractions.

2. Divide the numerator and denominator by all factors common to both.

3. The answer is the product of the factors remaining in the numerator divided by the product of the factors remaining in the denominator. A factor of 1 will always remain in both numerator and denominator.

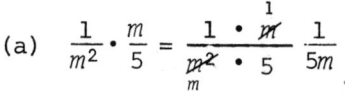

Example 1. Multiply the fractions.

(a) $\dfrac{1}{m^2} \cdot \dfrac{m}{5} = \dfrac{1 \cdot \overset{1}{\cancel{m}}}{\underset{m}{\cancel{m^2}} \cdot 5} = \dfrac{1}{5m}$.

(b) $\dfrac{2y^3}{3x^2} \cdot \dfrac{12x}{5y^2} = \dfrac{2y^3 \cdot \overset{4}{\cancel{12x}}}{\underset{1}{\cancel{3x^2}} \cdot 5y^2} = \dfrac{8y}{5x}$

(c) $\dfrac{x}{2x-6} \cdot \dfrac{4x-12}{x^2} = \dfrac{x}{2(x-3)} \cdot \dfrac{4(x-3)}{x^2}$

$\qquad\qquad = \dfrac{x \cdot \overset{2}{\cancel{4}}(\cancel{x-3})}{\underset{1}{\cancel{2}}(\cancel{x-3}) \cdot x^2} = \dfrac{2}{x}$

(d) $\dfrac{x+2}{6x^2} \cdot \dfrac{8x}{x^2-x-6} = \dfrac{(\cancel{x+2})}{\underset{3}{\cancel{6x^2}}} \cdot \dfrac{\overset{4}{\cancel{8x}}}{(\cancel{x+2})(x-3)}$

$\qquad\qquad = \dfrac{4}{3x(x-3)}$

(e) $\dfrac{10xy^3}{x^2-y^2} \cdot \dfrac{2x^2+xy-y^2}{15x^2y} = \dfrac{\overset{2}{\cancel{10xy^3}}}{(x+y)(x-y)} \cdot \dfrac{(x+y)(2x-y)}{\underset{3}{\cancel{15x^2y}}}$

$\qquad\qquad = \dfrac{2y^2(2x-y)}{3x(x-y)}$

DIVISION OF FRACTIONS

In Arithmetic

$$\dfrac{3}{5} \div \dfrac{4}{7} = \dfrac{3}{5} \cdot \boxed{\dfrac{7}{4}} = \dfrac{3 \cdot 7}{5 \cdot 4} = \dfrac{21}{20}$$

Invert the second fraction and multiply.

This method works because:

$$\dfrac{3}{5} \div \dfrac{4}{7} = \dfrac{\tfrac{3}{5}}{\tfrac{4}{7}} = \dfrac{\tfrac{3}{5}}{\tfrac{4}{7}} \cdot \left(\dfrac{\tfrac{7}{4}}{\tfrac{7}{4}}\right) = \dfrac{\tfrac{3}{5} \cdot \tfrac{7}{4}}{\tfrac{\cancel{4}}{\cancel{7}} \cdot \tfrac{\cancel{7}}{\cancel{4}}} = \dfrac{\tfrac{3}{5} \cdot \tfrac{7}{4}}{1} = \dfrac{3}{5} \cdot \dfrac{7}{4}$$

The value of this fraction is 1

Therefore, $\dfrac{3}{5} \div \dfrac{4}{7} = \dfrac{3}{5} \cdot \dfrac{7}{4}$.

<u>In Algebra</u>. We divide algebraic fractions the same way we divide fractions in arithmetic.

TO DIVIDE FRACTIONS

Invert the second fraction and multiply.

$$\frac{a}{b} \div \frac{c}{d} = \frac{a}{b} \cdot \frac{d}{c}$$

first fraction ————→↑   ↑←———— second fraction

Example 2. Divide the fractions.

(a) $\dfrac{4}{3x} \div \dfrac{12}{x^3} = \dfrac{\overset{1}{\cancel{4}}}{3x} \cdot \dfrac{x^3}{\underset{3}{\cancel{12}}} = \dfrac{x^2}{9}$

(b) $\dfrac{4r^3}{9s^2} \div \dfrac{8r^2s^4}{15rs} = \dfrac{\overset{1}{\cancel{4}}r^3}{\underset{3}{\cancel{9}}s^2} \cdot \dfrac{\overset{5}{\cancel{15}}rs}{\underset{2}{\cancel{8}}r^2s^4} = \dfrac{5r^2}{6s^5}$

(c) $\dfrac{3y^3 - 3y^2}{16y^5 + 8y^4} \div \dfrac{y^2 + 2y - 3}{4y + 12} = \dfrac{3y^2\cancel{(y - 1)}}{\underset{2}{\cancel{8}}y^4(2y + 1)} \cdot \dfrac{\overset{1}{\cancel{4}}\cancel{(y + 3)}}{\cancel{(y - 1)}\cancel{(y + 3)}}$

$$= \dfrac{3}{2y^2(2y + 1)}$$

(d) $\dfrac{y^2 - x^2}{4xy - 2y^2} \div \dfrac{2x - 2y}{2x^2 + xy - y^2}$

$$= \dfrac{(y + x)(y - x)}{2y\cancel{(2x - y)}} \cdot \dfrac{(x + y)\cancel{(2x - y)}}{2(x - y)} = \dfrac{(x + y)^2(y - x)}{4y(x - y)}$$

$$= -\dfrac{(x + y)^2\cancel{(x - y)}}{4y\cancel{(x - y)}} = -\dfrac{(x + y)^2}{4y}$$

↑————— Changing sign of fraction and numerator.

EXERCISES 903. Perform the indicated operations.

SET I

1. $\dfrac{5}{6} \div \dfrac{5}{3}$

2. $\dfrac{3}{8} \div \dfrac{21}{12}$

3. $\dfrac{4a^3}{5b^2} \cdot \dfrac{10b}{8a^2}$

4. $\dfrac{6d}{8c} \cdot \dfrac{12c^2}{9d}$

5. $\dfrac{3x^2}{16} \div \dfrac{x}{8}$

6. $\dfrac{4y^3}{7} \div \dfrac{4y^2}{21}$

7. $\dfrac{3x^4y^2z}{18xy} \cdot \dfrac{15z}{x^3yz^2}$

8. $\dfrac{21a^2b^5}{4b^2} \cdot \dfrac{6c}{7b^2c^3}$

9. $\dfrac{x}{x + 2} \cdot \dfrac{5x + 10}{x^3}$

10. $\dfrac{y - 2}{y} \cdot \dfrac{6}{3y - 6}$

11. $\dfrac{b^3}{a+3} \div \dfrac{4b^2}{2a+6}$ 12. $\dfrac{3n-6}{15n} \div \dfrac{n-2}{20n^2}$

13. $\dfrac{a+4}{a-4} \div \dfrac{a^2+8a+16}{a^2-16}$ 14. $\dfrac{x^3-5x}{9x} \div \dfrac{4x^3-20x}{12x^2}$

15. $\dfrac{5}{z+4} \cdot \dfrac{z^2-16}{(z-4)^2}$ 16. $\dfrac{u+3}{u^2-9} \cdot \dfrac{2u-6}{6}$

----

17. $\dfrac{3a-3b}{4c+4d} \cdot \dfrac{2c+2d}{b-a}$ 18. $\dfrac{2y-2x}{6} \cdot \dfrac{x+y}{x^2-y^2}$

19. $\dfrac{4x-8}{4} \cdot \dfrac{x+2}{x^2-4}$ 20. $\dfrac{2a+2b}{3} \cdot \dfrac{a-b}{a^2-b^2}$

21. $\dfrac{4a+4b}{ab^2} \div \dfrac{3a+3b}{a^2b}$ 22. $\dfrac{x^2-y^2}{x^2-2xy+y^2} \div \dfrac{x+y}{x-y}$

23. $\dfrac{x-y}{9x+9y} \div \dfrac{x^2-y^2}{3x^2+6xy+3y^2}$

24. $\dfrac{x^2-y^2}{8x^2-16xy+8y^2} \div \dfrac{x+y}{4x-4y}$

25. $\dfrac{2x^3y+2x^2y^2}{6x} \div \dfrac{x^2y^2-xy^3}{y-x}$

26. $\dfrac{2b^2c-2bc^2}{b+c} \div \dfrac{4bc^2-4b^2c}{4b+4c}$

SET II

1. $\dfrac{2}{3} \div \dfrac{8}{3}$ 2. $\dfrac{5}{8} \div \dfrac{5}{14}$

3. $\dfrac{5x^3}{4y^2} \cdot \dfrac{8y}{10x^2}$ 4. $\dfrac{a^3}{2a+6} \div \dfrac{a^2}{a+3}$

5. $\dfrac{a+2}{a+1} \cdot \dfrac{a^2+a}{a^2-4}$ 6. $\dfrac{2x-1}{y} \div \dfrac{2x^2+x-1}{y^2}$

7. $\dfrac{2u^2-14u}{5u^2} \cdot \dfrac{15u^3}{4u-28}$ 8. $\dfrac{-3v}{18v+90} \cdot \dfrac{6v^3+30v^2}{v^3}$

9. $\dfrac{3e^2}{28e-42} \div \dfrac{6e^3}{14e^2-21e}$ 10. $\dfrac{12f+16}{15f} \div \dfrac{6f^3+8f^2}{20f^4}$

11. $\dfrac{x^2+x-2}{x-1} \div \dfrac{x^2+5x+6}{x^2}$

12. $\dfrac{z^3}{z+4} \div \dfrac{z-1}{z^2+3z-4}$

13. $\dfrac{x^2+10x+25}{x^2-25} \cdot \dfrac{5-x}{x+5}$

14. $\dfrac{3-y}{y+1} \cdot \dfrac{4+5y+y^2}{y^2+y-12}$

Adding Like Fractions

<u>In Arithmetic.</u> *Like fractions* are fractions that have the same denominator.

<u>Example 1.</u> Examples of like fractions.

$$\frac{2}{3}, \frac{5}{3}, \frac{1}{3} \qquad \text{are like fractions.}$$

└─────── Same denominator.

<u>*Unlike fractions*</u> are fractions that have different denominators.

<u>Example 2.</u> Examples of unlike fractions.

$$\frac{1}{3}, \frac{2}{7}, \frac{3}{8} \qquad \text{are unlike fractions.}$$

└─────── Different denominators.

<u>ADDING LIKE FRACTIONS.</u> We know that

$$1 \text{ car} + 3 \text{ cars} + 7 \text{ cars} = (1 + 3 + 7) \text{ cars} = 11 \text{ cars.}$$

In the same way:

2 thirds + 5 thirds + 1 third = (2 + 5 + 1) thirds = 8 thirds

$$\text{so,} \quad \frac{2}{3} \quad + \quad \frac{5}{3} \quad + \quad \frac{1}{3} \quad = \quad \frac{2 + 5 + 1}{3} \quad = \quad \frac{8}{3}$$

TO ADD LIKE FRACTIONS

1. Add the numerators.

2. Write the sum of the numerators over the denominator of the like fractions.

$$\frac{a}{c} + \frac{b}{c} = \frac{a + b}{c}$$

3. Reduce the resulting fraction to lowest terms.

<u>Example 3.</u> Adding like arithmetic fractions.

(a) Add: $\dfrac{1}{9} + \dfrac{4}{9} + \dfrac{7}{9} = \dfrac{1 + 4 + 7}{9} = \dfrac{12}{9} = \dfrac{\overset{4}{\cancel{12}}}{\underset{3}{\cancel{9}}} = \dfrac{4}{3}$

(b) Add: $\dfrac{11}{23} + \dfrac{5}{23} = \dfrac{11 + 5}{23} = \dfrac{16}{23}$ Already lowest terms.

(c) Add: $\dfrac{3}{12} + \dfrac{1}{12} + \dfrac{4}{12} + \dfrac{7}{12} = \dfrac{3 + 1 + 4 + 7}{12} = \dfrac{\overset{5}{\cancel{15}}}{\underset{4}{\cancel{12}}} = \dfrac{5}{4}$

<u>In Algebra</u>. This same method is used for adding like fractions in algebra.

<u>SUBTRACTING LIKE FRACTIONS</u>. Any subtraction of fractions can always be changed into an addition of fractions.

$$\dfrac{a}{c} - \dfrac{b}{c} = \dfrac{a}{c} + \dfrac{-b}{c} = \dfrac{a\ -b}{c}$$

<u>Example 4</u>. Adding like algebraic fractions.

(a) $\dfrac{2}{x} + \dfrac{5}{x} = \dfrac{2 + 5}{x} = \dfrac{7}{x}$

(b) $\dfrac{7}{a - 2} - \dfrac{4}{a - 2} = \dfrac{7}{a - 2} + \dfrac{-4}{a - 2} = \dfrac{7 - 4}{a - 2} = \dfrac{3}{a - 2}$

(c) $\dfrac{3}{4a} - \dfrac{5}{4a} = \dfrac{3}{4a} + \dfrac{-5}{4a} = \dfrac{3 - 5}{4a} = \dfrac{-2}{4a} = -\dfrac{\overset{1}{\cancel{2}}}{\underset{2}{\cancel{4a}}} = -\dfrac{1}{2a}$

(d) $\dfrac{4x}{2x - y} - \dfrac{2y}{2x - y} = \dfrac{4x - 2y}{2x - y} = \dfrac{2(2x - y)}{(2x - y)} = \dfrac{2\cancel{(2x - y)}}{\cancel{(2x - y)}} = 2$

(e) $\dfrac{15}{d - 5} + \dfrac{-3d}{d - 5} = \dfrac{15 - 3d}{d - 5} = \dfrac{3(5 - d)}{d - 5} = -\dfrac{3(d - 5)}{d - 5} = -3$

Changing sign of fraction and numerator ⎯⎯⎯↑

When denominators differ only by sign, we can make the fractions like fractions by changing signs. (See Example 5.)

<u>Example 5</u>. Add: $\dfrac{9}{x - 2} + \dfrac{5}{2 - x}$

⎯⎯Changing sign of numerator and denominator

$\dfrac{9}{x - 2} + \dfrac{5}{2 - x} = \dfrac{9}{x - 2} + \dfrac{-5}{-(2 - x)} = \dfrac{9}{x - 2} + \dfrac{-5}{x - 2} = \dfrac{9 - 5}{x - 2} = \dfrac{4}{x - 2}$

⎣⎯ This denominator can be changed to $x - 2$ by a sign change

<u>EXERCISES 904</u>. Add the fractions.

SET I

1. $\dfrac{7}{a} + \dfrac{2}{a}$ 2. $\dfrac{5}{b} + \dfrac{2}{b}$

3. $\dfrac{6}{x - y} - \dfrac{2}{x - y}$ 4. $\dfrac{7}{m + n} - \dfrac{1}{m + n}$

5. $\dfrac{2}{3a} + \dfrac{4}{3a}$

6. $\dfrac{8}{5z} + \dfrac{2}{5z}$

7. $\dfrac{2y}{y+1} + \dfrac{2}{y+1}$

8. $\dfrac{3x}{x-4} - \dfrac{12}{x-4}$

9. $\dfrac{3}{x+3} + \dfrac{x}{x+3}$

10. $\dfrac{m}{m-4} - \dfrac{4}{m-4}$

----

11. $\dfrac{x-3}{y-2} - \dfrac{x+5}{y-2}$

12. $\dfrac{z+4}{a-b} - \dfrac{z+3}{a-b}$

13. $\dfrac{a+2}{2a+1} - \dfrac{1-a}{2a+1}$

14. $\dfrac{6x-1}{3x-2} - \dfrac{3x+1}{3x-2}$

15. $\dfrac{-x}{x-2} - \dfrac{2}{2-x}$

16. $\dfrac{-2a}{b-2a} + \dfrac{-b}{2a-b}$

17. $\dfrac{-15w}{1-5w} - \dfrac{3}{5w-1}$

18. $\dfrac{-35}{6w-7} - \dfrac{30w}{7-6w}$

19. $\dfrac{7z}{8z-4} + \dfrac{6-5z}{4-8z}$

20. $\dfrac{13-30w}{15-10w} - \dfrac{10w+17}{10w-15}$

SET II

1. $\dfrac{6}{x} - \dfrac{2}{x}$

2. $\dfrac{x+1}{a+b} + \dfrac{x-1}{a+b}$

3. $\dfrac{2a}{2a+3} + \dfrac{3}{2a+3}$

4. $\dfrac{2x+1}{x+4} - \dfrac{x-3}{x+4}$

5. $\dfrac{9x}{3x-y} - \dfrac{3y}{3x-y}$

6. $\dfrac{5a}{a-2b} - \dfrac{10b}{a-2b}$

7. $\dfrac{8}{z-4} - \dfrac{2z}{z-4}$

8. $\dfrac{15}{m-5} - \dfrac{3m}{m-5}$

9. $\dfrac{4x+y}{2x+y} + \dfrac{2x+2y}{2x+y}$

10. $\dfrac{7x-1}{3x-1} - \dfrac{x+1}{3x-1}$

11. $\dfrac{b}{b-2a} + \dfrac{2a}{2a-b}$

12. $\dfrac{11x-9y}{8x-6y} - \dfrac{13x-9y}{6y-8x}$

905

Lowest Common Denominator (LCD)

We ordinarily use the lowest common denominator (LCD) when adding or subtracting unlike fractions.

<u>In Arithmetic.</u> The lowest common denominator (LCD) is the smallest number that is exactly divisible by each of the denominators. Consider the problem:

$$\dfrac{1}{2} + \dfrac{3}{4}$$

In this example it is possible to determine the LCD by inspection: LCD = 4.
Then, since

$$\frac{1}{2} = \frac{2}{4}$$

therefore, $\frac{1}{2} + \frac{3}{4} = \frac{2}{4} + \frac{3}{4} = \frac{2 + 3}{4} = \frac{5}{4}$

Consider the problem:

$$\frac{7}{12} + \frac{4}{15}$$

Here the LCD is not easily found by inspection. To find the LCD in this case:

1. Find the prime factorization of each denominator.

$$12 = 2^2 \cdot 3 \qquad 15 = 3 \cdot 5$$

2. Write down each different factor that appears in the prime factorizations.

$$2, \quad 3, \quad 5$$

3. Raise each factor to the highest power it occurs in any denominator.

$$2^2, \quad 3, \quad 5$$

4. LCD $= 2^2 \cdot 3 \cdot 5 = 60$

<u>In Algebra</u>. This same method is used for finding the LCD for algebraic fractions.

TO FIND THE LCD

1. Factor each denominator completely. Repeated factors should be expressed as powers.

2. Write down each different factor that appears.

3. Raise each factor to the highest power it occurs in any denominator.

4. The LCD is the product of all the powers found in Step 3.

Example 1.　Find the LCD for $\dfrac{3}{2} + \dfrac{4}{y}$.

Solution

　1.　The denominators are already factored.

　2.　2 and y are the different factors.

　3.　2^1, y^1　(highest power of each factor).

　4.　LCD = $2^1 \cdot y^1 = 2y$

Example 2.　Find the LCD for $\dfrac{2}{x} + \dfrac{5}{x^2}$.

Solution

　1.　The denominators are already factored.

　2.　x　(x is the only different factor.)

　3.　x^2　(x^2 is the highest power in any denominator.)

　4.　LCD = x^2

Example 3.　Find the LCD for $\dfrac{7}{5b^3} + \dfrac{4}{15b^2}$.

Solution

　1.　$5 \cdot b^3$,　$3 \cdot 5 \cdot b^2$　　　Denominators in factored form.

　2.　3,　5,　b　　　All the different factors.

　3.　3^1,　5^1,　b^3　　　Highest powers.

　4.　LCD = $3^1 \cdot 5^1 \cdot b^3 = 15b^3$

Example 4.　Find the LCD for $\dfrac{7}{18x^2y} + \dfrac{5}{8xy^4}$.

Solution

　1.　$2 \cdot 3^2 \cdot x^2 \cdot y$,　$2^3 \cdot x \cdot y^4$　　Denominators in factored form.

　2.　2,　3,　x,　y　　　All the different factors.

　3.　2^3,　3^2,　x^2,　y^4　　　Highest powers.

　4.　LCD = $2^3 \cdot 3^2 \cdot x^2 \cdot y^4 = 72x^2y^4$

Example 5.　Find the LCD for $\dfrac{2}{x} + \dfrac{x}{x + 2}$.

Solution

　1.　The denominators are already factored.

　2.　x,　$(x + 2)$

　3.　x^1,　$(x + 2)^1$

　4.　LCD = $x(x + 2)$

Example 6. Find the LCD for $\dfrac{16a}{a^2b} + \dfrac{a-2}{2a(a-b)} - \dfrac{b+1}{4b^3(a-b)}$.

Solution

    1. a^2b, $2a(a-b)$, $2^2b^3(a-b)$

    2. 2, a, b, $(a-b)$ All the different factors.

    3. 2^2, a^2, b^3, $(a-b)^1$ Highest powers.

    4.   LCD $= 2^2a^2b^3(a-b)^1 = 4a^2b^3(a-b)$

Example 7. Find the LCD for $\dfrac{8}{3x-3} - \dfrac{5}{x^2+2x+1}$.

Solution

    1. $3x - 3 = 3(x-1)$; $x^2 + 2x + 1 = (x+1)^2$

    2. 3, $(x-1)$, $(x+1)$

    3. 3^1, $(x-1)^1$, $(x+1)^2$

    4.   LCD $= 3(x-1)(x+1)^2$

Example 8. Find the LCD for

$$\frac{2x-3}{x^2+10x+25} - \frac{14}{4x^2+20x} + \frac{4x-3}{x^2+2x-15}.$$

Solution

    1. $x^2 + 10x + 25 = (x+5)^2$

           $4x^2 + 20x = 4x(x+5) = 2^2x(x+5)$

          $x^2 + 2x - 15 = (x+5)(x-3)$

    2. 2, x, $(x+5)$, $(x-3)$

    3. 2^2, x, $(x+5)^2$, $(x-3)$

    4.   LCD $= 4x(x+5)^2(x-3)$

EXERCISES 905.   Find the LCD in each exercise.   Do *not* add the fractions.

SET I

1. $\dfrac{x}{3} + \dfrac{2}{x}$ 2. $\dfrac{3}{2y} - \dfrac{5}{y}$

3. $\dfrac{a-3}{12} - \dfrac{a+6}{4}$ 4. $\dfrac{y-2}{3} + \dfrac{y+5}{9}$

5. $\dfrac{7}{5x} + \dfrac{3}{2x}$ 6. $\dfrac{5}{3z} - \dfrac{9}{4z}$

7. $\dfrac{4}{x} + \dfrac{6}{x^3}$ 8. $\dfrac{3}{a^2} + \dfrac{5}{a^4}$

9. $\dfrac{7}{12u^3v^2} - \dfrac{11}{18uv^3}$ 10. $\dfrac{13}{50x^3y^4} - \dfrac{17}{20x^2y^5}$

11. $\dfrac{4}{a} + \dfrac{a}{a + 3}$

12. $\dfrac{5}{b} + \dfrac{b}{b - 5}$

13. $\dfrac{x}{2x + 4} - \dfrac{5}{4x}$

14. $\dfrac{4}{3x} + \dfrac{2x}{3x + 6}$

15. $\dfrac{3}{4z^2} + \dfrac{2z}{z^2 + 2z + 1} - \dfrac{4z}{z + 1}$

16. $\dfrac{2x}{x^2 - 2x + 1} - \dfrac{5}{x - 1} + \dfrac{11}{12x^3}$

----

17. $\dfrac{x - 4}{x^2 + 3x + 2} + \dfrac{3x + 1}{x^2 + 2x + 1}$

18. $\dfrac{2x + 3}{x^2 - x - 12} + \dfrac{x - 4}{x^2 + 6x + 9}$

19. $\dfrac{x^2 + 1}{12x^3 + 24x^2} - \dfrac{4x + 3}{x^2 - 4x + 4} + \dfrac{1}{x^2 - 4}$

20. $\dfrac{2y + 5}{y^2 + 6y + 9} - \dfrac{7y}{y^2 - 9} - \dfrac{11}{8y^2 - 24y}$

<u>SET II</u>

1. $\dfrac{5}{4y^2} + \dfrac{9}{6y}$

2. $\dfrac{5}{9x^2y} - \dfrac{7}{6xy^2}$

3. $\dfrac{2}{x} + \dfrac{x}{x + 5}$

4. $\dfrac{x}{2} + \dfrac{x}{5}$

5. $\dfrac{3}{2x} + \dfrac{5}{3x}$

6. $\dfrac{x + 1}{4} - \dfrac{x + 3}{2}$

7. $\dfrac{a}{3a + 6} - \dfrac{5}{3a}$

8. $\dfrac{3}{2x} + \dfrac{x}{x^2 + 4x + 4} - \dfrac{1}{x + 2}$

9. $\dfrac{9y}{x^2 - y^2} + \dfrac{6x}{(x + y)^2}$

10. $\dfrac{5}{8z^3} - \dfrac{8z}{z^2 - 4} + \dfrac{5z}{9z + 18}$

Adding Unlike Fractions

Equivalent fractions are fractions that have the same value.
If a fraction is multiplied by 1, its value is unchanged.

$$\left. \begin{array}{l} \dfrac{2}{2} = 1 \\[2mm] \dfrac{x}{x} = 1 \\[2mm] \dfrac{x + 2}{x + 2} = 1 \end{array} \right\}$$ Multiplying a fraction by expressions like these will produce equivalent fractions

For example:

$$\frac{5}{6} = \frac{5}{6} \cdot \frac{2}{2} = \frac{10}{12}$$ A fraction equivalent to $\frac{5}{6}$

$$\frac{x}{x + 2} = \frac{x}{x + 2} \cdot \frac{x}{x} = \frac{x^2}{x(x + 2)}$$ A fraction equivalent to $\frac{x}{x + 2}$

$$\frac{2}{x} = \frac{2}{x} \cdot \frac{x + 2}{x + 2} = \frac{2x + 4}{x(x + 2)}$$ A fraction equivalent to $\frac{2}{x}$

TO ADD UNLIKE FRACTIONS

1. Find the LCD.

2. Convert all fractions to equivalent fractions that have the LCD as denominator.

3. Add the resulting like fractions.

4. Reduce the resulting fraction to lowest terms.

In Arithmetic

Example 1. Find $\frac{1}{3} + \frac{5}{6}$.

Solution: LCD = 6

Since $\frac{1}{3} = \frac{2}{6}$;   then $\frac{1}{3} + \frac{5}{6} = \frac{2}{6} + \frac{5}{6} = \frac{2 + 5}{6} = \frac{7}{6}$.

Example 2. Find $\frac{1}{2} + \frac{2}{3} + \frac{3}{4}$.

Solution: LCD = 12

Since $\frac{1}{2} = \frac{6}{12}$, $\frac{2}{3} = \frac{8}{12}$, and $\frac{3}{4} = \frac{9}{12}$;

then $\frac{1}{2} + \frac{2}{3} + \frac{3}{4} = \frac{6}{12} + \frac{8}{12} + \frac{9}{12} = \frac{6 + 8 + 9}{12} = \frac{23}{12}$

In Algebra. This same method is used for adding unlike fractions in algebra.

Example 3. Add: $\frac{2}{x} + \frac{5}{x^2}$.

Solution

1. LCD = x^2 (Sec. 905, Example 2)

2. $\frac{2}{x} = \frac{2}{x} \cdot \frac{x}{x} = \frac{2x}{x^2}$

We multiply numerator and denominator by x in order to obtain an equivalent fraction whose denominator is the LCD x^2.

3. $\dfrac{2}{x} + \dfrac{5}{x^2} = \dfrac{2x}{x^2} + \dfrac{5}{x^2} = \dfrac{2x + 5}{x^2}$

Example 4. Add: $\dfrac{7}{18x^2y} + \dfrac{5}{8xy^4}$

Solution

1. LCD $= 72x^2y^4$ (Sec. 905, Example 4)

$$4y^3 = \dfrac{72x^2y^4}{18x^2y} = \dfrac{\text{LCD}}{\text{denominator of fraction}}$$

2. $\dfrac{7}{18x^2y} = \dfrac{7}{18x^2y} \cdot \dfrac{4y^3}{4y^3} = \dfrac{28y^3}{72x^2y^4}$

$\dfrac{5}{8xy^4} = \dfrac{5}{8xy^4} \cdot \dfrac{9x}{9x} = \dfrac{45x}{72x^2y^4}$

$$9x = \dfrac{72x^2y^4}{8xy^4} = \dfrac{\text{LCD}}{\text{denominator of fraction}}$$

3. $\dfrac{7}{18x^2y} + \dfrac{5}{8xy^4} = \dfrac{28y^3}{72x^2y^4} + \dfrac{45x}{72x^2y^4} = \dfrac{28y^3 + 45x}{72x^2y^4}$

Example 5. Add: $\dfrac{2}{x} + \dfrac{x}{x + 2}$

Solution

1. LCD $= x(x + 2)$ (Sec. 905, Example 5)

$$x + 2 = \dfrac{x(x + 2)}{x} = \dfrac{\text{LCD}}{\text{denominator of fraction}}$$

2. $\dfrac{2}{x} = \dfrac{2}{x} \cdot \dfrac{x + 2}{x + 2} = \dfrac{2(x + 2)}{x(x + 2)}$

$\dfrac{x}{x + 2} = \dfrac{x}{x + 2} \cdot \dfrac{x}{x} = \dfrac{x^2}{x(x + 2)}$

$$x = \dfrac{x(x + 2)}{x + 2} = \dfrac{\text{LCD}}{\text{denominator of fraction}}$$

3. $\dfrac{2}{x} + \dfrac{x}{x + 2} = \dfrac{2(x + 2)}{x(x + 2)} + \dfrac{x^2}{x(x + 2)} = \dfrac{2x + 4 + x^2}{x(x + 2)}$

4. $\dfrac{2x + 4 + x^2}{x(x + 2)} = \dfrac{x^2 + 2x + 4}{x(x + 2)}$

Example 6. Add: $3 - \dfrac{2a}{a + 2}$

Solution

1. LCD $= a + 2$

2. $3 = \dfrac{3}{1} \cdot \dfrac{a + 2}{a + 2} = \dfrac{3(a + 2)}{a + 2} = \dfrac{3a + 6}{a + 2}$

$\dfrac{2a}{a + 2} = \dfrac{2a}{a + 2}$

3. $3 - \dfrac{2a}{a + 2} = \dfrac{3a + 6}{a + 2} - \dfrac{2a}{a + 2} = \dfrac{3a + 6 - 2a}{a + 2} = \dfrac{a + 6}{a + 2}$

Example 7. Add: $\dfrac{z + 1}{z + 2} - \dfrac{z - 1}{z - 2}$

Solution

1. LCD $= (z + 2)(z - 2)$

2. $\dfrac{z + 1}{z + 2} = \dfrac{z + 1}{z + 2} \cdot \dfrac{z - 2}{z - 2} = \dfrac{z^2 - z - 2}{(z + 2)(z - 2)}$

$\dfrac{z - 1}{z - 2} = \dfrac{z - 1}{z - 2} \cdot \dfrac{z + 2}{z + 2} = \dfrac{z^2 + z - 2}{(z - 2)(z + 2)}$

3. $\dfrac{z + 1}{z + 2} - \dfrac{z - 1}{z - 2} = \dfrac{z^2 - z - 2}{(z + 2)(z - 2)} - \dfrac{z^2 + z - 2}{(z - 2)(z + 2)}$

$= \dfrac{z^2 - z - 2 - (z^2 + z - 2)}{(z + 2)(z - 2)}$

$= \dfrac{-2z}{(z + 2)(z - 2)} = \boxed{- \dfrac{2z}{z^2 - 4}} \leftarrow$

Changing sign of fraction and numerator. ——————

EXERCISES 906. Add the fractions.

SET I

1. $\dfrac{3}{a^2} + \dfrac{2}{a^3}$ 2. $\dfrac{5}{u} + \dfrac{4}{u^3}$ 3. $\dfrac{1}{2} + \dfrac{3}{x} - \dfrac{5}{x^2}$

4. $\dfrac{2}{3} - \dfrac{1}{y} + \dfrac{4}{y^2}$ 5. $\dfrac{2}{xy} - \dfrac{3}{y}$ 6. $\dfrac{5}{ab} - \dfrac{4}{a}$

7. $5 + \dfrac{2}{x}$ 8. $3 + \dfrac{4}{y}$ 9. $\dfrac{5}{4y^2} + \dfrac{9}{6y}$

10. $\dfrac{10}{5x} + \dfrac{3}{4x^2}$ 11. $3x - \dfrac{3}{x}$ 12. $4y - \dfrac{5}{y}$

13. $\dfrac{3}{a} + \dfrac{a}{a + 3}$ 14. $\dfrac{5}{b} + \dfrac{b}{b - 5}$

15. $\dfrac{x}{2x + 4} + \dfrac{-5}{4x}$

16. $\dfrac{4}{3x} + \dfrac{-2x}{3x + 6}$

17. $x + \dfrac{2}{x} - \dfrac{3}{x - 2}$

18. $m - \dfrac{3}{m} + \dfrac{2}{m + 4}$

19. $\dfrac{a + b}{b} + \dfrac{b}{a - b}$

20. $\dfrac{x - y}{x} - \dfrac{x}{x + y}$

21. $\dfrac{3}{2e - 2} - \dfrac{2}{3e - 3}$

22. $\dfrac{2}{3f + 6} - \dfrac{1}{5f + 10}$

----

23. $\dfrac{3}{m - 2} - \dfrac{5}{2 - m}$

24. $\dfrac{7}{n - 5} - \dfrac{2}{5 - n}$

25. $\dfrac{x + 1}{x - 1} - \dfrac{x - 1}{x + 1}$

26. $\dfrac{x - 5}{x + 5} - \dfrac{x + 5}{x - 5}$

27. $\dfrac{y}{x^2 - xy} + \dfrac{x}{y^2 - xy}$

28. $\dfrac{b}{ab - a^2} - \dfrac{a}{b^2 - ab}$

29. $\dfrac{2x}{x - 3} - \dfrac{2x}{x + 3} + \dfrac{36}{x^2 - 9}$

30. $\dfrac{x}{x + 4} - \dfrac{x}{x - 4} - \dfrac{32}{x^2 - 16}$

31. $\dfrac{x}{x^2 + 4x + 4} + \dfrac{1}{x + 2}$

32. $\dfrac{2x}{x^2 - 2x + 1} - \dfrac{5}{x - 1}$

SET II

1. $\dfrac{3}{x} + \dfrac{4}{x^2}$

2. $\dfrac{1}{3} - \dfrac{1}{a} + \dfrac{2}{a^2}$

3. $\dfrac{5}{xy} - \dfrac{3}{x}$

4. $2 + \dfrac{4}{z}$

5. $\dfrac{5}{6xy^2} + \dfrac{7}{8x^2y}$

6. $4m - \dfrac{5}{m}$

7. $\dfrac{2}{x} + \dfrac{x}{x + 2}$

8. $\dfrac{2}{x + 5} - \dfrac{3}{x - 5}$

9. $a + \dfrac{3}{a} - \dfrac{2}{a - 2}$

10. $\dfrac{2}{a + 3} - \dfrac{4}{a - 1}$

11. $\dfrac{a - b}{b} + \dfrac{b}{a + b}$

12. $\dfrac{x + 2}{x - 3} - \dfrac{x + 3}{x - 2}$

13. $\dfrac{x - 1}{x + 2} - \dfrac{x - 2}{x + 1}$

14. $\dfrac{5}{x - 3} - \dfrac{4}{3 - x}$

15. $\dfrac{x}{x - 1} - \dfrac{x}{x + 1} + \dfrac{2}{x^2 - 1}$

16. $\dfrac{x + 2}{x^2 + x - 2} + \dfrac{3}{x^2 - 1}$

Complex Fractions

A *simple fraction* is a fraction that has only one fraction line.

Examples of simple fractions:

$$\frac{2}{x}, \quad \frac{3+y}{12}, \quad \frac{7a-7b}{ab^2}, \quad \frac{5}{x+y}$$

A *complex fraction* is a fraction that has more than one fraction line.

Examples of complex fractions:

$$\frac{\frac{2}{x}}{3}, \quad \frac{a}{\frac{1}{c}}, \quad \frac{\frac{3}{z}}{\frac{5}{z}}, \quad \frac{\frac{3}{x}-\frac{2}{y}}{\frac{5}{x}+\frac{3}{y}}$$

The Parts of a Complex Fraction.

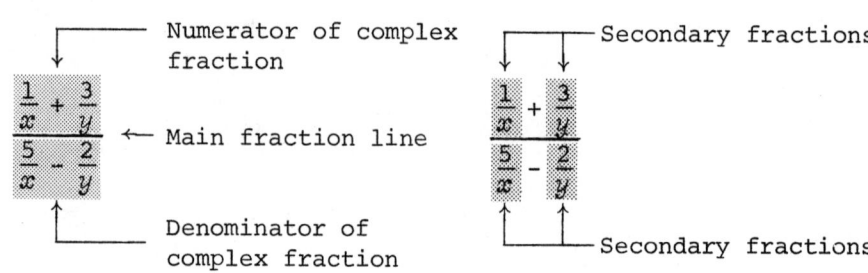

Numerator of complex fraction

← Main fraction line

Denominator of complex fraction

Secondary fractions

Secondary fractions

TO SIMPLIFY COMPLEX FRACTIONS

Method 1. Multiply both numerator and denominator of the complex fraction by the LCD of the secondary fractions, then simplify the results.

Method 2. First simplify the numerator and denominator of the complex fraction, then divide the simplified numerator by the simplified denominator.

Note that in some of the following examples the solution by Method 1 is easier than that by Method 2. In others, the opposite is true.

Example 1. Simplify the complex fraction

$$\dfrac{\dfrac{1}{2} + \dfrac{3}{4}}{\dfrac{5}{6} - \dfrac{2}{3}}$$

Method 1. The LCD of the secondary denominators 2, 4, 6, and 3 is 12.

$$\dfrac{12}{12} \cdot \dfrac{\dfrac{1}{2} + \dfrac{3}{4}}{\dfrac{5}{6} - \dfrac{2}{3}} = \dfrac{12\left(\dfrac{1}{2} + \dfrac{3}{4}\right)}{12\left(\dfrac{5}{6} - \dfrac{2}{3}\right)} = \dfrac{\dfrac{12}{1}\left(\dfrac{1}{2}\right) + \dfrac{12}{1}\left(\dfrac{3}{4}\right)}{\dfrac{12}{1}\left(\dfrac{5}{6}\right) - \dfrac{12}{1}\left(\dfrac{2}{3}\right)} = \dfrac{6 + 9}{10 - 8}$$

$$= \dfrac{15}{2} = 7\dfrac{1}{2}$$

└── This is 1.

Method 2

$$\dfrac{\dfrac{1}{2} + \dfrac{3}{4}}{\dfrac{5}{6} - \dfrac{2}{3}} = \left(\dfrac{1}{2} + \dfrac{3}{4}\right) \div \left(\dfrac{5}{6} - \dfrac{2}{3}\right) = \left(\dfrac{2}{4} + \dfrac{3}{4}\right) \div \left(\dfrac{5}{6} - \dfrac{4}{6}\right)$$

$$= \dfrac{5}{4} \div \dfrac{1}{6} = \dfrac{5}{\underset{2}{\cancel{4}}} \cdot \dfrac{\overset{3}{\cancel{6}}}{1} = \dfrac{15}{2} = 7\dfrac{1}{2}$$

Example 2. Simplify $\dfrac{4 + \dfrac{1}{4}}{2 - \dfrac{1}{2}}$.

Method 1. The LCD of the secondary denominators 4 and 2 is 4.

$$\dfrac{4}{4} \cdot \dfrac{4 + \dfrac{1}{4}}{2 - \dfrac{1}{2}} = \dfrac{4\left(4 + \dfrac{1}{4}\right)}{4\left(2 - \dfrac{1}{2}\right)} = \dfrac{\dfrac{4}{1}\left(\dfrac{4}{1}\right) + \dfrac{4}{1}\left(\dfrac{1}{4}\right)}{\dfrac{4}{1}\left(\dfrac{2}{1}\right) - \dfrac{4}{1}\left(\dfrac{1}{2}\right)} = \dfrac{16 + 1}{8 - 2} = \dfrac{17}{6} = 2\dfrac{5}{6}$$

Method 2. $\dfrac{4 + \dfrac{1}{4}}{2 - \dfrac{1}{2}} = \left(4 + \dfrac{1}{4}\right) \div \left(2 - \dfrac{1}{2}\right) = \left(\dfrac{16}{4} + \dfrac{1}{4}\right) \div \left(\dfrac{4}{2} - \dfrac{1}{2}\right)$

$$= \dfrac{17}{4} \div \dfrac{3}{2} = \dfrac{17}{\underset{2}{\cancel{4}}} \cdot \dfrac{\overset{1}{\cancel{2}}}{3} = \dfrac{17}{6} = 2\dfrac{5}{6}$$

In Algebra. These same two methods are used for simplifying complex algebraic fractions.

Example 3. Simplify $\dfrac{\dfrac{4b^2}{9a^2}}{\dfrac{8b}{3a^3}}$. $\longleftarrow$ main fraction line

Method 1. The LCD of the secondary denominators $9a^2$ and $3a^3$ is $9a^3$.

$$\dfrac{9a^3}{9a^3}\left(\dfrac{\dfrac{4b^2}{9a^2}}{\dfrac{8b}{3a^3}}\right) = \dfrac{\dfrac{9a^3}{1}\left(\dfrac{4b^2}{9a^2}\right)}{\dfrac{9a^3}{1}\left(\dfrac{8b}{3a^3}\right)} = \dfrac{4ab^2}{24b} = \dfrac{ab}{6}$$

$\longrightarrow$ The value of this fraction is 1.

Method 2. $\dfrac{\dfrac{4b^2}{9a^2}}{\dfrac{8b}{3a^3}} = \dfrac{4b^2}{9a^2} \div \dfrac{8b}{3a^3} = \dfrac{\overset{1}{\cancel{4b^2}}}{\underset{3}{\cancel{9a^2}}} \cdot \dfrac{\overset{1}{\cancel{3a^3}}}{\underset{2}{\cancel{8b}}} = \dfrac{ab}{6}$

Example 4. Simplify $\dfrac{\dfrac{2}{x} - \dfrac{3}{x^2}}{5 + \dfrac{1}{x}}$.

Method 1. The LCD of the secondary denominators x and x^2 is x^2.

$$\dfrac{x^2}{x^2}\left(\dfrac{\dfrac{2}{x} - \dfrac{3}{x^2}}{5 + \dfrac{1}{x}}\right) = \dfrac{\dfrac{x^2}{1}\left(\dfrac{2}{x}\right) - \dfrac{x^2}{1}\left(\dfrac{3}{x^2}\right)}{\dfrac{x^2}{1}\left(\dfrac{5}{1}\right) + \dfrac{x^2}{1}\left(\dfrac{1}{x}\right)} = \dfrac{2x - 3}{5x^2 + x}$$

Method 2. $\dfrac{\dfrac{2}{x} - \dfrac{3}{x^2}}{5 + \dfrac{1}{x}} = \left(\dfrac{2}{x} - \dfrac{3}{x^2}\right) \div \left(5 + \dfrac{1}{x}\right)$

$$= \left(\dfrac{2x}{x^2} - \dfrac{3}{x^2}\right) \div \left(\dfrac{5x}{x} + \dfrac{1}{x}\right)$$

$$= \dfrac{2x - 3}{x^2} \div \dfrac{5x + 1}{x}$$

$$= \dfrac{2x - 3}{x^2} \cdot \dfrac{x}{5x + 1} = \dfrac{2x - 3}{5x^2 + x}$$

Example 5. Simplify $\dfrac{1}{a^{-1} + b^{-1}}$.

Solution: $\dfrac{1}{a^{-1} + b^{-1}} = \dfrac{1}{\dfrac{1}{a} + \dfrac{1}{b}}$

<u>Method 1.</u> The LCD of the secondary denominators a and b
is ab.

$$\frac{ab}{ab}\left(\frac{1}{\dfrac{1}{a}+\dfrac{1}{b}}\right) = \frac{\dfrac{ab}{1}\left(\dfrac{1}{1}\right)}{\dfrac{ab}{1}\left(\dfrac{1}{a}\right)+\dfrac{ab}{1}\left(\dfrac{1}{b}\right)}$$

$$= \frac{ab}{b+a} \quad \text{or} \quad \frac{ab}{a+b}$$

<u>Method 2.</u>
$$\frac{1}{\dfrac{1}{a}+\dfrac{1}{b}} = 1 \div \left(\frac{1}{a}+\frac{1}{b}\right)$$

$$= 1 \div \left(\frac{b}{ab}+\frac{a}{ab}\right)$$

$$= 1 \div \frac{b+a}{ab}$$

$$= \frac{1}{1} \cdot \frac{ab}{b+a} = \frac{ab}{b+a} \quad \text{or} \quad \frac{ab}{a+b}$$

<u>EXERCISES 907.</u> Simplify each of the complex fractions.

<u>SET I</u>

1. $\dfrac{\dfrac{3}{4}-\dfrac{1}{2}}{\dfrac{5}{8}+\dfrac{1}{4}}$

2. $\dfrac{\dfrac{5}{6}-\dfrac{1}{3}}{\dfrac{2}{9}+\dfrac{1}{6}}$

3. $\dfrac{\dfrac{3}{5}+2}{2-\dfrac{3}{4}}$

4. $\dfrac{\dfrac{3}{16}+5}{6-\dfrac{7}{8}}$

5. $\dfrac{\dfrac{5x^3}{3y^4}}{\dfrac{10x}{9y}}$

6. $\dfrac{\dfrac{8a^4}{5b}}{\dfrac{4a^3}{15b^2}}$

7. $\dfrac{\dfrac{18cd^2}{5a^3b}}{\dfrac{12cd^2}{15ab^2}}$

8. $\dfrac{\dfrac{8x^2y}{7z^3}}{\dfrac{12xy^2}{21z^5}}$

9. $\dfrac{\dfrac{x+3}{5}}{\dfrac{2x+6}{10}}$

10. $\dfrac{\dfrac{a-4}{3}}{\dfrac{2a-8}{9}}$

11. $\dfrac{\dfrac{a}{b}+1}{\dfrac{a}{b}-1}$

12. $\dfrac{2+\dfrac{x}{y}}{2-\dfrac{x}{y}}$

13. $\dfrac{\dfrac{c}{d}+2}{\dfrac{c^2}{d^2}-4}$

14. $\dfrac{\dfrac{x^2}{y^2}-1}{\dfrac{x}{y}-1}$

----

15. $\dfrac{1}{1-\dfrac{1}{x}}$

16. $\dfrac{1}{1+\dfrac{1}{y}}$

17. $\dfrac{x+\dfrac{1}{y}}{y}$

18. $\dfrac{\dfrac{1}{a}-b}{b}$

19. $\dfrac{x+y^{-1}}{y}$

20. $\dfrac{a^{-1}-b}{b}$

21. $\dfrac{2+\dfrac{3}{z}}{4-\dfrac{5}{z}}$

22. $\dfrac{\dfrac{1}{x}+\dfrac{2}{x^2}}{3+\dfrac{4}{x^2}}$

23. $\dfrac{\dfrac{1}{x^2} - \dfrac{1}{y^2}}{\dfrac{1}{x} + \dfrac{1}{y}}$ 24. $\dfrac{\dfrac{1}{a^2} - \dfrac{1}{4}}{\dfrac{1}{a} - \dfrac{1}{2}}$ 25. $\dfrac{x^{-2} - y^{-2}}{x^{-1} + y^{-1}}$ 26. $\dfrac{a^{-2} - \dfrac{1}{4}}{a^{-1} - \dfrac{1}{2}}$

SET II

1. $\dfrac{\dfrac{5}{6} - \dfrac{1}{3}}{\dfrac{3}{2} - \dfrac{1}{4}}$ 2. $\dfrac{\dfrac{3}{4} + 2}{3 - \dfrac{1}{2}}$ 3. $\dfrac{\dfrac{3a^3}{5b^2}}{\dfrac{6a^2}{10b^3}}$ 4. $\dfrac{\dfrac{x - 2}{4}}{\dfrac{3x - 6}{12}}$

5. $\dfrac{\dfrac{a}{b} - 2}{2 + \dfrac{a}{b}}$ 6. $\dfrac{\dfrac{x^2}{y^2} - 4}{\dfrac{x}{y} + 2}$ 7. $\dfrac{2}{1 + \dfrac{1}{x}}$ 8. $\dfrac{1 - \dfrac{1}{a^2}}{\dfrac{1}{a} - \dfrac{1}{a^2}}$

9. $\dfrac{\dfrac{1}{a} + \dfrac{1}{b}}{\dfrac{1}{ab}}$ 10. $\dfrac{\dfrac{1}{x^2} - 9}{\dfrac{1}{x} + 3}$ 11. $\dfrac{a^{-1} + b^{-1}}{a^{-1}b^{-1}}$ 12. $\dfrac{x^{-2} - 9}{x^{-1} + 3}$

Solving Equations Having Fractions

In Sec. 404 we removed fractions from simple equations by multiplying both sides by the same number. In this section we extend this method to more complicated equations.

Polynomial equations whose highest-degree term is first-degree are called *first-degree equations*.

TO SOLVE AN EQUATION HAVING FRACTIONS
THAT SIMPLIFIES TO A FIRST-DEGREE EQUATION

1. *Remove fractions* by multiplying each term by the LCD.

2. *Remove grouping symbols.*

3. *Collect and combine like terms*; all terms with the unknown on one side, all other terms on the other side.

4. *Divide both sides by the coefficient of the unknown.*

Check apparent solutions in the original equation. Any value of a letter that makes any denominator in the equation zero is not a solution.

__Example 1.__   Solve $\dfrac{x}{2} + \dfrac{x}{3} = 5$.

Solution: The LCD of the fractions is 6. Multiply both sides by the LCD, 6.

$6\left(\dfrac{x}{2}\right) + 6\left(\dfrac{x}{3}\right) = 6\,(5)$

This results in *each term* of the equation being multiplied by the LCD, 6.

$\dfrac{\overset{3}{6}}{1}\left(\dfrac{x}{\underset{1}{2}}\right) + \dfrac{\overset{2}{6}}{1}\left(\dfrac{x}{\underset{1}{3}}\right) = \dfrac{6}{1}\left(\dfrac{5}{1}\right)$

$$3x + 2x = 30$$
$$5x = 30$$
$$x = 6$$

Check: $\dfrac{x}{2} + \dfrac{x}{3} = 5$

$$\dfrac{6}{2} + \dfrac{6}{3} = 5$$

$$3 + 2 = 5$$

__Example 2.__   Solve $\dfrac{x-4}{2} - \dfrac{x}{5} = \dfrac{1}{10}$.

Solution: LCD = 10

$\dfrac{\overset{5}{10}}{1}\left(\dfrac{x-4}{\underset{1}{2}}\right) - \dfrac{\overset{2}{10}}{1}\left(\dfrac{x}{\underset{1}{5}}\right) = \dfrac{10}{1}\left(\dfrac{1}{10}\right)$

Multiplying both sides by the LCD.

$$5(x-4) - 2x = 1$$
$$5x - 20 - 2x = 1$$
$$3x = 21$$
$$x = 7$$

Check: $\dfrac{x-4}{2} - \dfrac{x}{5} = \dfrac{1}{10}$

$$\dfrac{7-4}{2} - \dfrac{7}{5} = \dfrac{1}{10}$$

$$\dfrac{3}{2} - \dfrac{7}{5} = \dfrac{1}{10}$$

$$\dfrac{15}{10} - \dfrac{14}{10} = \dfrac{1}{10}$$

When an equation has only one fraction on each side of the equal sign, it is a proportion. Remember that any polynomial can be considered a fraction if it is divided by 1.

Proportions can be solved by setting the product of the means equal to the product of the extremes. Proportions can also be solved by multiplying both sides by the LCD.

__Example 3.__   Solve $\dfrac{3}{a} = 4$.

Solution: $\dfrac{3}{a} = \dfrac{4}{1}$

Writing $\dfrac{4}{1}$ makes the equation a proportion.

$4 \cdot a = 3 \cdot 1$

Product of means = product of extremes.

$a = \dfrac{3}{4}$

Dividing both sides by 4.

Check: $\dfrac{3}{a} = 4$

$$\dfrac{3}{\frac{3}{4}} = \dfrac{4}{1}$$

$$3 \cdot 1 = \dfrac{3}{\cancel{4}} \cdot \dfrac{\cancel{4}}{1}$$

$$3 = 3$$

Example 4.   Solve $\dfrac{9x}{x-3} = 6$.

Solution: $\dfrac{9x}{x-3} = \dfrac{6}{1}$ Writing $\dfrac{6}{1}$ makes the equation a proportion.

$9x \cdot 1 = 6(x-3)$ Product of means = product of extremes.

$9x = 6x - 18$ Removing ( ).

$\underline{-6x \qquad -6x}$

$3x = \qquad -18$ Getting x's on one side.

$x = -6$ Dividing both sides by 3.

Check: $\dfrac{9x}{x-3} = 6$

$$\dfrac{9(-6)}{-6-3} = 6$$

$$\dfrac{-54}{-9} = 6$$

$$6 = 6$$

Example 5.   Solve $\dfrac{x+1}{x-2} = \dfrac{7}{4}$.

Solution: $\dfrac{x+1}{x-2} = \dfrac{7}{4}$ This is a proportion.

$4(x+1) = 7(x-2)$ Product of means = product of extremes.

$4x + 4 = 7x - 14$ Removing ( ).

$18 = 3x$

$6 = x$ Dividing both sides by 3.

Check: $\dfrac{x+1}{x-2} = \dfrac{7}{4}$

$$\dfrac{6+1}{6-2} = \dfrac{7}{4}$$

$$\dfrac{7}{4} = \dfrac{7}{4}$$

Before beginning to solve an equation, note all excluded values of the variable by inspection. Any excluded value cannot be a solution of the equation.

Example 6.   Solve $\dfrac{x}{x-3} = \dfrac{3}{x-3} + 4$.

Note.   3 is an excluded value because it makes the denominators $x - 3$ zero.   Therefore, 3 cannot be a solution of this equation.

Solution: LCD = $x - 3$

$$\frac{\cancel{(x-3)}}{1} \cdot \frac{x}{\cancel{(x-3)}} = \frac{\cancel{(x-3)}}{1} \cdot \frac{3}{\cancel{(x-3)}} + \frac{(x-3)}{1} \cdot \frac{4}{1}$$

$$x \qquad\qquad = \qquad 3 \qquad + \quad 4(x-3)$$

$$x = 3 + 4x - 12$$
$$x = 4x - 9$$
$$9 = 3x$$
$$3 = x \qquad \text{Since 3 is an excluded value,}$$

this equation has *no solution* (that is a real number).

If we try to check the value 3 in the equation, we have:

Check: $\dfrac{x}{x-3} = \dfrac{3}{x-3} + 4$

$$\frac{3}{3-3} = \frac{3}{3-3} + 4$$

$$\boxed{\frac{3}{0}} = \boxed{\frac{3}{0}} + 4$$

$\uparrow \qquad \uparrow$ ——— not a real number

A word of caution.   Because students solve a proportion by cross-multiplication, they sometimes use cross-multiplication incorrectly in a product of fractions.

Correct application of cross-multiplication

This is an *equation.*

If $\qquad \dfrac{16}{6} = \dfrac{8}{3}$,

then $\quad 16 \cdot 3 = 6 \cdot 8$

$$48 = 48$$

Incorrect application of cross-multiplication

This is a *product.*

$$\frac{16}{6} \cdot \frac{8}{3} \neq \frac{16 \cdot 3}{6 \cdot 8}$$

Correct product

$$\frac{16}{6} \cdot \frac{8}{3} = \frac{16 \cdot 8}{6 \cdot 3} = \frac{128}{18}$$

<u>EXERCISES 908A.</u> Solve the equations.

<u>SET I</u>

1. $\dfrac{x}{3} + \dfrac{x}{4} = 7$ 2. $\dfrac{x}{5} + \dfrac{x}{3} = 8$

3. $\dfrac{10}{c} = 2$ 4. $\dfrac{6}{z} = 4$

5. $\dfrac{a}{2} - \dfrac{a}{5} = 6$ 6. $\dfrac{b}{3} - \dfrac{b}{7} = 12$

7. $\dfrac{9}{2x} = 3$ 8. $\dfrac{14}{3x} = 7$

9. $\dfrac{M-2}{5} + \dfrac{M}{3} = \dfrac{1}{5}$ 10. $\dfrac{y+2}{4} + \dfrac{y}{5} = \dfrac{1}{4}$

11. $\dfrac{7}{x+4} = \dfrac{3}{x}$ 12. $\dfrac{5}{x+6} = \dfrac{2}{x}$

13. $\dfrac{3x}{x-2} = 5$ 14. $\dfrac{4}{x+3} = \dfrac{2}{x}$

----

15. $\dfrac{x}{x^2+1} = \dfrac{2}{1+2x}$ 16. $\dfrac{3x}{3x^2+2} = \dfrac{1}{x+1}$

17. $\dfrac{2x-1}{3} + \dfrac{3x}{4} = \dfrac{5}{6}$ 18. $\dfrac{3z-2}{4} + \dfrac{3z}{8} = \dfrac{3}{4}$

19. $\dfrac{2(m-3)}{5} - \dfrac{3(m+2)}{2} = \dfrac{7}{10}$

20. $\dfrac{5(x-4)}{6} - \dfrac{2(x+4)}{9} = \dfrac{5}{18}$

21. $\dfrac{x}{x-2} = \dfrac{2}{x-2} + 5$ 22. $\dfrac{x}{x+5} = 4 - \dfrac{5}{x+5}$

<u>SET II</u>

1. $\dfrac{x}{5} + \dfrac{x}{2} = 7$ 2. $\dfrac{8}{z} = 4$

3. $\dfrac{a}{4} - \dfrac{a}{3} = 1$ 4. $\dfrac{y-1}{2} + \dfrac{y}{5} = \dfrac{3}{10}$

5. $\dfrac{3x+1}{3} - \dfrac{x}{2} = \dfrac{5}{6}$ 6. $\dfrac{6}{y-2} = \dfrac{3}{y}$

7. $\dfrac{5}{x-3} = \dfrac{2}{x}$ 8. $\dfrac{x}{x^2+1} = \dfrac{2}{2x+1}$

9. $\dfrac{2z-4}{3} + \dfrac{3z}{2} = \dfrac{5}{6}$ 10. $\dfrac{2(m-1)}{5} - \dfrac{3(m+1)}{2} = \dfrac{3}{10}$

306   Chapter 9: Fractions

11. $\dfrac{x}{x + 3} = 2 + \dfrac{3}{x + 3}$ 12. $\dfrac{y}{y - 3} + 10 = \dfrac{3}{y - 3}$

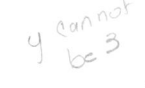

After removing fractions and grouping symbols, there may be second-degree terms. When this is the case, the equation can sometimes be solved by factoring (Sec. 808).

Polynomial equations whose highest-degree term is second-degree are called *second-degree* or *quadratic equations.*

TO SOLVE A QUADRATIC EQUATION BY FACTORING

1. Get *all* nonzero terms to one side by adding the same expression to both sides. *Only zero must remain on the other side.* Then arrange the terms in descending powers.

2. Factor the polynomial.

3. Set each factor equal to zero, and then solve for the unknown.

<u>Check</u> apparent solutions in the original equation. Any value of a letter that makes any denominator in the equation zero is not a solution.

<u>Example 7</u>. Solve $\dfrac{2}{x} + \dfrac{3}{x^2} = 1$.

Solution: LCD $= x^2$

$$\dfrac{x^2}{1}\left(\dfrac{2}{x}\right) + \dfrac{x^2}{1}\left(\dfrac{3}{x^2}\right) = \dfrac{x^2}{1}\left(\dfrac{1}{1}\right)$$

second-degree term

$$2x + 3 = x^2$$
$$0 = x^2 - 2x - 3$$
$$0 = (x - 3)(x + 1)$$
$$x - 3 = 0 \quad | \quad x + 1 = 0$$
$$x = 3 \quad | \qquad x = -1$$

Check for $x = 3$:

$$\dfrac{2}{x} + \dfrac{3}{x^2} = 1$$

$$\dfrac{2}{3} + \dfrac{3}{3^2} \overset{?}{=} 1$$

$$\dfrac{2}{3} + \dfrac{1}{3} = 1$$

Check for $x = -1$:

$$\dfrac{2}{x} + \dfrac{3}{x^2} = 1$$

$$\dfrac{2}{-1} + \dfrac{3}{(-1)^2} \overset{?}{=} 1$$

$$-2 + 3 = 1$$

Example 8. Solve $\dfrac{8}{x} = \dfrac{3}{x + 1} + 3$.

Solution: LCD $= x(x + 1)$

$$\frac{\cancel{x}(x + 1)}{1} \cdot \frac{8}{\cancel{x}} = \frac{x\cancel{(x + 1)}}{1} \cdot \frac{3}{\cancel{(x + 1)}} + \frac{x(x + 1)}{1} \cdot \frac{3}{1}$$

$$8(x + 1) = \qquad\quad 3x \qquad\quad + \quad 3x(x + 1)$$

Second-degree term

$$8x + 8 = \qquad\quad 3x + \boxed{3x^2} + 3x$$

$$0 = 3x^2 - 2x - 8$$

$$0 = (3x + 4)(x - 2)$$

$$
\begin{array}{c|c}
3x + 4 = 0 & x - 2 = 0 \\
3x = -4 & x = 2 \\
x = -\dfrac{4}{3} &
\end{array}
$$

You should check to see that both $x = 2$ and $x = -\dfrac{4}{3}$ make the two sides of the equation equal.

A word of caution. A common mistake students make is to confuse *an equation* such as $\dfrac{2}{x} + \dfrac{3}{x^2} = 1$ with *a sum* such as $\dfrac{2}{x} + \dfrac{3}{x^2}$.

The Equation	*The Sum*
Both sides are multiplied by the LCD to remove fractions.	Each fraction is changed into an equivalent fraction having the LCD for a denominator.
$\dfrac{2}{x} + \dfrac{3}{x^2} = 1 \qquad$ LCD $= x^2$.	$\dfrac{2}{x} + \dfrac{3}{x^2} \qquad$ LCD $= x^2$.
$\boxed{\dfrac{x^2}{1}} \cdot \dfrac{2}{x} + \boxed{\dfrac{x^2}{1}} \cdot \dfrac{3}{x^2} = \boxed{\dfrac{x^2}{1}} \cdot \dfrac{1}{1}$	This is 1. $= \dfrac{2}{x} \cdot \boxed{\dfrac{x}{x}} + \dfrac{3}{x^2}$
$2x \quad + \quad 3 \quad = \quad x^2$	$= \dfrac{2x}{x^2} + \dfrac{3}{x^2} = \dfrac{2x + 3}{x^2}$
This equation is then solved by factoring (Example 8). *Here the result* is two numbers (-1 and 3) that make both sides of the given equation equal.	*Here the result* is a fraction that represents the sum of the given fractions. The usual mistake made is to multiply both terms of *the sum* by the LCD.

(Continued)

$$\frac{x^2}{1} \cdot \frac{2}{x} + \frac{x^2}{1} \cdot \frac{3}{x^2} = 2x + 3$$

$$\neq \frac{2}{x} + \frac{3}{x^2}$$

The sum has been multiplied by x^2, and therefore is no longer equal to its original value.

EXERCISES 908B. Solve the equations.

SET I

1. $z + \frac{1}{z} = \frac{17}{z}$ 2. $y + \frac{3}{y} = \frac{12}{y}$ 3. $\frac{2}{x} - \frac{2}{x^2} = \frac{1}{2}$

4. $\frac{3}{x} - \frac{4}{x^2} = \frac{1}{2}$ 5. $\frac{x}{x+1} = \frac{4x}{3x+2}$ 6. $\frac{x}{3x-4} = \frac{3x}{2x+2}$

----

7. $\frac{1}{x-1} + \frac{2}{x+1} = \frac{5}{3}$ 8. $\frac{2}{3x+1} + \frac{1}{x-1} = \frac{7}{10}$

9. $\frac{3}{2x+5} + \frac{x}{4} = \frac{3}{4}$ 10. $\frac{5}{2x-1} - \frac{x}{6} = \frac{4}{3}$

SET II

1. $x + \frac{1}{x} = \frac{10}{x}$ 2. $\frac{5}{x} - \frac{1}{x^2} = \frac{9}{4}$ 3. $\frac{2x}{3x+1} = \frac{4x}{5x+1}$

4. $\frac{4}{x+1} = \frac{3}{x} + \frac{1}{15}$ 5. $\frac{1}{x-2} - \frac{4}{x+2} = \frac{1}{5}$ 6. $\frac{4y-3}{2} = \frac{5y}{y+2}$

Literal Equations

Literal equations are equations that have more than one letter. *Formulas* are literal equations that have meaning in real-life situations.

Example 1. Literal equations

Literal equations that *are not formulas*:

(a) $3x - 4y = 7$ (b) $\frac{4ab}{d} = 15$

Literal equations that *are formulas*:

(c) $A = P(1 + rt)$ Formula from business

(d) $I = \frac{nE}{R + nr}$ Formula from physics

```
TO SOLVE A LITERAL EQUATION

1.  Remove fractions (if there are any) by multiplying
    both sides by the LCD.

2.  Remove grouping symbols (if there are any).

3.  Collect like terms:  all terms containing the
    letter you are solving for on one side, all other
    terms on the other side.

4.  Factor out the letter you are solving for (if it
    appears in more than one term).

5.  Divide both sides by the coefficient of the letter
    you are solving for.
```

Example 2. When we solve a literal equation for one of its letters, the solution will contain the other letters as well as
numbers.

(a) Solve $3x + 4y = 12$ for x

$$3x + 4y = 12 \qquad \text{Subtract } 4y \text{ from both sides}$$

$$3x = 12 - 4y \qquad \text{Divide both sides by 3}$$

$$x = \frac{12 - 4y}{3} \qquad \text{Solution for } x$$

(b) Solve $3x + 4y = 12$ for y

$$3x + 4y = 12 \qquad \text{Subtract } 3x \text{ from both sides}$$

$$4y = 12 - 3x \qquad \text{Divide both sides by 4}$$

$$y = \frac{12 - 3x}{4} \qquad \text{Solution for } y$$

Sometimes a literal equation can be solved as a proportion.

Example 3. Solve $\dfrac{4ab}{d} = 15$ for a.

Solution: $\dfrac{4ab}{d} = \dfrac{15}{1} \qquad$ This is a proportion.

$$4ab \cdot 1 = 15 \cdot d \qquad \begin{array}{l}\text{Product of means}\\ \text{= product of extremes.}\end{array}$$

$$\frac{4ab}{4b} = \frac{15d}{4b} \qquad \text{Dividing both sides by } 4b.$$

$$a = \frac{15d}{4b} \qquad \text{Solution}$$

Example 4. Solve $A = P(1 + rt)$ for t.

Solution: $A = P(1 + rt)$

$$A = P + Prt \qquad \begin{array}{l}\text{Removing ( ) by using the}\\ \text{Distributive Rule.}\end{array}$$

$$A - P = Prt$$

Collecting terms with the letter you are solving for (t) on one side and all other terms on the other side.

$$\frac{A - P}{Pr} = \frac{\cancel{Prt}}{\cancel{Pr}}$$

Dividing both sides by Pr.

$$\frac{A - P}{Pr} = t$$

Solution

Example 5. Solve $I = \dfrac{nE}{R + nr}$ for n.

Solution: $\dfrac{I}{1} = \dfrac{nE}{R + nr}$ This is a proportion.

$$1 \cdot nE = I(R + nr)$$ Product of means = product of extremes.

$$\begin{array}{rl} nE & = IR + Inr \\ -Inr & \quad\; -Inr \end{array}$$ Removing ( ).

$$nE - Inr = IR$$ Getting all terms with n on one side.

$$n(E - Ir) = IR$$ n is a common factor.

$$\frac{n\cancel{(E - Ir)}}{\cancel{E - Ir}} = \frac{IR}{E - Ir}$$ Dividing both sides by $E - Ir$.

$$n = \frac{IR}{E - Ir}$$ Solution

EXERCISES 909. Solve for the letter listed after each equation.

SET I

1. $2x + y = 4$; x

2. $x + 3y = 6$; y

3. $y - z = -8$; z

4. $m - n = -5$; n

5. $2x - y = -4$; y

6. $3y - z = -5$; z

7. $2x - 3y = 6$; x

8. $3x - 2y = 6$; x

9. $2(x - 3y) = x + 4$; x

10. $3x - 14 = 2(y - 2x)$; x

11. $PV = k$; V

12. $I = Prt$; P

13. $S = \dfrac{a}{1 - r}$; r

14. $I = \dfrac{E}{R + r}$; R

----

15. $C = \dfrac{5}{9}(F - 32)$; F

16. $A = \dfrac{h}{2}(B + b)$; B

17. $\dfrac{1}{F} = \dfrac{1}{u} + \dfrac{1}{v}$; u

18. $Z = \dfrac{Rr}{R + r}$; R

19. $\dfrac{m + n}{x} - a = \dfrac{m - n}{x} + c$; x

20. $\dfrac{a - b}{x} + c = \dfrac{a + b}{x} - h; \ x$

SET II

1. $x + 2y = 5; \ x$ 2. $x - y = -4; \ y$

3. $2x - y = -4; \ x$ 4. $3x - 4y = 12; \ y$

5. $\dfrac{3xy}{z} = 10; \ x$ 6. $I = prt; \ r$

7. $A = P(1 + rt); \ r$ 8. $A = \dfrac{h}{2}(B + b); \ h$

9. $\dfrac{1}{F} = \dfrac{1}{u} + \dfrac{1}{v}; \ v$ 10. $\dfrac{a + b}{x} - c = \dfrac{a - b}{x} + h; \ x$

Word Problems Involving Fractions

<u>DISTANCE-RATE-TIME PROBLEMS</u> (Used in any field involving motion)

A physical law relating *distance* traveled d, *rate* of travel r, and *time* of travel t is

$$d = r \cdot t$$

For example, you know that if you are driving your car at an average speed of 50 mph, then

	$d = r \cdot t$
you travel a distance of 100 miles in 2 hr:	$100 = 50(2)$
you travel a distance of 150 miles in 3 hr:	$150 = 50(3)$

and so on.

METHOD FOR SOLVING
DISTANCE-RATE-TIME PROBLEMS

1. Draw the blank chart:

	d	$=$	r	$\cdot$	t

2. Fill in four of the boxes using a single letter and the given information to represent the unknowns.

3. Use the formula $d = r \cdot t$ to fill in the remaining two boxes.

4. Write the equation by using information in the chart along with an unused fact given in the problem.

5. Solve the resulting equation.

Example 1. Mr. Maxwell takes 30 min to drive to work in the
          morning, but he takes 45 min to return home over the same route
          during the evening rush hour. If his average morning speed is
          10 mph faster than his average evening speed, how far is it
          from his home to his work?

Let x = Speed returning from work
then $x + 10$ = Speed going to work

	d	$=$	r	$\cdot$	t
Going to work			$x + 10$		30 min $= \frac{1}{2}$ hr
Returning from work			x		45 min $= \frac{3}{4}$ hr

$\left.\right\}$ Use the given information to fill in these boxes.

Use the formula $d = r \cdot t$ to find what goes here.

	d	$=$	r	$\cdot$	t
Going to work	$\frac{1}{2}(x + 10)$		$x + 10$		30 min $= \frac{1}{2}$ hr
Returning from work	$\frac{3}{4}(x)$		x		45 min $= \frac{3}{4}$ hr

$$\text{Distance going to work} = \text{Distance returning from work}$$

$$\frac{1}{2}(x + 10) = \frac{3}{4}(x)$$

$$\frac{1}{2}x + 5 = \frac{3}{4}x$$

$$5 = \frac{1}{4}x$$

$$x = 20 \text{ mph}$$

$$\text{Distance} = rt = 20\left(\frac{3}{4}\right) = 15 \text{ mi}$$

Example 2. A boat cruises downstream for 4 hr before heading back.
          After traveling upstream for 5 hr, it is still 16 miles short
          of the starting point. If the speed of the stream is 4 mph,
          find the speed of the boat in still water.

Let x = Speed of boat in still water
then $x + 4$ = Speed of boat downstream
and $x - 4$ = Speed of boat upstream

	d	$=$	r	$\cdot$	t
Downstream	$(x + 4)4$		$x + 4$		4
Upstream	$(x - 4)5$		$x - 4$		5

$d = r \cdot t$
$d_1 = (x + 4)4$
$d = r \cdot t$
$d_2 = (x - 4)5$

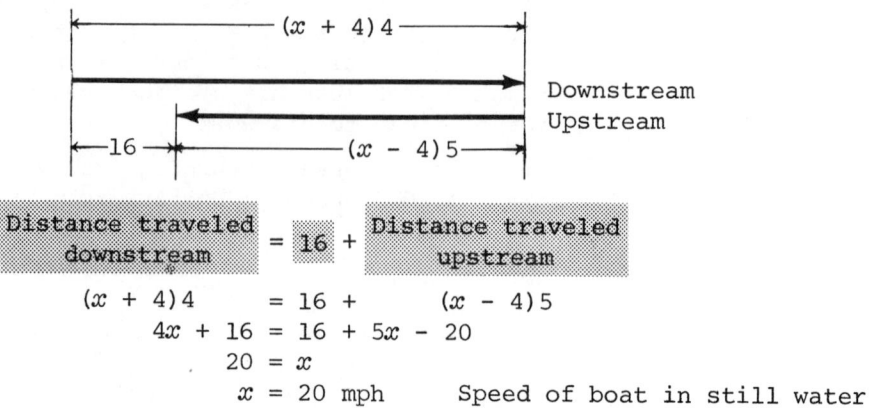

$$\text{Distance traveled downstream} = 16 + \text{Distance traveled upstream}$$

$$(x + 4)4 \quad = 16 + \quad (x - 4)5$$
$$4x + 16 = 16 + 5x - 20$$
$$20 = x$$
$$x = 20 \text{ mph} \qquad \text{Speed of boat in still water}$$

MIXTURE PROBLEMS (Business)

Mixture problems involve mixing two or more ingredients.

TWO IMPORTANT FACTS NECESSARY
TO SOLVE MIXTURE PROBLEMS

1. $\left(\begin{array}{c}\textit{Amount} \text{ of} \\ \text{ingredient A}\end{array}\right) + \left(\begin{array}{c}\textit{Amount} \text{ of} \\ \text{ingredient B}\end{array}\right) = \left(\begin{array}{c}\textit{Amount} \text{ of} \\ \text{mixture}\end{array}\right)$

2. $\left(\begin{array}{c}\textit{Cost} \text{ of} \\ \text{ingredient A}\end{array}\right) + \left(\begin{array}{c}\textit{Cost} \text{ of} \\ \text{ingredient B}\end{array}\right) = \left(\begin{array}{c}\textit{Cost} \text{ of} \\ \text{mixture}\end{array}\right)$

Example 3. A wholesaler makes up a 50-lb mixture of two kinds of coffee, one costing \$2.50 per pound, and the other costing \$2.60 per pound. How many pounds of each kind must be used if the mixture is to cost \$2.57 per pound?

Let $\quad x$ = Amount of \$2.50 coffee
then $50 - x$ = Amount of \$2.60 coffee

$$\text{Cost of ingredient A} + \text{Cost of ingredient B} = \text{Cost of mixture}$$

$$2.50x \quad + 2.60(50 - x) = 2.57(50)$$

$$250x + 260(50 - x) = 257(50) \quad \text{Multiplied both sides by}$$
$$250x + 13{,}000 - 260x = 12{,}850 \quad \text{LCD 100}$$
$$-10x = -150$$
$$x = 15 \text{ lb} \qquad (\$2.50 \text{ coffee})$$
$$50 - x = 50 - 15 = 35 \text{ lb} \quad (\$2.60 \text{ coffee})$$

Check: Cost of \$2.50 coffee = 15(2.50) = \$ 37.50
Cost of \$2.60 coffee = 35(2.60) = +91.00
$$\overline{\$128.50} \Big\rbrace \text{ Check}$$
Cost of mixture = 50(2.57) = \$128.50

SOLUTION PROBLEMS (Chemistry and Nursing)

Solution problems involve the mixing of liquids. They can be solved by the same method we used for mixture problems.

Example 4. How many liters of a 20% alcohol solution must be added to 3 liters of a 90% alcohol solution to make an 80% solution?

Let x = Number of liters of 20% solution
then $x + 3$ = Number of liters of 80% solution.

Amount of alcohol in 20% solution	+	Amount of alcohol in 90% solution	=	Amount of alcohol in 80% solution	
$0.20x$	+	$0.90(3)$	=	$0.80(x + 3)$	Multi-
$2x$	+	$9(3)$	=	$8(x + 3)$	ply
$2x$	+	27	=	$8x + 24$	by 10

$$3 = 6x$$
$$x = \frac{1}{2} \text{ liter of 20\% alcohol}$$

The following exercise set includes some word problems that have not been discussed. We leave it to students to devise their own solutions, guided by the general method given in Section 503.

EXERCISES 910.

SET I

1. The Malone family left San Diego by car at 7 AM, bound for San Francisco. Their neighbors the King family left in their car at 8 AM, also bound for San Francisco. By traveling 9 mph faster, the Kings overtook the Malones at 1 PM.
    (a) Find the average speed of each car.
    (b) Find the total distance traveled by each car before they met.
2. The Duran family left Ames, Iowa, by car at 6 AM, bound for Yellowstone National Park. Their neighbors the Silva family left in their car at 8 AM, also bound for Yellowstone. By traveling 10 mph faster, the Silvas overtook the Durans at 4 PM.
    (a) Find the average speed of each car.
    (b) Find the total distance traveled before they met.
3. Eric hiked from his camp to a lake in the mountains and returned to camp later in the day. He walked at a rate of 2 mph going to the lake and 5 mph coming back. If the trip to the lake took 3 hr longer than the trip back:
    (a) How long did it take him to hike to the lake?
    (b) How far is it from his camp to the lake?
4. Lee hiked from her camp up to an observation tower in the mountains and returned to camp later in the day. She walked up at the rate of 2 mph and jogged back at the rate of 6 mph. The trip to the tower took 2 hr longer than the return trip.
    (a) How long did it take her to hike to the tower?
    (b) How far is it from her camp to the tower?
5. Mr. Zaleva flew his private plane from his office to his company's storage facility bucking a 20-mph head wind all the way. He flew home the same day with the same wind at his back. The round trip took 10 hr of flying time. If the plane makes 100 mph in still air, how far is the storage facility from his office?

6. Mr. Summers drove his motor boat upstream a certain distance while pulling his son Brian on a water ski. He returned to the starting point pulling his other son Derek. The round trip took 25 min of skiing time. On both legs of the trip, the speedometer read 30 mph. If the speed of the current is 6 mph, how far upstream did he travel?

7. Mrs. Martinez mixes 15 lb of English toffee candy costing $1.25 a pound with caramels costing $1.50 a pound. How many pounds of caramels must she use to make a mixture costing $1.35 a pound?

8. Mr. Wong wants to mix 30 bushels of soybeans with corn to make a 100-bushel mixture costing $4.85 a bushel. How much can he afford to pay for each bushel of corn if soybeans cost $8.00 a bushel?

9. A 50-lb mixture of Delicious and Jonathan apples costs $14.50. If the Delicious apples cost 30¢ a pound and the Jonathan apples cost 20¢ a pound, how many pounds of each kind are there?

10. Mrs. Lavalle wants to mix 6 pounds of Brand A with Brand B to make a 10-pound mixture costing $11.50. How much can she afford to pay per pound for Brand B if Brand A costs $1.23 per pound?

11. Mrs. Edwards invested part of $24,000 at 15% and the remainder at 18%. Her total yearly income from these investments is $4,215. How much is invested at each rate?

12. Mr. McAllister invested part of $27,300 at 14% and the remainder at 21%. His total yearly income is $4,648. How much is invested at each rate?

13. How many milliliters of water must be added to 500 ml of a 40% solution of sodium bromide to reduce it to a 25% solution?

14. How many liters of pure alcohol must be added to 10 liters of a 20% solution of alcohol to make a 50% solution?

15. How many cubic centimeters (cc) of a 20% solution of sulfuric acid must be mixed with 100 cc of a 50% solution to make a 25% solution of sulfuric acid?

16. How many pints of a 2% solution of disinfectant must be mixed with 5 pints of a 12% solution to make a 4% solution of disinfectant?

17. The denominator of a fraction exceeds the numerator by 6. If 4 is added to the numerator and subtracted from the denominator, the resulting fraction equals $\frac{11}{10}$. What is the original fraction?

18. A fraction has a value of $\frac{1}{2}$. If 5 is added to the numerator and subtracted from the denominator, the value of the resulting fraction is $\frac{4}{5}$. What is the original fraction?

19. Manny has 20 coins that have a total value of $1.65. If all the coins are nickels or dimes, how many of each does he have?

20. Margaret has $2.60 in nickels, dimes and quarters. If there is one more dime than quarters and 3 times as many nickels as quarters, how many of each kind of coin does she have?

21. The sum of two consecutive integers is thirty-three. What are the integers?

22. The sum of the first two of three consecutive odd integers added to the sum of the last two is 140. Find the integers.

23. The sum of the digits of a two-digit number is thirteen. The number formed by reversing the digits is 27 more than the original number. Find the original number.

24. The sum of the digits of a two-digit number is seven. The number formed by reversing the digits is 27 less than the original number. Find the original number.

25. How many minutes after 8 o'clock will the hands of a clock first be together?

26. At what time between 8 and 9 o'clock will the hands of a clock be opposite one another?

27. A camera shop buys 18 lenses. If it had bought 15 lenses of higher quality, it would have paid $23 more per lens for the same total cost. Find the cost of each type of lens.

28. A hardware store buys 12 saws. If it had bought 8 saws of higher quality, it would have paid $2.75 more per saw for the same total cost. Find the cost of each type of saw.

SET II

1. Fran and Ron live 54 miles apart. Both leave their homes at 7 AM by bicycle, riding toward one another. They meet at 10 AM. If Ron's average speed is four-fifths of Fran's, how fast does each cycle?

2. Danny and Cathy live 60 miles apart. Both leave their homes at 10 AM by bicycle, riding toward one another. They meet at 2 PM. If Cathy's average speed is two-thirds of Danny's, how fast does each cycle?

3. Colin paddles a kayak downstream for 3 hr. After having lunch, he paddles upstream for 5 hr. At that time he is still 6 miles short of getting back to his starting point. If the speed of the stream is 2 mph, how fast does Colin row in still water? How far downstream did he travel?

4. The Wright family sails their houseboat upstream for 4 hr. After lunch they motor downstream for 2 hr. At that time they are still 12 miles away from the marina where they began. If the speed of the houseboat in still water is 15 mph, what is the speed of the stream? How far upstream did the Wrights travel?

5. A 10-pound mixture of nuts and raisins cost $25. If raisins cost $1.90 per pound and nuts $3.40 per pound, how many pounds of each are used?

6. Randy wants to mix dried figs with dried apricots to make an 8 pound mixture costing $2.70 per pound. If dried figs cost $1.80 per pound and dried apricots cost $4.20 per pound, how many pounds of each are used?

7. Ms Rennie invested part of $18,000 at 16% and the remainder at 20%. Her total yearly income from these investments is $3,120. How much is invested at each rate?

8. If 100 gal of 75% glycerin solution is made up by combining a 30% glycerin solution with a 90% glycerin solution, how much of each solution must be used?

9. If 1600 cc of 10% dextrose solution is made up by combining a 20% dextrose solution with a 4% dextrose solution, how much of each solution must be used?

10. The denominator of a fraction exceeds the numerator by twenty. If seven is added to the numerator and subtracted from the denominator, the resulting fraction equals 6/7. Find the fraction.

11. Ben bought 120 stamps consisting of 20¢, 15¢, and 3¢ stamps at a total cost of $12.80. He bought twice as many 20¢ stamps than 15¢ stamps and 20 more 3¢ stamps than 20¢ stamps. How many of each kind did he buy?

12. The sum of the first two of three consecutive odd integers added to the sum of the last two is 60. Find the integers.

13. The sum of the digits of a two digit number is 9. The number found by reversing the digits is 45 more than the original number. Find the original number.

14. At what time between 6 and 7 o'clock will the hands of a clock be together?

15. A drugstore buys eighteen cameras. If it had bought ten cameras of a higher quality, it would have paid $48 more per camera for the same total expenditure. Find the price of each type of camera.

16. *Brainteaser.* Two coins have a value of 60¢. One is not a dime. What are the coins?

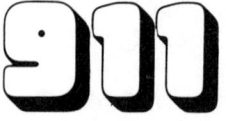

Chapter Summary

Algebraic Fractions (Sec. 901)

$$\text{terms of fraction} \left\{ \frac{P}{Q} \right.$$

numerator ← fraction line ← denominator (cannot be zero)

where P and Q are polynomials.

A simple fraction is a fraction having only one fraction line. (Sec. 907)

A complex fraction is a fraction having more than one fraction line. (Sec. 907)

The Three Signs of a Fraction (Sec. 901). Every fraction has three signs associated with it: the sign of the entire fraction, the sign of the numerator, and the sign of the denominator. *If any two of the three signs of a fraction are changed, the value of the fraction is unchanged.*

To Reduce a Fraction to Lowest Terms (Sec. 902)

1. *Factor* the numerator and denominator completely.
2. Divide numerator and denominator by all factors common to both.

To Multiply Fractions (Sec. 903)

1. Factor the numerator and denominator of the fractions.
2. Divide numerator and denominator by all factors common to both.
3. The answer is the product of factors remaining in the numerator, divided by the product of factors remaining in the denominator.

To Divide Fractions (Sec. 903)

Invert the second fraction and multiply.

$$\frac{a}{b} \div \frac{c}{d} = \frac{a}{b} \cdot \frac{d}{c}$$

first fraction ———↑   ↑—————— second fraction

To Find the LCD (Sec. 905)

1. Factor each denominator completely. Repeated factors should be expressed as powers.
2. Write down each different factor that appears.
3. Raise each factor to the highest power it occurs in any denominator.
4. The LCD is the product of all the powers found in Step 3.

To Add Like Fractions (Sec. 904)

1. Add their numerators.
2. Write the sum over the same denominator as that of the like fractions being added.
3. Reduce the resulting fraction to lowest terms.

To Add Unlike Fractions (Sec. 906)

1. Find the LCD.
2. Convert all fractions to equivalent fractions having the LCD as denominator.
3. Add the resulting like fractions.
4. Reduce resulting fraction to lowest terms.

To Simplify Complex Fractions (Sec. 907)

Method 1. Multiply both numerator and denominator of the complex fraction by the LCD of the secondary fractions.

Method 2. First simplify the numerator and denominator of the complex fraction, then divide the simplified numerator by the denominator.

To Solve an Equation Having Fractions (Sec. 908)

1. Remove fractions by multiplying each term by the LCD.
2. Remove grouping symbols (Sec. 305).

First-Degree Equations	*Quadratic Equations*
3. Collect and combine like terms: all terms with the unknown on one side, all other terms on the other side.	3. Get *all* nonzero terms to one side by adding the same expression to both sides. *Only zero must remain on the other side.* Then arrange the terms in descending powers.
4. Divide both sides by the coefficient of the unknown.	4. Factor the polynomial.
	5. Set each factor equal to zero, then solve for the unknown.

Check apparent solutions in the original equation. Any value of the letter that makes any denominator in the equation zero is not a solution.

Literal Equations are equations that have more than one letter (Sec. 909).

To Solve a Literal Equation (Sec. 909). Proceed in the same way used to solve an equation with a single letter. The solution will be expressed in terms of the other letters given in the literal equation, as well as in numbers.

REVIEW EXERCISES 911

SET I

In Exercises 1—6, what value(s) of the variable (if any) must be excluded?

1. $\dfrac{2x - 1}{x + 4}$

2. $8y - \dfrac{4}{5y}$

3. $\dfrac{x - 1}{x^2 - 3x - 10}$

4. $\dfrac{x - 2}{x^2 - 9}$

5. $\dfrac{x - 2}{2x^2 + x - 3}$

6. $\dfrac{x + 4}{x^3 + x^2 - 2x}$

In Exercises 7-10, use the rule about the three signs of a fraction to find the missing term.

7. $-\dfrac{2}{5} = \dfrac{-2}{?}$

8. $\dfrac{x - 6}{7} = -\dfrac{?}{-7}$

9. $\dfrac{2}{a - b} = -\dfrac{?}{b - a}$

10. $\dfrac{3 - x}{4} = \dfrac{x - 3}{?}$

In Exercises 11-20, reduce each fraction to lowest terms.

11. $\dfrac{4x^3 y}{2xy^2}$ 12. $\dfrac{6ab^4}{3a^3 b^3}$ 13. $\dfrac{2 + 4m}{2}$ 14. $\dfrac{3 - 6n}{3}$

15. $\dfrac{a^2 - 4}{a + 2}$ 16. $\dfrac{9 - y^2}{3 - y}$

17. $\dfrac{x + 3}{x^2 - x - 12}$ 18. $\dfrac{x - 5}{x^2 - 3x - 10}$

19. $\dfrac{a - b}{ax + ay - bx - by}$ 20. $\dfrac{x + y}{ax - bx + ay - by}$

In Exercises 21-36, perform the indicated operations.

21. $\dfrac{7}{z} - \dfrac{2}{z}$ 22. $\dfrac{8}{k} + \dfrac{2}{k}$ 23. $5 - \dfrac{3}{2x}$ 24. $7 - \dfrac{2}{3x}$

25. $\dfrac{3x}{x + 1} - \dfrac{2x - 1}{x + 1}$ 26. $\dfrac{4m}{2m - 3} - \dfrac{2m + 3}{2m - 3}$

27. $\dfrac{-5a^2}{3b} \div \dfrac{10a}{9b^2}$ 28. $\dfrac{21x^3}{4y^2} \div \dfrac{-7x}{8y^4}$

29. $\dfrac{3x + 6}{6} \cdot \dfrac{2x^2}{4x + 8}$ 30. $\dfrac{5x - 5}{10} \cdot \dfrac{4x^3}{2x - 2}$

31. $\dfrac{x + 4}{5} - \dfrac{x - 2}{3}$ 32. $\dfrac{y - 3}{2} - \dfrac{y + 4}{3}$

33. $\dfrac{a - 2}{a - 1} + \dfrac{a + 1}{a + 2}$ 34. $\dfrac{k + 3}{k - 2} - \dfrac{k + 2}{k - 3}$

35. $\dfrac{2x^2 - 6x}{x + 2} \div \dfrac{x}{4x + 8}$ 36. $\dfrac{4z^2}{z - 5} \div \dfrac{z}{2z - 10}$

In Exercises 37-42, simplify the complex fractions.

37. $\dfrac{\dfrac{5k^2}{3m^2}}{\dfrac{10k}{9m}}$ 38. $\dfrac{\dfrac{4x^3}{5y}}{\dfrac{8x^2}{10y^4}}$

39. $\dfrac{\dfrac{x}{y} + 2}{\dfrac{x}{y} - 2}$ 40. $\dfrac{3 - \dfrac{a}{b}}{2 + \dfrac{a}{b}}$

41. $\dfrac{x^{-1} + 2}{x^{-1}}$ 42. $\dfrac{x^{-1}}{x^{-1} + 3}$

In Exercises 43-54, solve the equations for the unknown letter.

43. $\dfrac{6}{m} = 5$ 44. $\dfrac{7}{m} = 8$ 45. $\dfrac{2m}{3} - m = 1$

46. $x - \dfrac{3x}{5} = 2$ 47. $\dfrac{z}{5} - \dfrac{z}{8} = 3$ 48. $\dfrac{k}{2} - \dfrac{k}{4} = 5$

49. $\dfrac{2x + 1}{3} = \dfrac{5x - 4}{2}$ 50. $\dfrac{3}{2} = \dfrac{3x + 4}{5x - 1}$

51. $\dfrac{4}{2z} + \dfrac{2}{z} = 1$ 52. $\dfrac{14}{3x} + \dfrac{42}{x} = 1$

53. $\dfrac{3}{x} - \dfrac{8}{x^2} = \dfrac{1}{4}$ 54. $\dfrac{4}{x^2} - \dfrac{3}{x} = \dfrac{5}{2}$

In Exercises 55-62, solve for the letter listed after each equation.

55. $3x - 4y = 12$; x 56. $2x - 7y = 14$; y

57. $\dfrac{2m}{n} = P$; n 58. $\dfrac{rs}{t} = 5$; t

59. $E = \dfrac{mv^2}{gr}$; m 60. $V = \dfrac{1}{3}Bh$; B

61. $\dfrac{F - 32}{C} = \dfrac{9}{5}$; C 62. $\dfrac{5(F - 32)}{C} = 9$; F

63. Mr. Maxwell takes 30 min to drive to work in the morning, but he takes 45 min to return home over the same route during the evening rush hour. If his average morning speed is 10 mph faster than his average evening speed, how far is it from his home to his work?

64. After sailing downstream for 2 hr, it takes a boat 7 hr to return to its starting point. If the speed of the boat in still water is 9 mph, what is the speed of the stream?

65. A dealer makes up a 15 lb mixture of 78¢ and 99¢ a pound candy. How many pounds of each must be used in order for the mixture to cost 85¢ a pound?

66. A dealer makes up a 30 lb mixture of 85¢ and 95¢ a pound nuts. How many pounds of each must be used in order for the mixture to cost 91¢ a pound?

67. How many cubic centimeters of water must be added to 500 cc of a 25% solution of potassium chloride to reduce it to a 5% solution?

68. How many cubic centimeters of water must be added to 10 cc of a 17% solution of zephiran chloride to reduce it to a 0.2% solution?

SET II

In Exercises 1—3, what value(s) of the variable (if any) must be excluded?

1. $\dfrac{x + 2}{x - 1}$ 2. $3x + \dfrac{5}{2x}$ 3. $\dfrac{x + 2}{x^2 + 2x - 3}$

In Exercises 4—6, use the rule about the three signs of a fraction to find the missing term.

4. $\dfrac{-3}{5} = \dfrac{?}{-5}$ 5. $\dfrac{6}{x - 3} = \dfrac{-6}{?}$ 6. $\dfrac{4 - x}{7} = -\dfrac{?}{7}$

In Exercises 7—10, reduce each fraction to lowest terms.

7. $\dfrac{6ab^3}{2ab}$

8. $\dfrac{x + 2}{x^2 - 2x - 8}$

9. $\dfrac{4z^3 + 4z^2 - 24z}{2z^2 + 4z - 6}$

10. $\dfrac{6k^3 - 12k^2 - 18k}{3k^2 + 3k - 36}$

In Exercises 11-18, perform the indicated operations.

11. $\dfrac{3}{x} + \dfrac{5}{x}$

12. $4 - \dfrac{3}{2x}$

13. $\dfrac{2a}{3a + 1} - \dfrac{3a - 1}{3a + 1}$

14. $\dfrac{x + 1}{2} - \dfrac{x - 3}{5}$

15. $\dfrac{y - 2}{y + 1} - \dfrac{y - 1}{y + 2}$

16. $\dfrac{15x^3}{4y^2} \div \dfrac{5x^2}{8y}$

17. $\dfrac{4x - 4}{2} \cdot \dfrac{6x^2}{3x - 3}$

18. $\dfrac{z^2 + 3z + 2}{z^2 + 2z + 1} \div \dfrac{z^2 + 2z - 3}{z^2 - 1}$

In Exercises 19-21, simplify the complex fractions.

19. $\dfrac{\dfrac{10a^2 b}{12a^4 b^3}}{\dfrac{5ab^2}{16a^2 b^3}}$

20. $\dfrac{2 + \dfrac{a}{b}}{\dfrac{a}{b} - 2}$

21. $\dfrac{x^{-2} - 9y^{-2}}{x^{-1} - 3y^{-1}}$

In Exercises 22-27, solve the equations for the unknown letter.

22. $\dfrac{3}{x} = 4$

23. $\dfrac{x}{3} - \dfrac{x}{2} = 2$

24. $\dfrac{x + 2}{5} + \dfrac{2x}{3} = 3$

25. $\dfrac{3x}{7} = \dfrac{x - 1}{5}$

26. $\dfrac{x + 2}{-2} = \dfrac{3}{x - 3}$

27. $\dfrac{17}{6x} + \dfrac{5}{2x^2} = \dfrac{2}{3}$

In Exercises 28-31, solve for the letter listed after each equation.

28. $\dfrac{P}{V} = C$; V

29. $V = LWH$; H

30. $V^2 = 2gS$; S

31. $5(x - 2y) = 14 + 3(2x - y)$; y

32. Nadya takes 20 min to drive to work in the morning, but she takes 36 min to return home over the same route during the evening rush hour. If her average morning speed is 16 mph faster than her average evening speed, how far is it from her apartment to her office?

33. Mrs. Walker paid $2.76 for a total of 12 cans of beef soup and tomato soup. If the beef soup costs 33¢ a can and the tomato soup 18¢ a can, how many cans of each kind of soup did she buy?

34. How many cubic centimeters of a 50% phenol solution must be added to 400 cc of a 5% solution to make it a 10% solution?

1. Evaluate $10 - (3\sqrt{4} - 5^2)$

2. Evaluate the formula using the values of the letters given with the formula.

$$V = \frac{25}{8}\left(\frac{H}{D} - \frac{A}{R}\right) \qquad H = 10, \; D = 18, \; A = 1, \; R = 5$$

3. Simplify. Write your answer using only positive exponents.

$$\left(\frac{24y^{-3}}{8y^{-1}}\right)^{-2}$$

In Exercises 4 and 5, perform the indicated operations and simplify.

4. $\dfrac{6x^2 - 2x}{2x}$

5. $(15z^2 + 11z + 4) \div (3z - 2)$

In Exercises 6-9, factor each expression.

6. $x^2 - x - 42$

7. $3w^2 - 48$

8. $20a^2 - 7ab - 3b^2$

9. $3x^2 - 6x - 2xy + 4y$

10. The sum of two numbers is 5. Their product is -24. What are the two numbers?

Chapter Nine Diagnostic Test

Name_____

_____

The purpose of this test is to see how well you understand the operations with fractions. We recommend that you work this diagnostic test *before* your instructor tests you on this chapter. Allow yourself about one hour to do this test.

   Complete solutions for all the problems on this test, together with section references, are given in the Answer Section. We suggest that you study the sections referred to for the problems you do incorrectly.

---

1. What value(s) of the variable must be excluded, if any, in each of the following expressions?

   (a) $\dfrac{3x}{x - 4}$

   (b) $\dfrac{5x + 4}{x^2 + 2x}$

   (1a) _____

   (1b) _____

---

2. Use the rule about the three signs of a fraction to find the missing term in each of the following expressions.

   (a) $-\dfrac{-4}{5} = \dfrac{4}{?}$

   (b) $\dfrac{-3}{x - y} = \dfrac{?}{y - x}$

   (2a) _____

   (2b) _____

Reduce each fraction to lowest terms.

3. $\dfrac{6x^3 y}{9x^2 y^2}$

   (3) _____

4. $\dfrac{x^2 + 8x + 16}{x^2 - 16}$

   (4) _____

5. $\dfrac{6a^2 + 11ab - 10b^2}{6a^2b - 4ab^2}$

(5) _____

_____

Perform the indicated operations. (Be sure to reduce fractions to lowest terms.)

6. $\dfrac{a}{a + 2} \cdot \dfrac{4a + 8}{6a^2}$

(6) _____

7. $\dfrac{3}{a - b} - \dfrac{2}{a - b}$

(7) _____

8. $4 + \dfrac{2}{x}$

(8) _____

9. $\dfrac{b + 1}{b} - \dfrac{b}{b - 1}$

(9) _____

10. $\dfrac{2x}{x^2 - 9} \div \dfrac{4x^2}{x - 3}$

(10) _____

_____

Simplify each of the following complex fractions.

11. $\dfrac{\dfrac{9x^5}{10y}}{\dfrac{3x^2}{20y^3}}$

(11) _____

12. $\dfrac{4 + \dfrac{10}{x}}{2 + \dfrac{5}{x}}$

(12) _____

Solve each of the following equations.

13. $\dfrac{y}{3} - \dfrac{y}{4} = 1$

(13) _____

14. $\dfrac{x - 2}{5} = \dfrac{x + 1}{2} + \dfrac{3}{5}$

(14) _____

15. $\dfrac{3}{a + 4} = \dfrac{5}{a}$

(15) _____

16. $\dfrac{2x - 5}{x} = \dfrac{x - 2}{3}$

(16) _____

17. Solve for y: $3x - 4y = 9$

(17) _____

18. Solve for T: $\dfrac{PV}{T} = k$

(18) _____

19. Solve for P: $PM + Q = PN$

(19) _____
_____

20. The denominator of a fraction is 6 more than its numerator. If one is subtracted from the numerator and added to the denominator, the value of the resulting fraction is $\dfrac{1}{3}$. What is the original fraction?

(20) _____
_____

TEN
Graphing

Many algebraic relationships are easier to understand if a picture called a *graph* is drawn. In this chapter we discuss how to draw such graphs.

The Rectangular Coordinate System

In Sec. 101 we discussed how any real number can be represented by a point on a *number line* (Fig. 1001A).

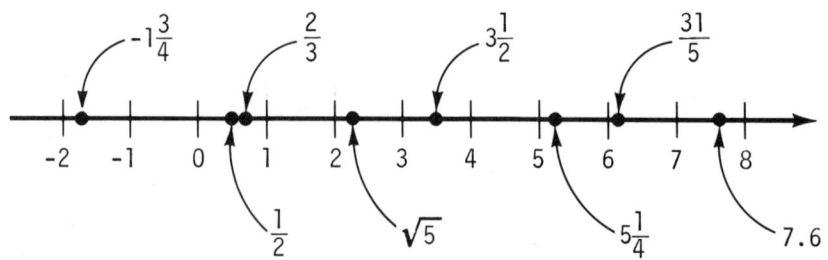

Figure 1001A

Horizontal Number Line

We draw another number line vertically with its zero point at the zero point of the horizontal number line. These two lines form the *axes* of a *rectangular coordinate system*. The rectangular coordinate system consists of a vertical number line called the *vertical axis* and a horizontal number line called the *horizontal axis* that meet at a point called the *origin*. The vertical and horizontal axes determine the *plane* of the rectangular coordinate system (Fig. 1001B).

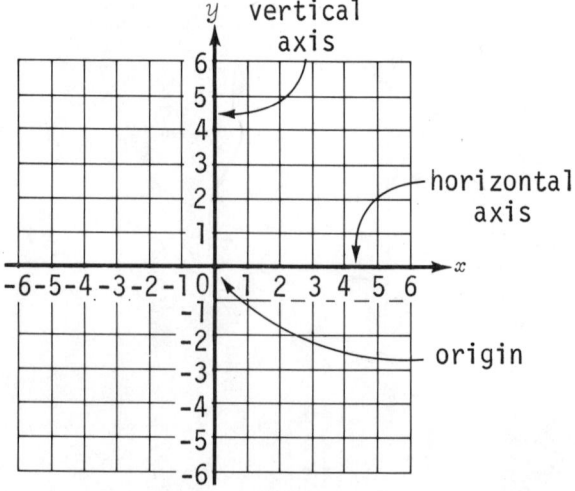

Figure 1001B

Rectangular Coordinate System

With a single number line, we could only represent a *single* real number by a point on that line. With two number lines forming a rectangular coordinate system, we can represent a *pair* of real numbers by a point in the plane of that rectangular coordinate system (Fig. 1001C).

Ordered Pairs. A point is represented by an *ordered pair* of numbers. The point (3, 2) is shown in Figure 1001C. We call 3 and 2 the *coordinates* of the point (3, 2). The first number (3) is called the *horizontal coordinate* of the point (3, 2). The second number (2) is called the *vertical coordinate* of the point (3, 2).

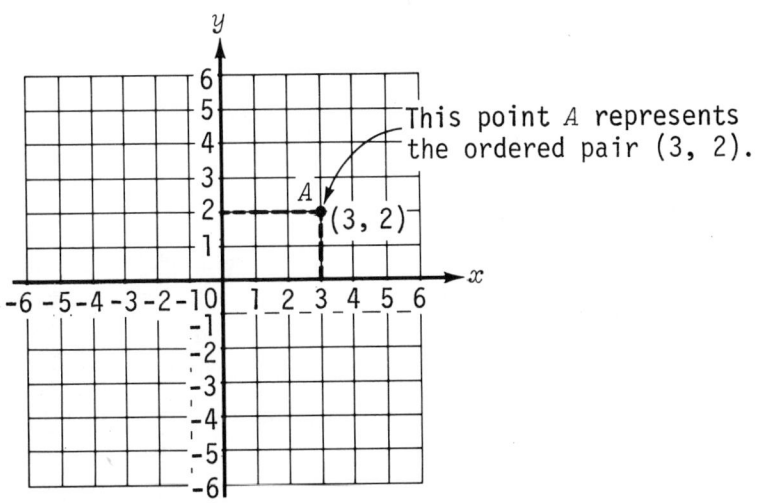

Figure 1001C

Graph of an Ordered Pair

A *positive* horizontal coordinate indicates the point is to the *right* of the vertical axis. A *negative* horizontal coordinate indicates the point is to the *left* of the vertical axis.

A *positive* vertical coordinate indicates the point is *above* the horizontal axis. A *negative* vertical coordinate indicates the point is *below* the horizontal axis.

All points on this dashed line have a horizontal coordinate of 3.　　All points on this dashed line have a vertical coordinate of 2.

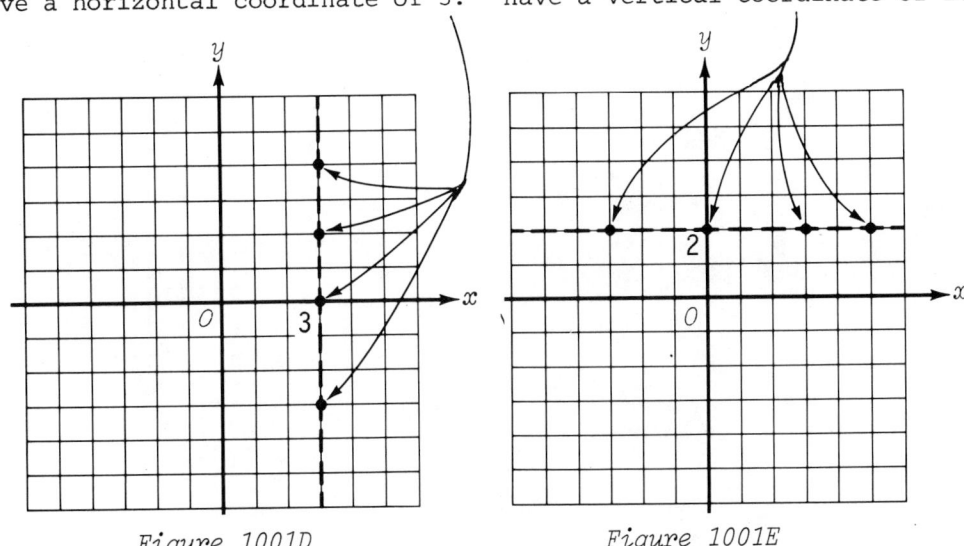

Figure 1001D　　　　　　　　　Figure 1001E

Note. When the order is changed
in an ordered pair, we get a
different point. For example,
(1, 4) and 4, 1) are two
different points (Fig. 1001F). ■

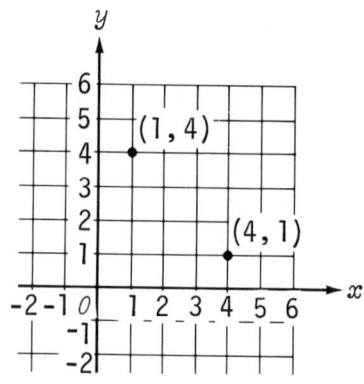

Figure 1001F

GRAPHING POINTS

Example 1.   Graph the following points:

(a)   (3, 5)   Start at the origin and move *right* 3 units,
                  then move *up* 5 units (point A in Fig.
                  1001G).

(b)   (-5, 2)   Start at the origin and move *left* 5 units,
                  then move *up* 2 units (point B in Fig.
                  1001G).

(c)   (-5, -4)   Start at the origin and move *left* 5 units,
                  then move *down* 4 units (point C in Fig.
                  1001G).

(d)   (0, -3)   Start at the origin, but because the first
                  number is zero, do not move either right
                  or left. Just move *down* 3 units (point D
                  in Fig. 1001G).

(e)   (4, -6)   Start at the origin and move *right* 4 units,
                  then move *down* 6 units (point E in Fig.
                  1001G).

The phrase "plot the points" means the same as "graph the
points."

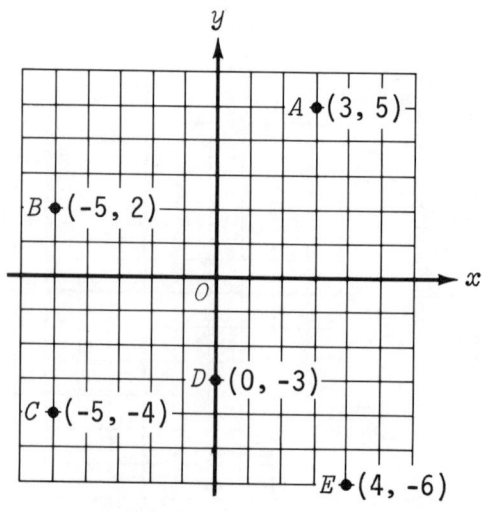

Figure 1001G

There are other names used in discussing a rectangular coordinate system. We show some of these in Fig. 1001H.

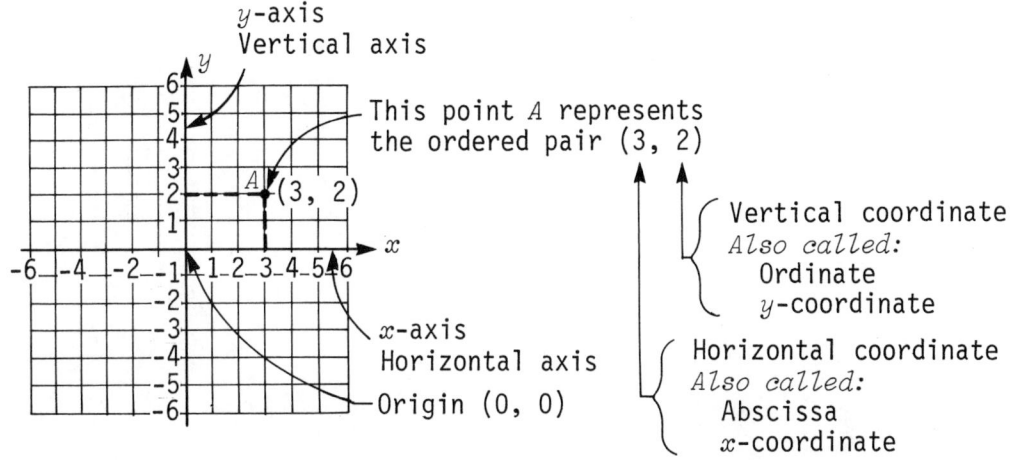

Figure 1001H

Graph of Ordered Pair

EXERCISES 1001

1. Graph each of the following points:

    (a) (3, 1)   (b) (-4, -2)   (c) (0, 3)
    (d) (5, -4)   (e) (4, 0)   (f) (-2, 4)

2. Graph each of the following points:

    (a) (2, 4)   (b) (2, -4)   (c) (3, 0)
    (d) (-3, -2)   (e) (0, 0)   (f) (0, -4)

3. Give the coordinates of each of the following points shown in Fig. 1001I.

    (a) *R*   (b) *N*   (c) *U*   (d) *S*

4. Give the coordinates of each of the following points shown in Fig. 1001I.

    (a) *M*   (b) *P*   (c) *Q*   (d) *T*

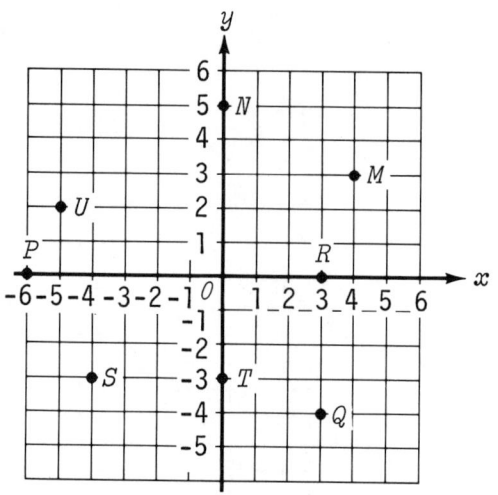

Figure 1001I

5. Write the x-coordinate of each of the following points shown in Fig. 1001J.

    (a) A (b) C (c) E (d) F

6. Write the y-coordinate of each of the following points shown in Fig. 1001J.

    (a) B (b) D (c) E (d) F

7. What is the y-coordinate of the origin?
8. What is the x-coordinate of the origin?

In Figure 1001J

9.   (a)   What is the abscissa of point F?
      (b)   What is the ordinate of point C?
10. (a)   What is the ordinate of point B?
      (b)   What is the abscissa of point D?

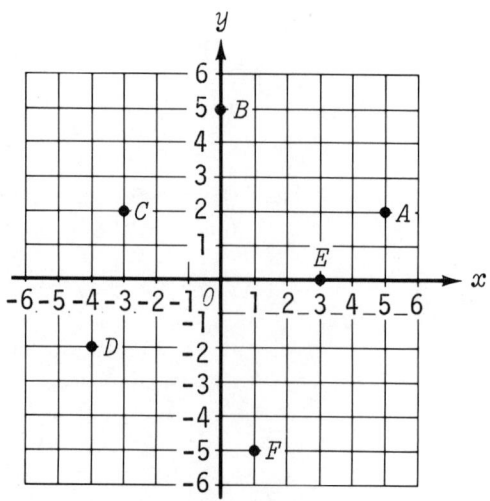

Figure 1001J

11. Draw the triangle whose vertices have the following coordinates:

   A (0, 0)   B (3, 2)   and   C (-4, 5)

12. Draw the triangle whose vertices have the following coordinates:

   A (-2, -3)   B (-2, 4)   C (3, 5)

SET II

1. Graph each of the following points:

   (a) (-2, 4)   (b) (2, -5)   (c) (-1, -3)

   (d) (3, 6)   (e) (-5, -1)   (f) (5, -2)

2. Give the coordinates of each of the following points shown in Fig. 1001K.

   (a) K   (b) L   (c) W   (d) U

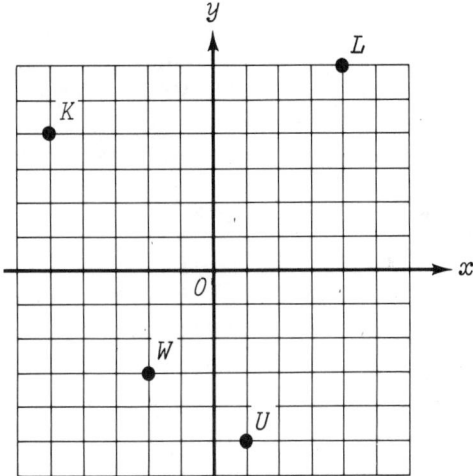

Figure 1001K

3. What name is given to the point (0, 0)?
4. List some other names for the x-coordinate of a point.
5. List some other names for the y-coordinate of a point.
6. Draw the triangle whose vertices have the following coordinates: A (-6, -4), B (2, -5), and C (5, 3).

Graphing Straight Lines

In the preceding section we showed how to graph points. In this section we show how to graph straight lines.

   Consider the equation $y = x + 1$. In order to graph this equation, we need to find values for x and y that make the equation true. For example if $x = 0$, then

$$y = x + 1$$
$$= (0) + 1 = 1$$

These values, $x = 0$ and $y = 1$, form an ordered pair $(0, 1)$ that represents a point on the graph of the equation $y = x + 1$. By choosing several values for x and finding the *corresponding values* for y, we obtain a set of points (ordered pairs) on the graph of $y = x + 1$. These ordered pairs are listed in the following *table of values*.

Equation: $y = x + 1$

Table of Values

x	y
0	1
2	3
5	6
-3	-2

When $x = 0$, $y = (0) + 1 = 1$

When $x = 2$, $y = (2) + 1 = 3$

When $x = 5$, $y = (5) + 1 = 6$

When $x = -3$, $y = (-3) + 1 = -2$

Each of these ordered pairs, called "a pair of corresponding values," represents a point on the line.

We plot the four points, contained in the table of values, in Fig. 1002A. You will note that the points appear to lie in a straight line. This suggests that the graph of $y = x + 1$ is a straight line. In fact any first-degree equation (in no more than two variables) has a graph that is a straight line. Such equations are called linear equations.

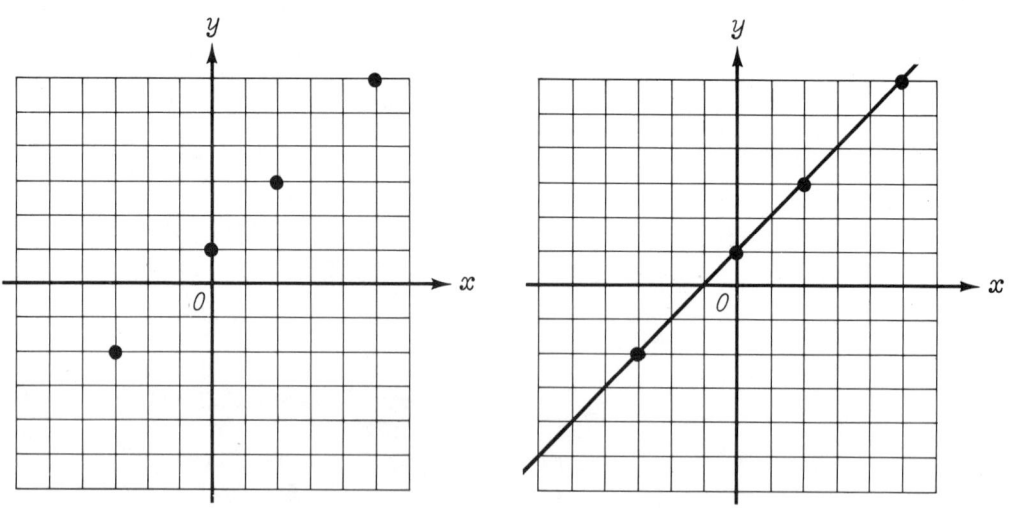

Figure 1002A   Figure 1002B

A straight line can be drawn if we know two points that lie on that line.

Although two points are all that are *necessary* to draw the line, it is *advisable* to plot a third point as a *check-point*. If the three points do not lie in a straight line, a mistake has been made in some calculation of the coordinates of the points.

In Fig. 1002B we have drawn the line through the points listed in the table of values. This line represents the graph of the equation $y = x + 1$.

<u>Example 1.</u> Graph the equation $3x - 5y = 15$.

     <u>Solution:</u> Substitute three values for x, and find the
                corresponding values for y.

Equation: $3x - 5y = 15$

If $x =$ 0, $3(0) - 5y = 15$

              $-5y = 15$

                 $y = -3$

If $x =$ 2, $3(2) - 5y = 15$

           $6 - 5y = 15$

              $-5y = 9$

                 $y = -\dfrac{9}{5}$ $-1\dfrac{4}{5}$

If $x =$ 5, $3(5) - 5y = 15$

         $15 - 5y = 15$

             $-5y = 0$

                 $y = 0$

x	y
0	-3
2	$-1\dfrac{4}{5}$
5	0

Plot the three points
from the table of values,
and draw a straight line
through them (Fig. 1002C).

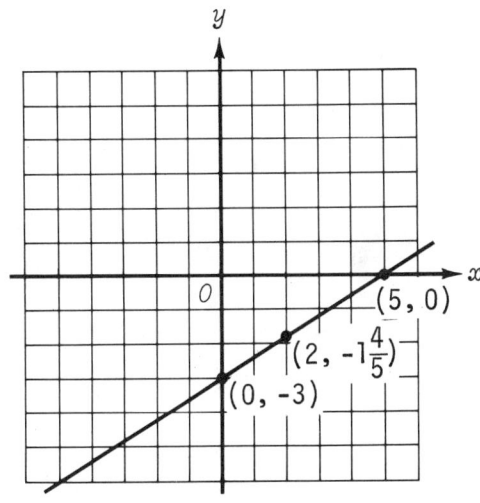

Figure 1002C

<u>INTERCEPTS.</u> Students often ask which
    points to use when plotting the graph
    of a straight line. We usually start
    by choosing zeros.

x	y
0	
	0

For example,

    if the equation of the line is $3x - 2y = -6$
                    If $x = 0$, $3(0) - 2y = -6$
                           $-2y = -6$
                              $y = 3$
                    If $y = 0$, $3x - 2(0) = -6$
                            $3x = -6$
                              $x = -2$

x	y
0	3
-2	0

The points we find by this method are called the *x-intercept* and the *y-intercept*. The *x*-intercept of an equation is the point where its graph meets the *x*-axis. The *y*-value at this point is zero (Fig. 1002D). The *y*-intercept of an equation is the point where its graph meets the *y*-axis. The *x*-value at this point is zero (Fig. 1002D).

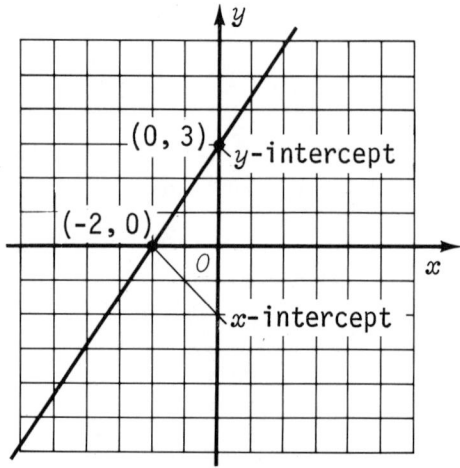

Figure 1002D

Example 2. Graph the equation $4x + 3y = 12$.

Solution: The *intercept method* of graphing a straight line is often easier to use than the method shown in Example 1.

x-intercept: Set $y = 0$. Then $4x + 3y = 12$
becomes $4x + 3(0) = 12$
$4x = 12$
$x = 3$

x	y
3	0
0	

Therefore, the *x*-intercept is (3, 0).

y-intercept: Set $x = 0$. Then $4x + 3y = 12$
becomes $4(0) + 3y = 12$
$3y = 12$
$y = 4$

x	y
3	0
0	4

Therefore, the *y*-intercept is (0, 4).

Check-point: Set $x = 6$. Then $4x + 3y = 12$
$4(6) + 3y = 12$
$24 + 3y = 12$
$3y = -12$
$y = -4$

Therefore, this check-point is (6, -4).

Plot the
x-intercept
(3, 0), the
y-intercept
(0, 4), and
the check-
point (6, -4);
then draw the
straight line
through them
(Fig. 1002E).

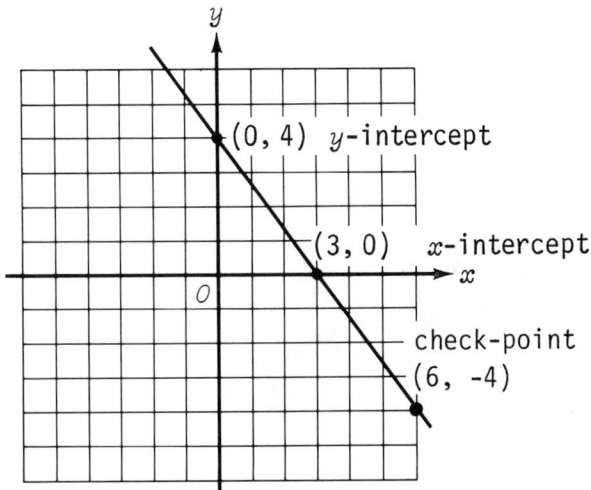

Figure 1002E

Example 3. Graph the equation $3x - 4y = 0$.

Solution:

x-intercept: Set $y = 0$. Then $3x - 4y = 0$
becomes $3x - 4(0) = 0$
$$3x = 0$$
$$x = 0$$

Therefore, the x-intercept is (0, 0) (origin). Since the
line goes through the origin, the y-intercept is also
(0, 0).
    We have found only one point on the line: (0, 0).
Therefore, we must find another point on the line. To find
another point, we must set either letter equal to a number
and then solve the equation for the other letter. For example,

Set $y = 3$. Then $3x - 4y = 0$
becomes $3x - 4(3) = 0$
$$3x = 12$$
$$x = 4$$

This gives the point (4, 3) on the line.

x	y
0	0
4	3
-4	-3

Check-point: Set $x = -4$, then $3x - 4y = 0$
$$3(-4) - 4y = 0$$
$$-12 - 4y = 0$$
$$-4y = 12$$
$$y = -3$$

Plot the points (0, 0), (4, 3), and (-4, -3); then draw the straight line through them (Fig. 1002F).

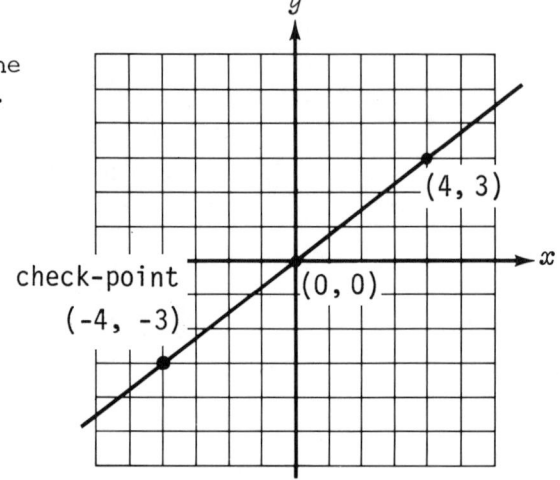

Figure 1002F

Some equations of a line have only one variable. Such equations have graphs that are either vertical or horizontal lines (Examples 4 and 5).

Example 4. Graph the equation $x = 3$.

Solution: The equation $x = 3$ is equivalent to
$$0y + x = 3.$$

If $y = 5$,
$$0(5) + x = 3$$
$$0 + x = 3$$
$$x = 3$$

If $y = -2$,
$$0(-2) + x = 3$$
$$0 + x = 3$$
$$x = 3$$

x	y
3	5
3	-2

You can see that no matter what value y has in this equation, x is always 3. Therefore, all the points having an x-value of 3 lie in a vertical line whose x-intercept is (3, 0) (Fig. 1002G).

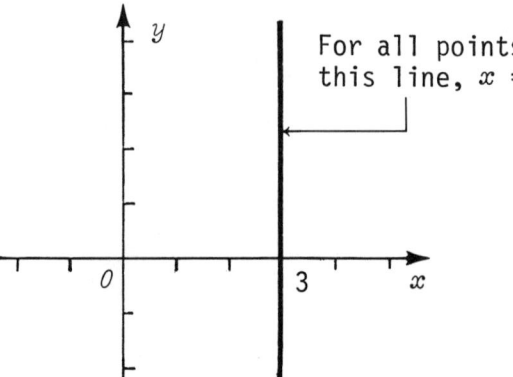

For all points on this line, $x = 3$

Figure 1002G

Example 5. Graph the equation $y + 4 = 0$ (Fig. 1002H)

Solution: $y + 4 = 0$
$$y = -4$$

In the equation $y + 4 = 0$, no matter what value x has, y is always -4. Therefore, all the points having a y-value of -4 lie in a horizontal line whose y-intercept is (0, -4) (Fig. 1002H).

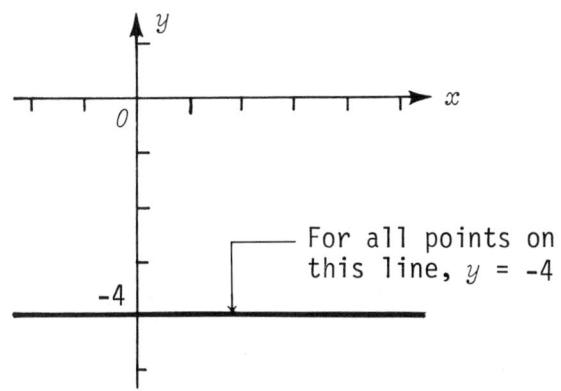

For all points on this line, $y = -4$

Figure 1002H

The methods used in these examples are summarized as follows:

TO GRAPH A STRAIGHT LINE

Method 1

1. Substitute a number in the equation for one of the letters and solve for the corresponding value of the other letter. Find three points in this way, and list them in a Table of Values. (The third point is a check-point.)

2. Graph the points that are listed in the Table of Values.

3. Draw a straight line through the points.

Method 2 (Intercept Method)

1. Find the x-intercept: Set $y = 0$; then solve for x.

2. Find the y-intercept: Set $x = 0$; then solve for y.

3. Draw a straight line through the x- and y-intercepts.

4. If both intercepts are (0, 0), an additional point must be found before the line can be drawn (Example 3).

Exceptions: The graph of $x = a$ is a vertical line (at $x = a$).
The graph of $y = b$ is a horizontal line (at $y = b$).

Note. Sometimes the x- and y-intercepts are very close together. To draw the line through them accurately would be very difficult. In this case, find another point on the line far enough away from the intercepts so that it is easy to draw an accurate line. To find the other point, set either variable equal to a number, and then solve the equation for the other variable. ■

In Exercises 1-22, graph each of the equations.

1. $x + y = 3$ 2. $x - y = 4$ 3. $2x - 3y = 6$

4. $3x - 4y = 12$ 5. $y = 8$ 6. $x = 9$

7. $x + 5 = 0$ 8. $y + 2 = 0$ 9. $3x = 5y + 15$

10. $2x = 5y + 10$ 11. $x = -2y$ 12. $y = -2x$

13. $4 - x = y$ 14. $6 - y = x$ 15. $y = x$

16. $x + y = 0$

----

17. $x = \dfrac{2}{3}y + 4$ 18. $y = \dfrac{3}{4}x + 1$ 19. $3x = 24 + 4y$

20. $2y = 14 - 7x$ 21. $5y = 9x + 160$ 22. $9x = 5(y - 32)$

In Exercises 23 and 24: (a) Graph the two equations for each exercise on the same set of axes. (b) What are the coordinates of the point where the two lines cross?

23. $\begin{aligned} x - y &= 5 \\ x + y &= 1 \end{aligned}$ 24. $\begin{aligned} 3x - 4y &= -12 \\ 3x + y &= 18 \end{aligned}$

In Exercises 1-11, graph each of the equations:

1. $x - y = 5$ 2. $4x - 3y = 12$ 3. $x = -4$

4. $y - 2 = 0$ 5. $3y = 6x - 18$ 6. $y = -3x$

7. $x - y = 0$ 8. $x = 0$ 9. $5x - y = 5$

10. $y = \dfrac{2}{3}x$ 11. $7x = 3y + 21$

In Exercise 12: (a) Graph the two equations on the same set of axes. (b) What are the coordinates of the point where the two lines cross?

12. $\begin{aligned} 2x + 3y &= 12 \\ 2x &= 3y \end{aligned}$

Equations of Straight Lines

In the last section we discussed the *graph* of a straight line. In this section we show how to write the *equation* of a line when certain facts about the line are known.

THE HORIZONTAL AND VERTICAL DISTANCES BETWEEN TWO POINTS.

Consider the two points $P_1(x_1, y_1)$ and $P_2(x_2, y_2)$ shown in Fig. 1003A. From this figure it can be seen that:

The horizontal distance
from P_1 to $P_2 = x_2 - x_1$

The vertical distance
from P_1 to $P_2 = y_2 - y_1$

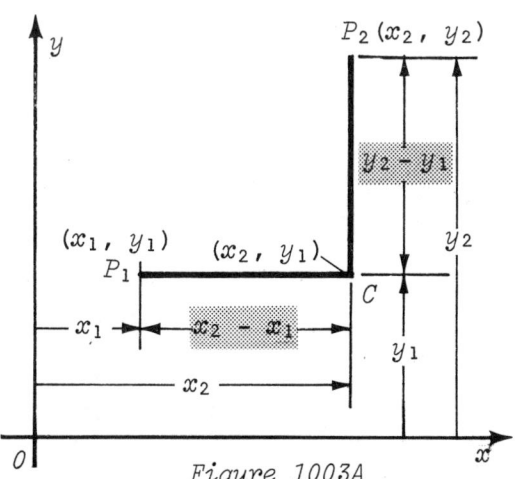

Figure 1003A

The horizontal and vertical distances between two points are used to find the slope of the line that passes through those two points.

THE SLOPE OF A LINE

If we imagine the line as representing a hill, then the *slope* of the line is a measure of the steepness of the hill. To measure the slope of a line, we choose any two points on the line, $P_1(x_1, y_1)$ and $P_2(x_2, y_2)$ (Figure 1003B).

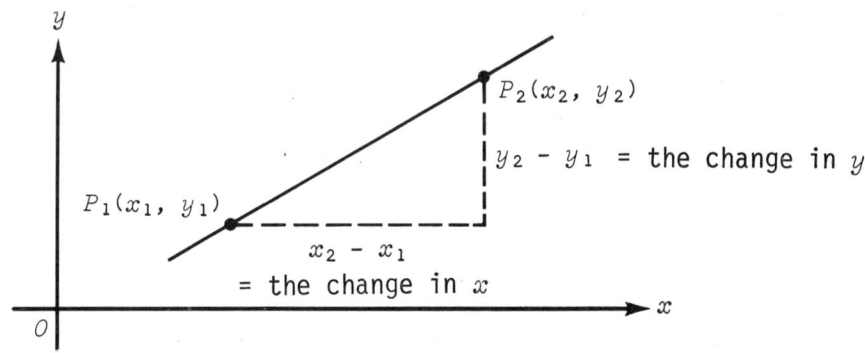

Figure 1003B

The letter m is used to represent the slope of a line. The slope is defined as follows:

SLOPE OF A LINE

$$\text{Slope} = \frac{\text{The change in } y}{\text{The change in } x}$$

$$m = \frac{y_2 - y_1}{x_2 - x_1} \quad \frac{Rise}{Run}$$

Example 1. Find the slope of the line through the points (-3, 5)
and (6, -1) (Figure 1003C).

Let $P_1 = (-3, 5)$

and $P_2 = (6, -1)$

$$m = \frac{y_2 - y_1}{x_2 - x_1}$$

$$= \frac{(-1) - (5)}{(6) - (-3)} = \frac{-6}{9} = -\frac{2}{3}$$

The slope is not changed if
the points P_1 and P_2 are
interchanged.

Let $P_1 = (6, -1)$

and $P_2 = (-3, 5)$

then $m = \dfrac{y_2 - y_1}{x_2 - x_1}$

$$= \frac{(5) - (-1)}{(-3) - (6)} = \frac{6}{-9} = -\frac{2}{3}$$

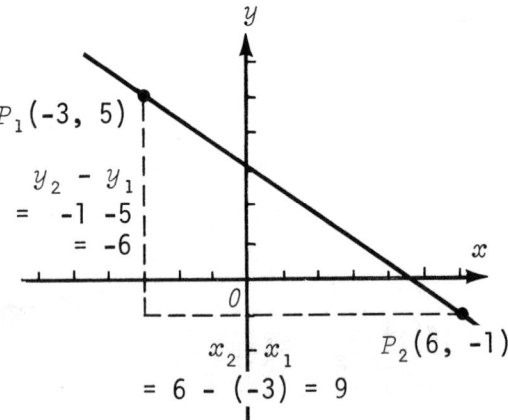

Figure 1003C

Example 2. Find the slope of the line through the points
$A(-2, -4)$ and $B(5, 1)$ (Figure 1003D).

$$m = \frac{y_2 - y_1}{x_2 - x_1}$$

$$= \frac{(1) - (-4)}{(5) - (-2)} = \frac{5}{7}$$

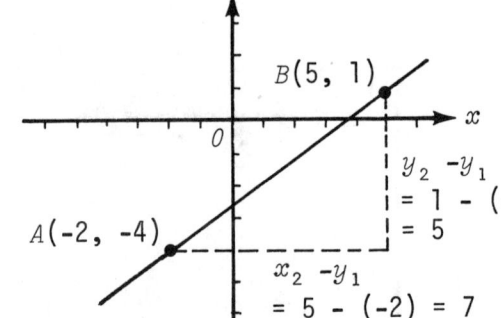

Figure 1003D

Example 3. Find the slope of the line through the points
$E(-4, -3)$ and $F(2, -3)$ (Figure 1003E).

$$m = \frac{y_2 - y_1}{x_2 - x_1}$$

$$= \frac{(-3) - (-3)}{(2) - (-4)} = \frac{0}{6} = 0$$

Whenever the slope is
zero, the line is
horizontal.

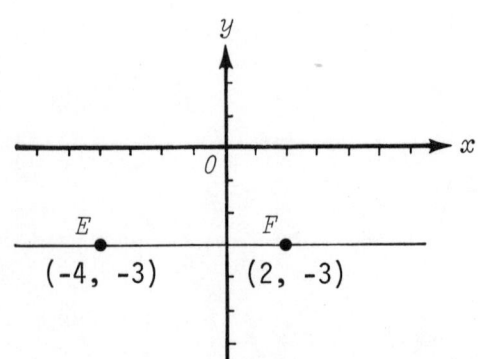

Figure 1003E

Example 4. Find the slope of the line through the points
R(4, 5) and S(4, -2) (Figure 1003F).

$$m = \frac{y_2 - y_1}{x_2 - x_1}$$

$$= \frac{(-2) - (5)}{(4) - (4)} = \frac{-7}{0}$$

Note that $\frac{-7}{0}$ is not a
real number. Therefore
the slope does not exist
when the line is vertical.

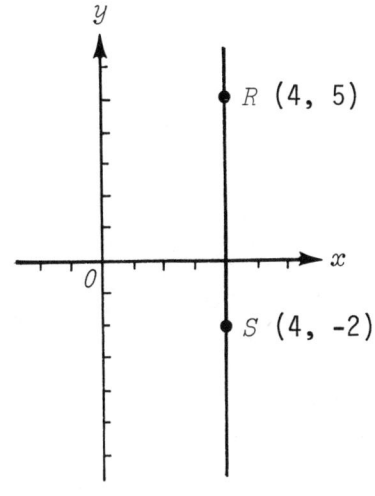

Figure 1003F

THE MEANING OF THE SIGN OF THE SLOPE.

The slope of a line is positive if a point moving along the
line in the positive x-direction (to the right) rises
(Fig. 1003D).

The slope of a line is negative if a point moving along
the line in the positive x-direction falls (Fig. 1003C).

The slope is zero if the line is horizontal (Fig. 1003E).

The slope does not exist if the line is vertical (Fig. 1003F).

EXERCISES 1003A

SET I

In Exercises 1-4, find (a) the vertical distance from the first
given point to the second, and (b) the horizontal distance from
the first given point to the second.

1. (-4, 8) and (7, -9)   2. (3, -10) and (-6, 14)
3. (16, -14) and (8, -11)   4. (-15, -13) and (-23, 17)

In Exercises 5-16, find the slope of the line through the
given pair of points.

5. (-2, 1) and (7, 3)   6. (-1, -3) and (5, 2)
7. (-1, -1) and (5, -3)   8. (-2, -1) and (6, -5)
9. (-5, -3) and (4, -3)   10. (-2, -4) and (3, -4)
11. (-7, 5) and (8, -3)   12. (12, -9) and (-5, -4)
13. (-6, -15) and (4, -5)   14. (-7, 8) and (-4, 5)
15. (-2, 5) and (-2, 8)   16. (6, -4) and (6, -11)

In Exercises 17-20, find the slope of the line by using any two points on the line.

17. $2x - 3y = 6$ 18. $x + 4y = 8$
19. $4x + 5y = 20$ 20. $3x - 5y = 15$

SET II

In Exercises 1 and 2, find (a) the vertical distance from the first given point to the second, and (b) the horizontal distance from the first given point to the second.

1. (-3, 5) and (6, -7)   2. (12, -10) and (4, -12)

In Exercises 3-8, find the slope of the line through the given pair of points.

3. (-3, 2) and (6, 4)   4. (-2, -2) and (4, -1)
5. (-4, -3) and (6, -3)   6. (-10, 2) and (-4, -8)
7. (-3, 8) and (9, 12)   8. (-7, 3) and (-7, -2)

In Exercises 9 and 10, find the slope of the line by using any two points on the line.

9. $6x - 3y = 12$ 10. $7x + 3y + 21 = 0$

EQUATIONS OF STRAIGHT LINES

GENERAL FORM OF THE EQUATION OF A LINE

$$Ax + By + C = 0$$

where A, B, and C are real numbers, and A and B are not both 0.

Whenever possible, write the general form having A *positive* and A, B, and C *integers*.

Example 5. Write $-\frac{2}{3}x + \frac{1}{2}y = 1$ in general form.

Solution: LCD = 6

$$\frac{6}{1}\left(-\frac{2}{3}x\right) + \frac{6}{1}\left(\frac{1}{2}y\right) = \frac{6}{1}\left(\frac{1}{1}\right)$$

$$-4x + 3y = 6$$

$$4x - 3y + 6 = 0 \quad \text{General form.}$$

<u>Point-Slope Form of the Equation of a Line.</u> Let $P_1(x_1, y_1)$ be a known point on a line whose slope is m. Let $P(x, y)$ represent any other point on that line. Then, using the definition of slope, we have:

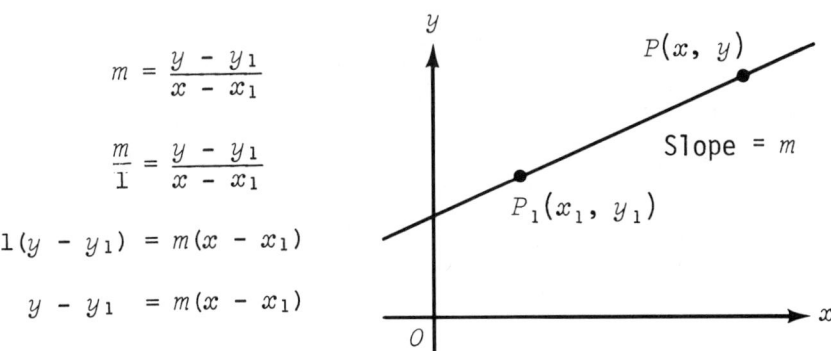

$$m = \frac{y - y_1}{x - x_1}$$

$$\frac{m}{1} = \frac{y - y_1}{x - x_1}$$

$$1(y - y_1) = m(x - x_1)$$

$$y - y_1 = m(x - x_1)$$

Therefore:

POINT-SLOPE FORM OF THE EQUATION OF A LINE

$$y - y_1 = m(x - x_1)$$

where m = slope of the line, and
$P_1(x_1, y_1)$ is a known point on the line.

<u>Example 6.</u> Write the equation of the line (in general form) that passes through (2, -3) and has a slope of 4.

<u>Solution:</u> $\quad y - y_1 = m(x - x_1) \quad$ Point-slope form.

$$y - (-3) = 4(x - 2)$$

$$y + 3 = 4x - 8$$

$$4x - y - 11 = 0 \qquad \text{General form.}$$

<u>Example 7.</u> Write the equation of the line (in general form) that passes through (-1, 4) and has a slope of $-\frac{2}{3}$.

<u>Solution:</u> $\qquad y - y_1 = m(x - x_1)$

$$y - 4 = -\frac{2}{3}[x - (-1)] \quad \text{Point-slope form.}$$

$$3y - 12 = -2(x + 1)$$

$$3y - 12 = -2x - 2$$

$$2x + 3y - 10 = 0 \qquad \text{General form.}$$

Slope-Intercept Form of the Equation of a Line.   Let $(0, b)$ be the y-*intercept* of a line whose slope is m.   Then

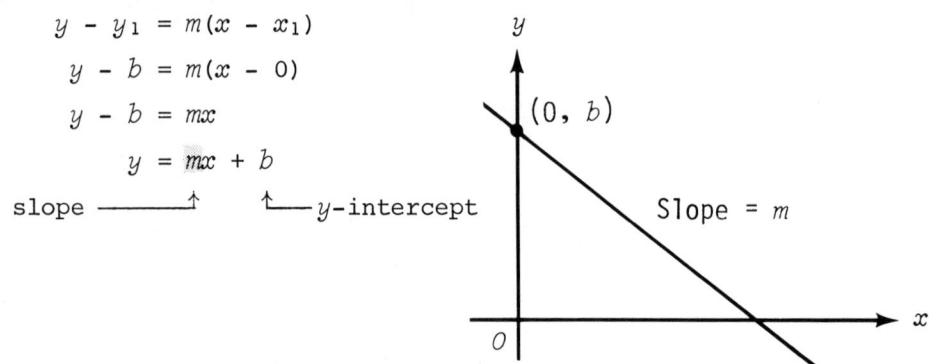

$$y - y_1 = m(x - x_1)$$
$$y - b = m(x - 0)$$
$$y - b = mx$$
$$y = mx + b$$

slope ——————↑   ↑——y-intercept

SLOPE-INTERCEPT FORM
OF THE EQUATION OF A LINE

$$y = mx + b$$

where m = slope of the line,
and b = y-intercept of the line.

Example 8.   Write the equation of the line (in general form) that has a slope of $-\dfrac{3}{4}$ and a y-intercept of -2.

Solution: $y = mx + b$

$$y = -\frac{3}{4}x - 2 \qquad \text{Slope-intercept form.}$$

$$4y = -3x - 8$$

$$3x + 4y + 8 = 0 \qquad \text{General form.}$$

In the following examples we choose the particular form of the equation of the line that makes the best use of the given information.

Example 9.   Find the equation of the line through $(2, -4)$ having a slope of zero.

Solution: $y - y_1 = m(x - x_1)$

$$y - (-4) = 0(x - 2) \qquad \text{Point-slope form.}$$

$$y + 4 = 0 \qquad \text{General form.}$$

$$y = -4 \qquad \text{(Sec. 1002, Example 5, and Fig. 1002H)}$$

Example 10. Find the equation of the vertical line through (3, -5).

Solution: Since the line is vertical, the slope does not exist. Therefore, we cannot use the point-*slope* form or the *slope*-intercept form. The x-coordinate of (3, -5) is 3. Therefore, every point on this vertical line has $x = 3$. This means that the equation of the line is $x = 3$ (Sec. 1002, Example 4, and Fig. 1002G).

Example 11. Find the equation of the line passing through the points (-15, -9) and (-5, 3).

Solution:

1. Find the slope from the two given points.

$$m = \frac{(-9) - (3)}{(-15) - (-5)} = \frac{-12}{-10} = \frac{6}{5}$$

2. Use this slope with *either* given point to find the equation of the line.

Using the point (-5, 3)	Using the point (-15, -9)
$y - y_1 = m(x - x_1)$	$y - y_1 = m(x - x_1)$
$y - 3 = \frac{6}{5}[x - (-5)]$	$y - (-9) = \frac{6}{5}[x - (-15)]$
$5y - 15 = 6(x + 5)$	$5(y + 9) = 6(x + 15)$
$5y - 15 = 6x + 30$	$5y + 45 = 6x + 90$
$0 = 6x - 5y + 45$	$0 = 6x - 5y + 45$

This shows that the same equation is obtained no matter which of the two given points is used.

It is sometimes useful to change the general form into the slope-intercept form. (Example 12)

Example 12. Write $2x + 3y + 6 = 0$ in slope-intercept form.

Solution: Solve the given equation for y.

$$2x + 3y + 6 = 0 \qquad \text{General form.}$$
$$3y = -2x - 6$$
$$y = -\frac{2}{3}x - 2 \qquad \text{Slope-intercept form.}$$

slope ⟶ ⟵ y-intercept

SET I

In Exercises 1-6, write each equation in general form.

1. $3x = 2y - 4$ 2. $2x = 3y + 7$

3. $y = -\dfrac{3}{4}x - 2$ 4. $y = -\dfrac{3}{5}x - 4$

5. $2(3x + y) = 5(x - y) + 4$

6. $3(2x - y) = 2(x + 3y) - 5$

In Exercises 7-10, write the equation of the line through the given point and having the indicated slope. (Write the equation in general form.)

7. $(3, 4)$, $m = \dfrac{1}{2}$ 8. $(5, 6)$, $m = \dfrac{1}{3}$

9. $(-1, -2)$, $m = -\dfrac{2}{3}$ 10. $(-2, -3)$, $m = -\dfrac{5}{4}$

In Exercises 11-14, write the equation of the line having the indicated slope and y-intercept. (Write the equation in general form.)

11. $m = \dfrac{3}{4}$, y-intercept = -3

12. $m = \dfrac{2}{7}$, y-intercept = -2

13. $m = -\dfrac{2}{5}$, y-intercept = $\dfrac{1}{2}$

14. $m = -\dfrac{5}{3}$, y-intercept = $\dfrac{3}{4}$

In Exercises 15-18, find the equation of the line that passes through the given points. (Write the equation in general form.)

15. $(4, -1)$ and $(2, 4)$ 16. $(5, -2)$ and $(3, 1)$

17. $(0, 0)$ and $(3, 4)$ 18. $(0, 0)$ and $(-2, -5)$

19. Write the equation of the horizontal line that passes through the point $(-3, 5)$.
20. Write the equation of the vertical line that passes through the point $(-2, -3)$.

In Exercises 21 and 22: (a) write the given equation in the slope-intercept form; (b) give the slope of the line; (c) give the y-intercept of the line.

21. $3x + 4y + 12 = 0$ 22. $2x + 5y - 15 = 0$

In Exercises 23 and 24, find the slope of the line through the given pair of points.

23. $(-4, 3)$ and $(-4, -2)$ 24. $(-5, 2)$ and $(-5, 7)$

SET II

In Exercises 1-3, write each equation in general form.

1. $5x = 4y - 7$ 2. $\frac{2}{3}x = 3y - \frac{1}{6}$

3. $3(2x - y) = 4(x + y) - 6$

In Exercises 4 and 5, write the equation of the line through the given point and having the indicated slope. (Write the equation in general form.)

4. $(-6, 3)$, $m = -\frac{1}{2}$ 5. $(5, -7)$, $m = -\frac{3}{4}$

In Exercises 6 and 7, write the equation of the line having the indicated slope and y-intercept. (Write the equation in general form.)

6. $m = -\frac{2}{3}$, y-intercept = -4

7. $m = \frac{5}{4}$, y-intercept = -3

In Exercises 8 and 9, find the equation of the line that passes through the given points. (Write the equation in general form.)

8. $(-3, 4)$ and $(5, -2)$ 9. $(5, -3)$ and $(-2, -4)$

10. Write the equation of the horizontal line that passes through the point $(-4, -2)$.

11. (a) Write $\frac{3}{4}x - 2y - 3 = 0$ in the slope-intercept form.
     (b) Give the slope of the line.
     (c) Give the y-intercept of the line.

12. Find the slope of the line through the points $(-3, 7)$ and $(-3, -5)$.

Graphing Curved Lines

In Section 1002 we showed how to graph straight lines. In this section we show how to graph *curved* lines.

Two points are all that we need to draw a straight line. To draw a curved line, we must find more than two points.

```
┌─────────────────────────────────────────────────────────┐
│                                                           │
│  TO GRAPH A CURVE                                         │
│                                                           │
│  1.  Use the equation to make a table of values.          │
│                                                           │
│  2.  Plot the points from the table of values.            │
│                                                           │
│  3.  Draw a smooth curve through the points, joining      │
│      them in order from left to right.                    │
│                                                           │
└─────────────────────────────────────────────────────────┘
```

<u>Example 1.</u> Graph the equation $y = x^2 - x - 2$.

<u>Solution:</u> Make a table of values by substituting values
of x in the equation and finding the corresponding
values for y.

x	y
-2	4
-1	0
0	-2
1	-2
2	0
3	4

If $x = -2$, then $y = (-2)^2 - (-2) - 2 = 4 + 2 - 2 = 4$.

If $x = -1$, then $y = (-1)^2 - (-1) - 2 = 1 + 1 - 2 = 0$.

If $x = 0$, then $y = (0)^2 - (0) - 2 = -2$.

If $x = 1$, then $y = (1)^2 - (1) - 2 = 1 - 1 - 2 = -2$.

If $x = 2$, then $y = (2)^2 - (2) - 2 = 4 - 2 - 2 = 0$.

If $x = 3$, then $y = (3)^2 - (3) - 2 = 9 - 3 - 2 = 4$.

In Fig. 1004A, we graph these points and draw a smooth
curve through them. *In drawing the smooth curve, start with
the point in the table of values having the smallest x-value.
Draw to the point having the next larger x-value.
Continue in this way through all the points.* The graph of
the equation $y = x^2 - x - 2$ is called a *parabola*.

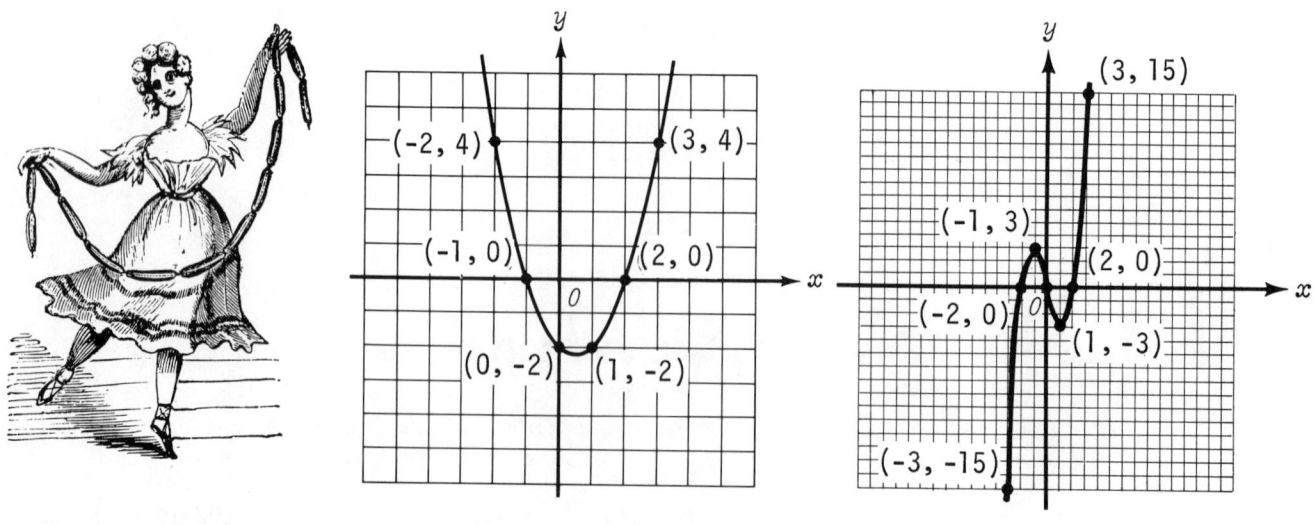

Figure 1004A   Figure 1004B

Example 2. Graph the equation $y = x^3 - 4x$.

Solution: First make a table of values.

If $x = -3$, then $y = (-3)^3 - 4(-3) = -27 + 12 = -15$.

If $x = -2$, then $y = (-2)^3 - 4(-2) = -8 + 8 = 0$.

If $x = -1$, then $y = (-1)^3 - 4(-1) = -1 + 4 = 3$.

If $x = 0$, then $y = (0)^3 - 4(0) = 0$.

If $x = 1$, then $y = (1)^3 - 4(1) = 1 - 4 = -3$.

If $x = 2$, then $y = (2)^3 - 4(2) = 8 - 8 = 0$.

If $x = 3$, then $y = (3)^3 - 4(3) = 27 - 12 = 15$.

x	y
-3	-15
-2	0
-1	3
0	0
1	-3
2	0
3	15

In Figure 1004B, we graph the points found in Example 2 and draw a smooth curve through them.

EXERCISES 1004

SET I

In Exercises 1-4, complete the table of values for each equation, and then draw its graph.

1. $y = x^2$

x	y
-2	
-1	
0	
1	
2	

2. $y = \dfrac{x^2}{4}$

x	y
-3	
-2	
-1	
0	
1	
2	
3	

3. $y = x^2 - 2x$ 4. $y = 3x - x^2$

x	y
-2	
-1	
0	
1	
2	
3	
4	

x	y
-2	
-1	
0	
1	
2	
3	
4	

5. Use integer values of x from -2 to +4 to make a table of values for the equation $y = 2x - x^2$. Graph the points and draw a smooth curve through them.

6. Use integer values of x from -3 to +1 to make a table of values for the equation $y = 2x + x^2$. Graph the points and draw a smooth curve through them.

----

7. Use integer values of x from -2 to +2 to make a table of values for the equation $y = x^3$. Graph the points and draw a smooth curve through them.

8. Use integer values of x from -2 to +2 to make a table of values for the equation $y = x^3 - 3x + 4$. Graph the points and draw a smooth curve through them.

SET II

In Exercises 1 and 2, complete the table of values for each equation, and then draw its graph.

1. $y = \dfrac{x^2}{2}$ 2. $y = x^2 + 4x$

x	y
-3	
-2	
-1	
0	
1	
2	
3	

x	y
-5	
-4	
-3	
-2	
-1	
0	
1	

3. Use integer values of x from -1 to $+6$ to make a table of values for the equation $y = 5x - x^2$. Graph the points and draw a smooth curve through them.

4. Use integer values of x from -2 to $+2$ to make a table of values for the equation $y = 1 - 2x - x^3$. Graph the points and draw a smooth curve through them.

Solving Inequalities Having One Letter and Graphing Them on the Number Line .

An *equation* is a statement that two expressions are *equal*. An *inequality* is a statement that two expressions are *not equal*.

An inequality has three parts:

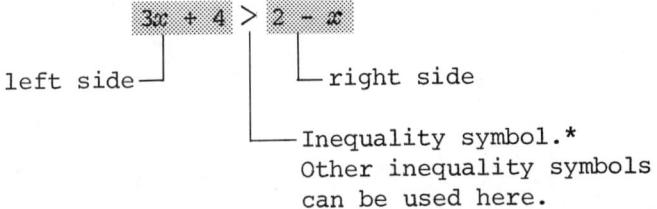

left side

right side

Inequality symbol.*
Other inequality symbols
can be used here.

*In this text we will discuss only inequalities that have the symbols $\neq$, $>$, $<$, $\leq$, or $\geq$.

TYPES OF INEQUALITIES

Unequal to symbol ($\neq$)

$a \neq b$ is read "a is unequal to b"

Example 1.   Unequal to symbol

(a)   Write $5 \neq 7$
Read   "5 is unequal to 7"

(b)   Write $5 \neq x - 3$
Read "5 is unequal to x minus 3"

Greater Than symbol ($>$)

$a > b$ is read "a is greater than b"

Example 2.   Greater than symbol

(a)   Write $11 > 2$
Read   "11 is greater than 2"

(b)   Write $3x - 4 > 7$
Read "$3x$ minus 4 is greater than 7"

Less Than symbol ($<$)

$a < b$ is read "a is less than b"

Example 3. Less than symbol

    (a)   Write $3 < 6$
          Read "3 is less than 6"
    (b)   Write $2x < 5 - x$
          Read "$2x$ is less than $5 - x$"

Less Than or Equal to symbol ($\leq$)

    $a \leq b$ is read "a is less than *or* equal to b."

This means if $\begin{cases} \text{either} & a < b \\ \text{or} & a = b \end{cases}$ is true, then $a \leq b$ is true.

Example 4. Less than or equal to symbol

    (a) $2 \leq 3$ is true, because $2 < 3$ is true.
    (b) $4 \leq 4$ is true, because $4 = 4$ is true.
    (c) Write $7 \leq 5x - 2$
         Read "7 is less than or equal to $5x - 2$."

Greater than or Equal to symbol ($\geq$)

    $a \geq b$ is read "a is greater than *or* equal to b."

This means if $\begin{cases} \text{either} & a > b \\ \text{or} & a = b \end{cases}$ is true, then $a \geq b$ is true.

Example 5. Greater than or equal to symbol

    (a) $5 \geq 1$ is true, because $5 > 1$ is true.
    (b) $7 \geq 7$ is true, because $7 = 7$ is true.
    (c) Write $x + 6 \geq 10$
         Read "x plus 6 is greater than or equal to 10."

The *sense* of an inequality symbol refers to the direction the symbol points.

$\left.\begin{array}{l} a > b \\ c > d \end{array}\right\}$ same sense $\left.\begin{array}{l} a < b \\ c > d \end{array}\right\}$ opposite sense

$\left.\begin{array}{l} e < f \\ g < h \end{array}\right\}$ same sense $\left.\begin{array}{l} e > f \\ g < h \end{array}\right\}$ opposite sense

FACTS ABOUT INEQUALITIES

The basic rules used to solve inequalities are the same as those used to solve equations, with the exception that *the sense must be changed when multiplying or dividing both sides by a negative number*.

Example 6. Illustrating the rules used with inequalities.

    (a) $\begin{array}{r} 10 > 5 \\ \underline{+\,6 +\,6} \\ 16 > 11 \end{array}$ Adding same number (6) to both sides.
                                      Sense is *not* changed.

(b)
$$7 < 12$$
$$\underline{-2 \quad -2}$$
$$5 < 10$$

Subtracting same number (2) from both sides.
Sense is *not* changed.

(c)
$$3 < 4$$
$$2(3) < 2(4)$$
$$6 < 8$$

Multiplying both sides by the same *positive* number (2).
Sense is *not* changed.

(d)
$$3 < 4$$
$$(-2)(3) \ ? \ (-2)(4)$$
$$-6 > -8$$

Multiplying both sides by the same *negative* number (-2).
Sense is changed.

(e)
$$9 > 6$$

$$\frac{9}{3} > \frac{6}{3}$$

Dividing both sides by the same *positive* number (3).

$$3 > 2$$

Sense is *not* changed.

(f)
$$9 > 6$$

$$\frac{9}{-3} \ ? \ \frac{6}{-3}$$

Dividing both sides by the same *negative* number (-3).

$$-3 < -2$$

Sense is changed.

SOLVING INEQUALITIES

An inequality is solved when we have nothing but the unknown letter on one side of the inequality symbol and everything else on the other side.

The method of solving inequalities is very much like the method used for solving equations. We show how the methods are alike or different in the following summary.

IN SOLVING EQUATIONS	IN SOLVING INEQUALITIES
Addition Rule: The same number may be added to both sides.	*Addition Rule:* The same number may be added to both sides.
Subtraction Rule: The same number may be subtracted from both sides.	*Subtraction Rule:* The same number may be subtracted from both sides.
Multiplication Rule: Both sides may be multiplied by the same number.	*Multiplication Rule:* 1. Both sides may be multiplied by the same *positive* number. 2. When both sides are multiplied by the same *negative* number, *the sense must be changed.*
Division Rule: Both sides may be divided by the same nonzero number.	*Division Rule:* 1. Both sides may be divided by the same *positive* number. 2. When both sides are divided by the same *negative* number, *the sense must be changed.*

Example 7.   Solve $x + 3 < 7$.

Solution:
$$x + 3 < 7$$
$$\underline{-3 \quad -3}$$
$$x \quad < 4$$

Adding -3 to both sides.
Solution.

This means that if we replace x by any number less than 4 in the given inequality, we get a true statement. For example, if we replace x by 3 (which is less than 4):

$$x + 3 < 7$$
$$3 + 3 < 7$$
$$6 < 7 \quad \textit{True}$$

Example 8.   Solve $2x - 5 > 1$.

Solution:
$$2x - 5 > 1$$
$$\underline{+5 \quad +5}$$
$$2x \quad > 6$$

Adding 5 to both sides.

$$\frac{2x}{2} > \frac{6}{2}$$ Dividing both sides by 2.
Sense is *not* changed.

$$x > 3 \quad \text{Solution}$$

Example 9.   Solve $3x - 2(2x - 7) \leq 2(3 + x) - 4$

Solution:
$$3x - 2(2x - 7) \leq 2(3 + x) - 4$$
$$3x - 4x + 14 \leq 6 + 2x - 4$$
$$-x + 14 \leq 2 + 2x$$
$$-3x \leq -12$$

$$\frac{-3x}{-3} \;?\; \frac{-12}{-3}$$ Dividing both sides by -3

$$x \geq 4$$ *Sense is changed.*
Solution

Example 10.   Solve $\dfrac{a}{3} - \dfrac{a}{7} \geq 12$.

Solution: LCD $= 3 \cdot 7 = 21$

$$\frac{\overset{7}{\cancel{21}}}{1} \frac{a}{\underset{1}{\cancel{3}}} - \frac{\overset{3}{\cancel{21}}}{1} \frac{a}{\underset{1}{\cancel{7}}} \geq \frac{21}{1} \frac{12}{1}$$

$$7a - 3a \geq 21(12)$$

$$4a \geq 21(12)$$

$$\frac{\cancel{4}a}{\cancel{4}} \geq \frac{21(\overset{3}{\cancel{12}})}{\cancel{4}}$$

$$a \geq 63$$

Example 11.   Solve $\dfrac{y + 3}{4} \leq \dfrac{y - 2}{3} + \dfrac{1}{4}$.

Solution: LCD $= 2^2 \cdot 3 = 12$

$$\dfrac{\overset{3}{\cancel{12}}}{1} \dfrac{y + 3}{\underset{1}{\cancel{4}}} \leq \dfrac{\overset{4}{\cancel{12}}}{1} \dfrac{y - 2}{\underset{1}{\cancel{3}}} + \dfrac{\overset{3}{\cancel{12}}}{1} \dfrac{1}{\cancel{4}}$$

$$3(y + 3) \leq 4(y - 2) + 3(1)$$

$$3y + 9 \leq 4y - 8 + 3$$

$$3y + 9 \leq 4y - 5$$

$$14 \leq y$$

or $y \geq 14$ $\Bigg\}$ Same meaning.

Example 12.   Solve: $4(x - 3) - 5 \neq 2x - 7$

Solution:
$$
\begin{array}{ll}
4(x - 3) - 5 \neq 2x - 7 & \\
4x - 12 - 5 \neq 2x - 7 & \text{Removing parentheses} \\
4x - 17 \neq 2x - 7 & \\
\underline{-2x \qquad\quad -2x} & \text{To get the } x\text{-term on} \\
2x - 17 \neq \quad\; - 7 & \text{only one side} \\
\underline{+ 17 \qquad\quad + 17} & \\
2x \qquad\;\; \neq \qquad 10 &
\end{array}
$$

$$\dfrac{2x}{2} \neq \dfrac{10}{2}$$

$$x \neq 5 \qquad\qquad \text{Solution}$$

The method used to solve inequalities may be summarized as follows.

TO SOLVE AN INEQUALITY

Proceed in the same way used to solve equations, with the *exception* that the sense must be changed when multiplying or dividing both sides by a negative number.

EXERCISES 1005A.   Solve the following inequalities.

SET I

1. $x - 5 < 2$	2. $x - 4 < 7$
3. $5x + 4 \leq 19$	4. $3x + 5 \leq 14$
5. $6x + 7 > 3 + 8x$	6. $4x + 28 > 7 + x$
7. $2x - 9 > 3(x - 2)$	8. $3x - 11 > 5(x - 1)$

----

9. $6(3 - 4x) + 12 \geq 10x - 2(5 - 3x)$

10. $7(2 - 5x) + 27 \geq 18x - 3(8 - 4x)$

11. $4(6 - 2x) \neq 5x - 2$

12. $6(2x - 5) + 29 \neq 3x - 7(11 - 4x)$

13. $2[3 - 5(x - 4)] < 10 - 5x$

14. $3[2 - 4(x - 7)] < 26 - 8x$

15. $\dfrac{x}{3} + \dfrac{x}{4} > 7$ 16. $\dfrac{x}{5} + \dfrac{x}{3} > 8$

17. $\dfrac{y - 5}{3} \leq \dfrac{y + 2}{5} + \dfrac{1}{3}$ 18. $\dfrac{x + 2}{4} - \dfrac{2}{3} \leq \dfrac{x - 2}{3}$

19. $12.85x - 15.49 \geq 22.06(9.66x - 12.74)$

20. $7.12(3.65x - 8.09) + 5.76 < 5.18x - 6.92(4.27 - 3.39x)$

SET II

1. $x + 3 \geq -4$ 2. $7x - 3 < 18$

3. $5x + 7 > 13 + 11x$ 4. $5x - 6 \leq 3(2 + 3x)$

5. $5(3 - 2x) + 25 \geq 4x - 6(10 - 3x)$

6. $4[2 - 3(x - 5)] < 2 - 6x$

7. $\dfrac{x}{6} + \dfrac{x}{3} > 12$ 8. $\dfrac{x + 1}{2} \leq \dfrac{x + 9}{5} + \dfrac{1}{2}$

9. $2(5 - 3x) \neq 7 - 4x$

10. $821.4x - 395.2 \geq 604.1(542.8x - 193.7)$

GRAPHING INEQUALITIES ON THE NUMBER LINE

We have just discussed *solving* inequalities in one letter. We now show how to *graph* the solution of an inequality on the number line (Examples 13 and 14).

Example 13. Solve $5x + 3 < 13$ and plot its solution on the number line.

Solution:
$$5x + 3 < 13$$
$$\underline{ - 3 \qquad -3}$$
$$5x \qquad < 10$$

$$x < 2 \qquad \text{Solution.}$$

Graph of solution.
The arrow indicates that all numbers to the left of 2 are solutions   Hollow circle because 2 is not a solution

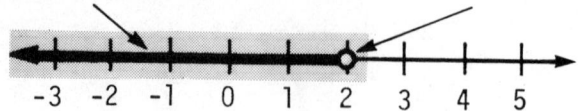

360   Chapter 10: Graphing

Example 14.   Solve $3x - 2 \geq -14$ and plot its solution on the
number line.

Solution:
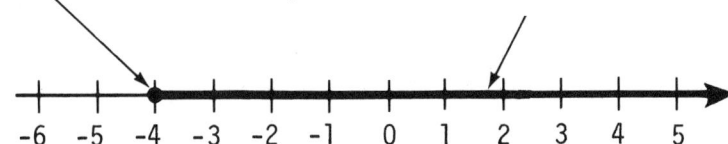

$$3x - 2 \geq -14$$
$$\underline{+ 2 \quad \quad + 2}$$
$$3x \quad \geq \overline{-12}$$

$$x \geq -4 \quad \quad \text{Solution.}$$

Solid circle because   The arrow together with the solid circle
-4 is a solution.   indicates that -4 and all numbers
to the right of -4 are solutions.

EXERCISES 1005B. Plot the graphs of the solutions to the
inequalities given in Exercises 1005A.

1006 Graphing Inequalities in the Plane

In Sec. 1005 we solved inequalities having one letter.
Then we graphed each solution *on the number line*. In this
section we graph the solutions of inequalities having no
more than two letters. The graphs in this section are
drawn *in the plane* of the rectangular coordinate system.

HALF-PLANES. Any line in a plane divides that plane into two
half-planes. For example, in Fig. 1006A the line *AB* divides
the plane into the two half-planes shown.

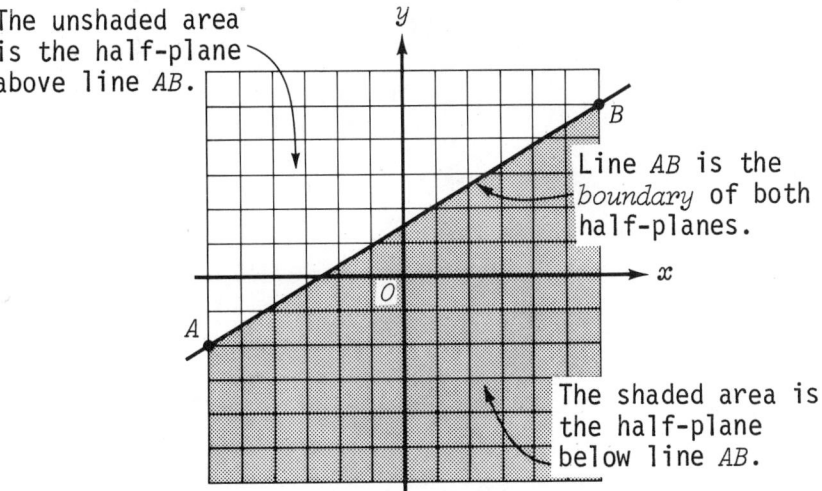

The unshaded area
is the half-plane
above line *AB*.

Line *AB* is the
boundary of both
half-planes.

The shaded area is
the half-plane
below line *AB*.

Figure 1006A

Any first-degree *inequality* (in no more than two variables) has a graph that is a half-plane.

The equation of the boundary line of the half-plane is obtained by replacing the inequality sign by an equal sign.

HOW TO DETERMINE WHEN BOUNDARY IS DASHED OR SOLID LINE

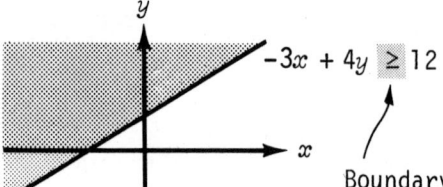

Boundary is a *solid* line when equality is included. In this case, the boundary line is part of the solution.

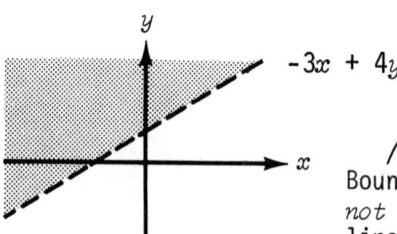

Boundary is a *dashed* line when equality is *not* included. In this case, the boundary line is *not* part of the solution.

HOW TO DETERMINE THE CORRECT HALF-PLANE

1. *If the boundary does not go through the origin*, substitute the coordinates of the origin (0, 0) into the inequality.

   If the resulting inequality is *true*, the solution is the half-plane containing (0, 0).
   If the resulting inequality is *false*, the solution is the half-plane *not* containing (0, 0).

2. *If the boundary goes through the origin*, select a point *not* on the boundary. Substitute the coordinates of this point into the inequality.

   If the resulting inequality is *true*, the solution is the half-plane containing the point selected.
   If the resulting inequality is *false*, the solution is the half-plane *not* containing the point selected.

TO GRAPH A FIRST-DEGREE INEQUALITY (IN THE PLANE)

1. The boundary line is *solid* if equality is included ($\geq$, $\leq$).
   The boundary line is *dashed* if equality is *not* included ($>$, $<$).

2. Graph the boundary line.

3. Select and shade the correct half-plane.

Example 1. Graph the inequality $2x - 3y < 6$.

Solution: Change $<$ to $=$ ─────────┐
                                        │
                                        │
Boundary line: $2x - 3y = 6$

1. The boundary is a *dashed* line because the equality is *not* included. ──────────────────┐
                                                                            │
                                                                            ↓
                      $2x - 3y < 6$

2. Plot the graph of the boundary line by the intercept method. (Figure 1006B)

x-intercept: Set $y = 0$ in $\quad 2x - 3y = 6$
                 Then $2x - 3(0) = 6$
                               $2x = 6$
                                $x = 3$

y-intercept: Set $x = 0$ in $\quad 2x - 3y = 6$
                 Then $2(0) - 3y = 6$
                              $-3y = 6$
                                $y = -2$

x	y
3	0
0	-2

Therefore the boundary line goes through (3, 0) and (0, -2).

3. *Select the correct half-plane.* The solution of the inequality is only one of the two half-planes determined by the boundary line. Substitute the coordinates of the origin (0, 0) into the inequality:

$$2x - 3y < 6$$
$$2(0) - 3(0) < 6$$
$$0 < 6 \quad \textit{True}$$

Therefore the half-plane containing the origin is the solution. The solution is the shaded area in Figure 1006B.

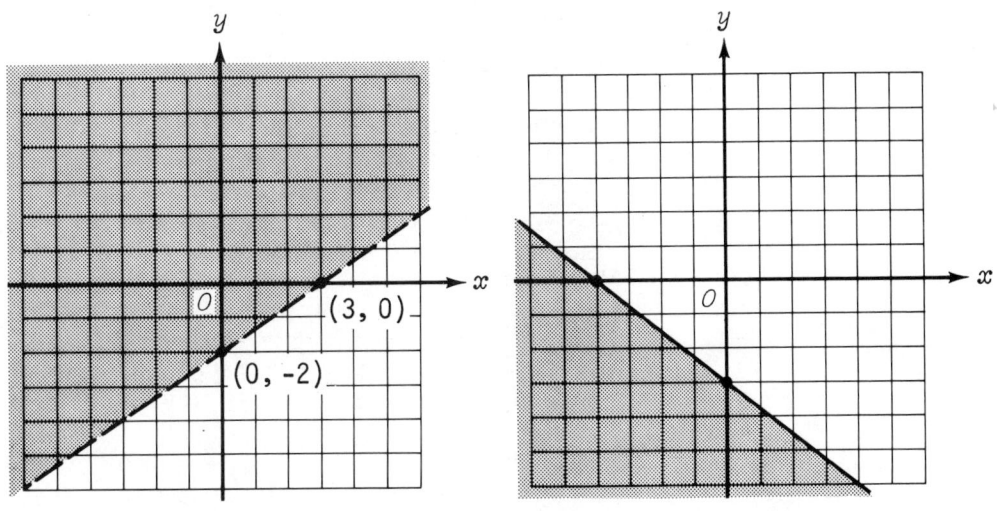

Figure 1006B   Figure 1006C

Example 2. Graph the inequality $3x + 4y \leq -12$.

Solution:

1. The boundary is a *solid* line because the equality is included.

$$3x + 4y \leq -12$$

2. Plot the graph of the boundary line: $3x + 4y = -12$
(Fig. 1006C).

    x-intercept: Set $y = 0$ in $3x + 4y = -12$
                            Then $3x + 4(0) = -12$
                                  $3x = -12$
                                    $x = -4$

x	y
-4	0
0	-3

    y-intercept: Set $x = 0$ Then $3(0) + 4y = -12$
                                      $4y = -12$
                                      $y = -3$

Therefore, the boundary line goes through $(-4, 0)$ and $(0, -3)$.

3. Select the correct half-plane. Substitute the coordinates of the origin $(0, 0)$:

$$3x + 4y \leq -12$$
$$3(0) + 4(0) \leq -12$$
$$0 \leq -12 \quad \textit{False}$$

Therefore the solution is the half-plane *not* containing $(0, 0)$. The solution is the shaded area in Fig. 1006C.

Some inequalities have equations with *only one variable*. Such inequalities have graphs whose *boundaries* are either *vertical* or *horizontal* lines.

Example 3. Graph the inequality $x + 4 < 0$.

Solution:

1. The boundary is a *dashed* line because the equality is *not* included.

$$x + 4 < 0$$

2. Plot the graph of the boundary line: $x + 4 = 0$
(See Figure 1006D.) $x = -4$

3. Select the correct half-plane. Substitute the coordinates of the origin $(0, 0)$:

$$x + 4 < 0$$
$$(0) + 4 < 0$$
$$4 < 0 \quad \textit{False}$$

Therefore the solution is the half-plane *not* containing $(0, 0)$. The solution is the shaded area in Fig. 1006D.

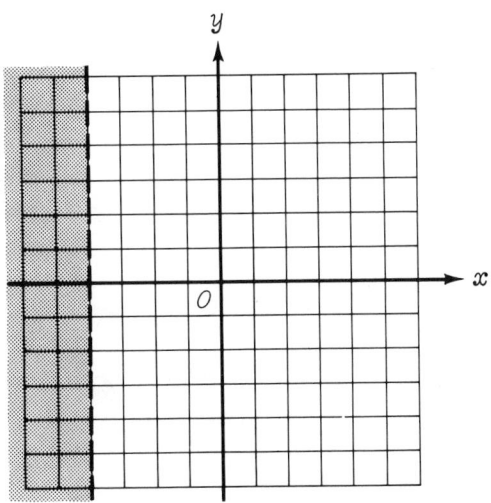

Figure 1006D

In Sec. 1005 we discussed how to graph the solution of
an inequality such as $x + 4 < 0$ on a *single number line*.

Since $x + 4 < 0$
then $x < -4$.

This arrow indicates that the solution
consists of all real numbers less
than -4.

```
      -8 -7 -6 -5 -4 -3 -2 -1  0  1  2  3  4
```

Example 3 of *this* section shows that the solution of this
same inequality, $x + 4 < 0$, represents an entire half-plane
when it is plotted in the rectangular coordinate system
(Fig. 1006D).

<u>Example 4.</u> Graph the inequality $2y - 5x \geq 0$.

Solution:

1. The boundary is a *solid* line because the equality is
    included.

$$2y - 5x \geq 0$$

2. Plot the graph of the boundary line:
    $2y - 5x = 0$ (Figure 1006E).

    <u>x-intercept</u>: Set $y = 0$. Then $2(0) - 5x = 0$
    $$-5x = 0$$
    $$x = 0$$

    <u>y-intercept</u>: Set $x = 0$. Then $2y - 5(0) = 0$
    $$2y = 0$$
    $$y = 0$$

Therefore the boundary line passes through the origin
(0, 0).

To find another point on the line: $2y - 5x = 0$

Set $x = 2$. Then $2y - 5(2) = 0$

$$2y - 10 = 0$$
$$2y = 10$$
$$y = 5$$

This gives the point $(2, 5)$ on the line.

x	y
0	0
0	0
2	5

3. Select the correct half-plane. Since the boundary goes through the origin $(0, 0)$, select a point *not* on the boundary, say $(1, 0)$. Substitute the coordinates of $(1, 0)$ into $2y - 5x \geq 0$.

$$2(0) - 5(1) \geq 0$$
$$-5 \geq 0 \quad \textit{False}$$

Therefore the solution is the half-plane *not* containing $(1, 0)$ (Figure 1006E).

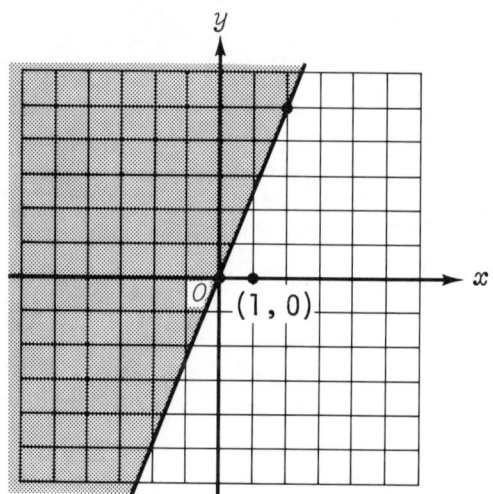

Figure 1006E

EXERCISES 1006. Graph each of the following inequalities (in the plane).

SET I

1. $x + 2y < 4$

2. $3x + y < 6$

3. $2x - 3y > 6$

4. $5x - 2y > 10$

5. $x \geq -2$

6. $y \geq -3$

7. $3y - 4x \geq 12$

8. $3x + 2y \geq -6$

9. $x + y > 0$

10. $x - y > 0$

11. $3x - 4y \geq 10$

12. $2x - 3y \leq 11$

----

13. $2(x + 1) + 3 \leq 3(2x - 1)$

14. $5(y - 1) + 2 \leq 2(3y + 2)$

15. $\dfrac{x}{5} - \dfrac{y}{3} > 1$

16. $\dfrac{y}{4} - \dfrac{x}{5} > 1$

17. $\dfrac{2x + y}{3} - \dfrac{x - y}{2} \geq \dfrac{5}{6}$

18. $\dfrac{4x - 3y}{5} - \dfrac{2x - y}{2} \geq \dfrac{2}{5}$

SET II

1. $4x + 2y < 8$

2. $2x - 7y \geq 14$

3. $y < 4$

4. $5x - 3y \geq 15$

5. $4x - y \leq 0$

6. $5x - 4y > 12$

7. $3x - 2(2x - 7) \leq 2(3 + x) - 4$

8. $\dfrac{x}{5} - \dfrac{y}{2} > 1$

9. $\dfrac{x - y}{2} - \dfrac{x - 4y}{7} \leq \dfrac{5}{14}$

Chapter Summary

Ordered Pairs. (Sec. 1001) An ordered pair of numbers is used to represent a point in the plane.

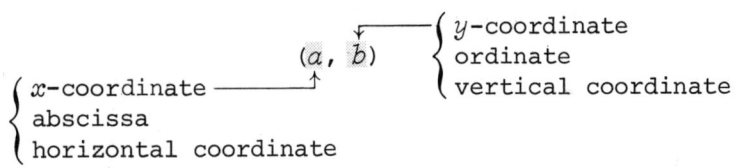

Equations of Straight Lines (Sec. 1003)

1. *General Form*: $Ax + By + C = 0$, where A and B are not both 0.

To Graph a Straight Line (Sec. 1002)

Method 1	*Method 2 (Intercept Method)*
1. Substitute a number in the equation for one of the letters and solve for the corresponding value of the other letter. Find three points in this way, and list them in a table of values. (The third point is a checkpoint.)	1. Find the x-intercept: Set $y = 0$; then solve for x.
	2. Find the y-intercept: Set $x = 0$; then solve for y.
2. Graph the points that are listed in the Table of Values.	3. Draw a straight line through the x- and y-intercepts.
3. Draw a straight line through the points.	4. If both intercepts are (0, 0), an additional point must be found before the line can be drawn.

Exceptions:
The graph of $x = a$ is a vertical line (at $x = a$).
The graph of $y = b$ is a horizontal line (at $y = b$).

To Graph a Curve (Sec. 1004)

1. Use the equation to make a Table of Values.
2. Plot the points from the Table of Values.
3. Draw a smooth curve through the points, joining them in order from left to right.

Inequality. An inequality is a statement that two expressions are not equal (Sec. 1005 and 1006).

Inequality in one letter (Sec. 1005)

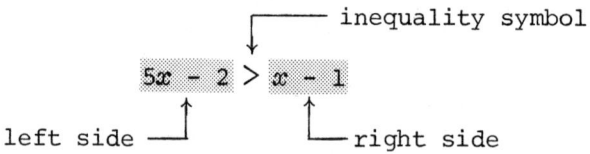

Inequality in two letters (Sec. 1006)

$$2x + 3 < y - 1$$

To Solve a First-Degree Inequality Having Only One Unknown Letter (Sec. 1005). Proceed in the same way used to solve equations, with the *exception* that the sense must be changed when multiplying or dividing both sides by a negative number.

Graphing Solutions on the Number Line (Sec. 1005).

To graph the solution $x > c$:

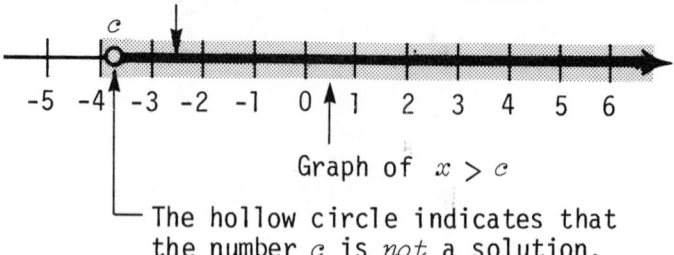

To graph the solution $x \leqslant b$:

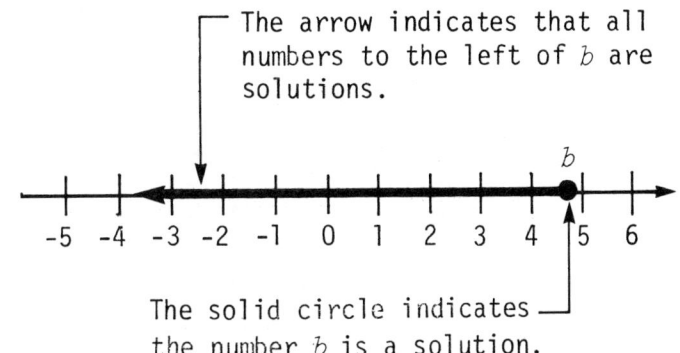

The arrow indicates that all numbers to the left of b are solutions.

The solid circle indicates the number b is a solution.

Other types of solutions, for example, $x < c$ and $x \geq c$, are graphed using the same procedures.

To Graph a First-Degree Inequality in the Plane (Sec. 1006)

1. The boundary line is *solid* if equality is included ($\geq, \leq$).
   The boundary line is *dashed* if equality is *not* included ($>, <$).
2. Graph the boundary line.
3. Select and shade the correct half-plane.

REVIEW EXERCISES 1007

SET I

1. Draw a rectangle whose vertices have the following coordinates: A (2, -5), B (2, 1), C (-3, 1), and D (-3, -5).
2. Draw a four-sided figure whose sides are straight lines and whose vertices have the following coordinates: E (3, -5), F (4, 0), G (0, 3), and H (-3, -2).
3. Given the point A (5, -3), find:
   (a) the abscissa of A.
   (b) the ordinate of A.
   (c) the y-coordinate of A.
4. Given the point B (-2, 4), find:
   (a) the ordinate of B.
   (b) the abscissa of B.
   (c) the x-coordinate of B.

In Exercises 5-14, graph each equation.

5. $x - y = 5$ 6. $y - x = 3$ 7. $x = y$

8. $x + y = 0$ 9. $x = -2$ 10. $y = -3$

11. $4y - 5x = 20$ 12. $5y - 4x = 20$ 13. $x + 2y = 0$

14. $y = -2x$

In Exercises 15 and 16, complete the table of values and then draw the graph.

15. $y = \dfrac{x^2}{2}$

x	y
-4	
-2	
-1	
0	
1	
2	
4	

16. $y = x^2 - 3x$

x	y
-2	
-1	
0	
1	
2	
3	
4	

In Exercises 17 and 18, find the slope of the line through the given pair of points.

17. (2, -6) and (-3, 5)   18. (3, -5) and (-2, 4)

In Exercises 19 and 20, write the equation of the line through the given point and having the indicated slope. (Write your answers in general form.)

19. (3, -5) and $m = -\dfrac{2}{3}$ 20. (-8, 4) and $m = -\dfrac{3}{4}$

In Exercises 21-24, solve the inequalities, and graph their solutions on the number line.

21. $x + 7 > 2$ 22. $x + 5 > 1$

23. $x - 3 \leq -8$ 24. $x - 6 \leq -10$

In Exercises 25-30, graph the inequalities in the plane.

25. $2x - 5y > 10$ 26. $3x - 7y < 21$

27. $x + 4y \leq 0$ 28. $3x - 2y \geq 0$

29. $x < 2$ 30. $y > 3$

In Exercises 31 and 32, complete the table of values, and then draw the graph.

31. $y = x^3 - 3x$

32. $y = x^3 + 3x^2 - 2$

x	y
-3	
-2	
-1	
0	
1	
2	
3	

x	y
-4	
-3	
-2	
-1	
0	
1	
2	

In Exercises 33 and 34, write the equation of the line having the indicated slope and y-intercept. (Write your answers in general form.)

33. $m = -\dfrac{1}{2}$, y-intercept = 6

34. $m = -\dfrac{1}{3}$, y-intercept = 9

In Exercises 35 and 36, find the equation of the line that passes through the given points. (Write your answers in general form.)

35. $(-3, 4)$ and $(1, -2)$ 36. $(-2, -4)$ and $(1, 3)$

37. Find the slope and y-intercept of the line $\dfrac{2x}{5} - \dfrac{3y}{2} = 3$.

38. Find the slope and y-intercept of the line $\dfrac{2x}{3} - \dfrac{5y}{2} = 5$.

In Exercises 39-42, graph each equation.

39. $x + 2(x - y) = 6$ 40. $x - 3(y - 2) = 0$

41. $\dfrac{2x + 3y}{5} - \dfrac{x - 3y}{4} = \dfrac{9}{10}$ 42. $\dfrac{x - y}{5} - \dfrac{x - 2y}{6} = \dfrac{4}{15}$

In Exercises 43-46, solve the inqualities, and graph their solutions on the number line.

43. $2(x - 4) - 5 \geq 7 + 3(2x - 1)$

44. $10 - 3(x + 2) \geq 9 - 2(4 - 3x)$

45. $\dfrac{3z}{5} - \dfrac{2z}{3} < \dfrac{1}{2}$ 46. $\dfrac{2w}{3} - \dfrac{5w}{6} < \dfrac{7}{12}$

In Exercises 47-50, graph the inequalities in the plane.

47. $\frac{x}{2} - \frac{y}{6} \geq 1$ 48. $\frac{y}{3} - \frac{x}{4} \leq 1$

49. $\frac{x - y}{3} \leq \frac{x - y}{2}$ 50. $\frac{2x - y}{4} \geq \frac{x - 3y}{5}$

SET II

1. Draw the four-sided figure whose sides are straight lines and whose vertices have the following coordinates: A (-4, -5), B (2, -4), C (5, 1), and D (-2, 3).
2. Given the point P (-7, 4) find:
   (a) the abscissa of P.
   (b) the ordinate of P.
   (c) the y-coordinate of P.

In Exercises 3-9, graph each equation.

3. $x - y = -4$ 4. $y + 2 = 0$

5. $x + 3y = 6$ 6. $x = \frac{3}{5} y$

7. $2x - 3y = 7$ 8. $y - 2(x - 3) = 0$

9. $\frac{5(x - 3)}{7} - \frac{3y}{2} = 2$

In Exercises 10 and 11, complete the table of values, and then draw the graph.

10. $y = 4x - x^2$ 11. $y = 2x - x^3$

x	y
-1	
0	
1	
2	
3	
4	
5	

x	y
-2	
-1	
0	
1	
2	

12. Find the slope of the line through the points (-13, -10) and (-8, 7).
13. Write the equation of the line through (4, -3) and having a slope of $-\frac{2}{5}$. (Write your answer in general form.)
14. Write the equation of the line having a slope of $-\frac{4}{3}$ and a y-intercept of 5. (Write your answer in general form.)

15. Write the equation of the line through the points (-4, 3) and (2, -1). (Write your answer in general form.)

16. Find the slope and y-intercept of the line
$$\frac{2}{3}x + 3y + 5 = 0.$$

In Exercises 17-20, solve the inequalities, and graph their solutions on the number line.

17. $x + 5 \geq -6$

18. $x - 7 < 2$

19. $7x - 2(5 + 4x) \leq 8$

20. $\frac{2(x + 6)}{10} + \frac{3x}{20} < 3$

In Exercises 21-25, graph the inequalities in the plane.

21. $2y - 5x \leq 11$

22. $2x - 3y \leq 0$

23. $x - 3 < 0$

24. $\frac{x}{5} - \frac{y}{4} > 1$

25. $\frac{x + y}{2} - \frac{2x + y}{5} > \frac{2}{5}$

CUMULATIVE REVIEW EXERCISES: CHAPTERS 1-9

1. Evaluate the formula using the values of the letters given with the formula.

$$A = \frac{h}{2}(B + b) \quad h = 5,\ B = 11,\ b = 7$$

2. Simplify. Write your answer using only positive exponents.

$$\left(\frac{35a}{15a^{-2}b}\right)^{-2}$$

In Exercises 3-6, perform the indicated operations and simplify.

3. $(6z^2 - z - 7) \div (3z - 5)$

4. $\frac{2x - 1}{x - 2} - \frac{1}{x + 1}$

5. $\frac{b + 1}{a^2 + ab} \div \frac{b^2 - b - 2}{a^3 - ab^3}$

6. $\dfrac{x^2 - \dfrac{4}{y^2}}{x + \dfrac{2}{y}}$

7. Solve for x: $\dfrac{2x - 4}{3} = \dfrac{4 - 6x}{5}$

8. Solve for x: $\dfrac{2x}{9} - \dfrac{11}{3} = \dfrac{5x}{6}$

9. Solve for k: $C = \dfrac{5}{2h} - \dfrac{h}{k}$

10. One number is 4 more than another. Their product is equal to $-\dfrac{7}{4}$. Find the two numbers.

Chapter Ten Diagnostic Test

Name_____

_____

The purpose of this test is to see how well you understand graphing. We recommend that you work this diagnostic test *before* your instructor tests you on this chapter. Allow yourself about fifty minutes to do this test.

Complete solutions for all the problems on this test, together with section references, are given in the Answer Section. We suggest that you study the sections referred to for the problems you do incorrectly.

---

1. Let $(2, -4)$ be the coordinates of point P.

    (a) What is the ordinate of point P?   (1a)_____

    (b) What is the y-coordinate of point P?   (1b)_____

    (c) What is the abscissa of point P?   (1c)_____

---

2. (a) Draw the triangle whose vertices have the following coordinates on the graph below: $A(0. -3)$, $B(4, 0)$, and $C(-3, 4)$.

    (b) Read the coordinates of the following points from the graph below: $D(\_,\_)$, $E(\_,\_)$, $F(\_,\_)$, $G(\_,\_)$.

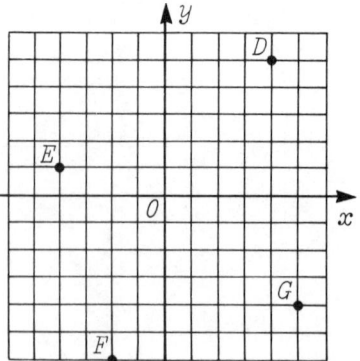

Graph each of the following equations.

3. $x = -2$

4. $x + y = 3$

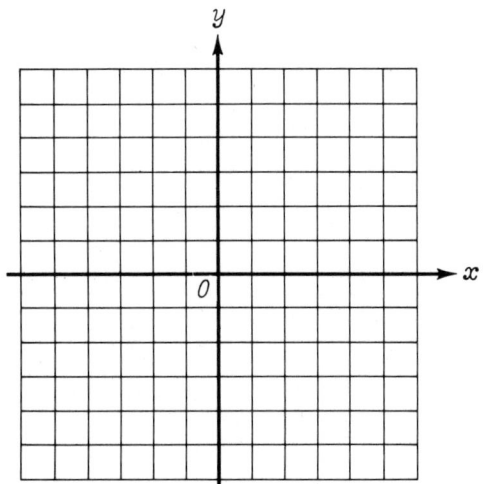 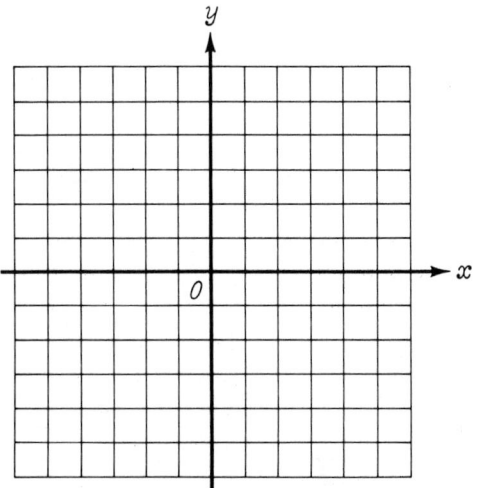

5. $2x - y = 4$

6. $4x + 5y = 18$

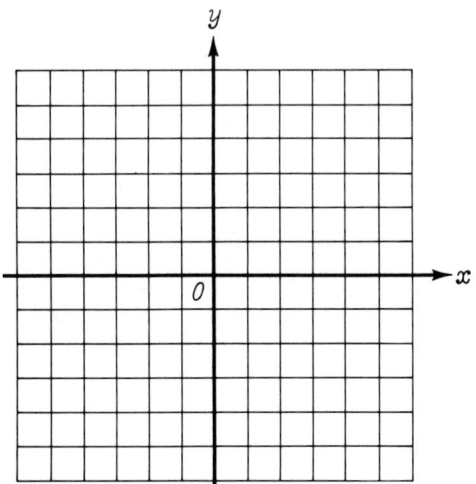 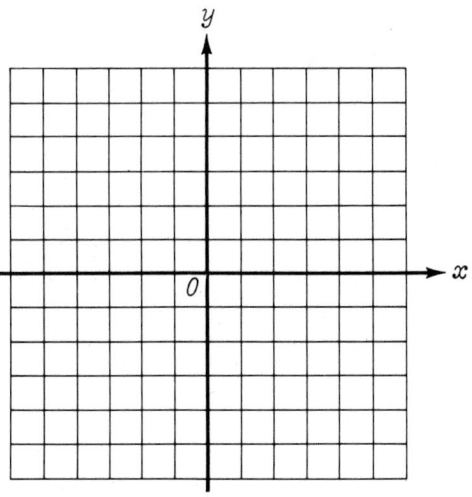

7. Complete the table of values and draw the graph of $y = x^2 + x - 6$.

x	y
-4	
-3	
-2	
-1	
0	
1	
2	
3	

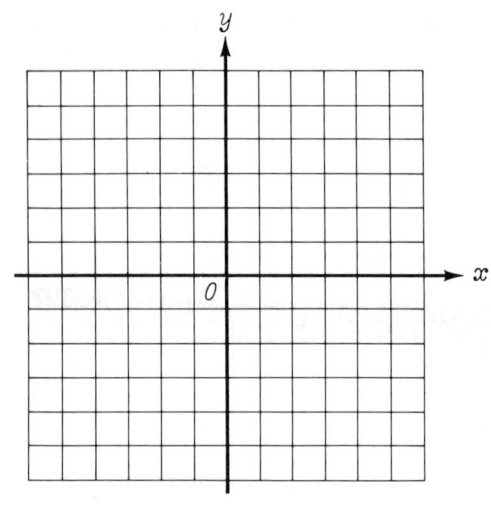

8. Graph the inequality $3x - 2y \leq 6$ in the plane.

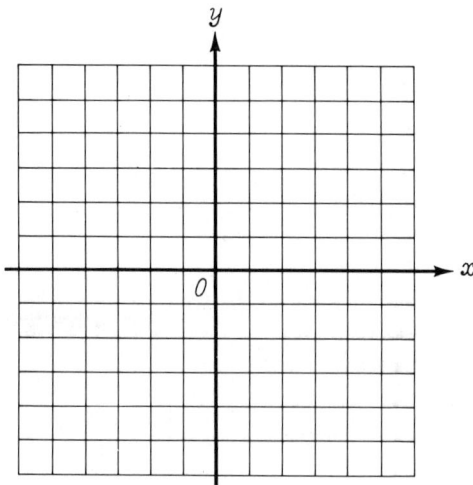

9. Solve the inequality $5x - 2 \leqslant 10 - x$, and graph the solution on the number line.

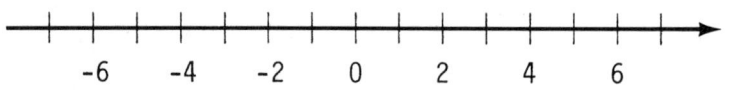

10. Given the points $A(-4, 2)$ and $B(1, -3)$, find:

(a) the slope of the line through A and B.

(a) $m = $ _____

(b) the equation of the line through A and B (written in general form).

(b) _____

ELEVEN

Systems of Equations

In previous chapters we showed how to solve a single equation for a single variable. In this chapter we show how to solve systems of two linear equations in two variables. Systems having *more* than two equations and variables are not discussed in this book.

 **Graphical Method**

BASIC DEFINITIONS.

<u>One Equation in One Variable.</u> *A solution of one equation in one variable* is a number that when put in place of the variable makes the two sides of the equation equal.

Example 1. 3 is a solution for $x + 2 = 5$

because $3 + 2 = 5$ is a true statement.

The expression "*3 satisfies the equation x + 2 = 5*" is often used.

<u>Two Equations in Two Variables</u>

$\begin{cases} x + y = 6 \\ x - y = 2 \end{cases}$ is called *a system of two equations in two variables.*

A solution of a system of two equations in two variables is an ordered pair that when substituted in each equation makes them both true.

Example 2. (4, 2) is the solution for the system $\begin{cases} x + y = 6 \\ x - y = 2 \end{cases}$

because $\begin{cases} x + y = 6 \\ 4 + 2 = 6 \ \textit{True} \end{cases}$ and $\begin{cases} x - y = 2 \\ 4 - 2 = 2 \ \textit{True} \end{cases}$.

This can be stated: *(4, 2) satisfies the system* $\begin{cases} x + y = 6 \\ x - y = 2 \end{cases}$.

GRAPHICAL METHOD FOR SOLVING A SYSTEM OF EQUATIONS.

In Sec. 1002 we showed how to graph a straight line. The graph of each equation in a system of linear equations in two variables is a straight line.

Example 3. Solve the system $\begin{cases} x + y = 6 \\ x - y = 2 \end{cases}$ graphically.

<u>Solution</u>: Draw the graph of each equation on the same set of axes (Fig. 1101A)

<u>Line (1)</u>: $x + y = 6$

x	y
6	0
0	6

x-intercept: If $y = 0$, then $x = 6$.
y-intercept: If $x = 0$, then $y = 6$.

Therefore, line (1) goes through (6, 0) and (0, 6).

Line (2): $x - y = 2$

x	y
2	0
0	-2

x-intercept: If $y = 0$, then $x = 2$.
y-intercept: If $x = 0$, then $y = -2$.

Therefore, line (2) goes through (2, 0) and (0, -2).

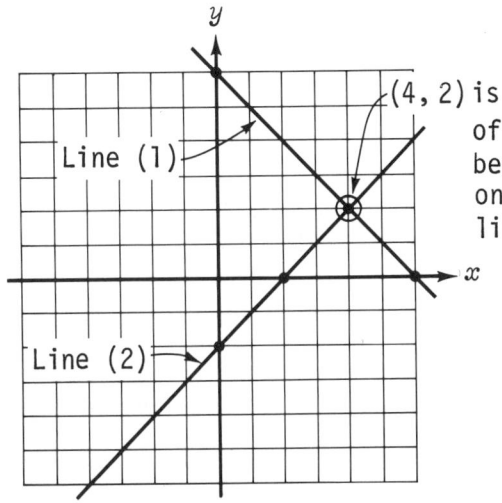

(4, 2) is the solution of this system because it is the only point that lies on *both* lines.

Line (1)

Line (2)

Figure 1101A Intersecting Lines

The coordinates of any point on line (1) satisfy the equation of line (1). The coordinates of any point on line (2) satisfy the equation of line (2). The only point that lies on *both* lines is (4, 2). Therefore, it is the only point whose coordinates satisfy *both* equations.

When the system has a solution, it is called a *consistent system*.

When each equation in the system has a different graph, they are called *independent equations*.

Example 4.   Solve the system $\begin{Bmatrix} 2x - 3y = 6 \\ 6x - 9y = 36 \end{Bmatrix}$ graphically.

Solution: Draw the graph of each equation on the same set of axes (Fig. 1101B).

Line (1): $2x - 3y = 6$ has intercepts (3, 0) and (0, -2).

Line (2): $6x - 9y = 36$ has intercepts (6, 0) and (0, -4).

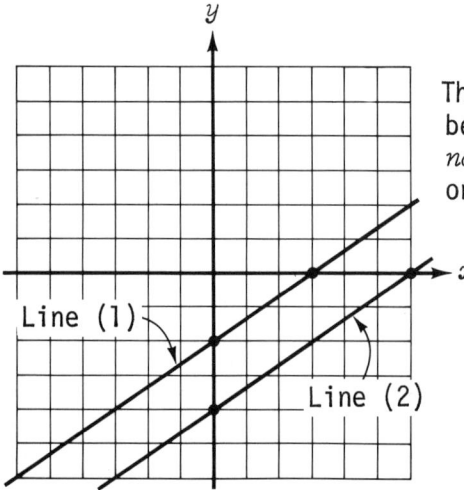

There is *no solution*
because there is
no point that lies
on *both* lines.

Line (1)

Line (2)

Figure 1101B Parallel Lines

Lines that never meet, such as these, are called *parallel
lines*.

When the system has no solution, it is called an *inconsistent system*.

Since each equation in this system has a different graph,
they are called *independent equations*.

<u>Example 5</u>. Solve the system $\begin{Bmatrix} 3x + 5y = 15 \\ 6x + 10y = 30 \end{Bmatrix}$ graphically.

<u>Solution</u>: Draw the graph of each equation on the same set
of axes.

<u>Line (1)</u>: $3x + 5y = 15$ has intercepts (5, 0) and (0, 3).

<u>Line (2)</u>: $6x + 10y = 30$ has intercepts (5, 0) and (0, 3).

Since each line goes through the same two points, they
must be the same line (Fig. 1101C).

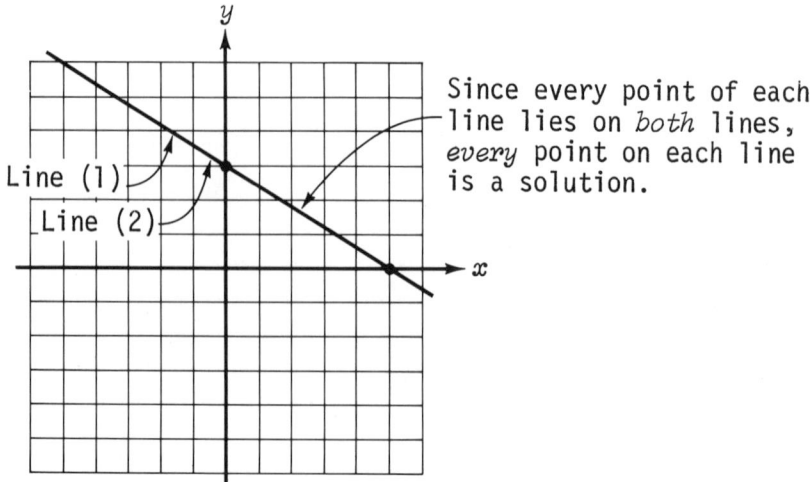

Since every point of each
line lies on *both* lines,
every point on each line
is a solution.

Line (1)

Line (2)

Figure 1101C Both Equations Have Same Graph

To find one of the many solutions, pick a value for one of the letters and substitute it into either equation. For example, let $x = 1$ in equation (1):

$$3x + 5y = 15$$
$$3(1) + 5y = 15$$
$$3 + 5y = 15$$
$$5y = 12$$
$$y = \frac{12}{5} = 2\frac{2}{5}$$

Therefore, $(1, 2\frac{2}{5})$ is a solution for this sytem. The intercepts (5, 0) and (0, 3) are also solutions. Since this system has solutions, it is a consistent system. When each equation in the system has the same graph, they are called *dependent equations*.

The graphical method is summarized in the following box.

TO SOLVE A SYSTEM OF EQUATIONS BY THE GRAPHICAL METHOD

1. Graph each equation of the system on the same set of axes.

2. There are three possibilities:
   (a) *The lines intersect at one point* (Fig. 1101A). The solution is the ordered pair representing the point of intersection.
   (b) *The lines never cross* (they are parallel). There is no solution (Fig. 1101B).
   (c) *Both equations have the same line for their graph.* Any ordered pair that represents a point on the line is a solution (Fig. 1101C).

EXERCISES 1101. Find the solution of each system graphically.

SET I

1. $2x + y = 6$
   $2x - y = -2$

2. $2x - y = -4$
   $x + y = 1$

3. $x - 2y = -6$
   $4x + 3y = 20$

4. $x - 3y = 6$
   $4x + 3y = 9$

5. $x + 2y = 0$
   $x - 2y = -2$

6. $2x + y = 0$
   $2x - y = -6$

7. $3x - 2y = -9$
   $x + y = 2$

8. $x + 2y = -4$
   $2x - y = -3$

----

9. $10x - 4y = 20$
   $6y - 15x = -30$

10. $12x - 9y = 36$
    $6y - 8x = -24$

11. $2x - 4y = -2$
    $-3x + 6y = 12$

12. $4x - 2y = 8$
    $-6x + 3y = 6$

SET II

1. $2x + y = -4$
   $x - y = -5$

2. $3x + 2y = 0$
   $3x - 2y = 12$

3. $3x - 4y = -3$
   $3x + 2y = 6$

4. $3x + 2y = 3$
   $5x - 4y = 16$

5. $12x - 9y = 36$
   $6y - 8x = -24$

6. $x - 2y = 10$
   $2y - x = 2$

 **Addition-Subtraction Method**

The graphical method for solving a system of equations has two disadvantages: (1) it is slow, and (2) it is not an exact method of solution. The method we discuss in this section has neither of these disadvantages.

Example 1. Solve the system $\left\{\begin{matrix} x + y = 6 \\ x - y = 2 \end{matrix}\right\}$.

Solution: Equation (1): $x + y = 6$
          Equation (2): $\underline{x - y = 2}$
                        $2x \quad\quad = 8$ By *adding the*
                        $x = 4$ *equations* vertically.

Then, substituting $x = 4$ into Equation (1), we have:

          Equation (1): $x + y = 6$
                        $4 + y = 6$
                        $y = 2$

Check: (See Sec. 1101, Example 2)

$\left\{\begin{matrix}(1): \quad x + y = 6 \\ \quad 4 + 2 = 6 \ true\end{matrix}\right\}$ and $\left\{\begin{matrix}(2): \quad x - y = 2 \\ \quad 4 - 2 = 2 \ true\end{matrix}\right\}$ So, (4, 2) is a solution.

Therefore, the solution for the system is $\left\{\begin{matrix} x = 4 \\ y = 2 \end{matrix}\right\}$, written (4, 2).

Example 2. Solve the system $\left\{\begin{matrix} 3x + 2y = 13 \\ 3x - 4y = 1 \end{matrix}\right\}$.

Solution: Equation (1): $3x + 2y = 13$
          Equation (2): $\underline{3x - 4y = 1}$
                        $6y = 12$ *By subtracting*
                                      Equation (2) from
                        $y = 2$ *Equation (1)*

Then, substituting $y = 2$ into Equation (2), we have:

$$\text{Equation (2):} \quad 3x - 4y = 1$$
$$3x - 4(2) = 1$$
$$3x = 9$$
$$x = 3$$

Therefore, the solution of the system is $\begin{Bmatrix} x = 3 \\ y = 2 \end{Bmatrix}$,

written (3, 2).

When we have found the value of one variable, that value may be substituted into *either* Equation (1) or Equation (2) to find the value of the other variable. Usually one equation is easier to work with than the other.

The systems in Examples 1 and 2 are simple because one letter can be eliminated by either *addition* or *subtraction*. *Sometimes we must multiply one or both equations by a number to make the coefficients of one of the letters the same.*

SYSTEMS THAT HAVE ONLY ONE SOLUTION

<u>Example 3.</u> Solve the system $\begin{Bmatrix} x - 2y = -6 \\ 4x + 3y = 20 \end{Bmatrix}$.

<u>Solution:</u> Equation (1): $\quad x - 2y = -6$ If both sides of
           Equation (2): $\quad 4x + 3y = 20$ Equation (1) are
                                          multiplied by 4,
                                          the coefficients
                                          of x will be the
                                          same in both
                                          equations.

$$4[x - 2y = -6] \Rightarrow^* \quad 4x - 8y = -24$$
$$4x + 3y = 20 \Rightarrow \quad \underline{4x + 3y = 20}$$
$$-11y = -44 \quad \text{By subtracting the}$$
$$y = 4 \quad\quad \text{bottom equation from}$$
the top one.

Then, substituting $y = 4$ in Equation (1), we have:

$$\text{Equation (1):} \quad x - 2y = -6$$
$$x - 2(4) = -6$$
$$x - 8 = -6$$
$$x = 2$$

Therefore, the solution of the system is $\begin{Bmatrix} x = 2 \\ y = 4 \end{Bmatrix}$,

written (2, 4).

---

* The symbol $\Rightarrow$, read "implies," means the second statement is true if the first statement is true. For example:
$$x - 2 = 0 \Rightarrow x = 2$$
Read "$x - 2 = 0$ implies $x = 2$"
means $x = 2$ is true if $x - 2 = 0$ is true.

Example 4. Solve the system $\left\{\begin{array}{l} 3x + 4y = 6 \\ 2x + 3y = 5 \end{array}\right\}$.

Solution: Equation (1): $3x + 4y = 6$ If Equation (1) is multiplied by 2 and Equation (2) is multipled by 3, the coefficients of x will be the same in the resulting equations.

Equation (2): $2x + 3y = 5$

This symbol means the equation is to be multiplied by 2.

2] $3x + 4y = 6 \Rightarrow 6x + 8y = 12$
3] $2x + 3y = 5 \Rightarrow 6x + 9y = 15$

Subtracting bottom equation from top one.

$$-y = -3$$

$$y = 3$$

The value $y = 3$ may be substituted into either Equation (1) or Equation (2) to find the value of x. It is usually easier to substitute in the equation having the smaller coefficients. We substitute $y = 3$ into Equation (2):

$$\text{Equation (2): } 2x + 3y = 5$$
$$2x + 3(3) = 5$$
$$2x + 9 = 5$$
$$2x = -4$$
$$x = -2$$

Therefore, the solution of the system is $\left\{\begin{array}{l} x = -2 \\ y = 3 \end{array}\right\}$, written (-2, 3).

Note: In Example 4, we subtracted the bottom equation from the top equation. We could have subtracted the *top* equation from the *bottom* equation. That would eliminate negative signs from the resulting equation.

$$6x + 8y = 12$$
$$6x + 9y = 15$$
$$y = 3 \quad \text{(No negative signs.)}$$

HOW TO CHOOSE THE NUMBERS EACH EQUATION IS MULTIPLIED BY. In Example 4, we multiplied Equation (1) by 2 and Equation (2) by 3. How were these numbers found?

The coefficients of x
were made the same

$$\begin{array}{l} 2\ ] \quad 3x + 4y = 6 \Rightarrow 6x + 8y = 12 \\ 3\ ] \quad 2x + 3y = 5 \Rightarrow 6x + 9y = 15 \end{array}$$

This pair of numbers is found by interchanging the coefficients of x.

In this **same** system, we show how to make the coefficients
of y the same:

The coefficients of y
were made the same

$$\begin{array}{l} 3\ ] \quad 3x + 4y = 6 \Rightarrow 9x + 12y = 18 \\ 4\ ] \quad 2x + 3y = 5 \Rightarrow 8x + 12y = 20 \end{array}$$

This pair of numbers is found by interchanging the coefficients of y.

<u>Example 5.</u>   Consider the system $\left\{\begin{array}{l} 10x - 9y = 5 \\ 15x + 6y = 4 \end{array}\right\}$.

This pair is found by interchanging
the coefficients of x.

$$\begin{array}{llll} 15\ ] & 3\ ] & 10x - 9y = 5 \Rightarrow 30x - 27y = 15 \\ 10\ ] & 2\ ] & 15x + 6y = 4 \Rightarrow 30x + 12y = \ \ 8 \end{array}$$

This pair is found by reducing the
ratio $\dfrac{15}{10} = \dfrac{3}{2}$.

This pair is found by interchanging
the coefficients of y.

$$\begin{array}{llll} 6\ ] & 2\ ] & 10x - 9y = 5 \Rightarrow 20x - 18y = 10 \\ 9\ ] & 3\ ] & 15x + 6y = 4 \Rightarrow 45x + 18y = 12 \end{array}$$

This pair is found by reducing the
ratio $\dfrac{6}{9} = \dfrac{2}{3}$.

<u>Example 6.</u>   Solve the system $\left\{\begin{array}{l} 2x + 3y = 6 \\ 3x + 6y = 8 \end{array}\right\}$.

<u>Solution:</u>

$$\begin{array}{lll} 3\ ] & 2x + 3y = 6 \Rightarrow & 6x + \ \ 9y = \ \ 18 \\ -2\ ] & 3x + 6y = 8 \Rightarrow & \underline{-6x - 12y = -16} \\ & & \qquad\quad -3y = \ \ \ \ 2 \\ \\ & & \qquad\qquad\ \ y = -\dfrac{2}{3} \end{array}$$

If -2 is used instead of 2, the resulting equations can be
added rather than *subtracted*. This method can be used
whenever both coefficients of the letter being eliminated
have the same sign.

Continuing with the solution, substitute $y = -\frac{2}{3}$ in $2x + 3y = 6$.

$$2x + 3y = 6$$

$$2x + \frac{\cancel{3}}{1}\left(\frac{-2}{\cancel{3}}\right) = 6$$

$$2x - 2 = 6$$

$$2x = 8$$

$$x = 4$$

Therefore, the solution of this system is $(4, -\frac{2}{3})$.

SYSTEMS THAT HAVE NO SOLUTION. In the preceding section we found that a system whose graphs are parallel lines has no solution (Sec. 1101, Example 4). Here we show how to identify systems that have no solution by using the *addition-subtraction method*.

Example 7. Solve the system $\begin{Bmatrix} 2x - 3y = 6 \\ 6x - 9y = 36 \end{Bmatrix}$.

Solution:

Equation (1): 6] 3] $2x - 3y = 6 \Rightarrow 6x - 9y = 18$
Equation (2): 2] 1] $6x - 9y = 36 \Rightarrow \underline{6x - 9y = 36}$
$$0 \neq -18$$

No values for x and y can make $0 = -18$.
Therefore, there is *no solution* for this system of equations.

SYSTEMS THAT HAVE MORE THAN ONE SOLUTION. In the preceding section, we found that a system whose equations have the same line for a graph has an infinite number of solutions (Sec. 1101, Example 5). Here we show how to identify such systems using the addition-subtraction method.

Example 8. Solve the system $\begin{Bmatrix} 4x + 6y = 4 \\ 6x + 9y = 6 \end{Bmatrix}$.

Solution:

Equation (1): 9] 3] $4x + 6y = 4 \Rightarrow 12x + 18y = 12$
Equation (2): 6] 2] $6x + 9y = 6 \Rightarrow \underline{12x + 18y = 12}$
$$0 = 0$$

This means both equations are equivalent to the same equation. Therefore, in this case, *any* ordered pair that satisfies Equation (1) *or* Equation (2) is a solution of the system (Sec. 1101, Example 5).

The addition-subtraction method is summarized in the following box.

TO SOLVE A SYSTEM OF EQUATIONS BY THE ADDITION-SUBTRACTION METHOD

1. Multiply the equations by numbers that make the coefficients of one of the letters the same.

2. Add (or subtract) the equations to eliminate the letter whose coefficients were made the same.

3. There are three possibilities:
   (a) *The resulting equation can be solved for the letter.* Substitute this value into either of the system's equations to find the value of the other letter. (one solution)
   (b) *Both letters drop out and an inequality results.* (no solution)
   (c) *Both letters drop out and an equality results.* *Any* ordered paid that satisfies either of the system's equations is a solution. (Many solutions)

Check your solutions in *both* of the original equations (Example 1).

EXERCISES 1102. Find the solution of each system by the addition-subtraction method. Check your solutions. Write "inconsistent" if no solution exists. Write "dependent" if many solutions exist.

SET I

1. $2x - y = -4$
   $x + y = -2$

2. $2x + y = 6$
   $x - y = 0$

3. $x - 2y = 10$
   $x + y = 4$

4. $x + 4y = 4$
   $x - 2y = -2$

5. $x - 3y = 6$
   $4x + 3y = 9$

6. $2x + 5y = 2$
   $3x - 5y = 3$

7. $x + y = 2$
   $3x - 2y = -9$

8. $x + 2y = -4$
   $2x - y = -3$

9. $x + 2y = 0$
   $2x - y = 0$

10. $2x + y = 0$
    $x - 3y = 0$

---

11. $4x + 3y = 2$
    $3x + 5y = -4$

12. $5x + 7y = 1$
    $3x + 4y = 1$

13. $6x - 10y = 6$
    $9x - 15y = -4$

14. $7x - 2y = 7$
    $21x - 6y = 6$

15. $3x - 5y = -2$
    $10y - 6x = 4$

16. $15x - 9y = -3$
    $6y - 10x = 2$

Addition-Subtraction Method   387

17. $\boxed{\blacksquare}$ $73x - 49y = 38$
         $56x + 82y = 91$

18. $\boxed{\blacksquare}$ $3.64x - 7.92y = 37.5$
         $5.25x + 4.06y = -35.9$

SET II

1. $x - y = -5$
   $3x + y = -3$

2. $x - 2y = 3$
   $3x + 7y = -4$

3. $x - 2y = 6$
   $3x - 2y = 12$

4. $3x + 5y = 4$
   $2x + 3y = 4$

5. $2x + 6y = 2$
   $3x + 9y = 3$

6. $4x - 3y = 7$
   $2x + 7y = 12$

7. $2x - 5y = 4$

8. $6x + 4y = 2$
   $3x - 2y = 3$

9. $\boxed{\blacksquare}$ $1.14x - 3.16y = 6.06$
     $8.61x + 5.32y = -12.3$

1103   Substitution Method

<u>Example 1.</u>   Solve the system $\begin{Bmatrix} x - 2y = 11 \\ 3x + 5y = -11 \end{Bmatrix}$.   Equation (1)
                                                   Equation (2)

<u>Solution:</u>   Equation (1): $x - 2y = 11$ is a literal equation.

1.   Solve Equation (1) for x: $x - 2y = 11$
                                    $\underline{+\ 2y \qquad +\ 2y}$
                                            $x = 11 + 2y$

2.   Substituting $11 + 2y$ in place of x in Equation (2), we have,

      Equation (2): $3x + 5y = -11$
                   $3(11 + 2y) + 5y = -11$
                      $33 + 6y + 5y = -11$
                            $11y = -44$
                                $y = -4$

3.   Substitute $y = -4$ in $x = 11 + 2y$
                           $x = 11 + 2(-4)$
                           $x = 11 - 8$
                           $x = 3$

Therefore, $(3, -4)$ is the solution for this system.

<u>Check:</u> $\begin{cases} (1): \ x - 2y = 11 \\ \qquad 3 - 2(-4) = 11 \\ \qquad\qquad 3 + 8 = 11 \ \textit{true} \end{cases}$

and $\begin{cases} (2): \ 3x + 5y = -11 \\ \quad 3(3) + 5(-4) = -11 \\ \qquad\quad 9 - 20 = -11 \ \textit{true} \end{cases}$

Therefore, $(3, -4)$ is a solution.

HOW TO CHOOSE WHICH LETTER TO SOLVE FOR

A. *One of the equations may already be solved for a letter.*

Example 2

(a) $\begin{cases} 2x - 5y = 4 \\ y = 3x + 7 \end{cases}$

$\quad\quad$ └─ Already solved for y.

$\quad\quad$ ┌─ Already solved for x.

(b) $\begin{cases} x = 9 - 4y \\ 5x - 3y = 8 \end{cases}$

B. *One of the letters may have a coefficient of 1.*

Example 3 $\quad\quad\quad\quad\quad\quad\quad\quad\quad\quad\quad\quad$ y has a coefficient of 1.

(a) $\begin{cases} 4x + y = 10 \Rightarrow y = 10 - 4x \\ -7x + 2y = 6 \end{cases}$

(b) $\begin{cases} 2x + 6y = 3 \\ x - 4y = 2 \Rightarrow x = 4y + 2 \end{cases}$

$\quad\quad\quad\quad\quad\quad\quad\quad\quad\quad\quad\quad$ x has a coefficient of 1.

C. *Choose the letter with the smallest coefficient.*

Example 4.

(a) $\begin{cases} 11x - 7y = 10 \\ 14x + 2y = 9 \Rightarrow y = \dfrac{9 - 14x}{2} \end{cases}$

└─ smallest of the $\quad\quad\quad\quad\quad$ └─ smallest possible
four coefficients. $\quad\quad\quad\quad\quad\quad\quad$ denominator in this case

(b) $\begin{cases} 3x + 9y = 7 \Rightarrow x = \dfrac{7 - 9y}{3} \\ 12x - 8y = 15 \end{cases}$

$\quad\quad\quad\quad\quad\quad\quad\quad\quad\quad\quad\quad$ └─ smallest possible
denominator in this case

$\quad\quad\quad\quad\quad\quad\quad\quad\quad\quad\quad\quad\quad$ ┌─ smallest of the
four coefficients

Example 5. Solve the system $\begin{cases} 6x + 3y = -1 \\ 4x + 9y = 4 \end{cases}$.

$\quad\quad$ Solution: No letter has a coefficient of 1. Solve
$\quad\quad\quad\quad\quad\quad\quad$ Equation (1) for y because it has the
$\quad\quad\quad\quad\quad\quad\quad$ smallest coefficient.

1. Solve Equation (1) for y:

$$6x + 3y = -1$$
$$\underline{-6x \quad\quad\quad -6x}$$
$$3y = -1 - 6x$$
$$y = \frac{-1 - 6x}{3}$$

2. Substituting $\frac{-1 - 6x}{3}$ in place of y in Equation (2),
we have,

Equation (2): $4x + 9y = 4$

$$4x + \overset{3}{\cancel{9}}\left(\frac{-1 - 6x}{\cancel{3}}\right) = 4$$

$$4x + 3(-1 - 6x) = 4$$

$$4x - 3 - 18x = 4$$

$$-14x = 7$$

$$x = \frac{7}{-14} = -\frac{1}{2}$$

3. Substitute $x = -\dfrac{1}{2}$ in $y = \dfrac{-1 - 6x}{3}$

$$y = \frac{-1 - \overset{3}{\cancel{6}}\left(-\frac{1}{\cancel{2}}\right)}{3}$$

$$y = \frac{-1 - 3(-1)}{3} = \frac{-1 + 3}{3}$$

$$y = \frac{2}{3}$$

Therefore, $\left(-\dfrac{1}{2}, \dfrac{2}{3}\right)$ is the solution for this system.

<u>Example 6.</u> Solve the system $\begin{cases} 6x + 5y = 2 \\ 5x + 3y = 4 \end{cases}$. Equation (1)
Equation (2)

$\uparrow$ smallest of the
four coefficients

<u>Solution:</u> No letter has a coefficient of 1. Solve
Equation (2) for y because it has the smallest coefficient.

1. Solve Equation (2) for y: $5x + 3y = 4$

$$3y = 4 - 5x$$

$$y = \frac{4 - 5x}{3}$$

2. Substituting $\dfrac{4 - 5x}{3}$ in place of y in Equation (1),
we have,

Equation (1): $6x + 5y = 2$

$$6x + 5\left(\frac{4 - 5x}{3}\right) = 2$$

LCD = 3 $3 \,]\; 6x + 5\left(\dfrac{4 - 5x}{3}\right) = 2$

$$(3)6x + (\cancel{3})5\left(\frac{4 - 5x}{\cancel{3}}\right) = (3)2$$

$$18x + 5(4 - 5x) = 6$$

$$18x + 20 - 25x = 6$$

$$-7x = -14$$

$$x = 2$$

3. Substitute $x = 2$ in $y = \dfrac{4 - 5x}{3}$

$$y = \frac{4 - 5(2)}{3} = \frac{4 - 10}{3} = \frac{-6}{3}$$

$$y = -2$$

Therefore, $(2, -2)$ is the solution for this system.

SYSTEMS THAT HAVE NO SOLUTION. We now show how to identify systems that have no solution by using the *substitution method.*

smallest coefficient

Example 7. Solve the system $\begin{cases} 2x - 3y = 6 \\ 6x - 9y = 36 \end{cases}$. Equation (1)
Equation (2)

Solution:

1. Solve equation (1) for x:

$$2x - 3y = 6 \Rightarrow 2x = 3y + 6$$

$$x = \frac{3y + 6}{2}$$

2. Substituting $\dfrac{3y + 6}{2}$ in place of x in Equation (2), we have,

Equation (2): $6x - 9y = 36$

$$\overset{3}{\cancel{6}}\left(\frac{3y + 6}{\cancel{2}}\right) - 9y = 36$$

$$3(3y + 6) - 9y = 36$$
$$\cancel{9y} + 18 - \cancel{9y} = 36$$
$$18 \ne 36 \qquad \text{An inequality}$$

No values for x and y can make $18 = 36$. Therefore, there is *no solution* for this system of equations.

SYSTEMS THAT HAVE MORE THAN ONE SOLUTION. We now show how to identify systems that have more than one solution by using the substitution method.

Example 8. Solve the system $\begin{cases} 9x + 6y = 6 \\ 6x + 4y = 4 \end{cases}$. Equation (1)
Equation (2)

smallest coefficient

Solution:

1. Solve Equation (2) for y:

$$6x + 4y = 4 \Rightarrow 4y = 4 - 6x$$

$$y = \frac{4 - 6x}{4}$$

$$y = \frac{\cancel{2}(2 - 3x)}{\cancel{4}_2}$$

$$y = \frac{2 - 3x}{2}$$

2. Substituting $\dfrac{2 - 3x}{2}$ in place of y in Equation (1), we have,

Equation (1): $9x + 6y = 6$

$$9x + \overset{3}{\cancel{6}}\left(\dfrac{2 - 3x}{\cancel{2}}\right) = 6$$

$$9x + 3(2 - 3x) = 6$$

$$\cancel{9x} + 6 - \cancel{9x} = 6$$

$$6 = 6 \qquad \text{An equality}$$

Therefore, *any* ordered pair that satisfies Equation (1), *or* Equation (2) is a solution of the system.

The substitution method is summarized in the following box.

TO SOLVE A SYSTEM OF EQUATIONS BY THE SUBSTITUTION METHOD

1. Solve one equation for one of the letters in terms of the other letter.

2. Substitute the expression obtained in Step 1 into the *other* equation (in place of the letter solved for in Step 1).

3. There are three possibilities:
   (a) _The resulting equation can be solved for the letter_. Substitute this value into either of the system's equations to find the value of the other letter. (One solution)
   (b) _Both letters drop out and an inequality results_. (No solution)
   (c) _Both letters drop out and an equality results_. *Any* ordered pair satisfying *either* of the system's equations is a solution. (Many solutions)

Check your solutions in *both* of the original equations (Example 1).

EXERCISES 1103. Find the solution of each system using the substitution method. Write "inconsistent" if no solution exists. Write "dependent" if many solutions exist.

SET I

1. $2x - 3y = 1$
   $x = y + 2$

2. $y = 2x + 3$
   $3x + 2y = 20$

3. $3x + 4y = 2$
   $y = x - 3$

4. $2x + 3y = 11$
   $x = y - 2$

5. $4x + y = 2$
   $7x + 3y = 1$

6. $5x + 7y = 1$
   $x + 4y = -5$

7. $4x - y = 3$
   $8x - 2y = 6$

8. $x - 3y = 2$
   $3x - 9y = 6$

----

9. $x + 3 = 0$
   $3x - 2y = 6$

10. $y - 4 = 0$
    $3y - 5x = 15$

11. $8x + 4y = 7$
    $3x + 6y = 6$

12. $5x - 4y = 2$
    $15x + 12y = 12$

13. $3x - 2y = 8$
    $2y - 3x = 4$

14. $4x - 5y = 15$
    $5y - 4x = 10$

15. $8x + 5y = 2$
    $7x + 4y = 1$

16. $4x - 9y = 7$
    $3x - 8y = 4$

17. $4x + 4y = 3$
    $6x + 12y = -6$

18. $4x + 9y = -11$
    $10x + 6y = 11$

📱 19. $44x + 75y = 63$
    $91x - 56y = 28$

📱 20. $5.21x - 8.7y = 3.44$
    $4.9x + 2.15y = 9.6$

SET II

1. $x - y = 1$
   $y = 2x - 3$

2. $x + 2y = -1$
   $x = 5 + y$

3. $x - 4y = 9$
   $3x + 8y = 7$

4. $3x + 4y = 18$
   $5x - y = 7$

5. $7x + 5y = -4$
   $4x + 3y = -2$

6. $4x + 7y = 9$
   $6x + 5y = -3$

7. $2x - y = 3$
   $y = 2x + 1$

8. $3x + 6y = 9$
   $4x + 8y = 12$

9. $2x - 6y = -15$
   $4x + 9y = 5$

📱 10. $14.9x + 27.3y = -35.2$
    $23.1x - 19.8y = 27.4$

1104

Using Systems of Equations to Solve Word Problems

In solving word problems involving more than one unknown, it is sometimes difficult to represent each unknown in terms of a single letter. In this section we eliminate that difficulty by using a different letter for each unknown. This means we will be using systems of equations to solve word problems.

```
TO SOLVE A WORD PROBLEM
USING A SYSTEM OF EQUATIONS

1.  Read the problem completely and determine
    how many unknown numbers there are.

2.  Draw a diagram showing the relationships in
    the problem whenever possible.

3.  Represent each unknown number by a different
    letter.

4.  Use the word statement to write a system of
    equations. There must be as many equations
    as unknown letters.

5.  Solve the system of equations using one of
    the following:
    (a)  Addition-subtraction method (Sec. 1102)
    (b)  Substitution method (Sec. 1103)
    (c)  Graphical method (Sec. 1101)
```

In Example 1 the word problem is solved first by using a single letter and a single equation. Then it is solved by using two letters and a system of equations.

Example 1. The sum of two numbers is 20. Their difference is 6. What are the numbers?

Solution:

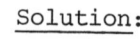

Using One Variable

Let x = larger number
then $20 - x$ = smaller number.

Their difference is 6.

$$x - (20 - x) = 6$$

$$x - 20 + x = 6$$

$$2x = 26$$

larger number: $x = 13$
smaller number:
$$20 - x = 7$$

The difficulty in using the one-variable method to solve this problem is that some students cannot decide whether to represent the second unknown number by $x - 20$ or by $20 - x$.

Using Two Variables

Let x = larger number
and y = smaller number.

The sum of two numbers is 20.

(1) $x + y = 20$

Their difference is 6.

(2) $x - y = 6$

Using the addition-subtraction method:

(1) $x + y = 20$
(2) $\underline{x - y = 6}$
$\quad 2x = 26$
$\quad\ x = 13$ Larger number.

Substituting $x = 13$ into equation (1), we have

(1) $x + y = 20$
$\ \ 13 + y = 20$
$\quad\ y = 7$ Smaller number.

Example 2. Doris has 17 coins in her purse that have a total
value of $1.15. If they are only nickels and dimes, how many
of each are there?

Solution: Let D = the number of dimes,
and N = the number of nickels.

Doris has 17 coins. They are only nickels and dimes.

(1)   17   = N + D

The coins in her purse have a total value of $1.15 (115¢).

amount of money in dimes	+	amount of money in nickels	=	total amount of money

(2) $10D$ + $5N$ =   115

(1) $N + D = 17$ ⎫ Arrange the equations so that like
(2) $5N + 10D = 115$ ⎬ terms are in the same column.
                              ⎭

(1) $N + D = 17 \Rightarrow N = 17 - D$
(2) $5N + 10D = 115$
       $5(17 - D) + 10D = 115$
       $85 - 5D + 10D = 115$
                $5D = 30$
                $D = 6$ Number of dimes.

and $N = 17 - D = 17 - 6 = 11$ Number of nickels.

Example 3. A 50-pound mixture of two different grades of coffee
costs $128.50. If grade A costs $2.50 a pound and grade B
costs $2.60 a pound, how many pounds of each grade were used?

Solution: Let a = number of pounds of grade A
and b = number of pounds of grade B.

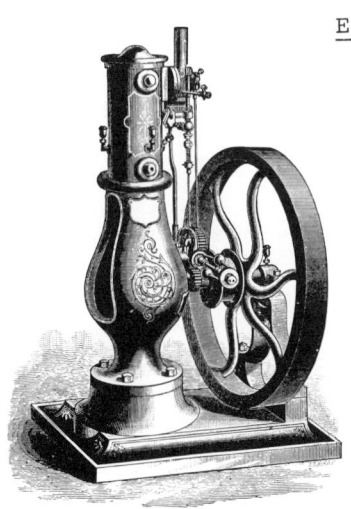

pounds of A	+	pounds of B	=	pounds of mixture

(1) a + b = $50 \Rightarrow b = 50 - a$

Because the sum of the weights of the two ingredients
must equal the weight of the mixture.

cost of A	+	cost of B	=	cost of mixture

(2) $250a$ + $260b$ =   12850

Because the sum of the costs of the two ingredients must
equal the cost of the mixture. (All costs are given in
cents.)

$$250a + 260b = 12850$$
$$250a + 260(50 - a) = 12850$$
$$250a + 13000 - 260a = 12850$$
$$-10a = -150$$
$$a = \frac{-150}{-10} = 15 \text{ lb of Grade A}$$
$$b = 50 - a = 50 - 15 = 35 \text{ lb of Grade B}$$

Some word problems should be solved using one unknown, while others are best solved using a system of equations.

HOW TO CHOOSE WHICH METHOD TO USE FOR SOLVING A WORD PROBLEM

1. Read the problem completely and determine how many unknown numbers there are.
2. If there is only one unknown number, use the one-variable method.
3. If there are more than one unknown number, try to represent all of them in terms of one letter. If this is too difficult, represent each unknown number by a different letter and then solve using a system of equations.

Systems having more than two equations or more than two variables are not discussed in this book.

EXERCISES 1104. Solve each of the following word problems by using a system of equations.

SET I

1. The sum of two numbers is 30. Their difference is 12. What are the numbers?
2. The sum of two numbers is 50. Their difference is 22. What are the numbers?
3. The sum of two angles is 90°. Their difference is 40°. Find the angles.
4. The sum of two angles is 180°. Their difference is 70°. Find the angles.
5. Find two numbers such that twice the smaller plus three times the larger is 34, and five times the smaller minus twice the larger is 9.
6. Find two numbers such that five times the larger plus three times the smaller is 47, and four times the larger minus twice the smaller is 20.

7. A 20-pound mixture of almonds and hazel nuts costs $19.75. If almonds cost 85¢ a pound and hazel nuts cost $1.40 a pound, find the number of pounds of each.
8. A 100-pound mixture of two different grades of coffee costs $72.50. If grade A costs 90¢ a pound and grade B costs 65¢ a pound, how many pounds of each grade were used?
9. Don spent $2.36 for 22 stamps. If he bought only 10-cent and 12-cent stamps, how many of each kind did he buy?
10. Sue spent $3.40 for 50 stamps. If she bought only 2-cent and 10-cent stamps, how many of each kind did she buy?

----

11. The length of a rectangle is 1 foot 6 inches longer than its width. Its perimeter is 19 feet. Find its dimensions.
12. The length of a rectangle is 2 feet 6 inches longer than its width. Its perimeter is 25 feet. Find its dimensions.

13. A fraction has the value $\frac{2}{3}$. If 4 is added to the numerator and the denominator is decreased by 2, the resulting fraction has the value $\frac{6}{7}$. What is the original fraction?

14. A fraction has the value $\frac{3}{4}$. If 4 is added to its numerator and 8 is subtracted from its denominator, the value of the resulting fraction is one. What is the original fraction?

15. A tie and a pin cost $1.10. The tie costs $1 more than the pin. What is the cost of each?

16. A number of birds are resting on two limbs of a tree. One limb is above the other. A bird on the lower limb says to the birds on the upper limb, "If one of you will come down here, we will have an equal number on each limb." A bird from above replies, "If one of you will come up here we will have twice as many up here as you will have down there." How many birds are sitting on each limb?

17. A pilot takes $2\frac{1}{2}$ hr to fly 1200 miles against the wind and only 2 hr to return with the wind. Find the average speed of the plane in still air and the average speed of the wind.

18. Jerry takes 6 hr to ride his bicycle 30 miles against the wind. He takes 2 hr to return with the wind. Find Jerry's average riding speed in still air and the average speed of the wind.

SET II

1. The sum of two numbers is 42. Their difference is 12. What are the numbers?

2. The sum of two angles is 90°. Their difference is 16°. Find the angles.

3. The length of a rectangle is 3 feet 6 inches longer than its width. Its perimeter is 13 feet. Find its dimensions.

4. Half the sum of two numbers is 15. Half their difference is 8. Find the numbers.

5. A fraction has a value of two-thirds. If 10 is added to its numerator and 5 is subtracted from its denominator, the value of the fraction becomes 1. What was the original fraction?

6. Beatrice has 15 coins having a total value of $1.75. If these coins are nickels and quarters, how many of each kind are there?

7. Several families went to a movie together. They spent $10.60 for 8 tickets. If adult tickets cost $1.95 and children's tickets cost 95¢, how many of each kind of ticket were bought?

8. A class received $233 for selling 200 tickets to the school play. If student tickets cost $1 each and nonstudent tickets cost $2 each, how many nonstudents attended the play?

9. A 100 lb mixture of Valencia and Navel oranges costs $22. If the Valencia oranges cost 20¢ a pound and the Navel oranges cost 25¢ a pound, how many pounds of each kind are there?

Chapter Summary

A solution of a system of two equations in two unknowns is an ordered pair that when substituted into each equation makes them both true (Sec. 1101).

In Solving a System of Equations, there are three possibilities (Sec. 1101, 1102, 1103).

1. _There is only one solution._
   (a) Graphical method: The lines intersect at one point.
   (b) Algebraic method:
       Addition-Subtraction } The equations can be
       Substitution   } solved for a single
                             } ordered pair.

2. _There is no solution._
   (a) Graphical method: The lines are parallel.
   (b) Algebraic method:
       Addition-Subtraction } Both letters drop out and
       Substitution   } an _inequality_ results.

3. _There are many solutions._
   (a) Graphical method: Both equations have the same line for a graph.
   (b) Algebraic method:
       Addition-Subtraction } Both letters drop out and
       Substitution   } an _equality_ results.

To Solve a Word Problem Using a System of Equations
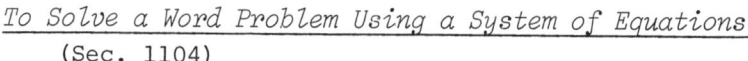
   (Sec. 1104)

1. Read the problem completely and determine how many unknown numbers there are.
2. Draw a diagram showing the relationships in the problem, whenever possible.
3. Represent each unknown number by a different letter.
4. Use the word statement to write a system of two equations in two unknowns.
5. Solve the system of equations using either:
   (a) Addition-Subtraction method (Sec. 1102)
   (b) Substitution method (Sec. 1103)
   (c) Graphical method (Sec. 1101)

In Exercises 1-8, find the solution of each system graphically.

1. $x + y = 6$
    $x - y = 4$

2. $x + y = 5$
    $x - y = -3$

3. $4x + 5y = 22$
    $3x - 2y = 5$

4. $7x - 8y = -9$
    $5x + 6y = 17$

5. $2x - 3y = 3$
    $3y - 2x = 6$

6. $5y - 3x = 10$
    $3x - 5y = 15$

7. $8x - 12y = 4$
    $6x - 9y = 3$

8. $9x - 12y = 3$
    $12x - 16y = 4$

In Exercises 9-14, find the solution of each system using the addition-subtraction method. Write "inconsistent" if no solution exists. Write "dependent" if many solutions exist.

9. $x + 5y = 11$
    $3x + 4y = 11$

10. $4x + 5y = 22$
    $3x + y = 11$

11. $4x - 8y = 4$
    $3x - 6y = 3$

12. $8x - 4y = 12$
    $6x - 3y = 9$

13. $3x - 5y = 15$
    $5y - 3x = 8$

14. $4x - 7y = 28$
    $7y - 4x = 20$

In Exercises 15-20, solve each system using the substitution method. Write "inconsistent" if no solution exists. Write "dependent" if many solutions exist.

15. $4x - 16y = 4$
    $3x - 12y = 3$

16. $8x - 4y = 8$
    $6x - 3y = 6$

17. $x = y + 2$
    $4x - 5y = 3$

18. $7x - 3y = 1$
    $y = x + 5$

19. $4x + 6y = -9$
    $2x - 8y = 23$

20. $6x + 8y = 15$
    $4x + 2y = -5$

In Exercises 21 and 22, solve each system by any convenient method. Write "inconsistent" if no solution exists. Write "dependent" if many solutions exist.

21. $4x + 3y = 8$
    $8x + 7y = 12$

22. $5x - 4y = -7$
    $-6x + 8y = 2$

23. The sum of two numbers is 84. Their difference is 22. What are the numbers?

24. The sum of two numbers is 6. Their difference is 40. What are the numbers?

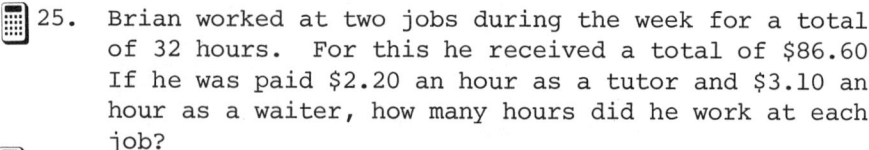
25. Brian worked at two jobs during the week for a total of 32 hours. For this he received a total of $86.60. If he was paid $2.20 an hour as a tutor and $3.10 an hour as a waiter, how many hours did he work at each job?

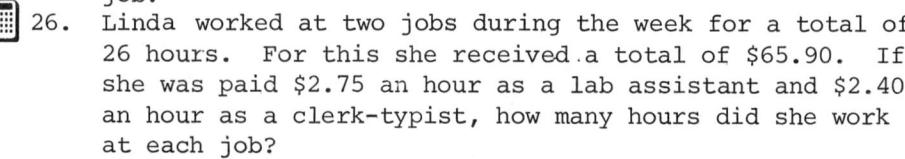
26. Linda worked at two jobs during the week for a total of 26 hours. For this she received a total of $65.90. If she was paid $2.75 an hour as a lab assistant and $2.40 an hour as a clerk-typist, how many hours did she work at each job?

27. A mail-order office paid $730 for a total of 80 rolls of stamps in two denominations. If one kind cost $10 per roll and the other kind cost $8 per roll, how many rolls of each kind were bought?

28. An office manager paid $39.60 for 20 boxes of legal-size and letter-size file folders. If legal-size folders cost $2.25 a box and letter-size folders cost $1.80 a box, how many boxes of each kind were bought?

SET II

1. Find the solution for the following system graphically.

$$3x + y = -9$$
$$3x - 2y = 0$$

In Exercises 2-4, find the solution of each system using the addition-subtraction method. Write "inconsistent" if no solution exists. Write "dependent" if many solutions exist.

2. $3x - 2y = 10$
    $5x + 4y = 24$

3. $6x + 4y = -1$
    $4x + 6y = -9$

4. $6x + 4y = 13$
    $8x + 10y = 1$

In Exercises 5-7, solve each system using the substitution method. Write "inconsistent" if no solution exists. Write "dependent" if many solutions exist.

5. $x - 3y = 15$
    $5x + 7y = -13$

6. $3x + 2y = 1$
    $7x + 3y = 9$

7. $4x - 6y = 2$
    $6x - 9y = 3$

In Exercises 8-10, solve each system by any convenient method. Write "inconsistent" if no solution exists. Write "dependent" if many solutions exist.

8. $5x + 4y = 2$
    $2x + 5y = 11$

9. $3x - 5y = 2$
    $2x + 7y = 22$

10. $5x - 7y = 17$
     $4x - 5y = 13$

11. The sum of two numbers is 95. Their difference is 19. What are the numbers?

12. The width of a rectangle is 5 meters shorter than its length. Its perimeter is 98 meters. Find its dimensions.

13. A 5 lb mixture of caramels and nougats costs $7.35. If nougats cost $2.10 a pound and caramels $1.20 a pound, how many pounds of each kind are there?

14. Armando worked at two jobs during the week for a total of 30 hours. For this he received a total of $87.60. If he was paid $2.60 an hour as a locker room attendant and $3.40 as a dishwasher, how many hours did he work at each job?

CUMULATIVE REVIEW EXERCISES: CHAPTERS 1-10

1. Simplify. Write your answer using only positive exponents.

$$\left(\frac{24w^{-2}z^4}{16w}\right)^{-3}$$

2. Evaluate the formula using the values of the letters given with the formula.

$$A = P(1 + r)^n \qquad P = 1000, \; r = 0.15, \; n = 2$$

3. Solve for x: $\dfrac{2 + 5x}{6x - 1} = \dfrac{3}{4}$

4. Solve for x: $\dfrac{3x - 1}{4} + 6 = \dfrac{5 - x}{5}$

5. Add and simplify.

$$\frac{1 + a}{2 - 3a} + \frac{2 + a}{4a}$$

6. Graph the equation $5x - 7y = 15$.

7. Draw the graph of $4y = x^2$. Use the following values for x in your table of values: -4, -2, -1, 0, 1, 2, 4.

8. Solve the inequality $2(x - 3) \leq 4$ and graph its solution on the number line.

9. Graph the inequality $3x - 4y > 12$ in the plane.

10. Write the equation (in general form) of the line that passes through the points $A(-3, 2)$ and $B(4, -1)$.

Chapter Eleven Diagnostic Test

Name_____

_____

The purpose of this test is to see how well you understand systems of equations. We recommend that you work this diagnostic test *before* your instructor tests you on this chapter. Allow yourself about fifty minutes to do this test.

Complete solutions for all the problems on this test, together with section references, are given in the Answer Section. We suggest that you study the sections referred to for the problems you do incorrectly.

---

1. Solve graphically: $\begin{Bmatrix} 3x + 2y = 2 \\ x - y = 4 \end{Bmatrix}$.

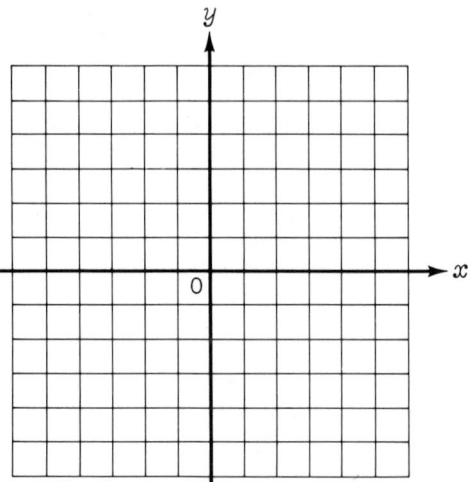

(1)_____

---

2. Solve by addition-subtraction: $\begin{Bmatrix} 2x + y = 7 \\ 3x - y = 3 \end{Bmatrix}$.

(2)_____$\left(\quad , \quad \right)$_____

---

3. Solve by addition-subtraction: $\left\{ \begin{array}{l} 3x - 4y = 1 \\ 5x - 3y = 9 \end{array} \right\}$.

(3)$(\quad , \quad)$

4. Solve by substitution: $\left\{ \begin{array}{l} 3x - 5y = 14 \\ x = y + 2 \end{array} \right\}$.

(4)$(\quad , \quad)$

5. Solve by substitution: $\left\{ \begin{array}{l} 3x + 4y = 1 \\ 2x - 5y = 16 \end{array} \right\}$.

(5)$(\quad , \quad)$

6. Solve by any convenient method: $\left\{ \begin{array}{l} 4x + 3y = 14 \\ 10x - 9y = 13 \end{array} \right\}$.

(6)$(\quad , \quad)$

7. Solve by any convenient method: $\left\{ \begin{array}{l} 6x - 9y = 2 \\ 15y - 10x = -5 \end{array} \right\}$.

(7)$(\quad , \quad)$

8. The sum of two numbers is 18. Their difference is 42.
   What are the numbers?

(8) _____

   _____
   Equations used to solve problem

   _____ smaller number

   _____ larger number

9. Linda paid $19.53 for 15 records at a special sale. If
   classical records sold for $2.99 per disc and pop records
   for 88¢ per disc, how many of each kind did she buy?

(9) _____

   _____
   Equations used to solve problem

   _____classical records

   _____pop records

10. The length of a rectangle is three centimeters more than
    its width. Its perimeter is 102 centimeters. Find the
    dimensions of the rectangle.

(10) _____

   _____
   Equations used to solve problem

   length_____

   width _____

TWELVE

Radicals

Roots of *numbers* were introduced in Sec. 112. Square roots of *algebraic terms* were discussed in Sec. 803. These are examples of *radicals*. In this chapter we will discuss simplification of and operations with *square roots*.

1201 Square Roots

The *square root* of a number N is a number which, when squared, gives N.

Every positive number has both a positive and a negative square root. The positive square root is called the *principal square root.*

<u>Example 1</u>. The square roots of 9 are 3 and -3.

(a) The positive square root of 9 is 3 because:

3 is called the *principal square root* of 9, written $3 = \sqrt{9}$.

$$3^2 = 3 \cdot \boxed{3} = \boxed{9}$$

9 is called *the square of 3,* written $3^2 = 9$.

(b) The negative square root of 9 is -3 because

-3 is a square root of 9, written $-3 = -\sqrt{9}$.

$$(-3)^2 = \boxed{(-3)} \cdot (-3) = 9$$

$\sqrt{9}$ stands for 3, the principal root.

Therefore, $-\sqrt{9} = -3$, the other square root.

When the symbol $\sqrt{N}$ is used, it *always* represents the *principal square root* of N. For example,

$\sqrt{4}$ represents the principal square root, 2.

$-\sqrt{4}$ represents the other square root, -2.

In the remainder of this chapter, we will only consider principal square roots.

<u>THE SQUARE OF A SQUARE ROOT</u>

$$\sqrt{25} = 5 \quad \text{because } 5^2 = 25.$$

This means $(\sqrt{25})^2 = 25$

THE SQUARE OF A SQUARE ROOT

$$(\sqrt{a})^2 = a$$

Example 2. Examples showing that when you square the square root of a number, you get that number.

    (a) $(\sqrt{16})^2 = 16$

    (b) $(\sqrt{7})^2 = 7$

    (c) $(\sqrt{x})^2 = x$

In this chapter we assume that all letters represent positive numbers.

THE PARTS OF A SQUARE ROOT. The parts of a square root are shown in Fig. 1201.

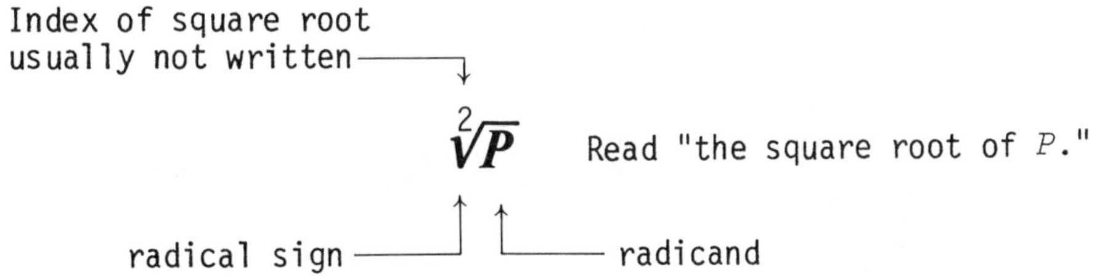

Index of square root
usually not written ⟶

$$\sqrt[2]{P}$$ Read "the square root of P."

radical sign ⟶   ⟵ radicand

Figure 1201

Example 3. Reading square roots.

    (a) $\sqrt{7}$ Read "the square root of 7."
                      7 is the radicand.

    (b) $\sqrt{2x}$ Read "the square root of $2x$."
                      $2x$ is the radicand.

    (c) $\sqrt{\dfrac{3x}{2y}}$ Read "the square root of the fraction $3x$ over $2y$."

                      $\dfrac{3x}{2y}$ is the radicand.

RATIONAL NUMBERS. A *rational number* is a number that can be expressed in the form $\dfrac{a}{b}$ where a and b are integers   ($b \neq 0$). Remember that the set of integers is

    $\{..., -3, -2, -1, 0, 1, 2, 3, ...\}$.

Example 4. Rational numbers.

    (a) $\dfrac{2}{3}$ All fractions are rational numbers.

    (b) $4 = \dfrac{4}{1}$ All integers are rational numbers.

    (c) $0.25 = \dfrac{25}{100}$ All terminating decimals are rational numbers.

    (d) $0.333 \ldots = \dfrac{1}{3}$ All repeating, nonterminating decimals are rational numbers.

(e) $2\frac{1}{2} = \frac{5}{2}$ All mixed numbers are rational numbers.

IRRATIONAL NUMBERS. An *irrational number* is a real number that *cannot* be expressed in the form $\frac{a}{b}$, where a and b are integers ($b \neq 0$). Remember that the set of integers is $\{..., -3, -2, -1, 0, 1, 2, 3, ...\}$.

Example 5. Irrational numbers.

(a) $\sqrt{2}$, $\sqrt{3}$, $\sqrt{5}$

(b) $\frac{1}{\sqrt{2}}$, $\frac{4}{\sqrt{5}}$

Rational *and* irrational numbers are real numbers and can therefore be represented by points on a number line (Sec. 1001, Fig. 1001A).

EXERCISES 1201

SET I

1. Which of the following are rational numbers?

-5; $\frac{3}{4}$; $2\frac{1}{2}$; $\sqrt{2}$; 3.5; $\sqrt{4}$; 3

2. Which of the following are irrational numbers?

$\frac{5}{6}$; -4; $\sqrt{3}$; $3\frac{1}{4}$; $\sqrt{9}$; 2

In Exercises 3 and 4, what is the radicand in each expression?

3. (a) $\sqrt{17}$ (b) $\sqrt{x + 1}$
4. (a) $\sqrt{15}$ (b) $\sqrt{m - n}$

In Exercises 5—14, evaluate each expression.

5. $\sqrt{36}$ 6. $\sqrt{49}$ 7. $(\sqrt{49})^2$ 8. $(\sqrt{36})^2$

----

9. $(\sqrt{a})^2$ 10. $(\sqrt{m^2})^2$ 11. $(\sqrt{a^2 b})^2$
12. $(\sqrt{xy^2})^2$ 13. $(\sqrt{x - y})^2$ 14. $(\sqrt{m + n})^2$

SET II

1. Which of the following are irrational numbers?

$2\frac{1}{2}$; -17; $\sqrt{13}$; -6.8; $\sqrt{25}$; 9; $\frac{5}{8}$

2. Give the radicand in each of the following expressions.

(a) $\sqrt{23}$ (b) $\sqrt{a + 4}$

In Exercises 3—7, evaluate each expression.

3. $\sqrt{64}$ 4. $(\sqrt{17})^2$ 5. $(\sqrt{x^2})^2$

6. $(\sqrt{h^3 k})^2$ 7. $(\sqrt{e - 4})^2$

Simplifying Square Roots

We will consider square roots of two kinds:

   1. Square roots *without* fractions in the radicand.
   2. Square roots *with* fractions in the radicand.

SQUARE ROOTS WITHOUT FRACTIONS IN THE RADICAND

$$\sqrt{x^2} = x \quad \text{because} \quad (x)^2 = x^2$$
$$\text{also} \quad \sqrt{x^2} = -x \quad \text{because} \quad (-x)^2 = x^2$$

Since x can be a positive number or a negative number, we don't know whether x or $-x$ is the principal root. However, $|x|$ must be positive (provided $x \neq 0$); therefore, $\sqrt{x^2} = |x|$ is the principal square root of x^2.

In this chapter we assume that all letters represent positive numbers unless otherwise indicated. For this reason we do not use the absolute value symbol to indicate a principal square root.

RULE I

TO FIND THE PRINCIPAL SQUARE ROOT OF A PRODUCT

$$\sqrt{ab} = \sqrt{a}\,\sqrt{b}$$

1. <u>Find the square root of each factor.</u>
   (Both numerical and literal factors are done the same way.)

   If the exponent of the factor is an even number:
   Divide the exponent by 2.

          — even exponent
   $$\sqrt{x^6} = x^{6 \div 2} = x^3$$

   If the exponent of the factor is an odd number:
   Write the factor as the product of two factors—one factor having an even exponent, the other factor having an exponent of 1.

          — odd exponent
   $$\sqrt{x^9} = \sqrt{x^8 x^1} = \sqrt{x^8}\,\sqrt{x^1}$$
   $$= x^4 \sqrt{x}$$

2. <u>Multiply the square roots of all the factors</u> found in Step I.

Example 1. Finding the principal square root of a
factor whose exponent is an *even* number.

(a) $\sqrt{5^2} = 5^{\frac{2}{2}} = 5^1$ Dividing exponent by 2.

(b) $\sqrt{x^2} = x^{\frac{2}{2}} = x^1$

(c) $\sqrt{3^4} = 3^{\frac{4}{2}} = 3^2$

(d) $\sqrt{x^6} = x^{\frac{6}{2}} = x^3$

Example 2. Finding the principal square root of a factor
whose exponent is an *odd* number.

                                 Factor $3^5 = \boxed{3^4} \cdot 3^1$

(a) $\sqrt{3^5} = \sqrt{3^4 \cdot 3^1}$

                                        The factor 3^4 is the
highest power of 3
whose exponent (4) is
exactly divisible by 2.

           $= \sqrt{3^4}\sqrt{3}$

           $= 3^2\sqrt{3}$

           $= 9\sqrt{3}$

(b) $\sqrt{x^7} = \sqrt{x^6 \cdot x^1}$ Factor $x^7 = \boxed{x^6} \cdot x^1$

           $= \sqrt{x^6}\sqrt{x}$ The factor x^6 is the
highest power of x
whose exponent (6) is
exactly divisible by 2.

           $= x^3\sqrt{x}$

When finding the principal square root of a number, first
express it in prime factored form (Sec. 801).

Example 3. Finding the principal square root of a product
of factors.

(a) $\sqrt{48} = \sqrt{2^4 \cdot 3}$

           $= \sqrt{2^4}\sqrt{3}$ Prime factored
form of 48.

           $= 2^2\sqrt{3}$

           $= 4\sqrt{3}$

$$
\begin{array}{r|l}
2 & 48 \\
2 & 24 \\
2 & 12 \\
2 & 6 \\
& 3
\end{array}
\qquad 48 = 2^4 \cdot 3
$$

(b) $\sqrt{75} = \sqrt{3 \cdot 5^2}$

           $= \sqrt{3}\sqrt{5^2}$ Prime factored
form of 75.

           $= \sqrt{3}(5)$

           $= 5\sqrt{3}$

$$
\begin{array}{r|l}
5 & 75 \\
5 & 15 \\
& 3
\end{array}
\qquad 75 = 3 \cdot 5^2
$$

A convenient arrangement of the work for finding the principal
square root of a product is shown in Example 4.

Example 4. Finding the principal square root of a product.

(a) $\sqrt{360} = \sqrt{2^3 \cdot 3^2 \cdot 5}$

$= \sqrt{2^2 \cdot \boxed{2} \cdot 3^2 \cdot \boxed{5}}$

$= 2 \cdot 3\sqrt{\boxed{2 \cdot 5}}$

$= 6\sqrt{10}$

2	360
2	180
2	90
3	45
3	15
	5

$360 = 2^3 \cdot 3^2 \cdot 5$

(b) $\sqrt{12x^4y^3} = \sqrt{2^2 \cdot \boxed{3} \cdot x^4 \cdot y^2 \cdot \boxed{y}}$

$= 2x^2y\sqrt{\boxed{3y}}$

2	12
2	6
	3

$12 = 2^2 \cdot 3$

(c) $\sqrt{24a^5b^7} = \sqrt{2^3 \cdot 3 \cdot a^5b^7}$

$= \sqrt{2^2 \cdot \boxed{2} \cdot \boxed{3} \cdot a^4 \cdot \boxed{a} \cdot b^6 \cdot \boxed{b}}$

$= 2a^2b^3\sqrt{\boxed{2 \cdot 3 \cdot ab}}$

$= 2a^2b^3\sqrt{6ab}$

2	24
2	12
2	6
	3

$24 = 2^3 \cdot 3$

Sometimes finding the square root of a number can be simplified if by inspection you can see that it has a factor that is a perfect square (Example 5).

Example 5

(a) $\sqrt{12} = \sqrt{\boxed{4 \cdot 3}}$ 4 and 3 are factors of 12 and
$= \sqrt{4} \cdot \sqrt{3}$ 4 is a perfect square.
$= 2 \cdot \sqrt{3}$
$= 2\sqrt{3}$

(b) $\sqrt{50} = \sqrt{2 \cdot \boxed{25}}$ 25 is a factor of 50 and is
$= \sqrt{2} \cdot \sqrt{25}$ a perfect square.
$= \sqrt{2} \cdot 5$
$= 5\sqrt{2}$

MULTIPLYING A SQUARE ROOT BY ITSELF

By Rule 1 $\sqrt{ab} = \sqrt{a}\sqrt{b}$

If $a = b$, then $\sqrt{aa} = \sqrt{a}\sqrt{a}$

$\sqrt{a^2} = \sqrt{a}\sqrt{a}$

$a = \sqrt{a}\sqrt{a}$ or $\sqrt{a}\sqrt{a} = a$

$$\boxed{\begin{array}{c} \text{MULTIPLYING A SQUARE ROOT BY ITSELF} \\ \sqrt{a}\,\sqrt{a} = a \end{array}}$$

<u>Example 6</u>. Examples of multiplying a square root by itself.

  (a) $\sqrt{5}\sqrt{5} = 5$

  (b) $\sqrt{7}\sqrt{7} = 7$

  (c) $\sqrt{2x}\sqrt{2x} = 2x$

  (d) $\sqrt{a+b}\sqrt{a+b} = a + b$

<u>SIMPLIFYING A SQUARE ROOT</u>. A square root without fractions is considered *simplified* if no prime factor of the radicand has an exponent equal to or greater than two.

<u>EXERCISES 1202A</u>

<u>SET I</u>

In Exercises 1—20, simplify each of the square roots.

 1. $\sqrt{25}$ 2. $\sqrt{100}$ 3. $\sqrt{81}$ 4. $\sqrt{64}$

 5. $\sqrt{4x^2}$ 6. $\sqrt{9y^2}$ 7. $\sqrt{16z^4}$ 8. $\sqrt{25b^6}$

 9. $\sqrt{12}$ 10. $\sqrt{20}$ 11. $\sqrt{18}$ 12. $\sqrt{45}$

13. $\sqrt{8}$ 14. $\sqrt{32}$ 15. $\sqrt{x^3}$ 16. $\sqrt{y^5}$

17. $\sqrt{m^7}$ 18. $\sqrt{n^9}$ 19. $\sqrt{24}$ 20. $\sqrt{54}$

In Exercises 21—34, find the products.

21. $\sqrt{6}\sqrt{6}$ 22. $\sqrt{3}\sqrt{3}$ 23. $\sqrt{4x}\sqrt{4x}$ 24. $\sqrt{7y}\sqrt{7y}$

In Exercises 25—34, simplify each of the square roots.

25. $\sqrt{a^2b^3}$ 26. $\sqrt{c^5d^2}$ 27. $\sqrt{40x^6y^2}$ 28. $\sqrt{135a^6b^8}$

29. $\sqrt{60h^5k^4}$ 30. $\sqrt{90m^7n^6}$ 31. $\sqrt{280y^5z^6}$

32. $\sqrt{270g^8h^9}$ 33. $\sqrt{500x^7y^9}$ 34. $\sqrt{216x^{11}y^{13}}$

In Exercises 35 and 36, find the products.

35. $\sqrt{a+b}\sqrt{a+b}$ 36. $\sqrt{m-n}\sqrt{m-n}$

In Exercises 1—15, simplify each of the square roots.

1. $\sqrt{36}$ 2. $\sqrt{49}$ 3. $\sqrt{25w^2}$ 4. $\sqrt{64u^6}$

5. $\sqrt{28}$ 6. $\sqrt{63}$ 7. $\sqrt{27}$ 8. $\sqrt{z^3}$

9. $\sqrt{a^5}$ 10. $\sqrt{40}$ 11. $\sqrt{h^3k^2}$ 12. $\sqrt{24m^4n^6}$

13. $\sqrt{50x^6y^5}$ 14. $\sqrt{140a^3b^8}$ 15. $\sqrt{250m^5n^7}$

In Exercises 16—18, find the products.

16. $\sqrt{13}\sqrt{13}$ 17. $\sqrt{11z}\sqrt{11z}$ 18. $\sqrt{x-7}\sqrt{x-7}$

__SQUARE ROOTS WITH FRACTIONS IN THE RADICAND.__ A second basic rule for working with square roots is:

PRINCIPAL SQUARE ROOT OF A FRACTION

RULE 2

$$\sqrt{\frac{a}{b}} = \frac{\sqrt{a}}{\sqrt{b}}$$

__Example 7.__ Finding the principal square root of a fraction.

(a) $\sqrt{\dfrac{4}{9}} = \dfrac{\sqrt{4}}{\sqrt{9}} = \dfrac{2}{3}$

(b) $\sqrt{\dfrac{25}{36}} = \dfrac{\sqrt{25}}{\sqrt{36}} = \dfrac{5}{6}$

(c) $\sqrt{\dfrac{x^4}{y^6}} = \dfrac{\sqrt{x^4}}{\sqrt{y^6}} = \dfrac{x^2}{y^3}$

(d) $\sqrt{\dfrac{50h^2}{2k^4}} = \sqrt{\dfrac{\overset{25}{\cancel{50}h^2}}{\cancel{2}k^4}} = \dfrac{\sqrt{25h^2}}{\sqrt{k^4}} = \dfrac{5h}{k^2}$

     ⬑————————————Simplify fraction first.

(e) $\sqrt{\dfrac{3x^2}{4}} = \dfrac{\sqrt{3x^2}}{\sqrt{4}} = \dfrac{x\sqrt{3}}{2}$

(f) $\sqrt{\dfrac{4}{5}} = \dfrac{\sqrt{4}}{\sqrt{5}} = \dfrac{2}{\sqrt{5}}$ ⟵————— This denominator is an irrational number.

An algebraic fraction is not considered simplified if a square root appears in the denominator.

__RATIONALIZING THE DENOMINATOR.__ When the denominator of a fraction is not a rational number, the procedure for changing it into a rational number is called _rationalizing the denominator._

Example 8.   Rationalize the denominator of each of the following fractions.

(a) $\dfrac{2}{\sqrt{5}} = \dfrac{2}{\sqrt{5}} \cdot \dfrac{\sqrt{5}}{\sqrt{5}} = \dfrac{2\sqrt{5}}{\sqrt{5}\sqrt{5}} = \dfrac{2\sqrt{5}}{5}$

$\uparrow$ $\uparrow$ $\uparrow$

— Denominator *is* now a rational number.

— Multiplying numerator and denominator by $\sqrt{5}$. Since the value of this fraction is 1, multiplying $\dfrac{2}{\sqrt{5}}$ by 1 does not change its value.

— Denominator is *not* a rational number.

(b) $\dfrac{6}{\sqrt{3}} = \dfrac{6 \cdot \sqrt{3}}{\sqrt{3} \cdot \sqrt{3}} = \dfrac{\overset{2}{6}\sqrt{3}}{\cancel{3}} = 2\sqrt{3}$

(c) $\dfrac{3xy}{\sqrt{x}} = \dfrac{3xy \cdot \sqrt{x}}{\sqrt{x} \cdot \sqrt{x}} = \dfrac{3xy\sqrt{x}}{x} = 3y\sqrt{x}$

THE SIMPLIFIED FORM OF AN EXPRESSION HAVING SQUARE ROOTS

1.   No prime factor of a radicand has an exponent equal to or greater than 2.

2.   No radicand contains a fraction.

3.   No denominator contains a square root.

EXERCISES 1202B.   Simplify each of the following expressions.

SET I

1. $\sqrt{\dfrac{9}{25}}$ 2. $\sqrt{\dfrac{36}{49}}$ 3. $\sqrt{\dfrac{16}{25}}$ 4. $\sqrt{\dfrac{81}{100}}$

5. $\sqrt{\dfrac{y^4}{x^2}}$ 6. $\sqrt{\dfrac{x^6}{v^8}}$ 7. $\sqrt{\dfrac{4x^2}{9}}$ 8. $\sqrt{\dfrac{16a^2}{49}}$

9. $\sqrt{\dfrac{2}{8k^2}}$ 10. $\sqrt{\dfrac{2m^2}{18}}$ 11. $\sqrt{\dfrac{4x^3y}{xy^3}}$ 12. $\sqrt{\dfrac{x^5y}{9xy^3}}$

13. $\dfrac{3}{\sqrt{7}}$ 14. $\dfrac{2}{\sqrt{3}}$ 15. $\dfrac{10}{\sqrt{5}}$ 16. $\dfrac{14}{\sqrt{2}}$

17. $\sqrt{\dfrac{m^2}{3}}$ 18. $\sqrt{\dfrac{k^2}{5}}$

----

19. $\sqrt{\dfrac{x^5 z^4}{36 y^2}}$ 20. $\sqrt{\dfrac{a^3 c^6}{25 b^2}}$ 21. $\sqrt{\dfrac{3 a^2 b}{4 b^3}}$ 22. $\sqrt{\dfrac{10 u v^2}{8 u}}$

23. $\sqrt{\dfrac{b^2 c^4}{16 d^3}}$ 24. $\sqrt{\dfrac{h^4 k^8}{49 p^5}}$ 25. $\sqrt{\dfrac{8 m^2 n}{2 n^2}}$ 26. $\sqrt{\dfrac{18 x y^2}{2 x^2}}$

SET II

1. $\sqrt{\dfrac{16}{49}}$ 2. $\sqrt{\dfrac{64}{81}}$ 3. $\sqrt{\dfrac{a^2}{b^6}}$ 4. $\sqrt{\dfrac{36 m^2}{25}}$

5. $\sqrt{\dfrac{3}{27 x^2}}$ 6. $\sqrt{\dfrac{h^3 k^3}{16 h k^5}}$ 7. $\dfrac{5}{\sqrt{10}}$ 8. $\dfrac{6}{\sqrt{15}}$

9. $\sqrt{\dfrac{e^2}{7}}$ 10. $\sqrt{\dfrac{r^3 s^6}{9 t^2}}$ 11. $\sqrt{\dfrac{15 z w^4}{18 z}}$

12. $\sqrt{\dfrac{d^4 e^6}{100 f^3}}$ 13. $\sqrt{\dfrac{45 t u^2}{5 t^2}}$

1203 Multiplying and Dividing Square Roots

<u>MULTIPLYING SQUARE ROOTS.</u> In Sec. 1202 we used Rule 1 in the following direction:

$\xrightarrow{\hspace{3cm}}$

$\sqrt{ab} = \sqrt{a}\sqrt{b}$ Using Rule 1 to find the square root of a product

$\sqrt{4 \cdot 3} = \sqrt{4}\sqrt{3}$

$\qquad\quad = 2\sqrt{3}$

In this section we use Rule 1 in the opposite way:

$\xrightarrow{\hspace{3cm}}$

$\sqrt{a}\sqrt{b} = \sqrt{ab}$ Using Rule 1 to find the product of square roots

$\sqrt{2}\sqrt{8} = \sqrt{2 \cdot 8}$

$\qquad\quad = \sqrt{16} = 4$

Therefore:

$$\boxed{\begin{array}{c} \text{Product of} \quad = \quad \text{Square root} \\ \text{Square Roots} \qquad\quad \text{of Product} \\[4pt] \sqrt{a}\,\sqrt{b} = \sqrt{ab} \end{array}}$$

Example 1. Multiplying square roots.

$$\underbrace{\text{Product of square roots}}_{} = \underbrace{\text{square root of product.}}_{}$$

(a) $\sqrt{2}\sqrt{2} = \sqrt{2 \cdot 2} = \sqrt{2^2} = 2$

(b) $\sqrt{2}\sqrt{8} = \sqrt{2 \cdot 8} = \sqrt{16} = 4$

(c) $\sqrt{4x}\sqrt{x} = \sqrt{4x \cdot x} = \sqrt{4x^2} = 2x$

(d) $\sqrt{3y}\sqrt{12y^3} = \sqrt{3y \cdot 12y^3} = \sqrt{36y^4} = 6y^2$

(e) $\sqrt{3}\sqrt{6}\sqrt{2} = \sqrt{3 \cdot 6 \cdot 2} = \sqrt{36} = 6$

(f) $\sqrt{5z}\sqrt{10}\sqrt{2z^3} = \sqrt{5z \cdot 10 \cdot 2z^3} = \sqrt{100z^4} = 10z^2$

(g) $\sqrt{3x}\,\sqrt{6x^2} = \sqrt{3x \cdot 6x^2} = \sqrt{18x^3}$ Multiplying the square roots

$\qquad\qquad = \sqrt{2 \cdot 9 \cdot x^2 \cdot x}$ $\Big\}$ Simplifying

$\qquad\qquad = 3x\sqrt{2x}$

(h) $\sqrt{3w^2}\,\sqrt{2}\,\sqrt{8w^3} = \sqrt{3w^2 \cdot 2 \cdot 8w^3} = \sqrt{48w^5}$ Multiplying square roots

$\qquad\qquad = \sqrt{3 \cdot 16 \cdot w^4 \cdot w}$ $\Big\}$ Simplifying

$\qquad\qquad = 4w^2\sqrt{3w}$

(i) $5\sqrt{2y^3} \cdot 3\sqrt{6y^4} = (5 \cdot 3)\sqrt{2y^3 \cdot 6y^4} = 15\sqrt{12y^7}$ Multiplying the square roots

$\qquad\qquad = 15\sqrt{3 \cdot 4 \cdot y^6 \cdot y}$

$\qquad\qquad = 15 \cdot 2 \cdot y^3\sqrt{3y}$ $\Big\}$ Simplifying

$\qquad\qquad = 30y^3\sqrt{3y}$

EXERCISES 1203A. Find the following products and simplify.

SET I

1. $\sqrt{3}\sqrt{3}$ 2. $\sqrt{7}\sqrt{7}$ 3. $\sqrt{4}\sqrt{4}$

4. $\sqrt{9}\sqrt{9}$ 5. $\sqrt{3}\sqrt{12}$ 6. $\sqrt{2}\sqrt{32}$

7. $\sqrt{9x}\sqrt{x}$ 8. $\sqrt{25y}\sqrt{y}$

9. $\sqrt{5}\sqrt{10}\sqrt{2}$ 10. $\sqrt{6}\sqrt{12}\sqrt{2}$

----

11. $\sqrt{5ab^2}\sqrt{20ab}$ 12. $\sqrt{3x^2y}\sqrt{27xy}$

13. $\sqrt{2a}\sqrt{6}\sqrt{3a}$ 14. $\sqrt{2}\sqrt{h^3}\sqrt{8h}$

15. $5\sqrt{2x} \cdot \sqrt{8x^3} \cdot 2\sqrt{3x^5}$ 16. $4\sqrt{2M^3} \cdot \sqrt{3M} \cdot 3\sqrt{12M^3}$

1. $\sqrt{11}\sqrt{11}$

2. $\sqrt{8}\sqrt{8}$

3. $\sqrt{18}\sqrt{2}$

4. $\sqrt{16a}\sqrt{a}$

5. $\sqrt{12mn}\sqrt{3m^2n}$

6. $\sqrt{3}\sqrt{6}\sqrt{2}$

7. $\sqrt{b^3}\sqrt{32}\sqrt{2b}$

8. $6\sqrt{5z^3} \cdot \sqrt{2z} \cdot 4\sqrt{8z^3}$

DIVIDING SQUARE ROOTS. In Sec. 1202 we used Rule 2 in the following direction:

$$\sqrt{\frac{a}{b}} = \frac{\sqrt{a}}{\sqrt{b}}$$ Using Rule 2 to find the square root of a quotient

$$\sqrt{\frac{4}{9}} = \frac{\sqrt{4}}{\sqrt{9}} = \frac{2}{3}$$

In this section we use Rule 2 in the opposite direction:

$$\frac{\sqrt{a}}{\sqrt{b}} = \sqrt{\frac{a}{b}}$$ Using Rule 2 to find the quotient of square roots

$$\frac{\sqrt{8}}{\sqrt{2}} = \sqrt{\frac{8}{2}}$$

$$= \sqrt{4} = 2$$

Therefore:

Quotient of Square Roots = Square Root of Quotient

$$\frac{\sqrt{a}}{\sqrt{b}} = \sqrt{\frac{a}{b}}$$

Example 2. Dividing square roots.

Quotient of square roots = square root of quotient.

(a) $\frac{\sqrt{8}}{\sqrt{2}} = \sqrt{\frac{8}{2}} = \sqrt{4} = 2$

(b) $\frac{\sqrt{a^5}}{\sqrt{a^3}} = \sqrt{\frac{a^5}{a^3}} = \sqrt{a^2} = a$

(c) $\frac{\sqrt{27x}}{\sqrt{3x^3}} = \sqrt{\frac{27x}{3x^3}} = \sqrt{\frac{9}{x^2}} = \frac{3}{x}$

(d) $\frac{\sqrt{28xy^3}}{\sqrt{7xy}} = \sqrt{\frac{28xy^3}{7xy}} = \sqrt{4y^2} = 2y$

(e) $\dfrac{\sqrt{5x}}{\sqrt{10x^2}} = \sqrt{\dfrac{5x}{10x^2}} = \sqrt{\dfrac{1}{2x}} = \dfrac{\sqrt{1}}{\sqrt{2x}} = \dfrac{1}{\sqrt{2x}} \cdot \dfrac{\sqrt{2x}}{\sqrt{2x}} = \dfrac{\sqrt{2x}}{2x}$

(f) $\dfrac{6\sqrt{25x^3}}{5\sqrt{3x}} = \dfrac{6}{5}\sqrt{\dfrac{25x^3}{3x}} = \dfrac{6}{5} \dfrac{\sqrt{25x^2}}{\sqrt{3}} = \dfrac{6}{5} \cdot \dfrac{5x}{\sqrt{3}} \cdot \dfrac{\sqrt{3}}{\sqrt{3}} = \dfrac{\overset{2}{6}x\sqrt{3}}{\underset{}{3}} = 2x\sqrt{3}$

<u>EXERCISES 1203B.</u>   Simplify each of the following expressions.

SET I

1. $\dfrac{\sqrt{20}}{\sqrt{5}}$ 2. $\dfrac{\sqrt{7}}{\sqrt{28}}$ 3. $\dfrac{\sqrt{32}}{\sqrt{2}}$

4. $\dfrac{\sqrt{98}}{\sqrt{2}}$ 5. $\dfrac{\sqrt{4}}{\sqrt{5}}$ 6. $\dfrac{\sqrt{9}}{\sqrt{7}}$

7. $\dfrac{\sqrt{15x}}{\sqrt{5x}}$ 8. $\dfrac{\sqrt{18y}}{\sqrt{3y}}$

----

9. $\dfrac{\sqrt{72x^3y^2}}{\sqrt{2xy^2}}$ 10. $\dfrac{\sqrt{27x^2y^3}}{\sqrt{3x^2y}}$ 11. $\dfrac{\sqrt{x^4y}}{\sqrt{5y}}$

12. $\dfrac{\sqrt{m^6n}}{\sqrt{3n}}$ 13. $\dfrac{4\sqrt{45m^3}}{3\sqrt{10m}}$ 14. $\dfrac{6\sqrt{400x^4}}{5\sqrt{6x}}$

SET II

1. $\dfrac{\sqrt{27}}{\sqrt{3}}$ 2. $\dfrac{\sqrt{2}}{\sqrt{50}}$ 3. $\dfrac{\sqrt{36}}{\sqrt{11}}$

4. $\dfrac{\sqrt{18m}}{\sqrt{6m}}$ 5. $\dfrac{\sqrt{75a^5b^3}}{\sqrt{3a^3b^3}}$ 6. $\dfrac{\sqrt{u^6v}}{\sqrt{7v}}$

7. $\dfrac{9\sqrt{20a^6}}{2\sqrt{15a^3}}$

1204   Adding Square Roots

<u>Like Square Roots</u> are square roots having the same radicand.

<u>Example 1.</u> Examples of like square roots.

(a) $3\sqrt{5}$, $2\sqrt{5}$, $-7\sqrt{5}$

(b) $2\sqrt{x}$, $-9\sqrt{x}$, $11\sqrt{x}$

<u>Unlike Square Roots</u> are square roots having different radicands.

Example 2. Examples of unlike square roots.

    (a) $2\sqrt{15}$, $-6\sqrt{11}$, $8\sqrt{24}$

    (b) $5\sqrt{y}$, $3\sqrt{x}$, $-4\sqrt{13}$

ADDING LIKE SQUARE ROOTS. Like square roots are added in the same way as any other like things: by adding their coefficients and then multiplying that sum by the like square root.

$$3 \text{ cars} + 2 \text{ cars} = (3 + 2) \text{ cars} = 5 \text{ cars}$$

$$3x \quad\quad + 2x \quad = (3 + 2)x \quad\quad = 5x$$

$$3\sqrt{7} \quad + 2\sqrt{7} \quad = (3 + 2)\sqrt{7} \quad = 5\sqrt{7}$$

The addition of like square roots is an application of the distributive rule.

$$ac \quad + \quad bc \quad = (a + b)c$$

Distributive Rule.

$$3\;\boxed{\sqrt{7}} + 2\;\boxed{\sqrt{7}} = (3 + 2)\;\boxed{\sqrt{7}}$$

Example 3

    (a) $5\sqrt{2} + 3\sqrt{2} = (5 + 3)\sqrt{2} = 8\sqrt{2}$

    (b) $6\sqrt{3} - 4\sqrt{3} = (6 - 4)\sqrt{3} = 2\sqrt{3}$

    (c) $7\sqrt{x} - 3\sqrt{x} = (7 - 3)\sqrt{x} = 4\sqrt{x}$

    (d) $\dfrac{3}{2}\sqrt{5} + \boxed{\dfrac{\sqrt{5}}{2}} = \left(\dfrac{3}{2} + \dfrac{1}{2}\right)\sqrt{5} = 2\sqrt{5}$

$$\dfrac{\sqrt{5}}{2} = \dfrac{1}{2}\sqrt{5} \text{ because } \dfrac{1}{2}\sqrt{5} = \dfrac{1}{2}\cdot\dfrac{\sqrt{5}}{1} = \dfrac{\sqrt{5}}{2}$$

ADDING UNLIKE SQUARE ROOTS. Simplifying *unlike* square roots *sometimes* results in *like* square roots, which can then be added.

TO ADD UNLIKE SQUARE ROOTS

1. Simplify each square root in the sum.

2. Combine any terms with like square roots that result from Step 1.

Example 4. $\sqrt{8} + \sqrt{18}$

    Solution: $\sqrt{4 \cdot 2} + \sqrt{9 \cdot 2} = 2\sqrt{2} + 3\sqrt{2} = 5\sqrt{2}$

Example 5. $\sqrt{12} - \sqrt{27} + 5\sqrt{3}$

$\sqrt{4 \cdot 3} - \sqrt{9 \cdot 3} + 5\sqrt{3} = 2\sqrt{3} - 3\sqrt{3} + 5\sqrt{3} = 4\sqrt{3}$

Example 6. $\sqrt{20} - 2\sqrt{45} - \sqrt{15}$

$\sqrt{4 \cdot 5} - 2\sqrt{9 \cdot 5} - \sqrt{3 \cdot 5}$

$= 2\sqrt{5} - 2 \cdot 3\sqrt{5} - \sqrt{15}$

$= 2\sqrt{5} - 6\sqrt{5} - \sqrt{15} = -4\sqrt{5} - \sqrt{15}$

Example 7. $2\sqrt{\dfrac{1}{2}} - 6\sqrt{\dfrac{1}{8}} - 10\sqrt{\dfrac{4}{5}}$

$\dfrac{2}{1} \cdot \dfrac{\sqrt{1}}{\sqrt{2}} - \dfrac{6}{1} \cdot \dfrac{\sqrt{1}}{\sqrt{8}} - \dfrac{10}{1} \cdot \dfrac{\sqrt{4}}{\sqrt{5}}$

$= \dfrac{2}{1} \cdot \dfrac{1}{\sqrt{2}} \cdot \dfrac{\sqrt{2}}{\sqrt{2}} - \dfrac{6}{1} \cdot \dfrac{1}{\sqrt{4 \cdot 2}} - \dfrac{10}{1} \cdot \dfrac{2}{\sqrt{5}} \cdot \dfrac{\sqrt{5}}{\sqrt{5}}$ Rationalizing the denominators

$= \dfrac{\cancel{2}}{1} \cdot \dfrac{\sqrt{2}}{\cancel{2}} - \dfrac{\cancel{6}^{3}}{1} \cdot \dfrac{1}{\cancel{2}\sqrt{2}} \cdot \dfrac{\sqrt{2}}{\sqrt{2}} - \dfrac{\cancel{10}^{2}}{1} \cdot \dfrac{2\sqrt{5}}{\cancel{5}}$

$= \sqrt{2} - \dfrac{3}{2}\sqrt{2} - 4\sqrt{5}$

$= \left(1 - \dfrac{3}{2}\right)\sqrt{2} - 4\sqrt{5} = -\dfrac{1}{2}\sqrt{2} - 4\sqrt{5}$

Although we cannot add the unlike square roots in the expression $-\dfrac{1}{2}\sqrt{2} - 4\sqrt{5}$, we can *evaluate* this expression using either Table I or a calculator (Example 8).

Example 8. Evaluate $-\dfrac{1}{2}\sqrt{2} - 4\sqrt{5}$.

Using Table 1: $\sqrt{2} = 1.414$

$\sqrt{5} = 2.236$

Therefore, $-\dfrac{1}{2}\sqrt{2} - 4\sqrt{5} = -\dfrac{1}{2}(1.414) - 4(2.236)$

$= -0.707 - 8.944$

$= -9.651$

Using Calculator: $\sqrt{2} = 1.414213562$

$\sqrt{5} = 2.236067977$

Therefore, $-\frac{1}{2}\sqrt{2} - 4\sqrt{5} = -\frac{1}{2}(1.414213562) - 4(2.236067077)$

$$= -0.7071067812 - 8.94427191$$

$$= -9.651379691$$

$$= -9.651 \quad \text{Rounded off to three decimal places.}$$

Notice that when the calculator answer is rounded off to the same number of decimal places as the answer obtained using Table 1, we get the same number, -9.651. However, these numbers may differ slightly because of the roundoff process.

Example 9. $\sqrt{2}(3\sqrt{2} - 5) = \sqrt{2} \cdot (3\sqrt{2}) + \sqrt{2}(-5)$

$$= 3\sqrt{2 \cdot 2} - 5\sqrt{2}$$

$$= 3 \cdot 2 - 5\sqrt{2}$$

$$= 6 - 5\sqrt{2}$$

Example 10. $(2\sqrt{3} - 5)(4\sqrt{3} - 6)$

$2\sqrt{3} \cdot 4\sqrt{3} = 8 \cdot 3 = 24 \qquad (-5)(-6) = 30$

Solution: $(2\sqrt{3} - 5)(4\sqrt{3} - 6)$

$-20\sqrt{3}$

$-12\sqrt{3}$ Adding like radicals.

$$= 24 - 32\sqrt{3} + 30$$

$$= 54 - 32\sqrt{3}$$

Example 11. $(3\sqrt{5} - 7x)^2$

$(3\sqrt{5})(3\sqrt{5}) = 9 \cdot 5 = 45 \qquad (-7x)(-7x) = 49x^2$

Solution: $(3\sqrt{5} - 7x)^2 = (3\sqrt{5} - 7x)(3\sqrt{5} - 7x)$

$-21\sqrt{5}x$

$-21\sqrt{5}x$ Adding like radicals.

$$= 45 - 42\sqrt{5}x + 49x^2$$

Example 12.

$$\frac{3\sqrt{14} - \sqrt{8}}{\sqrt{2}} = \frac{3\sqrt{14}}{\sqrt{2}} - \frac{\sqrt{8}}{\sqrt{2}} = 3\sqrt{\frac{14}{2}} - \sqrt{\frac{8}{2}}$$

$$= 3\sqrt{7} - \sqrt{4} = 3\sqrt{7} - 2$$

RATIONALIZING A BINOMIAL DENOMINATOR CONTAINING SQUARE ROOTS

The *conjugate* of a binomial containing square roots is a binomial having the same two terms in which the sign of the second term is changed.

Example 13. Conjugates of binomials that contain square roots.

(a) The conjugate of $1 - \sqrt{2}$ is $1 + \sqrt{2}$.

(b) The conjugate of $2\sqrt{3} + 5$ is $2\sqrt{3} - 5$.

(c) The conjugate of $\sqrt{x} - \sqrt{y}$ is $\sqrt{x} + \sqrt{y}$.

The product of a binomial containing square roots, and its conjugate, is a rational number. For example:

The conjugate of $1 - \sqrt{2}$ is $1 + \sqrt{2}$.

Then since $(a - b)(a + b) = a^2 - b^2$,

therefore $(1 - \sqrt{2})(1 + \sqrt{2}) = (1)^2 - (\sqrt{2})^2$

$$= 1 - 2 = -1 \quad \text{Rational number}$$

Because of this fact, the following procedure should be used when a binomial denominator contains a square root.

TO RATIONALIZE A BINOMIAL DENOMINATOR CONTAINING SQUARE ROOTS

Multiply numerator and denominator by the conjugate of the denominator:

$$\frac{a}{b + \sqrt{c}} \cdot \frac{b - \sqrt{c}}{b - \sqrt{c}} = \frac{a(b - \sqrt{c})}{b^2 - c}$$

<u>Example 14.</u> Rationalizing binomial denominators containing square roots.

(a) $\dfrac{2}{1 + \sqrt{3}} = \dfrac{2}{1 + \sqrt{3}} \cdot \boxed{\dfrac{1 - \sqrt{3}}{1 - \sqrt{3}}} = \dfrac{2(1 - \sqrt{3})}{(1)^2 - (\sqrt{3})^2} = \dfrac{2(1 - \sqrt{3})}{1 - 3}$

$= \dfrac{2(1 - \sqrt{3})}{-2} = \dfrac{\cancel{2}(1 - \sqrt{3})}{\underset{-1}{\cancel{-2}}}$

$= \sqrt{3} - 1$

Multiplying numerator and denominator by $1 - \sqrt{3}$ (the conjugate of the denominator $1 + \sqrt{3}$). Since the value of this fraction is 1, multiplying $\dfrac{2}{1 + \sqrt{3}}$ by 1 does not change its value.

(b) $\dfrac{6}{\sqrt{5} - \sqrt{3}} = \dfrac{6}{\sqrt{5} - \sqrt{3}} \cdot \boxed{\dfrac{\sqrt{5} + \sqrt{3}}{\sqrt{5} + \sqrt{3}}} = \dfrac{6(\sqrt{5} + \sqrt{3})}{(\sqrt{5})^2 - (\sqrt{3})^2} = \dfrac{6(\sqrt{5} + \sqrt{3})}{5 - 3}$

$= \dfrac{\overset{3}{\cancel{6}}(\sqrt{5} + \sqrt{3})}{\cancel{2}} = 3\sqrt{5} + 3\sqrt{3}$

Multiplying numerator and denominator by $\sqrt{5} + \sqrt{3}$ (the conjugate of the denominator $\sqrt{5} - \sqrt{3}$).

A word of caution. A common mistake is to confuse the square root of a *sum* with the sum of square roots.

$\sqrt{16 + 9}$ is the *square root of a sum.*

$\sqrt{16} + \sqrt{9}$ is the *sum of square roots.*

The sum of the square roots, $\sqrt{16} + \sqrt{9}$

$= 4 + 3 = 7$

The square root of the sum, $\sqrt{16 + 9}$

$= \sqrt{25}$

$= 5$

and certainly, $5 \ne 7$

EXERCISES 1204

SET I

In Exercises 1—26, find each of the sums.

1. $2\sqrt{3} + 5\sqrt{3}$ 2. $4\sqrt{2} + 3\sqrt{2}$ 3. $3\sqrt{x} - \sqrt{x}$

4. $5\sqrt{a} - \sqrt{a}$ 5. $\dfrac{3}{2}\sqrt{2} - \dfrac{\sqrt{2}}{2}$ 6. $\dfrac{4}{3}\sqrt{3} - \dfrac{\sqrt{3}}{3}$

7. $5 \cdot 8\sqrt{5} + \sqrt{5}$ 8. $3 \cdot 4\sqrt{7} + \sqrt{7}$ 9. $\sqrt{25} + \sqrt{5}$

10. $\sqrt{16} - \sqrt{6}$ 11. $2\sqrt{3} + \sqrt{12}$ 12. $3\sqrt{2} + \sqrt{8}$

13. $2\sqrt{50} - \sqrt{32}$ 14. $3\sqrt{24} - \sqrt{54}$ 15. $3\sqrt{32} - \sqrt{8}$

16. $4\sqrt{27} - 3\sqrt{12}$ 17. $\sqrt{\dfrac{1}{2}} + \sqrt{8}$ 18. $\sqrt{\dfrac{1}{3}} + \sqrt{12}$

19. $\sqrt{24} - \sqrt{\dfrac{2}{3}}$ 20. $\sqrt{45} - \sqrt{\dfrac{4}{5}}$ 21. $10\sqrt{\dfrac{3}{5}} + \sqrt{60}$

22. $8\sqrt{\dfrac{3}{16}} + \sqrt{48}$

----

23. $\sqrt{\dfrac{25}{2}} - \dfrac{3}{\sqrt{2}}$ 24. $5\sqrt{\dfrac{1}{5}} - \sqrt{\dfrac{9}{20}}$

25. $3\sqrt{\dfrac{1}{6}} + \sqrt{12} - 5\sqrt{\dfrac{3}{2}}$ 26. $3\sqrt{\dfrac{5}{2}} + \sqrt{20} - 5\sqrt{\dfrac{1}{10}}$

In Exercises 27–38, find each of the products.

27. $\sqrt{2}(\sqrt{2} + 1)$ 28. $\sqrt{3}(\sqrt{3} + 1)$ 29. $\sqrt{3}(2\sqrt{3} + 1)$

30. $\sqrt{5}(3\sqrt{5} + 1)$ 31. $\sqrt{x}(\sqrt{x} - 3)$ 32. $\sqrt{y}(4 - \sqrt{y})$

33. $(\sqrt{7} + 2)(\sqrt{7} + 3)$ 34. $(\sqrt{3} + 2)(\sqrt{3} + 4)$

35. $(\sqrt{8} - 3\sqrt{2})(\sqrt{8} + 2\sqrt{5})$ 36. $(\sqrt{2} + 4\sqrt{3})(\sqrt{12} - 2\sqrt{3})$

37. $(\sqrt{2x} + 3)^2$ 38. $(\sqrt{7x} - 4)^2$

In Exercises 39–42, find the quotients and simplify.

39. $\dfrac{\sqrt{8} + \sqrt{18}}{\sqrt{2}}$ 40. $\dfrac{\sqrt{12} + \sqrt{27}}{\sqrt{3}}$ 41. $\dfrac{\sqrt{20} + 5\sqrt{10}}{\sqrt{5}}$

42. $\dfrac{2\sqrt{6} + \sqrt{14}}{\sqrt{6}}$

In Exercises 43 and 44, write the conjugate for each expression.

43. (a) $2 + \sqrt{3}$ (b) $2\sqrt{5} - 7$

44. (a) $3\sqrt{2} - 5$ (b) $\sqrt{7} + 4$

In Exercises 45–52, rationalize the denominators and simplify.

45. $\dfrac{3}{\sqrt{2} - 1}$ 46. $\dfrac{5}{\sqrt{2} - 1}$ 47. $\dfrac{6}{\sqrt{3} - \sqrt{2}}$

48. $\dfrac{8}{\sqrt{2} - \sqrt{3}}$ 49. $\dfrac{6}{\sqrt{5} + \sqrt{2}}$ 50. $\dfrac{4}{\sqrt{7} + \sqrt{5}}$

51. $\dfrac{x - 4}{\sqrt{x} + 2}$　　　52. $\dfrac{y - 9}{\sqrt{y} - 3}$

In Exercises 53-56, evaluate each expression using Table I or a calculator. Round off answers to two decimal places.

53. $\dfrac{1}{3}\sqrt{7} - 2\sqrt{3}$　　　　　　54. $3\sqrt{6} - \dfrac{1}{4}\sqrt{5}$

55. $\dfrac{3 + 2\sqrt{11}}{6}$　　　　　　56. $\dfrac{3 - 2\sqrt{11}}{6}$

SET II

In Exercises 1—13, find each of the sums.

1. $3\sqrt{7} + 2\sqrt{7}$　　　2. $4\sqrt{m} - \sqrt{m}$　　　3. $\dfrac{2}{3}\sqrt{5} - \dfrac{\sqrt{5}}{3}$

4. $6 \cdot 5\sqrt{3} + \sqrt{3}$　　　5. $\sqrt{11} - \sqrt{9}$　　　6. $5\sqrt{2} + \sqrt{18}$

7. $\sqrt{45} - 3\sqrt{20}$　　　8. $4\sqrt{28} - 2\sqrt{63}$　　　9. $\sqrt{20} + \sqrt{\dfrac{1}{5}}$

10. $\sqrt{75} - \sqrt{\dfrac{4}{3}}$　　　11. $6\sqrt{\dfrac{5}{9}} + \sqrt{45}$　　　12. $\sqrt{\dfrac{16}{3}} - \dfrac{6}{\sqrt{3}}$

13. $10\sqrt{\dfrac{1}{15}} + \sqrt{60} - 8\sqrt{\dfrac{3}{5}}$

In Exercises 14-19, find each of the products.

14. $\sqrt{5}(\sqrt{5} - 1)$　　　15. $\sqrt{2}(3\sqrt{2} + 1)$　　　16. $\sqrt{z}(3 - \sqrt{z})$

17. $(\sqrt{6} + 5)(\sqrt{6} + 2)$　　　　18. $(\sqrt{2} - 5\sqrt{8})(\sqrt{2} + 4\sqrt{8})$

19. $(3\sqrt{y} - 5)^2$

In Exercises 20 and 21, find the quotients and simplify.

20. $\dfrac{\sqrt{15} + \sqrt{10}}{\sqrt{5}}$　　　21. $\dfrac{5\sqrt{32} + \sqrt{24}}{\sqrt{8}}$

22. Write the conjugate for each expression.
   (a) $5 - \sqrt{7}$　　　　　　(b) $-2 + \sqrt{3}$

In Exercises 23-26, rationalize the denominators and simplify.

23. $\dfrac{10}{1 + \sqrt{2}}$　　　　24. $\dfrac{13}{\sqrt{6} - \sqrt{5}}$

25. $\dfrac{15}{\sqrt{3} + \sqrt{8}}$　　　　26. $\dfrac{m^2 - 16}{2 - \sqrt{m}}$

In Exercises 27 and 28, evaluate each expression using Table I or a calculator. Round off answers to two decimal places.

27. $\frac{1}{4}\sqrt{13} - 3\sqrt{6}$

28. $\frac{-5 + 2\sqrt{5}}{7}$

Radical Equations

Radical Equations. A *radical equation* is an equation in which the unknown letter appears in a radicand. In this text we will consider only radical equations that have square roots.

Example 1. Radical equations.

(a) $\sqrt{x} = 7$

(b) $\sqrt{x + 2} = 3$

(c) $\sqrt{2x - 3} = \sqrt{x} + 5$

If two numbers are equal,

then their squares are equal

If $a = b$

then $a^2 = b^2$

Example 2. Squaring square roots.

(a) Since these are equal: $\sqrt{25} = 5$

    their squares are equal. $(\sqrt{25})^2 = (5)^2$

                                   $25 = 25$

(b) If these are equal: $\sqrt{x} = 3$

    their squares are equal. $(\sqrt{x})^2 = (3)^2$

                                   $x = 9$

(c) If these are equal: $\sqrt{x - 1} = 6$

    their squares are equal. $(\sqrt{x - 1})^2 = (6)^2$

                                $x - 1 = 36$

                                    $x = 37$

```
┌─────────────────────────────────────────────────────────┐
│                                                           │
│  TO SOLVE A RADICAL EQUATION                              │
│                                                           │
│  1.  Arrange the terms so that one term with a radical    │
│      is by itself on one side of the equation.            │
│                                                           │
│  2.  Square both sides of the equation.                   │
│                                                           │
│  3.  Collect like terms.                                  │
│                                                           │
│  4.  If a radical still remains, repeat Steps, I, 2, and 3.│
│                                                           │
│  5.  Solve the resulting equation for the letter.         │
│                                                           │
│  Check apparent solutions in the original equation.       │
│                                                           │
└─────────────────────────────────────────────────────────┘
```

Example 3.   Solve $\sqrt{x} = 7$.

  Solution: $\sqrt{x} = 7$ Check: $\sqrt{x} = 7$

  $(\sqrt{x})^2 = (7)^2$ $\sqrt{49} \stackrel{?}{=} 7$

  $x = 49$ $7 = 7$

Example 4.   Solve $\sqrt{x + 2} = 3$.

  Solution: $\sqrt{x + 2} = 3$ Check: $\sqrt{x + 2} = 3$

  $(\sqrt{x + 2})^2 = (3)^2$ $\sqrt{7 + 2} \stackrel{?}{=} 3$

  $x + 2 = 9$ $\sqrt{9} \stackrel{?}{=} 3$

  $x = 7$ $3 = 3$

A word of caution. It is necessary to check any apparent
solution of a radical equation by substituting it in the
original radical equation. This is necessary because in
solving radical equations it is possible to get an apparent solution that does *not* satisfy the original equation
(Example 5).   ■

Example 5.   Solve $\sqrt{2x + 1} = x - 1$.

  Solution: $\sqrt{2x + 1} = x - 1$

  $(\sqrt{2x + 1})^2 = (x - 1)^2$

  $2x + 1 = x^2 - 2x + 1$ ── When squaring
                                  $(x - 1)$, do not
                                  forget this middle
                                  term.

  $0 = x^2 - 4x$

  $0 = x(x - 4)$

  $x = 0 \ | \ x - 4 = 0$
  $ x = 4$

Check for $x = 0$:

$$\sqrt{2x + 1} \overset{?}{=} x - 1$$

$$\sqrt{2(0) + 1} \overset{?}{=} (0) - 1$$

$$\sqrt{1} \neq -1 \qquad \text{The symbol } \sqrt{1} \text{ } always \text{ stands for the } principal \text{ square root of 1, which is 1}$$

$$1 \neq -1 \qquad (not -1).$$

Therefore, *0 is not a solution of* $\sqrt{2x + 1} = x - 1$ because it does not satisfy the equation.

Check for $x = 4$:

$$\sqrt{2x + 1} = x - 1$$

$$\sqrt{2(4) + 1} \overset{?}{=} (4) - 1$$

$$\sqrt{9} \overset{?}{=} 3$$

$$3 = 3$$

Therefore, *4 is a solution* because it does satisfy the equation.

EXERCISES 1205   Solve each of the following equations.

SET I

1. $\sqrt{x} = 5$

2. $\sqrt{x} = 4$

3. $\sqrt{2x} = 4$

4. $\sqrt{3x} = 6$

5. $\sqrt{x - 3} = 2$

6. $\sqrt{x + 4} = 6$

7. $\sqrt{2x + 1} = 9$

8. $\sqrt{5x - 4} = 4$

9. $\sqrt{3x + 1} = 5$

10. $\sqrt{7x + 8} = 6$

11. $\sqrt{x + 1} = \sqrt{2x - 7}$

12. $\sqrt{3x - 2} = \sqrt{x + 4}$

----

13. $\sqrt{3x - 2} = x$

14. $\sqrt{5x - 6} = x$

15. $\sqrt{4x - 1} = 2x$

16. $\sqrt{6x - 1} = 3x$

17. $\sqrt{x - 3} + 5 = x$

18. $\sqrt{4x + 5} + 5 = 2x$

19. $\sqrt{3.14x + 6.75} = 4.96$

20. $9.02 = \sqrt{8.63x - 4.75}$

SET II

1. $\sqrt{x} = 8$

2. $\sqrt{5x} = 10$

3. $\sqrt{x - 6} = 3$

4. $\sqrt{6x + 1} = 5$

5. $\sqrt{9x - 5} = 7$

6. $\sqrt{9 - 2x} = \sqrt{5x - 12}$

7. $x = \sqrt{3x + 10}$

8. $\sqrt{3x + 2} = 3x$

9. $2x = \sqrt{40 - 12x}$

10. $\sqrt{x - 6} + 8 = x$

 11. $\sqrt{50.9x - 83.1} = 11.3$

The Pythagorean Theorem

Right Triangles. A triangle that has a *right angle* (square corner) is called a *right triangle*. The *diagonal* of a rectangle divides the rectangle into two right triangles. The parts of a right triangle are shown in Fig. 1206A.

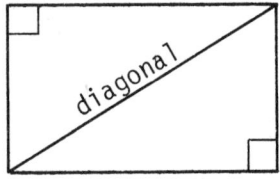

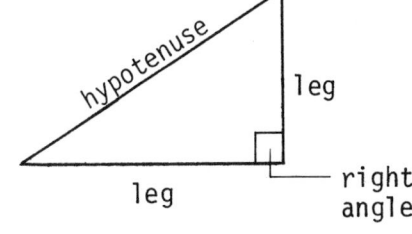

Rectangle   Right Triangle

Figure 1206A

THE PYTHAGOREAN THEOREM

The square of the hypotenuse of a right triangle is equal to the sum of the squares of the other sides.

$$c^2 = a^2 + b^2$$

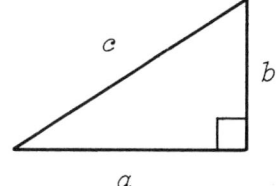

Note: The Pythagorean theorem applies only to *right triangles*.

The Pythagorean Theorem can be verified by comparing the areas shown in Fig. 1206B.

The area of the large square $(a + b)^2$ is equal to the area of the inside square c^2 plus the area of four equal triangles, $4\left(\dfrac{1}{2}ab\right)$.

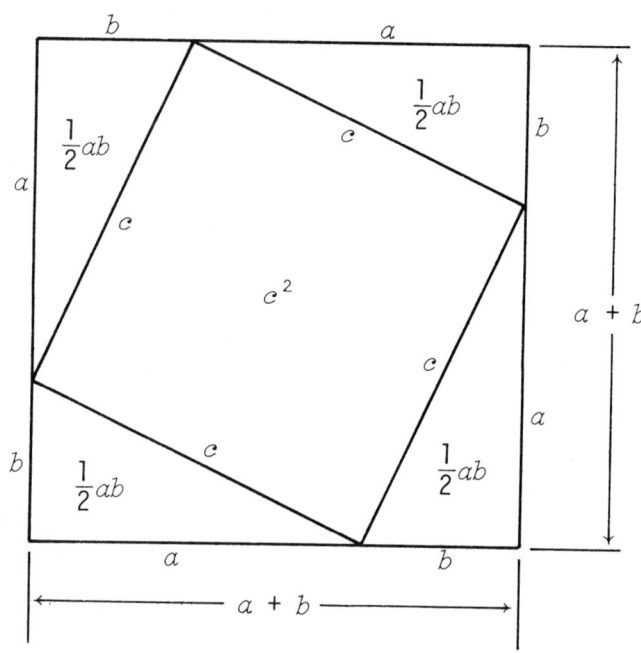

Figure 1206B

$$(a + b)^2 = c^2 + \frac{\overset{2}{\cancel{4}}}{1}\left(\frac{1}{\cancel{2}}ab\right)$$

$$a^2 + 2ab + b^2 = c^2 + 2ab$$

$$\underline{ - 2ab } \qquad \underline{ - 2ab }$$

$$a^2 + b^2 = c^2 \qquad \text{Pythagorean Theorem}$$

Example 1. Using the Pythagorean Theorem to show whether or not a given triangle is a right triangle.

(a)

$$5^2 \overset{?}{=} 3^2 + 4^2$$

$$25 \overset{?}{=} 9 + 16$$

$$25 = 25$$

Therefore the given triangle *is* a right triangle.

(b)

$$(\sqrt{29})^2 \overset{?}{=} 5^2 + 2^2$$

$$29 \overset{?}{=} 25 + 4$$

$$29 = 29$$

Therefore the given triangle *is* a right triangle.

(c)

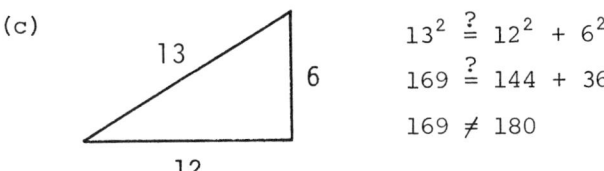

$$13^2 \stackrel{?}{=} 12^2 + 6^2$$

$$169 \stackrel{?}{=} 144 + 36$$

$$169 \neq 180$$

Therefore this triangle *is not* a right triangle.

The Pythagorean Theorem can be used to find one side of a right triangle when the other two sides are known.

<u>Example 2</u>. Find the hypotenuse of a right triangle whose legs are 8 and 6 cm.

<u>Solution</u>:

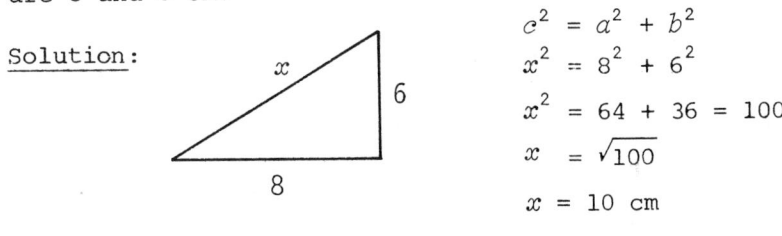

$$c^2 = a^2 + b^2$$

$$x^2 = 8^2 + 6^2$$

$$x^2 = 64 + 36 = 100$$

$$x = \sqrt{100}$$

$$x = 10 \text{ cm}$$

<u>Note</u>.

$$x^2 = 100$$

$$x^2 - 100 = 0$$

$$(x - 10)(x + 10) = 0$$

$x - 10 = 0$	$x + 10 = 0$
$x = +10$	$x = -10$

$x = 10$, -10 are solutions of this equation

However, -10 cannot be a solution of this *geometric problem* because we usually consider lengths in geometric figures as positive numbers. For this reason in the problems of this section we will take only the positive (*principal*) square root.

<u>Example 3</u>. Use the Pythagorean Theorem to find x in the given right triangle.

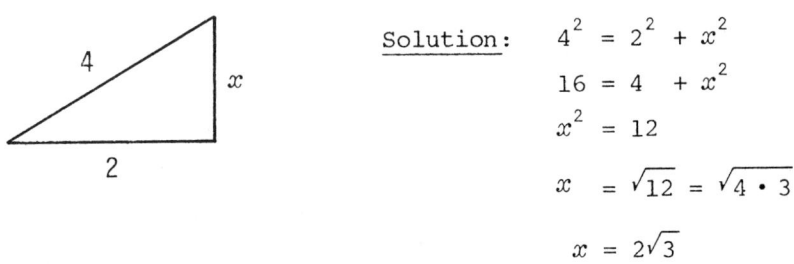

<u>Solution</u>:

$$4^2 = 2^2 + x^2$$

$$16 = 4 + x^2$$

$$x^2 = 12$$

$$x = \sqrt{12} = \sqrt{4 \cdot 3}$$

$$x = 2\sqrt{3}$$

<u>Example 4</u>. Find the length of the diagonal of a rectangle having a length of 6 ft and a width of 4 ft.

<u>Solution</u>: Let x = the length of the diagonal.

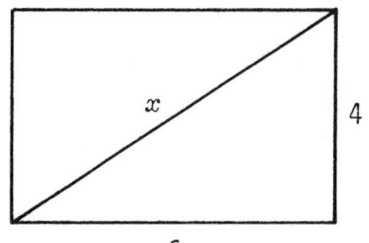

$$x^2 = 6^2 + 4^2$$
$$x^2 = 36 + 16 = 52$$
$$x = \sqrt{52} = \sqrt{4 \cdot 13}$$
$$x = 2\sqrt{13} \text{ ft}$$

<u>Example 5.</u> The length of a rectangle is 2 meters more than its width. If the length of its diagonal is 10 meters, find the dimensions of the rectangle.

Let x = Width

then $x + 2$ = Length

$$(10)^2 = (x)^2 + (x + 2)^2$$
$$100 = x^2 + x^2 + 4x + 4$$
$$0 = 2x^2 + 4x - 96 \qquad \text{Divide both}$$
$$0 = x^2 + 2x - 48 \qquad \text{sides by 2}$$
$$0 = (x + 8)(x - 6)$$

$x + 8 = 0 \quad | \quad x - 6 = 0$

     $x = -8 \quad | \qquad x = 6$ m Width

Not a solution $| \; x + 2 = 8$ m Length

<u>EXERCISES 1206</u>

<u>SET I</u>

Use the Pythagorean Theorem to find x in each of the following figures.

1.
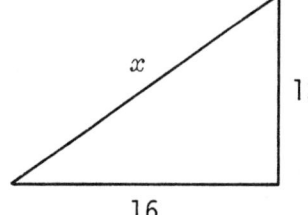

2.
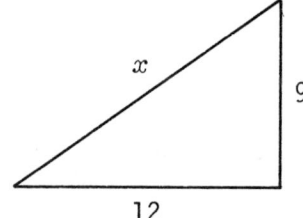

3.
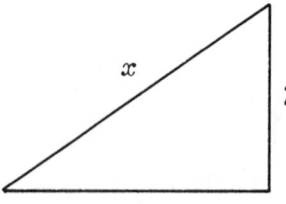

4.
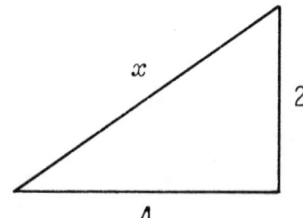

5.
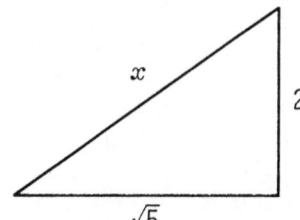

6.
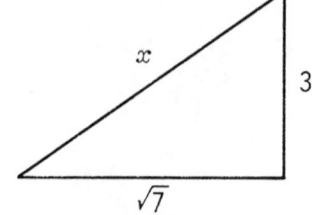

432   Chapter 12:   Radicals

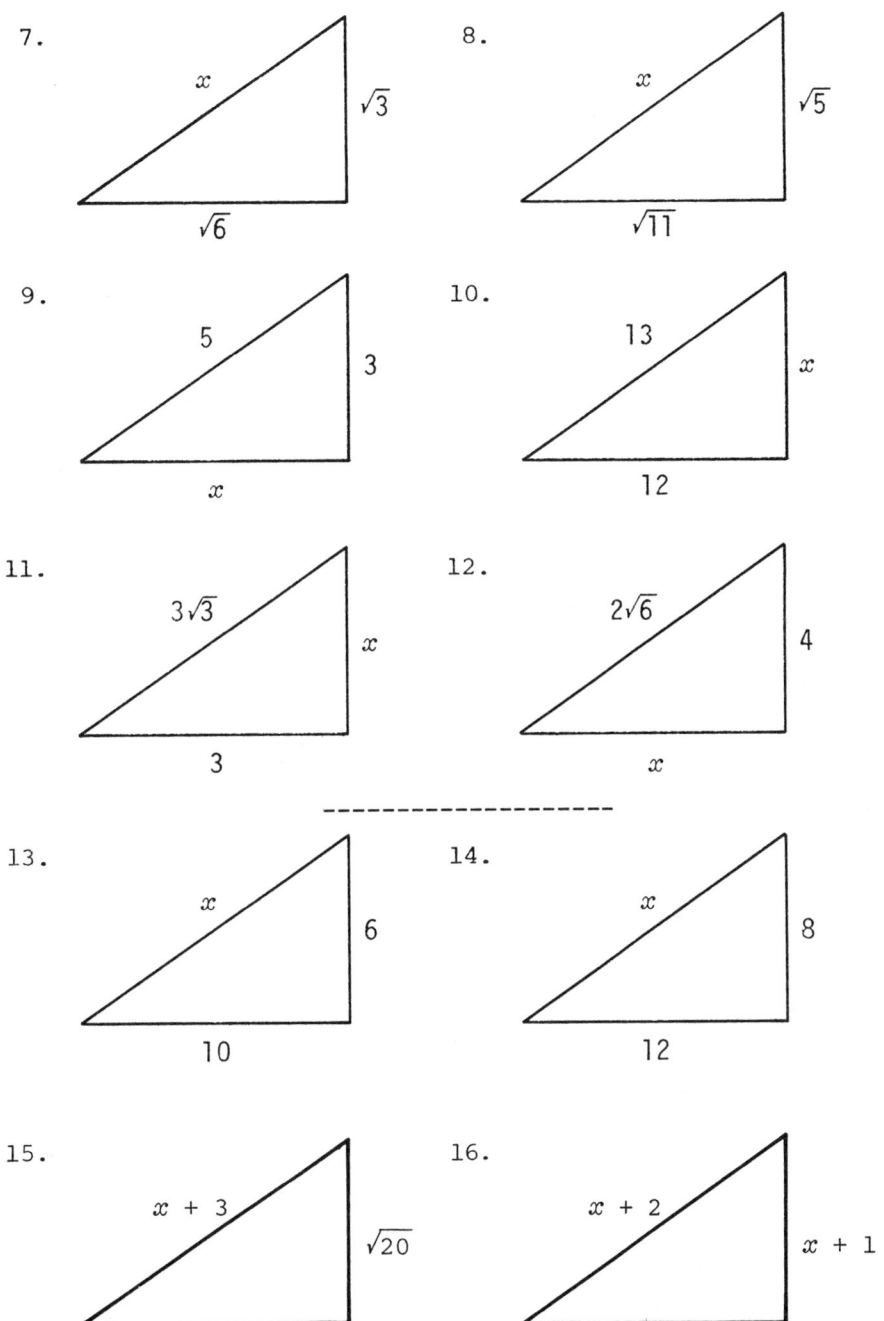

7. x $\sqrt{3}$ $\sqrt{6}$

8. x $\sqrt{5}$ $\sqrt{11}$

9.   5   3 x

10.   13 x 12

11. $3\sqrt{3}$ x 3

12. $2\sqrt{6}$ 4 x

13. x 6   10

14. x 8   12

15. $x+3$ $\sqrt{20}$ $x+1$

16. $x+2$ $x+1$ $\sqrt{17}$

17. Find the width of a rectangle having a diagonal of 25 cm and a length of 24 cm.

18. Find the width of a rectangle having a diagonal of 41 inches and a length of 40 inches.

19. One leg of a right triangle is 4 meters less than twice the other leg. If its hypotenuse is 10 meters, how long are the two legs?

20. The length of a rectangle is 3 yards more than its width. If the length of its diagonal is 15 yards, find the dimensions of the rectangle.

21. Find the diagonal of a square whose side is 41.6 cm.
22. Find the width of a rectangle having a diagonal of 4.53 m and a length of 3.67 m.

SET II

Use the Pythagorean Theorem to find x in each of the following figures.

1.

```
        x   /|
          /  | 15
        /____|
          20
```

2.

```
        x   /|
          /  | 3
        /____|
          6
```

3.

```
        x   /|
          /  | 2
        /____|
         √21
```

4.

```
        x   /|
          /  | √17
        /____|
         √19
```

5.

```
        13  /|
          /  | 5
        /____|
          x
```

6.

```
       3√5  /|
          /  | x
        /____|
          6
```

7.

```
        _____
        |        /  |
        |  x   /    | 6
        |    /      |
        |__/_____|
            15
```

8.

```
       x + 2  /|
            /  | √51
          /    |
        /_____|
         x - 1
```

9. Find the width of a rectangle having a diagonal of $10\sqrt{3}$ feet and a length of 15 feet.
10. The width of a rectangle is 4 cm less than its length. If the length of the diagonal is $4\sqrt{5}$ cm, find the dimensions of the rectangle.
11. Find the diagonal of a square whose side is 7.13 inches. Use Table I or a calculator and express your answer correct to two decimal places.

Chapter Summary

Square Roots (Sec. 1201). The *square root* of a number N, is a number which when squared gives N.

A positive real number N has two square roots, a positive root called the *principal square root*, written $\sqrt{N}$, and a negative square root, written $-\sqrt{N}$.

The Parts of a Square Root (Sec. 1201)

Index of square root
usually not written ⟶

$$\sqrt[2]{P}$$ Read "the square root of P."

radical sign ⟶ ⟵ radicand

Rational Numbers (Sec. 1201). A rational number is a real number that can be expressed in the form $\dfrac{a}{b}$, where a and b are integers ($b \neq 0$).

Irrational Numbers (Sec. 1201). An irrational number is a real number that *cannot* be expressed in the form $\dfrac{a}{b}$, where a and b are integers ($b \neq 0$).

Square Root Rules (Secs. 1201-1203)

1. *The square root of a product.* $\sqrt{ab} = \sqrt{a}\sqrt{b}$

2. *The square root of a quotient.* $\sqrt{\dfrac{a}{b}} = \dfrac{\sqrt{a}}{\sqrt{b}}$

3. *The product of square roots.*

Product of square roots	=	Square root of product

   $$\sqrt{a}\sqrt{b} = \sqrt{ab}$$

   $$\sqrt{a}\sqrt{a} = a$$

   $$(\sqrt{a})^2 = a$$

4. *The quotient of square roots.*

Quotient of square roots	=	Square root of quotient

   $$\dfrac{\sqrt{a}}{\sqrt{b}} = \sqrt{\dfrac{a}{b}}$$

To Find the Square Root of a Single Factor (Sec. 1202)

1. If the exponent of the factor is even:
    Divide the exponent by 2.

2. If the exponent of the factor is odd:
    Write the factor as the product of two factors—
    one factor having an even exponent, the other
    factor having an exponent of 1.

The Simplified Form of an expression having square roots
    (Sec. 1202).

1. No prime factor of a radicand has an exponent equal
    to or greater than 2.
2. No radicand contains a fraction.
3. No denominator contains a square root.

Conjugates (Sec. 1204). The conjugate of a binomial containing
    square roots is a binomial having the same two terms in
    which the sign of the second term is changed. For example:

$$\text{The conjugate of } 1 + \sqrt{2} \text{ is } 1 - \sqrt{2}$$

To Rationalize the Denominator

A. Monomial: $\dfrac{1}{\sqrt{a}} = \dfrac{1}{\sqrt{a}} \cdot \dfrac{\sqrt{a}}{\sqrt{a}} = \dfrac{\sqrt{a}}{a}$
    (Sec. 1202)

B. Binomial: $\dfrac{a}{b + \sqrt{c}} = \dfrac{a}{b + \sqrt{c}} \cdot \dfrac{b - \sqrt{c}}{b - \sqrt{c}} = \dfrac{a(b - \sqrt{c})}{b^2 - c}$
    (Sec. 1204)

To Add Square Roots (Sec. 1204)

A. Like roots: Add their coefficients and then multiply
    that sum by the like square root.
B. Unlike roots that can be simplified into like roots:
    1. Simplify each radical.
    2. Add any resulting like square roots.

The Pythagorean Theorem (Sec. 1206). The square of the
    hypotenuse of a right triangle is equal to the sum of
    the squares of the other sides.

$$c^2 = a^2 + b^2$$

To Solve a Radical Equation (Sec. 1205).

1. Arrange the terms so that one term with a radical is by itself on one side of the equation.
2. Square both sides of the equation.
3. Collect like terms.
4. If a radical still remains, repeat Steps 1, 2, and 3.
5. Solve the resulting equation for the letter.

REVIEW EXERCISES 1207

SET I

1. Which of the numbers $\sqrt{3}$, $2\frac{1}{2}$, $2\sqrt{5}$, 3.6, $\sqrt{5}$, $\frac{5}{2}$

    (a) are irrational numbers?
    (b) have like square roots?

2. Which of the numbers $7\frac{3}{4}$, $\sqrt{2}$, $\sqrt{3}$, 5.8, $3\sqrt{2}$

    (a) are rational numbers?
    (b) are like square roots?

In Exercises 3 and 4, what is the radicand in each expression?

3. (a) $\sqrt{9x}$ (b) $\sqrt{\frac{1}{2}}$ (c) $\sqrt{x-5}$

4. (a) $\sqrt{\frac{3}{5}}$ (b) $\sqrt{3x+4}$ (c) $\sqrt{4x}$

In Exercises 5—32, simplify each expression.

5. $\sqrt{81}$ 6. $\sqrt{100}$ 7. $(\sqrt{3})^2$ 8. $(\sqrt{5})^2$

9. $(\sqrt{2x})^2$ 10. $(\sqrt{3y})^2$

11. $(\sqrt{a+b})^2$ 12. $(\sqrt{a-b})^2$

13. $\sqrt{x^3}$ 14. $\sqrt{y^5}$ 15. $\sqrt{16x^2y^4}$ 16. $\sqrt{36a^4b^2}$

17. $\sqrt{a^3b^3}$ 18. $\sqrt{x^5y^5}$ 19. $\sqrt{8}\sqrt{8}$ 20. $\sqrt{11}\sqrt{11}$

21. $\sqrt{2}\sqrt{32}$ 22. $\sqrt{3}\sqrt{12}$ 23. $3\sqrt{5} + \sqrt{5}$

24. $4\sqrt{2} - \sqrt{2}$ 25. $\sqrt{18} - \sqrt{8}$ 26. $\sqrt{27} - \sqrt{12}$

27. $\frac{1}{\sqrt{5}}$ 28. $\frac{1}{\sqrt{7}}$ 29. $\frac{6}{\sqrt{3}}$

30. $\frac{20}{\sqrt{10}}$ 31. $\sqrt{8} - \sqrt{\frac{1}{2}}$ 32. $\sqrt{54} - \sqrt{\frac{2}{3}}$

In Exercises 33—40, solve each equation.

33. $\sqrt{x} = 4$ 34. $\sqrt{y} = 3$

35. $\sqrt{3a} = 6$ 36. $\sqrt{4b} = 10$

37. $\sqrt{2x - 1} = 5$ 38. $\sqrt{3x + 2} = 4$

39. $\sqrt{5a - 4} = \sqrt{3a + 2}$ 40. $\sqrt{3b - 2} = \sqrt{b + 4}$

In Exercises 41 and 42, use the Pythagorean Theorem.

41. Solve for x.   42. Solve for x.

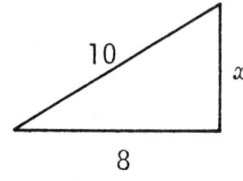

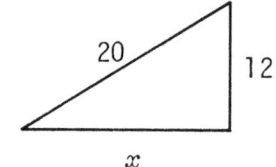

In Exercises 43—54, simplify each expression.

43. $\sqrt{2}(\sqrt{8} + \sqrt{18})$ 44. $\sqrt{3}(\sqrt{12} + \sqrt{27})$

45. $(\sqrt{5} + 3)(\sqrt{5} - 3)$ 46. $(5 + \sqrt{2})(5 - \sqrt{2})$

47. $(2\sqrt{3} + 1)^2$ 48. $(3\sqrt{2} - 1)^2$

49. $(3\sqrt{2} + 1)(2\sqrt{2} - 1)$ 50. $(5\sqrt{3} - 1)(3\sqrt{3} + 1)$

51. $\dfrac{8}{\sqrt{3} - 2}$ 52. $\dfrac{6}{2 + \sqrt{5}}$

53. $\dfrac{10}{\sqrt{6} - 2}$ 54. $\dfrac{8}{3 - \sqrt{7}}$

 55. Find the diagonal of a square whose side is 5 meters. Use Table I or a calculator and express your answer correct to two decimal places.

56. Find the width of a rectangle having a diagonal of 13 inches and a length of 12 inches.

In Exercises 57—60, solve each equation.

57. $\sqrt{7x - 6} = x$ 58. $\sqrt{9x - 8} = x$

59. $\sqrt{2x + 7} = \sqrt{x} + 2$ 60. $\sqrt{5x - 4} = \sqrt{x} + 2$

SET II

1. Which of the numbers $-\dfrac{7}{12}$, $\sqrt{6}$, $-4\dfrac{2}{3}$, $\sqrt{5}$,   6.8, $-3\sqrt{6}$
   (a) are irrational numbers?
   (b) have like square roots?

2. Give the radicand in each expression.

   (a) $\sqrt{4 - z}$ (b) $\sqrt{\dfrac{2}{3}}$ (c) $\sqrt{5a}$

In Exercises 3—22, simplify each expression.

3. $\sqrt{64}$ 4. $(\sqrt{11})^2$ 5. $(\sqrt{7z})^2$ 6. $(\sqrt{m-n})^2$

7. $\sqrt{w^7}$ 8. $\sqrt{25t^4s^2}$ 9. $\sqrt{u^3v^5}$ 10. $\sqrt{6}\sqrt{6}$

11. $\sqrt{18}\sqrt{2}$ 12. $5\sqrt{6} - 2\sqrt{6}$ 13. $\sqrt{45} - \sqrt{20}$

14. $\dfrac{1}{\sqrt{13}}$ 15. $\dfrac{12}{\sqrt{6}}$ 16. $\sqrt{60} - \sqrt{\dfrac{3}{5}}$

17. $\sqrt{5}(\sqrt{5} - \sqrt{20})$ 18. $(\sqrt{6} - 2)(\sqrt{6} + 2)$

19. $(3 - 2\sqrt{7})^2$ 20. $(4\sqrt{x} - 1)(\sqrt{x} + 3)$

21. $\dfrac{3}{1 - \sqrt{2}}$ 22. $\dfrac{12}{\sqrt{5} + 3}$

In Exercises 23—28, solve each equation.

23. $\sqrt{z} = 5$ 24. $\sqrt{5h} = 10$

25. $\sqrt{4x - 3} = 5$ 26. $\sqrt{7 - 3m} = \sqrt{m + 3}$

27. $x = \sqrt{x + 20}$ 28. $\sqrt{4x - 7} = \sqrt{x} + 1$

In Exercises 29 and 30, use the Pythagorean Theorem.

29. Solve for x.

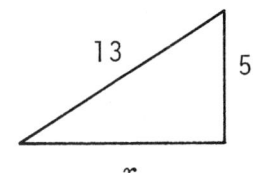

30. Find the diagonal of a rectangle having a width of 8 cm and a length of 10 cm. Use Table I or a calculator to express your answer correct to two decimal places.

CUMULATIVE REVIEW EXERCISES: CHAPTERS 1-11

1. Simplify. Write your answer using only positive exponents.

   $$\left(\frac{30x^4y^{-3}}{12y^{-1}}\right)^{-2}$$

2. Simplify the following expression. Then factor if possible.

   $$(2h - 6)^2 - 2[-4h(3 - h)]$$

3. Divide and simplify.

   $$\frac{x^2 + x - 2}{x^2 - 1} \div \frac{x^2 - 2x - 8}{x^2 - 4x}$$

4. Solve the inequality $3(x - 2) \le 6$ and graph its solution on the number line.

5. Solve the equation for x: $\dfrac{2x - 3}{2} = \dfrac{5x + 4}{6} - \dfrac{5}{3}$

6. Subtract and simplify.

$$\dfrac{2x}{x + 2} - \dfrac{5}{x - 1}$$

7. Solve graphically: $\left\{\begin{array}{l} 4x - 3y = -9 \\ 3y + x = -6 \end{array}\right\}$

8. Solve by addition-subtraction: $\left\{\begin{array}{l} 3x + 2y = 8 \\ 2x - y = 17 \end{array}\right\}$

9. Solve by substitution: $\left\{\begin{array}{l} 2x - 5y = 2 \\ 3x - 7y = 2 \end{array}\right\}$

10. The sum of two numbers is $\dfrac{1}{2}$. Their difference is $7\dfrac{1}{2}$. Find the two numbers.

Chapter Twelve Diagnostic Test

Name_____

_____

The purpose of this test is to see how well you understand operations with radicals. We recommend that you work this diagnostic test *before* your instructor tests you on this chapter. Allow yourself about one hour to do this test.

Complete solutions for all the problems on this test, together with section references, are given in the Answer Section. We suggest that you study the sections referred to for the problems you do incorrectly.

---

1. Which of the following are irrational numbers?

$$2\frac{1}{2}, \quad \sqrt{9}, \quad \frac{3}{4}, \quad \sqrt{3}, \quad -4, \quad \sqrt{5}$$

(1)_____

Simplify each of the following expressions.

2. $\sqrt{9x^2}$ 3. $\sqrt{18}$

(2)_____   (3)_____

4. $\sqrt{x^4 y^3}$ 5. $\sqrt{\dfrac{36}{49}}$

(4)_____   (5)_____

6. $\sqrt{\dfrac{18}{2m^2}}$

(6)_____

Find each of the following products and simplify.

7. $\sqrt{6}\sqrt{6}$ 8. $\sqrt{2}\sqrt{18x^2}$

(7)_____   (8)_____

9. $\sqrt{3}(2\sqrt{3} - 5)$

(9)_____

10. $(\sqrt{7} + \sqrt{3})(\sqrt{7} - \sqrt{3})$

(10)_____

11. $(5\sqrt{x} + 1)(5\sqrt{x} + 4)$

(11)_____

Simplify each of the following.

12. $\dfrac{\sqrt{6}}{\sqrt{24}}$

(12)_____

13. $\dfrac{\sqrt{4}}{\sqrt{6}}$

(13)_____

14. $\dfrac{\sqrt{15} - \sqrt{27}}{\sqrt{3}}$

(14)_____

15. $\dfrac{\sqrt{a^6 b}}{\sqrt{2b}}$

(15)_____

16. $\dfrac{4}{1 + \sqrt{3}}$

(16)_____

Find each of the following sums.

17. $4\sqrt{x} - \sqrt{x}$

(17)_____

18. $3\sqrt{2} - \sqrt{18}$

(18)_____

19. $\sqrt{27} + 3\sqrt{\dfrac{4}{3}}$

(19)_____

Use the Pythagorean Theorem to find x in each of the right triangles.

20.

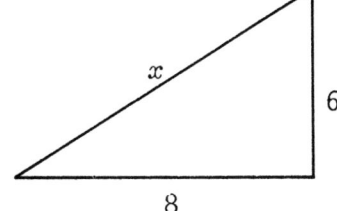

(20)_____

21.

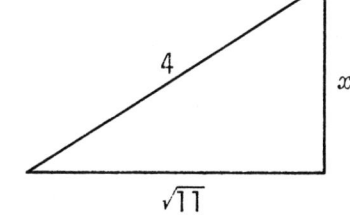

(21)_____

22. Find the diagonal of a square whose side is 6.

(22) Diagonal_____

Solve each of the following equations.

23. $\sqrt{2x} = 6$

(23)_____

24. $\sqrt{4x + 5} = 5$

(24)_____

25. $\sqrt{5x - 6} = x$

(25)_____

_____

THIRTEEN
Quadratic Equations

In this chapter we discuss several methods for solving quadratic equations. We have already solved quadratic equations by factoring in Secs. 807 and 908.

1301   General Form of Quadratic Equations

QUADRATIC EQUATIONS. A *quadratic equation* is a polynomial equation whose highest-degree term is second-degree. Quadratic equations are also called second-degree equations.

Example 1. Examples of quadratic equations.

    (a) $3x^2 + 7x + 2 = 0$

    (b) $\frac{1}{2}x^2 = \frac{2}{3}x - 4$

    (c) $x^2 - 4 = 0$

    (d) $5x^2 - 15x = 0$

GENERAL FORM (STANDARD FORM). Any quadratic equation can be arranged as follows:

THE GENERAL FORM OF A QUADRATIC EQUATION

$$ax^2 + bx + c = 0$$

where a, b, and c are real numbers ($a \neq 0$)

In this text, *when we write the general form of a quadratic equation, all coefficients will be integers. It is also helpful to write the general form in such a way that a is positive.*

TO CHANGE A QUADRATIC EQUATION INTO GENERAL FORM

1. *Remove fractions* by multiplying each term by the LCD.

2. *Remove grouping symbols* (Sec. 305).

3. *Collect and combine like terms* (Sec. 405).

4. Arrange all nonzero terms in descending powers on one side, leaving only zero on the other side.

Example 2. Changing quadratic equations into general form.

(a)
$$7x = 5 - 2x^2$$
$$2x^2 + 7x - 5 = 0$$ General form $\begin{cases} a = 2 \\ b = 7 \\ c = -5 \end{cases}$

└── Writing the general form so that a is positive.

(b)
$$5x^2 = 3$$
$$5x^2 + 0x - 3 = 0$$ General form $\begin{cases} a = 5 \\ b = 0 \\ c = -3 \end{cases}$

(c)
$$6x = 11x^2$$
$$0 = 11x^2 - 6x + 0$$
$$11x^2 - 6x + 0 = 0$$ General form $\begin{cases} a = 11 \\ b = -6 \\ c = 0 \end{cases}$

(d)
$$\frac{2}{3}x^2 - 5x = \frac{1}{2}$$
$$\frac{6}{1} \cdot \frac{2}{3}x^2 + \frac{6}{1} \cdot (-5x) = \frac{6}{1} \cdot \frac{1}{2}$$ Multiplied each term by the LCD, 6

$$4x^2 - 30x = 3$$
$$4x^2 - 30x - 3 = 0$$ General form $\begin{cases} a = 4 \\ b = -30 \\ c = -3 \end{cases}$

(e)
$$x(x - 2) = 5$$
$$x^2 - 2x = 5$$
$$x^2 - 2x - 5 = 0$$ General form $\begin{cases} a = 1 \\ b = -2 \\ c = -5 \end{cases}$

(f)
$$(x + 2)(2x - 3) = 3x - 7$$
$$2x^2 + x - 6 = 3x - 7$$
$$2x^2 - 2x + 1 = 0$$ General form $\begin{cases} a = 2 \\ b = -2 \\ c = 1 \end{cases}$

EXERCISES 1301. Write each of the following quadratic equations in general form and identify a, b, and c.

SET I

1. $2x^2 = 5x + 3$ 2. $3x^2 = 4 - 2x$

3. $6x^2 = x$ 4. $2x - 3x^2 = 0$

5. $\dfrac{3x}{2} + 5 = x^2$ 6. $4 - x^2 = \dfrac{2x}{3}$

7. $x^2 - \dfrac{5x}{4} + \dfrac{2}{3} = 0$ 8. $2x^2 + \dfrac{3x}{5} = \dfrac{1}{3}$

----

9. $x(x - 3) = 4$ 10. $2x(x + 1) = 12$

11. $3x(x + 1) = (x + 1)(x + 2)$

12. $(x + 1)(x - 3) = 4x(x - 1)$

▦ 13. $8.63x = 5.91 - 3.82x^2$ ▦ 14. $11.4x - 16.8x^2 = 15.7$

1. $5x = 4x^2 + 1$ 2. $5x^2 = x$

3. $\dfrac{4x}{3} + 2 = x^2$ 4. $3x^2 + \dfrac{x}{4} = \dfrac{1}{5}$

5. $(x - 1)(3x) = 7$ 6. $3x(x + 1) = (x + 2)(x - 3)$

 7. $4.65x(8.06 - 3.44x) = 7.51$

1302 Solving Quadratic Equations by Factoring

We will use the same method for solving quadratic equations by factoring as was used in Secs. 808 and 908.

> TO SOLVE A QUADRATIC EQUATION BY FACTORING
>
> 1. Arrange the equation in general form (Sec. 1301).
>
> $$ax^2 + bx + c = 0$$
>
> 2. Factor the polynomial.
> 3. Set each factor equal to zero and solve for the unknown letter.
>
> <u>Check</u> apparent solutions in the original equation.

<u>Example 1.</u> Solve $x^2 - 2x - 8 = 0$.

    <u>Solution:</u> $x^2 - 2x - 8 = 0$ Equation is already

                $(x + 2)(x - 4) = 0$ in general form.

$$x + 2 = 0 \,\big|\, x - 4 = 0$$
$$x = -2 \,\big|\,\quad x = 4$$

<u>Check for $x = -2$:</u>   <u>Check for $x = 4$:</u>

     $x^2 - 2x - 8 = 0$ $x^2 - 2x - 8 = 0$

$(-2)^2 - 2(-2) - 8 = 0$ $(4)^2 - 2(4) - 8 = 0$

       $4 + 4 - 8 = 0$ *true* $16 - 8 - 8 = 0$ *true*

Therefore, -2 and 4 are solutions.

     We can also solve equations of this type by getting all terms to the *right* side, leaving only zero on the *left* side (Example 2).

Example 2. Solve $3x = 5 - 2x^2$.

Solution:
$$3x = 5 - 2x^2$$
$$\underline{-3x \qquad\qquad -3x}$$
$$0 = 5 - 2x^2 - 3x$$

$$0 = 2x^2 + 3x - 5 \qquad \text{Writing equation so that}$$
$$\text{coefficient of } x^2 \text{ is}$$
$$\textit{positive}.$$

$$0 = (x - 1)(2x + 5)$$

$$
\begin{array}{l|l}
x - 1 = 0 & 2x + 5 = 0 \\
\quad\;\; x = 1 & \qquad 2x = -5 \\
 & \qquad\;\; x = -\dfrac{5}{2}
\end{array}
$$

Example 3. Solve $x^2 = \dfrac{3 - 5x}{2}$.

Solution:
$$\frac{x^2}{1} = \frac{3 - 5x}{2}$$

$$2 \cdot x^2 = 1 \cdot (3 - 5x) \qquad \text{Product of means}$$
$$2x^2 = 3 - 5x \qquad\qquad\; = \text{product of}$$
$$\text{extremes.}$$

$$2x^2 + 5x - 3 = 0$$

$$(2x - 1)(x + 3) = 0$$

$$
\begin{array}{l|l}
2x - 1 = 0 & x + 3 = 0 \\
\quad\; 2x = 1 & \qquad x = -3 \\
\quad\;\; x = \dfrac{1}{2} &
\end{array}
$$

Example 4. Solve $\dfrac{x - 1}{x - 3} = \dfrac{12}{x + 1}$.

Solution:
$$\frac{x - 1}{x - 3} = \frac{12}{x + 1}$$

$$(x - 1)(x + 1) = 12(x - 3) \qquad \text{Product of means}$$
$$x^2 - 1 = 12x - 36 \qquad\qquad = \text{product of extremes.}$$

$$x^2 - 12x + 35 = 0$$

$$(x - 7)(x - 5) = 0$$

$$
\begin{array}{l|l}
x - 7 = 0 & x - 5 = 0 \\
\quad\;\; x = 7 & \quad\;\; x = 5
\end{array}
$$

Example 5. Solve $(6x + 2)(x - 4) = 2 - 11x$.

Solution:

$$(6x + 2)(x - 4) = 2 - 11x$$
$$6x^2 - 22x - 8 = 2 - 11x$$
$$6x^2 - 11x - 10 = 0$$
$$(3x + 2)(2x - 5) = 0$$

$3x + 2 = 0$	$2x - 5 = 0$
$3x = -2$	$2x = 5$
$x = -\dfrac{2}{3}$	$x = \dfrac{5}{2}$

Example 6. The length of a rectangle is 8 more than its width. If its area is 48, find its dimensions.

Solution

Let W = width,
then L = length.

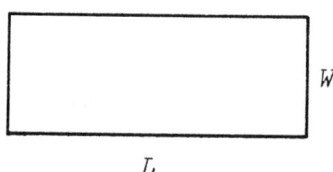

Its area is 48 .

(1) LW = 48

The length of the rectangle is 8 more than its width .

(2) L = 8 + W

Substitute $8 + W$ in place of L in equation (1).

(1)
$$LW = 48$$
$$(8 + W)W = 48$$
$$8W + W^2 = 48$$
$$W^2 + 8W - 48 = 0$$
$$(W + 12)(W - 4) = 0$$

$W + 12 = 0$	$W - 4 = 0$
$W = -12$	$W = 4$ (width)
	$L = 8 + W$
No meaning.	$L = 8 + 4 = 12$ (length)

This problem can also be solved using a single letter as follows:

450   Chapter 13: Quadratic Equations

Solution

Let W = width,
then $W + 8$ = length (L).

Its area is 48..

$$W(W + 8) = 48$$

$$W^2 + 8W = 48$$

$$W^2 + 8W - 48 = 0$$

$$(W + 12)(W - 4) = 0$$

$W + 12 = 0$	$W - 4 = 0$
$W = -12$	$W = 4$ (width)
	$W + 8 = 4 + 8$
No meaning.	$L = 12$ (length)

Area = $WL = W(W + 8)$

EXERCISES 1302. Solve by factoring.

SET I

1. $x^2 + x - 6 = 0$ 2. $x^2 - x - 6 = 0$

3. $x^2 + x = 12$ 4. $x^2 + 2x = 15$

5. $2x^2 - x = 1$ 6. $2x^2 + x = 1$

7. $\dfrac{x}{8} = \dfrac{2}{x}$ 8. $\dfrac{x}{3} = \dfrac{12}{x}$

9. $\dfrac{x + 2}{3} = \dfrac{-1}{x - 2}$ 10. $\dfrac{x + 3}{2} = \dfrac{-4}{x - 3}$

11. $x^2 + 9x + 8 = 0$ 12. $x^2 + 7x + 6 = 0$

13. $2x^2 + 4x = 0$ 14. $3x^2 - 9x = 0$

15. $x^2 = x + 2$ 16. $x^2 = x + 6$

17. $\dfrac{x}{2} + \dfrac{2}{x} = \dfrac{5}{2}$ 18. $\dfrac{x}{3} + \dfrac{2}{x} = \dfrac{7}{3}$

----

19. $\dfrac{x - 1}{4} + \dfrac{6}{x + 1} = 2$ 20. $\dfrac{3x + 1}{5} + \dfrac{8}{3x - 1} = 3$

21. $2x^2 = \dfrac{2 - x}{3}$ 22. $4x^2 = \dfrac{14x - 3}{2}$

23. The length of a rectangle is 5 more than its width. If its area is 24, find its dimensions.

24. The length of a rectangle is 4 more than its width. If its area is 77, find its dimensions.

25. One leg of a right triangle is 2 more than the other. The hypotenuse is 10. Find the length of the longer leg.

26. One leg of a right triangle is 7 more than the other. The hypotenuse is 13. Find the length of the longer leg.

27. If the product of two consecutive even integers is increased by 4, the result is 84. Find the integers.

28. Bruce drives from Los Angeles to the Mexican border and back to Los Angeles, a total distance of 240 miles. His average speed returning to Los Angeles was 20 mph faster than his average speed going to Mexico. If his total driving time was 5 hr, what was his average speed driving from Los Angeles to Mexico?

SET II

1. $x^2 + 2x - 8 = 0$

2. $x^2 + 4x = 5$

3. $3x^2 - 2x = 1$

4. $\dfrac{x}{27} = \dfrac{3}{x}$

5. $\dfrac{x + 1}{1} = \dfrac{3}{x - 1}$

6. $x^2 + 6x + 5 = 0$

7. $2x^2 - 6x = 0$

8. $x^2 + x = 0$

9. $\dfrac{x}{2} - \dfrac{3}{x} = \dfrac{5}{4}$

10. $\dfrac{2x + 1}{5} + \dfrac{10}{2x + 1} = 3$

11. $3x^2 = \dfrac{11x + 10}{2}$

12. The length of a rectangle is 5 more than its width. Its area is 36, find its dimensions.

13. One leg of a right triangle is 3 more than the other. The hypotenuse is 15. Find the length of the shorter leg.

14. The length of a rectangle is 3 times its width. If the numerical sum of its area and perimeter is 80, find its dimensions.

15. The tens digit of a two-digit number is 4 more than the units digit. If the product of the units digit and tens digit is 21, find the number.

16. Ruth drives from Creston to Des Moines, a distance of 90 miles. Then she continues on from Des Moines to Omaha, a distance of 120 miles. Her average speed was 10 mph faster on the second part of the journey than on the first part. If the total driving time was 6 hr, what was her average speed on the first leg of the journey?

Incomplete Quadratic Equations

An *incomplete quadratic equation* is one in which b or c (or both) is zero. The only letter that *cannot* be zero is a. If a were zero, the equation would not be a quadratic.

Example 1. Incomplete quadratic equations.

(a) $12x^2 + 5 = 0$ ($b = 0$)

(b) $7x^2 - 2x = 0$ ($c = 0$)

(c) $3x^2 = 0$ (b and $c = 0$)

TO SOLVE A QUADRATIC EQUATION WHEN $c = 0$

1. Find the greatest common factor (GCF)
    (Sec. 802).
2. Then solve by factoring.
$$ax^2 + bx = 0$$
$$x(ax + b) = 0$$

$$x = 0 \quad | \quad ax + b = 0$$
$$ax = -b$$
$$x = -\frac{b}{a}$$

Example 2. Solve $12x^2 = 3x$.

Solution:

$$12x^2 - 3x = 0 \qquad \text{General form.}$$
$$3x(4x - 1) = 0 \qquad \text{GCF} = 3x$$

$$3x = 0 \quad | \quad 4x - 1 = 0$$
$$x = 0 \quad | \quad 4x = 1$$
$$x = \frac{1}{4}$$

A word of caution. In doing Example 2, a common mistake
students make is to divide both sides of the equation by x.

$$12x^2 = 3x$$
$$12x = 3 \qquad \text{Dividing both sides by } x.$$
$$x = \frac{1}{4} \qquad \text{Using this method, we only found the}$$
solution $x = \frac{1}{4}$, *not* $x = 0$.

By dividing both sides of the equation by x, we lost the
solution $x = 0$.

*Do not divide both sides of an equation by an expression
containing the unknown letter, because you may lose solutions.* ■

Example 3. Solve $\frac{2}{5}x = 3x^2$.

Solution: LCD = 5 $\dfrac{5}{1} \cdot \dfrac{2}{5} x = 5 \cdot (3x^2)$

$$2x = 15x^2$$

$$15x^2 - 2x = 0 \qquad \text{General form.}$$

$$x(15x - 2) = 0$$

$$x = 0 \quad \bigg| \quad 15x - 2 = 0$$
$$15x = 2$$
$$x = \frac{2}{15}$$

$\underline{\pm \text{ Symbol}}.$ The symbol "$\pm$" is read "plus or minus."

"± 2" is read "plus or minus 2."

"$x = \pm 2$" is read "x equals +2 or -2."

This means $x = +2$ or $x = -2$.

A positive real number, N, has two square roots: a positive root called the *principal square root*, written $\sqrt{N}$, and a negative square root, written $-\sqrt{N}$. We can represent these two square roots by the symbol $\pm\sqrt{N}$.

$\underline{\text{Example 4}}.$ Solve $x^2 - 4 = 0$.   (Here $b = 0$.   Refer to following box for method of solution.)

$\underline{\text{Solution}}:$ $x^2 - 4 = 0$

$$x^2 = 4$$
$$\sqrt{x^2} = \pm\sqrt{4}$$
$$x = \pm 2$$

$\underline{\text{Justification for the} \pm \text{ sign}}.$ This equation can be solved by factoring.

$$x^2 - 4 = 0 \qquad \bigg| \quad x + 2 = 0 \quad \bigg| \quad x - 2 = 0$$
$$(x + 2)(x - 2) = 0 \qquad \bigg| \qquad x = -2 \quad \bigg| \qquad x = 2$$

This shows why we must use $\pm$.

TO SOLVE A QUADRATIC EQUATION WHEN $b = 0$

1. Arrange the equation so that the second-degree term is on one side and the constant term c is on the other side.

2. Divide both sides by the coefficient a of x^2.

3. Take the square root of both sides and simplify the square root.

4. There is both a positive and a negative answer (written $\pm$).

$$ax^2 + c = 0$$
$$ax^2 = -c$$
$$x^2 = -\frac{c}{a}$$

$$x = \pm\sqrt{-\frac{c}{a}}$$

We write both square roots, because we want *all* solutions of the equation.

$$x = \pm\sqrt{-\frac{c}{a}}$$

This square root can be evaluated *only* if either a or c is negative (*not* both).

5. When the radicand $-\frac{c}{a}$ is:

Positive: The square roots are real numbers.
Negative: The square roots are not real numbers.

Example 5. Solve $4x^2 - 9 = 0$.

Solution:
$$4x^2 - 9 = 0$$
$$4x^2 = 9$$
$$x^2 = \frac{9}{4}$$
$$x = \pm\sqrt{\frac{9}{4}}$$
$$x = \pm\frac{3}{2}$$

Example 6. Solve $3x^2 - 5 = 0$.

Solution:

$$3x^2 - 5 = 0$$

$$3x^2 = 5$$

$$x^2 = \frac{5}{3}$$

$$x = \pm\sqrt{\frac{5}{3}} = \pm\frac{\sqrt{5}}{\sqrt{3}} \cdot \frac{\sqrt{3}}{\sqrt{3}} = \pm\frac{\sqrt{15}}{3}$$

$$x = \pm\frac{\sqrt{15}}{3}$$

We can use Table I, or a calculator, to evaluate $\sqrt{15}$ and express the answer as approximate decimals.

$$x = \pm\frac{\sqrt{15}}{3} = \pm\frac{3.873}{3} = \pm1.291 \doteq \pm1.29 \qquad \text{Rounded off to two decimal places.}$$

Example 7. Solve $x^2 + 25 = 0$.

Solution:

$$x^2 + 25 = 0$$

$$x^2 = -25$$

$$x = \pm\sqrt{-25} \qquad \text{Solution is not a real number because radicand is negative.}$$

Equations of this type, where the radicand of a square root is negative, have roots that are *complex numbers*. Complex numbers are not discussed in this text.

EXERCISES 1303. Solve each equation.

SET I

1. $8x^2 = 4x$ 2. $15x^2 = 5x$

3. $x^2 - 9 = 0$ 4. $x^2 - 36 = 0$

5. $5x^2 = 4$ 6. $3x^2 = 25$

7. $8 - 2x^2 = 0$ 8. $27 - 3x^2 = 0$

9. $2(x + 3) = 6 + x(x + 2)$

10. $5(2x - 3) - x(2 - x) = 8(x - 1) - 7$

----

11. $2x(3x - 4) = 2(3 - 4x)$

12. $5x(2x - 3) = 3(4 - 5x)$

In Exercises 13 and 14, use Table I or a calculator and express your answers rounded off to two decimal places.

13. A rectangle is 8 inches long and 4 inches wide. Find the length of its diagonal.
14. A rectangle is 9 feet long and 3 feet wide. Find the length of its diagonal.
15. It takes Mina 3 hr longer to do a job than it does Merwin. After Mina has worked on the job for 5 hr, Merwin joins her. Together they finish the job in 3 hr. How long would it take each of them to do the entire job working alone?
16. Find the diagonal of a square whose side is $\sqrt{10}$.

<u>SET II</u>

1. $12x = 8x^2$

2. $x^2 - 16 = 0$

3. $5x^2 = 25$

4. $64 - 4x^2 = 0$

5. $x(x + 2) = (x - 1)2x$

6. $\dfrac{2x^2}{3} = 4x$

In Exercise 7, use Table I or a calculator and express your answer rounded off to two decimal places.

7. The legs of a right triangle are 5 and 7 centimeters. Find the length of the hypotenuse.
8. The length of the diagonal of a square is $\sqrt{32}$. What is the length of its sides?
9. It takes Darryl 2 hr longer to do a job than it does Jeannie. After Darryl has worked on the job for 1 hr, Jeannie joins him. Together they finish the job in 3 hr. How long would it take each of them to do the entire job working alone?

13O4 The Quadratic Formula

The methods we have shown in previous sections can only be used to solve *some* quadratic equations. The method we show in this section can be used to solve *all* quadratic equations.

In Example 1 we use a method called *completing the square* to solve a quadratic equation.

<u>Example 1.</u> Solve $x^2 - 4x + 1 = 0$.

<u>Solution</u>: $x^2 - 4x + 1 = 0$

$x^2 - 4x = -1$ Subtracting 1 from both sides.

$$x^2 - 4x \boxed{+ 4} = -1 \boxed{+ 4}$$

Adding 4 to both sides makes the left side a perfect square.

$$(x - 2)^2 = 3$$

Factoring left side.

$$\sqrt{(x - 2)^2} = \pm\sqrt{3}$$

Taking square root of both sides.

$$x - 2 = \pm\sqrt{3}$$

Simplifying radical.

$$x = 2 \pm \sqrt{3}$$

Adding 2 to both sides.

<u>Check for $x = 2 + \sqrt{3}$</u>:

$$x^2 \quad - \quad 4x \quad + 1 = 0$$
$$(2 + \sqrt{3})^2 - 4(2 + \sqrt{3}) + 1 \overset{?}{=} 0$$
$$4 + 4\sqrt{3} + 3 - 8 - 4\sqrt{3} + 1 \overset{?}{=} 0$$
$$0 = 0$$

We leave the check for $x = 2 - \sqrt{3}$ for the student.

The method of completing the square can be used to solve *any* quadratic equation. We now use it to solve the general form of the quadratic equation and in this way derive the *quadratic formula*.

<u>DERIVATION OF THE QUADRATIC FORMULA</u>

$$ax^2 + bx + c = 0$$

General form.

$$ax^2 + bx = -c$$

Taking c to right side.

$$x^2 + \frac{b}{a}x = -\frac{c}{a}$$

Dividing both sides by a.

$$x^2 + \frac{b}{a}x + \boxed{\frac{b^2}{4a^2}} = \boxed{\frac{b^2}{4a^2}} - \frac{c}{a} = \frac{b^2}{4a^2} - \frac{4ac}{4a^2}$$

Adding $\boxed{\dfrac{b^2}{4a^2}}$ to both sides to make left side a perfect square.

$$\left(x + \frac{b}{2a}\right)^2 = \frac{b^2 - 4ac}{4a^2}$$

Factoring left side and adding the fractions on right side.

$$x + \frac{b}{2a} = \pm\sqrt{\frac{b^2 - 4ac}{4a^2}}$$

Taking square root of both sides.

$$x + \frac{b}{2a} = \pm\frac{\sqrt{b^2 - 4ac}}{\sqrt{4a^2}} = \pm\frac{\sqrt{b^2 - 4ac}}{2a}$$

Simplifying radicals.

$$x = -\frac{b}{2a} \pm \frac{\sqrt{b^2 - 4ac}}{2a}$$

Adding $-\dfrac{b}{2a}$ to both sides.

Therefore $\quad x = \dfrac{-b \pm \sqrt{b^2 - 4ac}}{2a}$

The *quadratic formula*.

The procedure for using the quadratic formula can be summarized as follows:

TO SOLVE A QUADRATIC EQUATION BY FORMULA

1. Arrange the equation in general form (Sec. 1301).

$$ax^2 + bx + c = 0$$

2. Substitute the values of a, b, and c into the *quadratic formula*

$$x = \frac{-b \pm \sqrt{b^2 - 4ac}}{2a} \qquad (a \neq 0)$$

3. Simplify your answers.

<u>Check</u> your answers by substituting them in the *original* equation.

Example 2. Solve $x^2 - 5x + 6 = 0$ by formula.

Solution

Substitute $\left\{ \begin{array}{l} a = 1 \\ b = -5 \\ c = 6 \end{array} \right\}$ in the formula $x = \dfrac{-b \pm \sqrt{b^2 - 4ac}}{2a}$

$$x = \frac{-(-5) \pm \sqrt{(-5)^2 - 4(1)(6)}}{2(1)}$$

$$x = \frac{5 \pm \sqrt{25 - 24}}{2} = \frac{5 \pm \sqrt{1}}{2}$$

$$x = \frac{5 \pm 1}{2} = \left\{ \begin{array}{l} \dfrac{5 + 1}{2} = \dfrac{6}{2} = 3 \\[2mm] \dfrac{5 - 1}{2} = \dfrac{4}{2} = 2 \end{array} \right.$$

This equation can also be solved by factoring.

Solution:
$$x^2 - 5x + 6 = 0$$
$$(x - 2)(x - 3) = 0$$

$$\begin{array}{c|c} x - 2 = 0 & x - 3 = 0 \\ x = 2 & x = 3 \end{array}$$

Solving a quadratic equation by factoring is ordinarily shorter than using the formula. Therefore, first check to see if the equation can be solved by factoring. If it cannot, use the formula.

Example 3. Solve $x^2 - 6x - 3 = 0$.

Solution

Substitute $\begin{cases} a = 1 \\ b = -6 \\ c = -3 \end{cases}$ in the formula $x = \dfrac{-b \pm \sqrt{b^2 - 4ac}}{2a}$

$$x = \frac{-(-6) \pm \sqrt{(-6)^2 - 4(1)(-3)}}{2(1)}$$

$$= \frac{6 \pm \sqrt{36 + 12}}{2} = \frac{6 \pm \sqrt{48}}{2}$$

$$= \frac{6 \pm 4\sqrt{3}}{2} = \frac{\cancel{2}(3 \pm 2\sqrt{3})}{\cancel{2}} = 3 \pm 2\sqrt{3}$$

Example 4. Solve $\frac{1}{4}x^2 = 1 - x$.

Solution: LCD = 4

$$\boxed{\frac{4}{1}} \cdot \frac{1}{4}x^2 = \boxed{4} \cdot (1 - x) \qquad \text{First, changing equation to general form.}$$

$$x^2 = 4 - 4x$$

$$x^2 + 4x - 4 = 0 \qquad \text{General form.}$$

Substitute $\begin{cases} a = 1 \\ b = 4 \\ c = -4 \end{cases}$ into $x = \dfrac{-b \pm \sqrt{b^2 - 4ac}}{2a}$

$$x = \frac{-(4) \pm \sqrt{(4)^2 - 4(1)(-4)}}{2(1)}$$

$$= \frac{-4 \pm \sqrt{16 + 16}}{2} = \frac{-4 \pm \sqrt{32}}{2}$$

$$= \frac{-4 \pm 4\sqrt{2}}{2} = \frac{\cancel{2}(-2 \pm 2\sqrt{2})}{\cancel{2}} = -2 \pm 2\sqrt{2}$$

Example 5. Solve $4x^2 - 5x + 2 = 0$.

Solution

Substitute $\begin{cases} a = 4 \\ b = -5 \\ c = 2 \end{cases}$ into $x = \dfrac{-b \pm \sqrt{b^2 - 4ac}}{2a}$

$$x = \frac{-(-5) \pm \sqrt{(-5)^2 - 4(4)(2)}}{2(4)}$$

$$= \frac{5 \pm \sqrt{25 - 32}}{8} = \frac{5 \pm \sqrt{\boxed{-7}}}{8} \longleftarrow \text{Solution is not a real number because radicand is negative.}$$

We can use Table I or a calculator to evaluate the square root and express the answers as approximate decimals.

<u>Example 6.</u> Solve $x^2 - 5x + 3 = 0$. Express the answers as decimals correct to two decimal places.

<u>Solution</u>

Substitute $\left\{ \begin{array}{l} a = 1 \\ b = -5 \\ c = 3 \end{array} \right\}$ into $x = \dfrac{-b \pm \sqrt{b^2 - 4ac}}{2a}$

$$x = \frac{-(-5) \pm \sqrt{(-5)^2 - 4(1)(3)}}{2(1)}$$

$$= \frac{5 \pm \sqrt{25 - 12}}{2} = \frac{5 \pm \sqrt{13}}{2} \qquad \left(\begin{array}{l} \sqrt{13} \doteq 3.606 \text{ from} \\ \text{Table I} \end{array} \right)$$

$$\doteq \frac{5 \pm 3.606}{2} = \left\{ \begin{array}{l} \dfrac{5 + 3.606}{2} = \dfrac{8.606}{2} = 4.303 \doteq 4.30 \\[2ex] \dfrac{5 - 3.606}{2} = \dfrac{1.394}{2} = 0.697 \doteq 0.70 \end{array} \right.$$

We suggest you use a calculator to check these answers in the original equation.

<u>EXERCISES 1304.</u> Use the quadratic formula to solve each of the following equations.

SET I

1. $3x^2 - x - 2 = 0$ 2. $2x^2 + 3x - 2 = 0$

3. $x^2 - 4x + 1 = 0$ 4. $x^2 - 4x - 1 = 0$

5. $\dfrac{x}{2} + \dfrac{2}{x} = \dfrac{5}{2}$ 6. $\dfrac{x}{3} + \dfrac{2}{x} = \dfrac{7}{3}$

7. $2x^2 = 8x - 5$ 8. $3x^2 = 6x - 2$

9. $\dfrac{1}{x} + \dfrac{x}{x - 1} = 3$ 10. $\dfrac{2}{x} - \dfrac{x}{x + 1} = 4$

11. A number less its reciprocal is $\dfrac{2}{3}$. What is the number? (The reciprocal of a number n is $\dfrac{1}{n}$)

12. If a number is subtracted from twice its reciprocal, the result is $\dfrac{5}{4}$. What is the number?

In Exercises 13-20, use Table I or a calculator to complete the solutions, giving answers correct to two decimal places.

13. The length of a rectangle is 2 more than its width. If its area is 2, find its dimensions.
14. The length of a rectangle is 4 more than its width. If its area is 6, find its dimensions.

----

15. $4x^2 + 4x = 1$ 16. $9x^2 - 6x = 2$

17. $3x^2 + 2x + 1 = 0$ 18. $4x^2 + 3x + 2 = 0$

19. The perimeter of a square is numerically 6 less than its area. Find the length of its side.
20. The area of a square is numerically 2 more than its perimeter. Find the length of its side.

SET II

1. $x^2 - 4x + 2 = 0$ 2. $4x^2 = 12x - 7$

3. $x^2 = \dfrac{3 - 5x}{2}$ 4. $\dfrac{x}{3} + \dfrac{1}{x} = \dfrac{7}{6}$

5. $\dfrac{2}{x} = \dfrac{3x}{x + 2} - 1$ 6. $3x^2 + 4 = 2x$

7. The perimeter of a square is numerically 3 more than its area. Find the length of its side.

8. A number is equal to the sum of its reciprocal and $\dfrac{2}{5}$. What is the number?

In Exercises 9 and 10, use Table I or a calculator to complete the solutions, giving answers correct to two decimal places.

9. $5x^2 + 4x = 3$

10. The length of a rectangle is 2 more than its width. If its area is 6, find its dimensions.

Chapter Summary

Quadratic Equations (Sec. 1301). A _quadratic equation_ is a polynomial equation whose highest-degree term is second-degree.

The General Form (Sec. 1301) of a quadratic equation is:
$$ax^2 + bx + c = 0$$
where a, b, and c are real numbers ($a \neq 0$)

Methods of Solving Quadratic Equations

1. Factoring   (1) Arrange in general form.
   (Sec. 1302)   (2) Factor the polynomial.
                      (3) Set each factor equal to zero
                           and solve for the letter.
                      (4) Check answers in original equation.

2. Formula   (1) Arrange in general form.
   (Sec. 1304)   (2) Substitute values of a, b, and c into

$$x = \frac{-b \pm \sqrt{b^2 - 4ac}}{2a} \cdot \begin{array}{l} \textit{Quadratic} \\ \textit{Formula} \end{array}$$

                      (3) Simplify the answers.

3. Incomplete quadratic (Sec. 1303)

   (a) When $c = 0$ Find the greatest common factor
                       (GCF), then solve by factoring.

   (b) When $b = 0$ (1) Write equation as $ax^2 = -c$.
                       (2) Divide both sides by a.
                       (3) Take square root of both sides
                            and simplify.
                       (4) There are two answers, $\pm$.

When the radicand is negative, the roots are not real numbers.
Such numbers are not discussed in this text.

REVIEW EXERCISES 1305. Solve the following quadratic equations
   by any convenient method.

SET I

1. $x^2 + x = 6$ 2. $x^2 = 3x + 10$

3. $x^2 - 25x = 0$ 4. $x^2 - 49x = 0$

5. $x^2 - 2x - 4 = 0$ 6. $x^2 - 4x + 1 = 0$

7. $x^2 = 5x$ 8. $x^2 = 7x$

9. $\dfrac{2x}{3} = \dfrac{3}{8x}$ 10. $\dfrac{3x}{5} = \dfrac{5}{12x}$

11. $\dfrac{x + 2}{3} = \dfrac{1}{x - 2} + \dfrac{2}{3}$ 12. $\dfrac{x + 2}{4} = \dfrac{2}{x + 2} + \dfrac{1}{2}$

13. $5(x + 2) = x(x + 5)$ 14. $3(x + 4) = x(x + 3)$

----

15. $\dfrac{2}{x} + \dfrac{x}{x + 1} = 5$ 16. $\dfrac{3}{x} - \dfrac{x}{x + 2} = 2$

17. $3x^2 + 2x + 1 = 0$ 18. $2x^2 - 3x + 4 = 0$

19. $(x + 5)(x - 2) = x(3 - 2x) + 2$

20. $(2x - 1)(3x + 5) = x(x + 7) + 4$

In Exercises 21 and 22, use Table I or a calculator to complete the solution, giving answers correct to two decimal places.

21. The length of a rectangle is 4 more than its width. Its area is 7. Find its dimensions.
22. The width of a rectangle is 6 less than its length. Its area is 6. Find its dimensions.

SET II

1. $x^2 + x = 12$ 2. $x^2 - 36 = 0$

3. $x^2 - 2x - 2 = 0$ 4. $x^2 = 11x$

5. $\dfrac{2x}{3} = \dfrac{3}{8x}$ 6. $\dfrac{x + 2}{4} = \dfrac{1}{x - 2} + 1$

7. $2(x + 1) = x(x - 4)$ 8. $\dfrac{3}{x} + \dfrac{x}{x - 1} = 2$

9. $3x^2 - x = 0$ 10. $4x^2 = 2x - 1$

11. One leg of a right triangle is 2 units longer than the other. The hypotenuse is $2\sqrt{2}$. Find the length of each leg.

CUMULATIVE REVIEW EXERCISES: CHAPTERS 1-12

1. Simplify. Write your answer using only positive exponents.

$$\left(\frac{18s^{-1}t^{-3}}{12s}\right)^{-2}$$

2. Find the product: $(2\sqrt{3} - 3)(4\sqrt{3} + 5)$

3. Divide and simplify.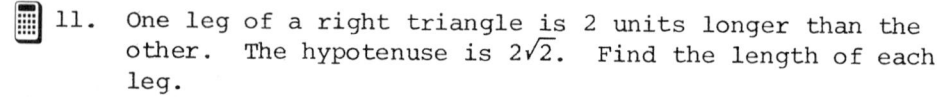

$$\frac{x^2 + 3x}{2x^2 + 7x + 5} \div \frac{x^2 - 9}{x^2 - 2x - 3}$$

4. Solve for x: $\dfrac{3x - 5}{4} + 2 = \dfrac{3 + 4x}{3}$

5. Solve by any convenient method: $\begin{cases} 3x + 4y = 3 \\ 2x - 5y = 25 \end{cases}$

6. Solve for x. $\sqrt{6x + 13} = 3$

7. Rationalize the denominator and simplify.

$$\frac{14}{3 - \sqrt{2}}$$

8. Find the sum: $5\sqrt{18} - 6\sqrt{\dfrac{9}{2}}$

9. Solve for x: $\sqrt{5x + 3} = 10x$

10. One leg of a right triangle is 2 cm more than the other. If the hypotenuse is 10 cm, find the length of the shorter leg.

Chapter Thirteen Diagnostic Test

Name_____

_____

The purpose of this test is to see how well you understand quadratic equations. We recommend that you work this diagnostic test *before* your instructor tests you on this chapter. Allow yourself about forty-five minutes to do this test.

Complete solutions for all the problems on this test, together with section references, are given in the Answer Section. We suggest that you study the sections referred to for the problems you do incorrectly.

Write each of the following quadratic equations in general form and identify a, b, and c in each equation.

1. $5x + 3x^2 = 7$

(1) _____ $\begin{cases} a = \text{_____} \\ b = \text{_____} \\ c = \text{_____} \end{cases}$
General form

2. $2(x + 1) = 3(2 - x^2)$

(2) _____ $\begin{cases} a = \text{_____} \\ b = \text{_____} \\ c = \text{_____} \end{cases}$
General form

Solve each of the following equations by factoring.

3. $x^2 + 3x = 10$

(3) _____

4. $6x^2 = 5 - 7x$

(4) _____

Solve each of the following equations.

5. $3x^2 = 12x$

(5) _____

6. $5x^2 = 20$

(6) _____

7. $x(x - 4) = x$

(7) _____

Use the quadratic formula $x = \dfrac{-b \pm \sqrt{b^2 - 4ac}}{2a}$ to solve each of the following equations.

8. $2x^2 - 5x - 3 = 0$

(8) _____

9. $2(x + 1) = x^2$

(9) _____

_____

10. The length of a rectangle is 5 more than its width.
    Its area is 36. Find its length and width.

(10) _____
     Equation used to solve problem

     Width_____

     Length_____

_____

APPENDIX 1

Sets

Ideas in all branches of mathematics, such as arithmetic, algebra, geometry, calculus, and statistics, can be explained in terms of sets. For this reason, you will find it helpful to have a basic understanding of sets. We have already used sets in the text and in writing answers and solutions for the exercises.

Basic Definitions

SET. A *set* is a collection of objects or things.

Example 1. Examples of sets.

    (a)   A 48-piece set of dishes
    (b)   A basket of birthday presents
    (c)   A basket containing an apple, a pillow, and a cat
    (d)   The number of students attending college in the United States
    (e)   The set of natural numbers

ELEMENT OF A SET. The objects or things that make up a set are called its *elements* (or *members*). Sets are usually represented by listing their elements within braces { } as we did in Sec. 101 when we described the set of natural numbers and the set of whole numbers.

Example 2. Examples showing the elements of sets.

    (a)   Set $\{1, 2, 3, \ldots\}$ has elements 1, 2, 3, and so on.
    (b)   Set $\{5, 7, 9\}$ has elements 5, 7, and 9.
    (c)   Set $\{a, d, f, h, k\}$ has elements a, d, f, h, and k.
    (d)   Set $\{$Ben, Kay, Frank, Albert$\}$ has elements Ben, Kay, Frank, and Albert.
    (e)   Set $\{\square, \Sigma, \Delta, \odot\}$ has elements $\square$, Σ, Δ, and $\odot$.

    It is sometimes helpful to think of the braces as a basket or box that contains the elements of the set. This basket, { }, may contain just a few elements, many elements, or no elements at all. A set is usually named by a capital letter, such as A, N, W, and so on. The expression "$A = \{1, 5, 7\}$" is read "A is the set whose elements are 1, 5, and 7."

ROSTER METHOD OF REPRESENTING A SET. A class roster is a list of the members of the class. When we represent a set by $\{3, 8, 9, 11\}$, we are representing the set by a roster (or list) of its members. This method of representing a set is called the *roster method*.

THE SYMBOL $\in$. The expression $2 \in A$ is read "2 is an element of set A" (or "2 is a member of set A"). If $A = \{2, 3, 4,\}$, we can say: $2 \in A$, $3 \in A$, and $4 \in A$. If we wish to show that a number or object is *not* a member of a given set, we use the symbol $\notin$, which is read "is not an element of" or "is not a member of." If $A = \{2, 3, 4\}$, then $5 \notin A$, which is read "5 is not an element of set A." To help you remember this symbol, notice that $\in$ looks like the first letter of the word *element*.

Example 3. Examples showing the use of $\in$ and $\notin$.

(a) If $B = \{5, 9\}$, then $5 \in B$, $9 \in B$, $3 \notin B$, and $1 \notin B$.
(b) If $C = \{b, e, g, m\}$, then $g \in C$, $e \in C$, and $k \notin C$.
(c) If $D = \{$Abe, Helen, John$\}$, then Helen $\in D$ but Mary $\notin D$.

CARDINAL NUMBER OF A SET. The cardinal number of a set is the number of elements in that set. The symbol $n(A)$ is read "the cardinal number of set A" and means the number of elements in set A. When the set is represented by the roster method, its cardinal number is found by counting its elements.

Example 4. Examples of the cardinal number of a set.

(a) If $A = \{5, 8, 6, 9\}$, then $n(A) = 4$.
(b) If $H = \{$Ed, Mabel$\}$, then $n(H) = 2$.
(c) If $Q = \{a, h, l, s, t, v\}$, then $n(Q) = 6$.
(d) If $E = \{2, 4, 3, 2\}$, then $n(E) = 3$. The cardinal number is 3 instead of 4 because the set has only 3 *different* elements.

EQUAL SETS. Two sets are equal if they both have exactly the same members.

Example 5. Examples of equal sets and unequal sets.

(a) $\{1, 5, 7\} = \{5, 1, 7\}$. Notice that both sets have exactly the same elements, even though they are not listed in the same order.
(b) $\{1, 5, 5, 5\} = \{5, 1\}$. Notice that both sets have exactly the same elements. It is not necessary to write the same element more than once when writing the roster of a set.
(c) $\{7, 8, 11\} \neq \{7, 11\}$. These sets are not equal because they both do not have exactly the same elements.

THE EMPTY SET (OR NULL SET). If we think of the braces $\{\ \}$ as a basket, then the set $A = \{1, 5, 7\}$ has three elements in its basket: 1, 5, and 7. Set $B = \{1, 5\}$ has two elements in its basket, and set $C = \{5\}$ has only one element. Set $D = \{\ \}$ is empty, having no elements in its basket. A set having no elements is called the *empty set* (or *null set*). We use symbols $\{\ \}$ or $\emptyset$ to represent the empty set. Whenever either symbol appears, read it as "the empty set."

Example 6. Examples of the empty set.

(a) The set of all people in this classroom who are 10 ft tall $= \emptyset$.
(b) The set of all digits that are greater than 10 $= \{\ \}$.

A word of caution

$\phi = \{\ \}$ has *no* elements
$\{\phi\}$ has *one* element, ϕ; therefore, $\{\phi\} \neq \{\ \}$.
$\{0\}$ has *one* element, 0; therefore, $\{0\} \neq \{\ \}$.

also $\phi \neq \{\phi\}$ and $\phi \neq \{0\}$, for the same reason.

UNIVERSAL SET. A *universal set* is a set containing all the
elements being considered in a particular problem. We
use the symbol U to represent the universal set under
consideration.

Example 7.

(a) Suppose we are going to consider only digits.
     Then $U = \{0, 1, 2, 3, 4, 5, 6, 7, 8, 9\}$, since
     U contains *all* digits.
(b) Suppose we are going to consider whole numbers.
     Then $U = \{0, 1, 2, 3, \ldots\}$, since U contains *all*
     whole numbers.
(c) Suppose we are going to consider sets of football
     players at ELAC in 1978. Then U is the set of
     football players at ELAC in 1978.
(d) Suppose we are going to consider different sets
     of cats. Then U is the set of *all* cats.

Notice that there can be different universal sets.
We might want to consider the set of all students in this
class as the universal set if we were going to deal only
with class members. On the other hand, we might use the
set of all 50 of the United States as our universal set
if we were going to consider only sets of states.

FINITE SET. If in counting the elements of a set the counting comes to an end, the set is called a *finite set*. This
means that the number of elements in a finite set must be
a particular whole number (which we call its cardinal
number).

Example 8. Examples of Finite Sets.

(a) $A = \{5, 9, 10, 13\}$. $n(A) = 4$.
(b) D = the set of digits. $n(D) = 10$.
(c) C = the set of whole numbers less than 100.
     $n(C) = 100$.
(d) $\emptyset = \{\ \}$. $n(\emptyset) = 0$.

INFINITE SET. If in counting the elements of a set the
counting never comes to an end, the set is called an
infinite set. A set is infinite if it is not finite.
The cardinal number of an infinite set is not a whole
number.

Example 9. Examples of Infinite Sets.

(a) $N = \{1, 2, 3, \ldots\}$
(b) $W = \{0, 1, 2, 3, \ldots\}$
(c) The set of all fractions.

EXERCISES 1

1. Can the collection $\{\square, X, =, 5\}$ be called a set?
2. Are $\{2, 7\}$ and $\{7, 2\}$ equal sets?
3. Are $\{2, 2, 7, 7\}$ and $\{7, 2\}$ equal sets?
4. Write the set of digits < 3 (see Sec. 101 for the
    meaning of $<$ and $>$).

5. Write the set of digits > 9.
6. Write the set of whole numbers < 3.
7. Write the set of whole numbers > 9.
8. Write the set of whole numbers > 4 and < 6.
9. Write the set of whole numbers > 4 and < 5.
10. Write the set of whole numbers < 4 and < 5.
11. Write all the elements of the set {2, a, 3}.
12. Write all the elements in the set of digits.
13. Write the cardinal number of each of the following sets:
    (a) {1, 1, 3, 5, 5, 5}
    (b) {0}
    (c) {a, b, g, x}
    (d) The set of whole numbers < 8.
    (e) ∅
14. The empty set has no elements. Therefore, the statement ∅ = { } is true.
    (a) The statement ∅ = {0} is not true. Explain.
    (b) The statement { } = {∅} is not true. Explain.
15. State which of the following sets are finite and which are infinite:
    (a) The set of digits.
    (b) The set of whole numbers.
    (c) The set of days in the week.
    (d) The set of books in the ELAC library.
    (e) The set of fish in all the seas of the earth at this instant.

16. State which of the following statements are true and which are false:
    (a) If A = {5, 11, 19}, then 11 ∈ A.
    (b) If B = {x, y, z, w}, then a ∉ B.
    (c) If C = {Ann, Bill, Charles}, then Dan ∈ C.
    (d) 0 ∈ ∅.
    (e) ∅ ∉ { }.
17. Given the universal set U = {7, 12, 15, 20, 23}:
    (a) Write the set of numbers < 15.
    (b) Write the set of numbers > 20.
18. Given the universal set U = {5, 7, 11, 14, 20}:
    (a) Write the set of numbers > 7 and < 14.
    (b) Write the set of numbers < 7 and < 20.

3 Subsets

DEFINITION. A set A is called a *subset* of set B if every member of A is also a member of B. "A is a subset of B" is written "$A \subseteq B$."

Example 1. Examples of subsets.

(a) A = {3, 5} is a subset of B = {3, 5, 7} because every member of A is also a member of B. Therefore, $A \subseteq B$.
(b) P = {a, c, g, f} is a subset of Q = {d, f, a, g, h, c} because every member of P is also a member of Q. Therefore, $P \subseteq Q$.
(c) X = {Joe, Betty} is a subset of Y = {Mary, Betty, Jack, Joe} because every member of X is also a member of Y. Therefore, $X \subseteq Y$.

(d) $D = \{4, 7\}$ is *not* a subset of $E = \{7, 8, 5\}$ because
     $4 \in D$, but $4 \notin E$. Therefore, $D \nsubseteq E$, read "D is not a
     subset of E."

(e) $K = \{d, f, m\}$ is *not* a subset of $L = \{f, m\}$ because
     $d \in K$, but $d \notin L$. Therefore, $K \nsubseteq L$, read "K is not
     a subset of L."

PROPER SUBSET.   Subset A is called a *proper subset* of B if
    there is at least one member of B that is not a member of
    subset A.   "A is a proper subset of B" is written "$A \subset B$."

Example 2. Examples of proper subsets.

(a) Subset $A = \{3, 5\}$ is a proper subset of
     $B = \{3, 5, 7\}$ because $7 \in B$, but $7 \notin A$. Therefore,
     $A \subset B$.

(b) Subset $X = \{$Joe, Betty$\}$ is a proper subset of
     $Y = \{$Mary, Betty, Jack, Joe$\}$ because Mary $\in Y$, but
     Mary $\notin X$. Therefore, $X \subset Y$.

IMPROPER SUBSET.   Subset A is called an *improper subset* of
    B if there is no member of B that is not also a
    member of A.

Example 3. Examples of improper subsets.

(a) Subset $A = \{10, 12\}$ is an improper subset of
     $B = \{12, 10\}$, because no member of B is not also
     a member of A. Note that $A = B$. This means that
     A is an improper subset of A. In other words, *any
     set is an improper subset of itself*. Therefore:

(b) D is an improper subset of D.

The empty set is a proper subset of every set except
itself.

ALL THE SUBSETS OF A SET.   By considering set $A = \{3, 5, 7\}$
    we find all its subsets are $\emptyset$, $\{3\}$, $\{5\}$, $\{7\}$, $\{3, 5\}$,
    $\{3, 7\}$, $\{5, 7\}$, $\{3, 5, 7\}$. Of these eight subsets, only
    $A = \{3, 5, 7\}$ is an improper subset of A; the seven others
    are proper subsets of A.

Example 4. Examples of subsets of a set.

(a) All the subsets of $\{6, 8\}$ are $\emptyset$, $\{6\}$, $\{8\}$, $\{6, 8\}$.
     Of these four subsets, only $\{6, 8\}$ is an improper
     subset.

(b) All the subsets of $\{a\}$ are $\emptyset$, $\{a\}$. Of these two
     subsets, only $\{a\}$ is an improper subset.

EXERCISES 2

1. $M = \{1, 2, 3, 4, 5\}$. State whether each of the follow-
    ing sets is a proper subset, an improper subset, or
    not a subset of M.

    (a) $A = \{3, 5\}$ (b) $B = \{0, 1, 7\}$
    (c) $\emptyset$ (d) $C = \{2, 4, 1, 3, 5\}$

2. $P = \{x, z, w, r, t, y\}$. State whether each of the
   following sets is a proper subset, an improper subset,
   or not a subset of P.

   (a) $D = \{x, y, r\}$ (b) P
   (c) $\emptyset$ (d) $E = \{x, y, z, s, t\}$

3. Write all the subsets of $\{R, G, Y\}$.
4. Write all the subsets of $\{\square, \triangle\}$.

3 Union and Intersection of Sets

<u>VENN DIAGRAMS</u>. A useful tool for helping you understand set
     concepts is the Venn diagram. A simple Venn diagram is
     shown in Fig. 3A.

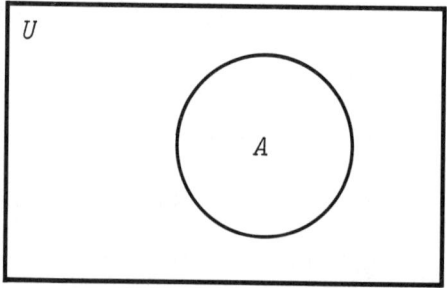

Figure 3A, Venn Diagram

It is customary to represent the universal set U by a
rectangle and the other sets by circles enclosed in the
U-rectangle. Just as we enclose all members of a particular set within braces in conventional set notation, in
Venn diagrams we think of all members of a set A as being
enclosed in a circle marked by the A. Using the same
reasoning, we see that all elements in the universe under
consideration are enclosed in the U-rectangle.

<u>UNION OF SETS</u>. The union of sets A and B, written $A \cup B$
     is the set that contains all the elements of A as well as
     all the elements of B.

In Fig. 3B, $A \cup B$ is represented by the shaded area.
In terms of set notation, suppose $A = \{b, c, g\}$ and
$B = \{1, 2, 5, 7\}$. Then $A \cup B = \{b, c, g, 1, 2, 5, 7\}$.

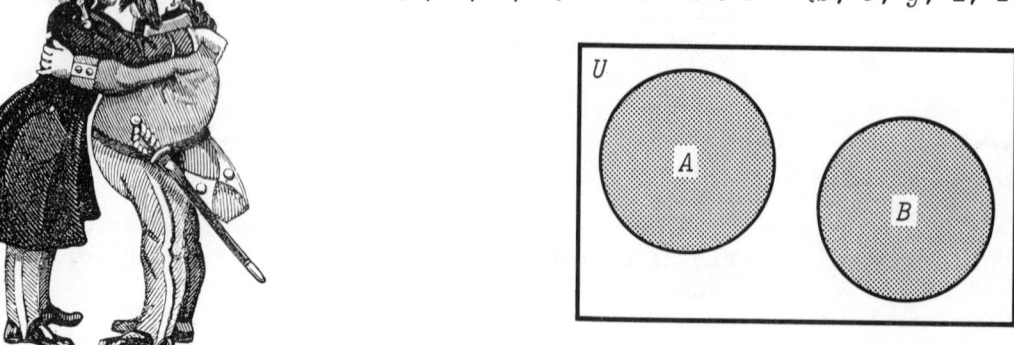

Figure 3B, $A \cup B$

You will notice in the illustration just given that no members of A and B are in both sets. When this is the case, the sets A and B are called *disjoint sets*.

Example 1. Examples of union of sets.

(a) If $C = \{x, y\}$ and $D = \{4\}$, then $C \cup D = \{x, y, 4\}$
(b) If $E = \{\text{Mary, Helen}\}$ and $G = \{\text{high, low}\}$, then
$E \cup G = \{\text{Mary, Helen, high, low}\}$.
(c) If $H = \{4, 8, 26\}$ and $K = \{15, 17\}$, then
$H \cup K = \{4, 8, 26, 15, 17\}$.
(d) If $S = \{2, 5, 9\}$ and $T = \{9, 2, 7\}$, then
$S \cup T = \{2, 5, 7, 9\}$.
(e) If $P = \{a, 4, 3, c\}$ and $Q = \{3, k, a\}$, then
$P \cup Q = \{a, 4, 3, c, k\}$.
(f) If $A = \{2, 3, 4\}$ and $B = \{ \}$, then
$A \cup B = \{2, 3, 4\} = A$.

INTERSECTION OF SETS. The intersection of sets C and D, written $C \cap D$, is the set that contains only elements in both C and D. Consider $C = \{g, f, m\}$ and $D = \{g, m, t, z\}$. Then $C \cap D = \{g, m\}$, because g and m are the only elements in both C and D. In the Venn diagram (Fig. 3C) the shaded area represents $C \cap D$ because that area lies in both circles.

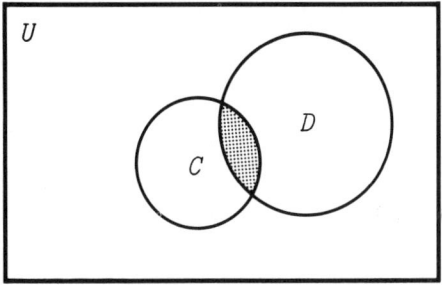

Figure 3C, $C \cap D$

To be certain you can distinguish between the union and intersection of sets, two Venn diagrams (Figs. 3D and 3E) are shown for the same sets, P and Q.

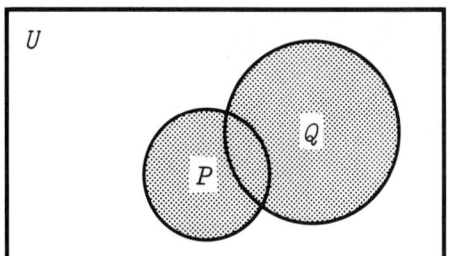

Shaded Area is $P \cup Q$
Figure 3D

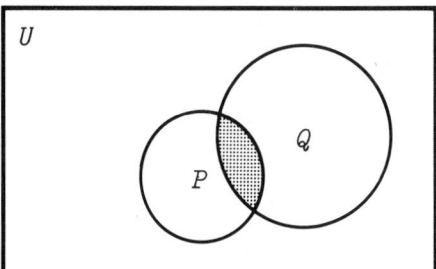

Shaded Area is $P \cap Q$
Figure 3E

Example 2.   Examples of intersection of sets.

(a)   If A = {John, Henry} and B = {Bill, Henry, Tom},
      then $A \cap B$ = {Henry} and $A \cup B$ = {John, Henry, Bill,
      Tom}.
(b)   If G = {1, 5, 7} and H = {2, 5, 6, 7, 8}, then
      $G \cap H$ = {5, 7} and $G \cup H$ = {1, 5, 7, 2, 6, 8}.
(c)   If K = {a, 6, b} and M = {c, 5, 4}, then
      $K \cap M$ = { } and $K \cup M$ = {a, 6, b, c, 5, 4}.

DISJOINT SETS.   Disjoint sets are sets whose intersection is
      the empty set.   A Venn diagram showing disjoint sets is
      Fig. 3B, in which sets A and B are disjoint.

Example 3.   Examples of disjoint sets.

(a)   If A = {1, 2} and B = {3, 4}, then $A \cap B$ = $\emptyset$.
      Therefore, A and B are disjoint sets.
(b)   If P = {a, b, c} and Q = {2, 8}, then $P \cap Q$ = $\emptyset$.
      Therefore, P and Q are disjoint sets.
(c)   If R = {5, 7, 9} and T = {9, 10, 12}, then
      $R \cap T$ = {9} $\neq \emptyset$.   Therefore, R and T are *not*
      disjoint sets.

EXERCISES 3

1.   Write the union and intersection of each pair of
     given sets:
     (a)   {1, 5, 7}, {2, 4}
     (b)   {a, b}, {x, y, z, a}
     (c)   { }, {k, 2}
     (d)   {river, boat}, {boat, streams, down}

2.   Given that A = {1, 3, 5, 7}, B = {2, 4, 6}, C = {1, 2,
     3, 4}, and D = {5, 6, 7}.   Find the following:
     (a) $A \cup B$ (b) $C \cup D$ (c) $A \cap B$ (d) $B \cap D$

3.   Given that A = {Bob, John}, B = {Charles, Tom, Bob},
     C = {Tom, John, Dick}, and D = {Ray, Bob}.   Find any
     two sets that are disjoint.

4.   Given the Venn diagram below, write each of the follow-
     ing sets in roster notation.   (The small letters within
     a particular circle in the diagram are elements of that
     set.)

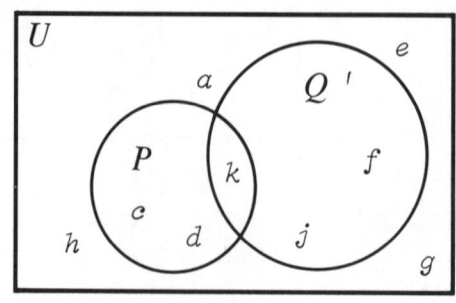

(a) P (b) Q (c) $P \cup Q$ (d) $P \cap Q$ (e) U

5. Given $X = \{2, 5, 6, 11\}$ and $Y = \{7, 5, 11, 13\}$.
   (a) Find $X \cap Y$.
   (b) Find $Y \cap X$.
   (c) Is $X \cap Y = Y \cap X$?

6. Given sets $K = \{a, 4, 7, b\}$, $L = \{m, 4, 6, b\}$, and $M = \{n, 4, 7, t\}$.
   (a) Write $K \cap L$ in roster notation.
   (b) Find $n(K \cap L)$.
   (c) Write $L \cup M$ in roster notation.
   (d) Find $n(L \cup M)$.

7. Shade in $A \cup B$ in the Venn diagram given here.

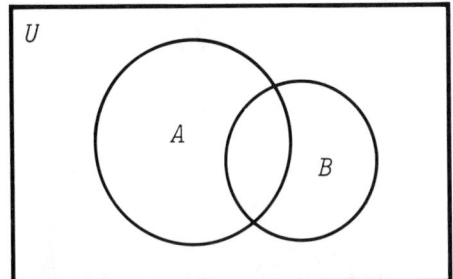

8. Shade in $P \cap Q$.

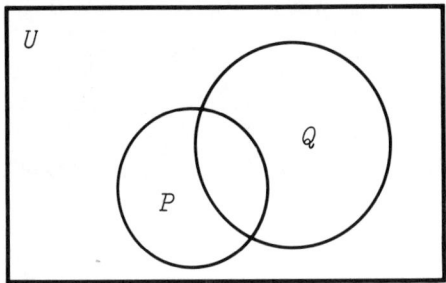

9. Write the name of the set representing the shaded area.

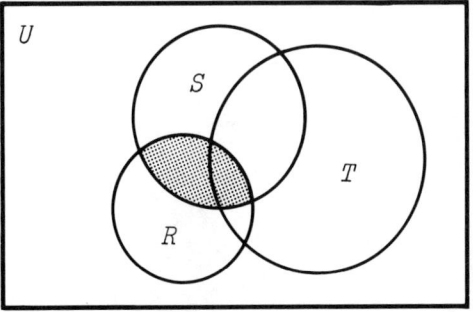

10. Write the name of the set representing the shaded area.

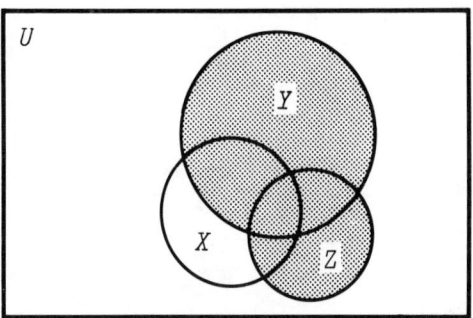

APPENDIX 2

Brief Review of Arithmetic

This brief review is given as an aid for those students who need to refresh their knowledge of arithmetic. For a more complete treatment, see C. L. Johnston and Alden T. Willis, *Essential Arithmetic*, *3rd Ed.* (Belmont, Calif.: Wadsworth Publishing Company, 1981.)

WHOLE NUMBERS. All whole numbers can be considered as decimals.

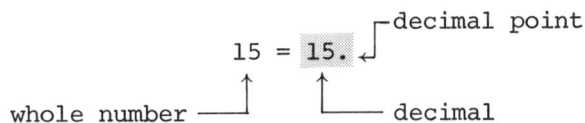

$$15 = 15.$$

Therefore, all operations with whole numbers can be done in the same way as the operations with decimals.

DECIMALS

Decimal Places. The number of decimal places in a number is the number of digits written to the right of the decimal point.

75.14 (2 decimal places)   1.086 (3 decimal places)

Approximately Equal. The symbol ≐ (read "approximately equal to") is used to show that two numbers are approximately equal to each other.

78 ≐ 80   is read "78 is approximately equal to 80."

π ≐ 3.14   is read "π is approximately equal to 3.14."

0.99 ≐ 1   is read "0.99 is approximately equal to 1."

Rounding Off

876. ≐ 880   rounded to tens
44.62 ≐ 44.6   rounded to 1 decimal place
36.50 ≐ 36.   rounded to units ⎫ When exactly in the middle,
35.50 ≐ 36.   rounded to units ⎬ round off so last digit is
⎭ even.
0.16504 ≐ 0.17   rounded to 2 decimal places.

Addition and Subtraction. Write the numbers with their decimal points in the same vertical line.

Add: 17.6 + 2.65 + 439 + 0.015

```
  17.6
   2.65
 439.
   0.015
 459.265
```

Subtract: 26.54 from 518.3

$$
\begin{array}{r}
5\,1\,8.3\,0 \\
2\,6.5\,4 \\
\hline
4\,9\,1.7\,6
\end{array}
$$

Multiplication. The number of decimal places in a product
is the sum of the number of decimal places in the numbers
being multiplied.

$$
\begin{array}{r}
5\,6.7\,5 \quad \text{(2 decimal places)} \\
3.8 \quad \text{(\underline{1} decimal place)} \\
\hline
4\,5\,4\,0\,0 \quad 3 \\
1\,7\,0\,2\,5 \\
\hline
2\,1\,5.6\,5\,0 \quad \text{(3 decimal places)}
\end{array}
$$

$$
\begin{array}{r}
1\,5\,6 \,|\, 0\,0 \\
7\,5 \,|\, 0\,0\,0 \\
7\,8\,0 \,| \\
1\,0\,9\,2 \qquad | \\
\hline
1,\,1\,7\,0,0 \,|\, 0\,0,0\,0\,0
\end{array}
$$

Division

$$
\begin{array}{r}
2\,4.8\,8 \doteq 24.9 \text{ Rounded to tenths.} \\
3.8_\wedge \overline{\smash)9\,4.5_\wedge6\,0} \\
7\,6 \\
\hline
1\,8\,5 \\
1\,5\,2 \\
\hline
3\,3\,6 \\
3\,0\,4 \\
\hline
3\,2\,0 \\
3\,0\,4 \\
\hline
1\,6
\end{array}
$$

Changing a Fraction to a Decimal. Divide the numerator by
the denominator.

$$
\frac{5}{12} = 1\,2\overline{\smash)5.0\,0\,0}
$$
$$
\begin{array}{r}
0.4\,1\,6 \doteq 0.42 \text{ Rounded to 2 decimal} \\
\text{places.} \\
4\,8 \\
\hline
2\,0 \\
1\,2 \\
\hline
8\,0 \\
7\,2 \\
\hline
8
\end{array}
$$

Changing a Decimal to a Fraction

$$
0.48 = 48 \text{ hundredths} = \frac{48}{100} = \frac{12}{25}
$$

To Multiply a Decimal by a Power of 10, move the decimal point
to the *right* as many places as the number of zeros in the
power of ten.

$$
23.4 \times 100 = 2340_{\overrightarrow{2}} \qquad 1.56 \times 10^3 = 1560_{\overrightarrow{3}}
$$

To Divide a Decimal by a Power of 10, move the decimal point
to the *left* as many places as the number of zeros in the
power of ten.

$$
\frac{72.8}{10} = 7.28_{\overleftarrow{1}} \qquad \frac{875}{10^2} = 8.75_{\overleftarrow{2}}
$$

ORDER OF OPERATIONS

A. If there are any parentheses in the expression, that part of the expression within a pair of parentheses is evaluated first, then the entire expression.

B. Any evaluation always proceeds in three steps:
1. Powers and roots are done in any order.
2. Multiplication and division are done in order from left to right.
3. Addition and subtraction are done in order from left to right.

(1) $12 \div 3 \times 4$
     $4 \quad \times 4 = 16$

(2) $4 \times 3^2 \div 6 - 2$
     $4 \times 9 \div 6 - 2$
     $\qquad 36 \div 6 - 2$
     $\qquad\quad 6 \quad - 2 = 4$

(3) $5(8 - 2) + 6(4)$
     $5(6) \qquad + 6(4)$
     $\quad 30 \qquad + \quad 24 = 54$

(4) $5\sqrt{16} \div 4 - 2$
     $5(4) \div 4 - 2$
     $\quad 20 \div 4 - 2$
     $\qquad 5 \quad - 2 = 3$

FRACTIONS

To Raise a Fraction to Higher Terms, multiply both numerator and denominator by the same number (not zero).

$$\frac{2}{3} = \frac{2 \cdot 2}{3 \cdot 2} = \frac{4}{6} \Rightarrow \frac{2}{3} \text{ and } \frac{4}{6} \text{ are called } \textit{equivalent fractions.}$$

To Reduce a Fraction to Lower Terms, divide both numerator and denominator by a number that is a divisor of both.

$$\frac{\overset{3}{\cancel{15}}}{\underset{15}{\cancel{75}}} = \frac{\overset{1}{\cancel{3}}}{\underset{5}{\cancel{15}}} = \frac{1}{5} \quad \begin{cases} \dfrac{15}{75} \text{ and } \dfrac{1}{5} \text{ are equivalent fractions.} \\[2em] \dfrac{1}{5} \text{ is } \dfrac{15}{75} \text{ reduced to } \textit{lowest terms.} \end{cases}$$

To Change an Improper Fraction into a Mixed Number, divide the numerator by the denominator and express the remainder as a fraction.

$$\frac{17}{3} = 3\overline{)17} \quad \overset{5 \quad R2}{} = 5\frac{2}{3}$$

To Change a Mixed Number into an Improper Fraction

$$\frac{\text{whole number} \times \text{denominator} + \text{numerator}}{\text{denominator}}$$

$$2\frac{3}{5} = \frac{2 \times 5 + 3}{5} = \frac{10 + 3}{5} = \frac{13}{5}$$

<u>Adding</u>

$$\frac{3}{8} = \frac{9}{24}$$

$$+\frac{5}{6} = \frac{20}{24}$$

$$\frac{29}{24} = 1\frac{5}{24}$$

$$
\begin{array}{c|cc}
2 & 8 & 6 \\
\hline
 & 4 & 3
\end{array}
$$

$$\text{LCD} = 2 \cdot 4 \cdot 3$$
$$= 24$$

<u>Subtracting</u>

$$13\frac{1}{2} = 13\frac{3}{6} = 12 + 1 + \frac{3}{6} = 12 + \frac{6}{6} + \frac{3}{6} = 12\frac{9}{6}$$

$$-9\frac{2}{3} = -9\frac{4}{6} \qquad\qquad\qquad\qquad = -9\frac{4}{6}$$

$$3\frac{5}{6}$$

<u>Multiplying</u>

$$\overset{2}{\cancel{6}} \times \overset{2}{\cancel{14}} = \frac{4}{5}$$
$$\underset{1}{\cancel{7}} \quad \underset{5}{\cancel{15}}$$

<u>Dividing</u>

$$\frac{5}{8} \div 3\frac{3}{4} = \frac{5}{8} \div \frac{15}{4} = \overset{1}{\cancel{5}} \times \overset{1}{\cancel{4}} = \frac{1}{6}$$
$$\qquad\qquad\qquad\qquad \underset{2}{\cancel{8}} \quad \underset{3}{\cancel{15}}$$

<u>To Simplify a Complex Fraction</u>, divide the numerator of the complex fraction by the denominator.

$$\frac{\dfrac{5}{12}}{\dfrac{15}{16}} = \frac{5}{12} \div \frac{15}{16} = \overset{1}{\cancel{5}} \times \overset{4}{\cancel{16}} = \frac{4}{9}$$
$$\qquad\qquad\qquad\quad \underset{3}{\cancel{12}} \quad \underset{3}{\cancel{15}}$$

$$\frac{3 - \dfrac{1}{5}}{\dfrac{1}{3} + \dfrac{1}{5}} = \frac{\dfrac{15}{5} - \dfrac{1}{5}}{\dfrac{5}{15} + \dfrac{3}{15}} = \frac{\dfrac{14}{5}}{\dfrac{8}{15}} = \frac{14}{5} \div \frac{8}{15} = \overset{7}{\cancel{14}} \times \overset{3}{\cancel{15}} = \frac{21}{4} = 5\frac{1}{4}$$
$$\qquad\qquad\qquad\qquad\qquad\qquad\qquad\qquad\qquad \underset{1}{\cancel{5}} \quad \underset{4}{\cancel{8}}$$

EXERCISES 4

In Exercises 1-4, reduce each fraction to lowest terms.

1. $\dfrac{6}{9}$ 　　　2. $\dfrac{12}{20}$ 　　　3. $\dfrac{49}{24}$ 　　　4. $\dfrac{210}{240}$

In Exercises 5-8, change each improper fraction into a mixed number and reduce if possible.

5. $\dfrac{5}{2}$ 　　　6. $\dfrac{11}{8}$ 　　　7. $\dfrac{47}{25}$ 　　　8. $\dfrac{78}{33}$

In Exercises 9-12, change each mixed number into an improper fraction.

9. $3\frac{7}{8}$ 10. $2\frac{7}{9}$ 11. $2\frac{5}{6}$ 12. $8\frac{3}{5}$

In Exercises 13-38, perform the indicated operation.

13. $\frac{2}{3} + \frac{1}{4}$ 14. $\frac{2}{7} + \frac{3}{14}$ 15. $\frac{7}{10} - \frac{2}{5}$

16. $\frac{3}{4} - \frac{2}{5}$ 17. $\frac{3}{16} \times \frac{20}{9}$ 18. $\frac{6}{35} \times \frac{15}{8}$

19. $\frac{4}{3} \div \frac{8}{9}$ 20. $\frac{5}{2} \div \frac{5}{8}$ 21. $2\frac{2}{3} + 1\frac{3}{5}$

22. $3\frac{1}{4} + 4\frac{1}{2}$ 23. $5\frac{4}{5} - 3\frac{7}{10}$ 24. $4\frac{5}{6} - 2\frac{2}{3}$

25. $4\frac{1}{5} \times 2\frac{1}{7}$ 26. $2\frac{1}{3} \times 4\frac{1}{2}$ 27. $2\frac{2}{5} \div 1\frac{1}{15}$

28. $2\frac{1}{4} \div 3\frac{3}{8}$ 29. $\dfrac{\frac{5}{8}}{\frac{5}{6}}$ 30. $\dfrac{\frac{3}{5}}{\frac{6}{5}}$

31. Add 34.5 + 1.74 + 18 + 0.016.
32. Add 74.1 + 19 + 1.55 + 0.095.
33. Subtract 34.67 from 356.4.
34. Subtract 81.94 from 418.5.
35. 100×7.45
36. 1000×3.54

37. $\dfrac{46.8}{100}$

38. $\dfrac{89.5}{1000}$

In Exercises 39-42, perform the indicated operations. Then round off your answer to the indicated place.

39. 70.9×94.78 (1 decimal place)
40. 40.8×68.59 (1 decimal place)
41. $6.007 \div 7.25$ (2 decimal places)
42. $8.009 \div 4.67$ (2 decimal places)

43. Change $5\frac{3}{4}$ to a decimal.

44. Change $4\frac{3}{5}$ to a decimal.

45. Change 0.65 to a fraction.
46. Change 0.25 to a fraction.
47. Change 5.9 to a mixed number.
48. Change 4.3 to a mixed number.

Answers

EXERCISES 101, SET I   (page 6)

1. 5   2. 5   3. 1   4. 0
5. 9   6. 99   7. 15, 16
8. 0, 1, 2, 3, 4   9. 10   10. 100
11. 8 > 7   12. 0 < 1
13. Yes 14. Yes   15. 0   16. 0
17. 7, seven   18. 60, sixty
19. Yes 20. Yes   21. 3   22. 4

EXERCISES 102, SET I   (page 9)

1. Minus seventy-five or negative seventy-five
2. Minus forty-nine or negative forty-nine
3. -54   4. -109
5. -2 because it is to the right of -4 on
   the number line.
6. 0   7. -62   8. -45° F   9. -1
10. It cannot be found.
11. >, zero is to the right of -3 on the
    number line.
12. >
13. <, -5 is to the left of 2 on the number
    line.
14. <
15. -5, -5 is to the right of -10 on the
    number line.
16. -15   17. -9, -8, -7
18. -1, 0, 1, 2

EXERCISES 103, SET I   (page 14)

1. Since they have the same sign,   2. 8
   add their absolute values:
   4 + 5 = 9
   Sum has the same sign: +
   Therefore, the sum is 9.

3. Since they have the same sign,   4. -8
   add their absolute values:
   3 + 4 = 7
   Sum has the same sign: -
   Therefore, the sum is -7.

5. Since they have different signs,   6. -5
   subtract their absolute values:
   6 - 5 = 1
   Sum has sign of number with
   larger absolute value: -
   Therefore, the sum is -1.

7. Since their signs are different,   8. 5
   subtract their absolute values:
   7 - 3 = 4
   Sum has the sign of the number
   with larger absolute value: +
   Therefore, the sum is 4.

9. Since their signs are different,   10. 12
   subtract their absolute values:
   15 - 5 = 10
   Sum has sign of number with
   larger absolute value: +
   Therefore, sum is 10.

11. Since they have the same sign,   12. -54
    add their absolute values:
    27 + 13 = 40
    Sum has the same sign: -
    Therefore, the sum is -40.

13. Since their signs are different,   14. 65
    subtract their absolute values:
    121 - 80 = 41
    Sum has sign of number with
    larger absolute value: +
    Therefore, sum is 41.

15. Since their signs are different,   16. 105
    subtract their absolute values:
    105 - 73 = 32
    Sum has sign of number with
    larger absolute value: +
    Therefore, sum is 32.

17. Since they have the same sign,   18. 56
    add their absolute values:
    15 + 21 = 36
    Sum has same sign: +
    Therefore, the sum is 36.

19. $|-6| = 6$. The absolute value   20. 3
    of a number is never negative.
    Thus $|-6| + (-2)$
        = (6) + (-2) the signs are
    unlike, we find the difference
    in their absolute values:
    6 - 2 = 4
    Sum has sign of number with
    larger absolute value: +
    Therefore, sum is 4.

21. Since the signs are different,   22. 88.373
    subtract their absolute values:
    6.075 - 3.146 = 2.929
    Sum has sign of number with
    larger absolute value: +
    Therefore, the sum is 2.929.

23. Since they have different signs,   24. 17° F
    subtract their absolute values:
    53 - 35 = 18
    Sum has sign of number with
    larger absolute value: +
    Therefore, the sum is 18° F.

EXERCISES 104, SET I   (page 17)

1. (10) - (4)   (10)   2. 7
   = (10) + (-4)   + (-4)
   = 6   +6

3. (-3) - (-2)   (-3)   4. -1
   = (-3) + (+2)   + (+2)
   = -1   -1

5. (-6) - (+2)   (-6)   6. -13
   = (-6) + (-2)   + (-2)
   = -8   -8

7. (9) - (-5)   (9)   8. 10
   = (9) + (+5)   + (+5)
   = 14   14

9. (2) - (-7)   (2)   10. 8
   = (2) + (+7)   + (7)
   = 9   9

11. (-15) - (11)   (-15)   12. -40
    = (-15) + (-11) + (-11)
    = -26   -26

13. (+5) - (-2)   (+5)   14. -5
    = (+5) + (+2)   + (+2)
    = 7   7

15. (156) - (-97)   (156)   16. 373
    = (156) + (+97) + (97)
    = 253   253

17. (-354) - (-286) (-354)   18. -109
    = (-354) + (+286) + (+286)
    = -68   -68

19. ($473.29) - ($238.43)   20. $578.89
    = (473.29) + (-238.43)
    = $234.86

21. $(356) - (184)$
    $= (356) + (-184)$
    $= 172$

$\begin{array}{r} (\ 356) \\ +\ (-184) \\ \hline 172 \end{array}$

22. 64

23. $\left(-5\frac{1}{4}\right) - \left(2\frac{1}{2}\right)$

$\begin{array}{r} \left(-5\frac{1}{4}\right) \\ +\ \left(-2\frac{2}{4}\right) \\ \hline -7\frac{3}{4} \end{array}$

$= \left(-5\frac{1}{4}\right) + \left(-2\frac{1}{2}\right)$

$= -7\frac{3}{4}$

24. $-10\frac{1}{2}$

25. $(-7.000) - (-2.009)$
    $= (-7.000) + (+2.009)$
    $= -4.991$

$\begin{array}{r} (-7.000) \\ +\ (+2.009) \\ \hline -4.991 \end{array}$

26. -7.72

27. $42 - (-7)$
    $= 42 + (+7)$
    $= 49$

$\begin{array}{r} (42) \\ +\ (-7) \\ \hline 49 \end{array}$

28. $43.1°$ F

   Therefore, the rise in
   temperature was 49° F.

29. Find the sum of the two negative numbers: $\begin{array}{r} -141 \\ -\ 68 \\ \hline \end{array}$

   Altitude $= \overline{-209}$ ft

30. 9800 ft

31. $(29,028) - (-36,198)$
    $= (29,028) + (+36,198)$
    $= 65,226$ ft

$\begin{array}{r} (29,028) \\ +\ (36,198) \\ \hline 65,226 \end{array}$

   (This is 12.35 miles)

32. 3997 ft

EXERCISES 105, SET I (page 21)

1. $3(-2) = -(3 \times 2)$
   $= -6$

2. -24

3. $(-5)(2) = -(5 \times 2)$
   $= -10$

4. -35

5. $(-8)(-2) = +(8 \times 2)$
   $= 16$

6. 42

7. $8(-4) = -(8 \times 4)$
   $= -32$

8. -45

9. $(-7)(9) = -(7 \times 9)$
   $= -63$

10. -48

11. $(-10)(-10) = +(10 \times 10)$
    $= 100$

12. 81

13. $(8)(-7) = -(8 \times 7)$
    $= -56$

14. -72

15. $(-26)(10) = -(26 \times 10)$
    $= -260$

16. -132

17. $(-20)(-10) = +(20 \times 10)$
    $= 200$

18. 600

19. $(75)(-15) = -(75 \times 15)$
    $= -1125$

20. -1118

21. $(-30)(5) = -(30 \times 5)$
    $= -150$

22. -300

23. $(-7)(-20) = +(7 \times 20)$
    $= 140$

24. 360

25. $(-3.5)(-1.4) = +(3.5 \times 1.4)$
    $= 4.90$

26. 7.52

27. $(2.74)(-100) = -(2.74 \times 100)$
    $= -274$

28. -304

29. $\left(2\frac{1}{3}\right)\left(-3\frac{1}{2}\right) = \left(\frac{7}{3}\right)\left(-\frac{7}{2}\right)$
    $= -\frac{49}{6} = -8\frac{1}{6}$

30. $13\frac{13}{20}$

EXERCISES 106, SET I, (page 23)

1. 2   Positive because numbers have same signs.
2. 3
3. -4 Negative because numbers have different signs.
4. -2
5. -5 Negative because numbers have different signs.
6. -2
7. 2   Positive because numbers have same signs.
8. 5
9. -5 Negative because numbers have different signs.
10. -6
11. -4 Negative because numbers have different signs.
12. -5
13. 3   Positive because numbers have same sign.
14. 3
15. -3 Negative because signs are unlike.
16. -4
17. 9   Positive because signs are the same.
18. 7
19. -15 Negative because numbers have different signs.
20. -2.5
21. -3 Negative because numbers have different signs.
22. -7
23. -3 Negative because numbers have different signs.
24. -3

25. $\frac{-15}{6} = \frac{-5}{2} = -2\frac{1}{2}$

26. $-2\frac{1}{4}$

27. $\frac{7.5}{-0.5} = \frac{75}{-5} = \frac{15}{-1} = -15$

28. -5

29. $\frac{-6.3}{-0.9} = \frac{-63}{-9} = 7$

30. 8

31. $\frac{-367}{100} = -3.67$

32. -4.86

33. $\frac{78.5}{-96.5} \doteq -0.81$

34. $\doteq -1.17$

35. $\frac{2\frac{1}{2}}{-5} = \left(2\frac{1}{2}\right) \div (-5) = \left(\frac{5}{2}\right) \div \left(\frac{-5}{1}\right) = \frac{5}{2} \cdot \left(\frac{1}{-5}\right) = -\frac{1}{2}$

36. $-\frac{1}{5}$

EXERCISES 108, SET I (page 29)

1. True, because of the Commutative Property of Addition. (Order of numbers changed.)
2. True. Commutative Property of Addition.
3. True. Associative Property of Addition. (Grouping changed.)
4. True. Associative Property of Addition.
5. $6 - 2 \overset{?}{=} 2 - 6$
   $4 \neq -4$
   False. Commutative Property does not hold for subtraction.
6. False. Subtraction is not commutative.
7. True. Associative Property of Multiplication.
8. True. Associative Property of Multiplication.
9. $8 \div 4 \overset{?}{=} 4 \div 8$

   $2 \neq \frac{1}{2}$

   False. Commutative Property does not hold for division.
10. False. Commutative Property does not hold for division.
11. True. Commutative Property of Multiplication.
12. True. Commutative Property of Multiplication.
13. False. $(4)(-5) \overset{?}{=} (-5) + (4)$
    $-20 \neq -1$

14. False. $-14 \neq -5$
15. True. Commutative Property of Addition.
16. True. Commutative Property of Addition.
17. True. Commutative Property of Addition.
18. True. Commutative Property of Addition.
19. True. Associative and Commutative Properties of Addition.
20. True. Both the Commutative Property of Multiplication and the Associative Property of Multiplication were used.
21. False. Subtraction is not commutative.
22. False. Subtraction is not commutative.
23. True. Associative Property of Multiplication. (Grouping changed.)
24. True. Associative Property of Multiplication. (Grouping changed.)
25. True. Commutative Property of Addition. (Order changed.)
26. True. Commutative Property of Addition. (Order changed.)

EXERCISES 109, SET I   (page 32)

1. 0
2. 0
3. 4
4. 9
5. -6
6. -10
7. 0
8. 0
9. 11
10. 10
11. Not possible
12. Not possible
13. 0
14. 0
15. Cannot be determined
16. Cannot be determined
17. -789
18. -546
19. Not possible
20. Not possible.

EXERCISES 110, SET I (page 34)

1. $3^3 = 3 \cdot 3 \cdot 3 = 27$
2. 16
3. $(-5)^2 = (-5)(-5) = 25$
4. -216
5. $7^2 = 7 \cdot 7 = 49$
6. 81
7. $0^3 = 0 \cdot 0 \cdot 0 = 0$
8. 0
9. $(-10)^1 = -10$
10. 100
11. $10^3 = 10 \cdot 10 \cdot 10 = 1000$
12. 10,000
13. $(-10)^5 = (-10)(-10)(-10)(-10)(-10)$
    $= -100,000$
14. 1,000,000
15. $2^4 = 2 \cdot 2 \cdot 2 \cdot 2 = 16$
16. 32
17. $(-2)^6 = (-2)(-2)(-2)(-2)(-2)(-2)$
    $= 64$
18. -128
19. $2^8 = 2 \cdot 2 \cdot 2 \cdot 2 \cdot 2 \cdot 2 \cdot 2 \cdot 2$
    $= 256$
20. 625
21. $40^3 = 40 \cdot 40 \cdot 40 = 64,000$
22. 0
23. $(-12)^3 = (-12)(-12)(-12)$
    $= -1728$
24. 225
25. $(-1)^5 = (-1)(-1)(-1)(-1)(-1)$
    $= -1$
26. -1
27. $-2^2 = -(2 \cdot 2) = -4$
28. -9
29. $(-1)^{99} = -1$
30. $(-1)^{98} = 1$
31. 161.29
32. 237.16

EXERCISES 112A, SET I (page 36)

1. 4
   because $4^2 = 16$
2. 5
3. $-\sqrt{4} = -(\sqrt{4}) = -(2) = -2$
4. -3
5. 9
   because $9^2 = 81$
6. 6
7. 10
   because $10^2 = 100$
8. 12
9. $-\sqrt{81} = -(\sqrt{81}) = -(9) = -9$
10. -11
11. 8
    because $8^2 = 64$
12. 13

EXERCISES 112B, SET I, (page 37)

1. Try 15: $15^2 = 225$, therefore, 15 is too small.
   Try 16: $16^2 = 256$, therefore, $\sqrt{256} = 16$.
2. 19
3. Try 25: $25^2 = 625$, therefore, 25 is too large.
   Try 22: $22^2 = 484$, therefore, 22 is too large.
   Try 21: $21^2 = 441$, therefore, $\sqrt{441} = 21$.
4. 25
5. Try 18: $18^2 = 324$, therefore, 18 is too large.
   Try 17: $17^2 = 289$, therefore, $\sqrt{289} = 17$.
6. 18
7. If the number we are taking the square root of is an odd number, then its square root must be an odd number.
   Try 29: $29^2 = 841$, therefore, 29 is too large.
   Try 27: $27^2 = 729$, therefore, $\sqrt{729} = 27$.
8. 36

EXERCISES 112C, SET I   (page 38)

1. Locate 13 in the N column, then read $\sqrt{13} = 3.606$ immediately to the right of 13 in the $\sqrt{N}$ column.
2. 4.243
3. Locate 37 in the N column, then read $\sqrt{37} = 6.083$ immediately to the right of 37 in the $\sqrt{N}$ column.
4. 7.071
5. Locate 79 in the N column, then read $\sqrt{79} = 8.888$ to the right of 79 in the $\sqrt{N}$ column.
6. 7.746
7. Locate 86 in the N column, then read $\sqrt{86} = 9.274$ to the right of 86 in the $\sqrt{N}$ column.
8. 9.592

EXERCISES 112D, SET I   (page 40)

1. By trial, we find: $2^3 = 2 \cdot 2 \cdot 2 = 8$;
   $3^3 = 3 \cdot 3 \cdot 3 = 27$;
   $4^3 = 4 \cdot 4 \cdot 4 = 64$
   Therefore, $\sqrt[3]{64} = 4$.
2. 3
3. 3 (See the trial in the solution for Exercise 1.)
4. 5
5. -3
   because $(-3)(-3)(-3) = -27$
6. -5
7. $-\sqrt[4]{1} = -(\sqrt[4]{1}) = -(1) = -1$
8. 2
9. -5
   because $(-5)(-5)(-5) = -125$
10. -2
11. Not a real number
12. Not a real number
13. -10
    because $(-10)(-10)(-10) = -1000$
14. -4
15. -1
    Any odd root of -1 is -1.
16. -2
17. 3
    because $3 \cdot 3 \cdot 3 \cdot 3 = 81$
18. 6
19. Not a real number
20. Not a real number

1. 8, 9   2. 0, 1, 2   3. 99
4. 10   5. -9   6. -1
7. (a) 12, 13, 14
    (b) -2, -1, 0, 1, 2
    (c) -20, -19, -18
8. (a) 18, 19
    (b) -3, -2, -1, 0, 1
    (c) -17, -16, -15
9. Since they have different signs,   10. -1
    subtract their absolute values:
    3 - 2 = 1
    Sum has same sign as number
    with larger absolute value: +
    Therefore, sum is 1.
11. 3. Positive because numbers   12. 2
         have same sign.
13. $(-5) - (-3)$ (-5) 14. -5
     $= (-5) + (+3)$ $\underline{+ \ (\ 3)}$
     $= -2$ -2
15. $(+5) - |-2|$ $(\ 5)$ 16. 5
     $= (+5) - (2)$ $\underline{+ \ (-2)}$
     $= (+5) + (-2)$ 3
     $= 3$
17. 12. Positive because both   18. 20
          numbers have same sign.
19. $-3^2 = -(+3^2) = -(+9) = -9$ 20. -16
21. $(-10) - (-6)$ (-10) 22. 3
     $= (-10) + (+6)$ $\underline{+ \ (\ +6)}$
     $= -4$ -4
23. -3. Negative because they   24. -3
          have unlike signs.
25. $0^3 = 0 \cdot 0 \cdot 0 = 0$ 26. 0
27. $(-5)^2 = (-5)(-5) = 25$ 28. 16
29. Since they have the same sign,   30. -11
     find sum of their absolute values:
     10 + 2 = 12
     Sum has same sign: -
     Therefore, the sum is -12.
31. -24. Negative because numbers   32. -35
           have opposite signs.
33. 5.   Positive because both numbers   34. 8
           have the same sign.
35. 0.   Zero divided by any number   36. 0
           other than zero is zero.
37. 6   38. 8
     because $6^2 = 36$
39. $-2^4 = -(2 \cdot 2 \cdot 2 \cdot 2)$ 40. -64
     $= -(16) = -16$
41. $\sqrt[3]{-8} = -2$ 42. -4
     because $(-2)^3 = (-2)(-2)(-2) = -8$
43. 0. Zero times any number is zero.   44. 0
45. -5. Negative because signs   46. -7
          are unlike.
47. 12.369
48. 13.601
49. (a) True. Associative Property of
              Multiplication.
     (b) True. Commutative Property of Addition.
     (c) False. 5 - (-2) = 5 + 2 = 7
              (-2) - 5 = (-2) + (-5) = -7
     (d) True. Associative Property of Addition.
     (e) True. Commutative Property of
              Multiplication.
     (f) True. Commutative Property of Addition.

50. (a) True. Associative Property of
              Multiplication.
     (b) True. Commutative Property of Addition.
     (c) False.
     (d) True. Associative Property of Addition.
     (e) True. Commutative Property of
              Multiplication.

CHAPTER ONE DIAGNOSTIC TEST (page 45)

Following each problem number is the textbook section
reference (in parentheses) where that kind of problem
is discussed.

1. (101) <   2. (101) >
3. (101) <   4. (101) 99
5. (101) -9   6. (101) 0, 1, 2
7. (102) negative thirty-five
           or minus thirty-five
8. (103) $(38) - (-20)$ $(\ 38)$
           $= (38) + (+20)$ $\underline{+ \ (+20)}$
           $= 58$ 58
           Therefore, the rise in temperature
           was $58°$ F.
9. (103; 105) False, because
                $(-9)(3) \stackrel{?}{=} (3) + (-9)$
                $-27 \neq -6$
10. (108) True. Associative Property of Addition.
11. (107) True. Commutative Property of
                   Multiplication.
12. (103) -4
13. (104) $20 - (-10)$ (20)
            $= 20 + (+10)$ $\underline{+ \ (10)}$
            $= 30$ 30
14. (105) 50
15. (106) -3   16. (110) 36
17. (103) 3   18. (109) 0
19. (104) $(-10) - (+5)$ (-10)
            $= (-10) + (-5)$ $\underline{+ \ (\ -5)}$
            $= -15$ -15
20. (109) Not possible
21. (105) -40   22. (106) $-\dfrac{5}{6}$
23. (110) -64   24. (106) 4
25. (103) -14   26. (109) 0
27. (106) -3   28. (109) 0
29. (105) -24   30. (109) Not determined
31. (110) 16   32. (112) 7
33. (112) 9   34. (112) 4
35. (112) -2

EXERCISES 201, SET I   (page 50)

1.   12 - 8 - 6   2. 2
      =   4   - 6 = -2
3.   17 - 11 + 13 - 9   4. 12
      =   6   + 13 - 9
      =   19   - 9 = 10
5.   7 + 2 · 4   6. 28
      = 7 +   8   = 15
7.   9 - 3 · 2   8. -10
      = 9 -   6   = 3
9.   10 ÷ 2 · 5   10. 60
      =   5   · 5 = 25
11.   12 ÷ 6 ÷ 2   12. $\dfrac{1}{3}$
      =   2   ÷ 2 = 1
13. $(-12) ÷ 2 \cdot (-3)$ 14. -36
      $= (-6) \cdot (-3) = 18$
15. $(8 - 2) \cdot 6$ 16. 16
      =   (6)   · 6 = 36

17. $(-485)^2 \cdot 0 \cdot (-5)^2$
    $= \qquad 0 \qquad \cdot (-5)^2 = 0$

18. 0

19. $12 \cdot 4 + 16 \div 8$
    $= \quad 48 \quad + 16 \div 8$
    $= \quad 48 \quad + \quad 2 \quad = 50$

20. 15

21. $28 \div 4 \cdot 2(6)$
    $= \quad 7 \quad \cdot 2(6)$
    $= \qquad 14(6) \qquad = 84$

22. -48

23. $(-2)^2 + (-4)(5) - (-3)^2$
    $= \quad 4 \quad + (-20) \quad - \quad (9) = -25$

24. -3

25. $2 \cdot 3 + 3^2 - 4 \cdot 2$
    $= 2 \cdot 3 + 9 \quad - 4 \cdot 2$
    $= \quad 6 \quad + 9 \quad - \quad 8 \quad = 7$

26. 624

27. $(10^2)\sqrt{16} + 5(4) - 80$
    $= (100)(4) + 5(4) - 80$
    $= \quad 400 \quad + 20 \quad - 80 = 340$

28. 39

29. $2\sqrt{9}(2^3 - 5)$
    $= 2\sqrt{9}(8 - 5)$
    $= 2\sqrt{9}(3)$
    $= 2(3)(3) = 6(3) = 18$

30. 240

31. $(3 \cdot 5^2 - 15 \div 3) \div (-7)$
    $= (3 \cdot 25 - 15 \div 3) \div (-7)$
    $= (\quad 75 \quad - \quad 5 \quad) \quad \div (-7)$
    $= \qquad (70) \qquad \div (-7) = -10$

32. -20

33. $2.573 - 5.846(1.098)$
    $= 2.573 - 6.418908$
    $= \qquad -3.845908 \quad \doteq -3.85$

34. $\doteq -11.28$

35. $82.49 \div 23.06(51.73)$
    $\doteq \qquad 3.57719(51.73)$
    $\doteq \qquad\qquad 185.05$

36. $\doteq 84.43$

EXERCISES 202, SET I (page 53)

1. $2(-6) \div 3(8 - 4)$
   $= 2(-6) \div 3(4)$
   $= (-12) \div 3(4)$
   $= \quad (-4)(4) \quad = -16$

2. -50

3. $24 - [(-6) + 18]$
   $= 24 - \qquad [12] \quad = 12$

4. 11

5. $[12 - (-19)] - 16$
   $= \quad [31] \qquad - 16 = 15$

6. 6

7. $[11 - (5 + 8)] - 24$
   $= [11 - \quad (13)] \quad - 24$
   $= \qquad [-2] \qquad - 24 = -26$

8. -25

9. $20 - [5 - (7 - 10)]$
   $= 20 - [5 - \quad (-3)]$
   $= 20 - \qquad [8] \qquad = 12$

10. 3

11. $\dfrac{7 + (-12)}{8 - 3}$
    $= \dfrac{-5}{5} = -1$

12. -4

13. $15 - \{4 - [2 - 3(6 - 4)]\}$
    $= 15 - \{4 - [2 - 3(2)]\}$
    $= 15 - \{4 - [2 - 6]\}$
    $= 15 - \{4 - [-4]\}$
    $= 15 - \{8\} = 7$

14. 30

15. $32 \div (-2)^3 - 5\left\{7 - \dfrac{6 - 2}{5}\right\}$
    $= 32 \div (-2)^3 - 5\left\{7 - \dfrac{4}{5}\right\}$
    $= 32 \div (-2)^3 - 5\left\{\dfrac{31}{5}\right\}$
    $= 32 \div (-8) - 31 = (-4) - 31 = -35$

16. -16

17. $\sqrt{3^2 + 4^2}$
    $= \sqrt{9 + 16} = \sqrt{25} = 5$

18. 12

19. $\sqrt{16.3^2 - 8.35^2}$
    $= \sqrt{265.69 - 69.7225}$
    $= \sqrt{195.9675} \doteq 14.0$

20. $\doteq 45.4$

21. $(1.5)^2 \div (-2.5) + \sqrt{35}$
    $= 2.25 \quad \div (-2.5) + 5.916$
    $= \qquad -0.90 \qquad + 5.916 \doteq 5.0$

22. $\doteq -55$

23. $18.91 - [64.3 - (8.6^2 + 14.2)]$
    $= 18.91 - [64.3 - (73.96 + 14.2)]$
    $= 18.91 - [64.3 - 88.16]$
    $= 18.91 - [-23.86] = 42.77$

24. $\doteq 8.40$

24. $\doteq 8.40$

EXERCISES 203, SET I (page 56)

1. $b^2 = (-5)^2 = (-5)(-5) = 25$

2. -49

3. $2a - 3b$
   $= 2(3) - 3(-5)$
   $= \quad 6 \quad + \quad 15 \quad = 21$

4. 26

5. $x - y - 2b$
   $= (4) - (-7) - 2(-5)$
   $= \quad 4 \quad + \quad 7 \quad + \quad 10 \quad = 21$

6. 29

7. $3b - ab + xy$
   $= 3(-5) - (3)(-5) + (4)(-7)$
   $= \quad -15 \quad + \quad 15 \quad - \quad 28 \quad = -28$

8. -27

9. $x^2 - y^2$
   $= (4)^2 - (-7)^2$
   $= 16 \quad - \quad 49 \quad = -33$

10. 24

11. $4 + a(x + y)$
    $= 4 + (3)[(4) + (-7)]$
    $= 4 + \quad 3[-3]$
    $= 4 - \quad 9 \quad = -5$

12. 15

13. $2(a - b) - 3c$
    $= 2[(3) - (-5)] - 3(-1)$
    $= \quad 2[8] \qquad - 3(-1)$
    $= \qquad 16 \qquad + \quad 3 \quad = 19$

14. 17

15. $3x^2 - 10x + 5$
    $= 3(4)^2 - 10(4) + 5$
    $= 3(16) - 10(4) + 5$
    $= \quad 48 \quad - \quad 40 \quad + 5 = 13$

16. 156

17. $a^2 - 2ab + b^2$
    $= (3)^2 - 2(3)(-5) + (-5)^2$
    $= \quad 9 \quad - 2(3)(-5) + \quad 25$
    $= \quad 9 \quad + \quad 30 \quad + \quad 25 = 64$

18. 121

19. $\dfrac{3x}{y + b} = \dfrac{3(4)}{(-7) + (-5)}$
    $= \dfrac{12}{-12} = -1$

20. 3

21. $\dfrac{E + F}{EF} = \dfrac{(-1) + (3)}{(-1)(3)}$
    $= \dfrac{2}{-3} = -\dfrac{2}{3}$

22. $-\dfrac{9}{20}$

23. $\dfrac{(1 + G)^2 - 1}{H}$
    $= \dfrac{[1 + (-5)]^2 - 1}{-4}$
    $= \dfrac{[-4]^2 - 1}{-4} = \dfrac{16 - 1}{-4} = \dfrac{15}{-4}$
    $= -3\dfrac{3}{4}$

24. $\dfrac{1}{3}$

25. $2E - [F - (3K - H)]$
$= 2(-1) - [(3) - \{3(0) - (-4)\}]$
$= 2(-1) - [(3) - \{0 + 4\}]$
$= 2(-1) - [3 - \{4\}]$
$= 2(-1) - [-1]$
$= -2 + 1 = -1$

26. 1

27. $G - \sqrt{G^2 - 4EH}$
$= (-5) - \sqrt{(-5)^2 - 4(-1)(-4)}$
$= (-5) - \sqrt{25 - 4(-1)(-4)}$
$= (-5) - \sqrt{25 - 16}$
$= (-5) - \sqrt{9} = -5 - 3 = -8$

28. $\doteq -9.3$

29. $\dfrac{\sqrt{2H - 5G}}{0.2F^2}$

$= \dfrac{\sqrt{2(-4) - 5(-5)}}{0.2(3)^2}$

$= \dfrac{\sqrt{-8 + 25}}{0.2(9)} = \dfrac{\sqrt{17}}{1.8}$

$\doteq \dfrac{4.123}{1.8} \doteq 2.29$

30. 20

EXERCISES 204, SET I   (page 58)

1. $A = \frac{1}{2}bh = \frac{1}{2}\left(\frac{15}{1}\right)\left(\frac{14}{1}\right) = 105$

2. 486

3. $I = \dfrac{E}{R} = \dfrac{110}{22} = 5$

4. $6\frac{2}{3}$

5. $I = prt = 600(0.09)(4.5) = 243$

6. 140

7. $q = \dfrac{DQ}{H} = \dfrac{5(420)}{30} = 70$

8. 125

9. $S = P(1 + i)^n$
$= 1000(1 + 0.06)^2$
$= 1123.60$

10. 2332.80

11. $A = \pi R^2 \doteq 3.14(10)^2$
$= 3.14(100) = 314$

12. $\doteq 1256$

13. $F = \frac{9}{5}C + 32 = \frac{9}{5}(-25) + 32$

14. -31

$= -45 + 32 = -13$

15. $A = P(1 + rt)$
$= 500(1 + 0.09(2.5))$
$= 500(1 + 0.225)$
$= 500(1.225) = 612.50$

16. 498

17. $C = \frac{5}{9}(F - 32) = \frac{5}{9}(-10 - 32)$

18. $-21\frac{2}{3}$

$= \frac{5}{9}(-42) = -23\frac{1}{3}$

19. $V = \frac{4}{3}\pi R^3 \doteq \frac{4}{3}(3.14)(3)^3$

20. $\doteq 904.32$

$= \frac{4}{3}(3.14)(27)$

$= 113.04$

21. $C = \dfrac{a}{a + 12} \cdot A$

22. 12

$= \dfrac{6}{6 + 12} \cdot 30$

$= \dfrac{6}{18} \cdot 30 = 10$

23. $S = R\left[\dfrac{(1 + i)^n - 1}{i}\right]$

24. 151.505

$= 100\left[\dfrac{(1 + 0.01)^2 - 1}{0.01}\right]$

$= 100\left[\dfrac{(1.01)^2 - 1}{0.01}\right] = 100\left[\dfrac{0.0201}{0.01}\right]$

$= 100(2.01) = 201$

25. $Y = 0.2Q - 0.015Q^2$
$= 0.2(4.7) - 0.015(4.7)^2$
$= 0.94 - 0.015(22.09)$
$\doteq 0.609$

26. $\doteq 0.643$

27. $M = \dfrac{17.6Vtf}{H}$

28. $\doteq 0.0226$

$= \dfrac{17.6(145)\left(\dfrac{1}{125}\right)(5.89)}{3250}$

$\doteq 0.0370$

REVIEW EXERCISES 205, SET I   (page 60)

1. $26 - 14 + 8 - 11$
$= 12 + 8 - 11$
$= 20 - 11 = 9$

2. -13

3. $11 - 7 \cdot 3$
$= 11 - 21 = -10$

4. 12

5. $15 \div 5 \cdot 3$
$= 3 \cdot 3 = 9$

6. 9

7. $[16 - (-8)] - 22$
$= [24] - 22 = 2$

8. 58

9. $6 - [8 - (3 - 4)]$
$= 6 - [8 - (-1)] = 6 - [9] = -3$

10. 13

11. $(56)^2(0) - 8 \div (-2)$
$= 0 + 4 = 4$

12. -3

13. $\dfrac{6 + (-14)}{3 - 7} = \dfrac{-8}{-4} = 2$

14. -4

15. $\sqrt{6^2 + 8^2}$

16. 6

$= \sqrt{36 + 64} = \sqrt{100} = 10$

17. $3x - y + z = 3(-2) - 3 + (-4)$
$= -6 - 3 - 4$
$= -13$

18. -20

19. $6 - x(y - z) = 6 - (-2)(3 - (-4))$
$= 6 - (-2)(7)$
$= 6 + 14 = 20$

20. 25

21. $5x^2 - 3x + 10$
$= 5(-2)^2 - 3(-2) + 10$
$= 5(4) - 3(-2) + 10$
$= 20 + 6 + 10 = 36$

22. 33

23. $y^2 - 2yz + z^2$
$= (3)^2 - 2(3)(-4) + (-4)^2$
$= 9 - 2(3)(-4) + 16$
$= 9 - 6(-4) + 16$
$= 9 + 24 + 16 = 49$

24. -17

25. $x - 2[y - x(y + z)]$
$= -2 - 2[3 - (-2)(3 + (-4))]$
$= -2 - 2[3 + 2(-1)]$
$= -2 - 2[3 - 2]$
$= -2 - 2(1) = -2 - 2 = -4$

26. 27

27. $\dfrac{(x + y)^2 - z^2}{x - 2y} = \dfrac{(1)^2 - (-4)^2}{-2 - 2(3)}$

28. $6\frac{5}{6}$

$= \dfrac{1 - 16}{-2 - 6} = \dfrac{-15}{-8} = 1\frac{7}{8}$

29. $C = \dfrac{a}{a + 12}(35)$

30. 10

$= \dfrac{8}{8 + 12}\left(\dfrac{35}{1}\right)$

$= \dfrac{8}{20}\left(\dfrac{35}{1}\right) = 14$

31. $I = prt = 100(0.07)(4.5)$
$= 7(4.5) = 31.5$

32. 110

33. $C = \frac{5}{9}(F - 32) = \frac{5}{9}(15\frac{1}{2} - 32)$
$= \frac{5}{9}\left(-\frac{33}{2}\right) = -9\frac{1}{6}$

34. $-5\frac{5}{6}$

35. $S = P(1 + i)^n = 700(1 + 0.05)^2$
$= 700(1.05)^2$
$= 700(1.1025)$
$= 771.75$

36. 665.50

37. $Y = 0.2Q - 0.015Q^2$
$= 0.2(5.8) - 0.015(5.8)^2$
$= 1.16 - 0.015(33.64)$
$= 1.16 - 0.5046 = 0.6554$

38. $\doteq 5605$

REVIEW EXERCISES FROM CHAPTER 1 (page 62)

1. $(-16)(-2) = 32$
2. -21
3. $(-5) - (-11) = (-5) + (11) = 6$
4. -4
5. $(-15)(0)(4) = 0$
6. -8
7. $(-27) + (10) = -17$
8. 4
9. $\frac{-48}{-12} = 4$
10. 0
11. $(25)^2 = (25)(25) = 625$
12. -45
13. $-2^4 = -(2^4) = -16$
14. -4
15. $\frac{-12}{0}$ is not possible
16. 2
17. $\sqrt{64} = 8$ because $8^2 = 64$
18. 0
19. $(8) - (17) = (8) + (-17) = -9$
20. -29

CHAPTER TWO DIAGNOSTIC TEST (page 63)

Following each problem number is the textbook section reference (in parentheses) where that kind of problem is discussed.

1. (201) $17 - 9 - 6 + 11$
$= 8 - 6 + 11$
$= 2 + 11 = 13$

2. (201) $5 + 2 \cdot 3 = 5 + 6 = 11$

3. (201) $12 \div 2 \cdot 3 = 6 \cdot 3 = 18$

4. (201) $-5^2 + (-4)^2$
$= -25 + 16 = -9$

5. (201) $(2) \cdot 3^2 - 4 = (2) \cdot 9 - 4$
$= 18 - 4 = 14$

6. (201) $3\sqrt{25} - 5(-4)$
$= 3 \cdot 5 - 5(-4)$
$= 15 + 20 = 35$

7. (202) $\frac{8 - 12}{-6 + 2} = \frac{-4}{-4} = 1$

8. (202) $(2^3 - 8)(5^2 + 4^2)$
$= (8 - 8)(25 + 16)$
$= 0(41) = 0$

9. (202) $10 - [6 - (5 - 7)]$
$= 10 - [6 - (-2)]$
$= 10 - [6 + 2]$
$= 10 - [8] = 2$

10. (202) $\{-10 - [5 + (4 - 7)]\} - 3$
$= \{-10 - [5 + (-3)]\} - 3$
$= \{-10 - [2]\} - 3$
$= \{-12\} - 3 = -15$

11. (202) $\sqrt{10^2 - 6^2}$
$= \sqrt{100 - 36} = \sqrt{64} = 8$

12. (202) $48 \div (-4)^2 - 3\left[10 - \frac{10}{-2}\right]$

$= 48 \div (-4)^2 - 3[10 - (-5)]$
$= 48 \div (-4)^2 - 3[15]$
$= 48 \div 16 - 3[15]$
$= 3 - 45 = -42$

13. (203) $3a + bx - cy$ $\begin{cases} a = -2 \\ b = 4 \\ c = -3 \\ x = 5 \\ y = -6 \end{cases}$
$= 3(-2) + 4(5) - (-3)(-6)$
$= -6 + 20 - 18$
$= 14 - 18 = -4$

14. (203) $4x - [a - (3c - b)]$ $\begin{cases} a = -2 \\ b = 4 \\ c = -3 \\ x = 5 \\ y = -6 \end{cases}$
$= 4(5) - [-2 - (3(-3) - 4)]$
$= 4(5) - [-2 - (-9 - 4)]$
$= 4(5) - [-2 - (-13)]$
$= 4(5) - [11]$
$= 20 - 11 = 9$

15. (203) $x^2 + 2xy - y^2$ $\begin{cases} x = 5 \\ y = -6 \end{cases}$
$= (5)^2 + 2(5)(-6) - (-6)^2$
$= 25 + 2(5)(-6) - 36$
$= 25 - 60 - 36$
$= -35 - 36 = -71$

16. (204) $C = \frac{5}{9}(F - 32)$ $\qquad F = -4$
$= \frac{5}{9}(-4 - 32) = \frac{5}{9}(-36)$
$= \frac{5}{9}\left(-\frac{\overset{4}{\cancel{36}}}{1}\right)$
$= 5(-4) = -20$

17. (204) $A = \pi R^2$ $\begin{cases} \pi \doteq 3.14 \\ R = 20 \end{cases}$
$\doteq (3.14)(20)^2$
$= 3.14(400)$
$= 1256$

18. (204) $C = \frac{a}{a + 12} \cdot A$ $\begin{cases} a = 7 \\ A = 38 \end{cases}$
$= \frac{7}{7 + 12}(38)$
$= \frac{7}{19}\left(\frac{38}{1}\right)$
$= 14$

19. (204) $A = P(1 + rt)$
$= 600(1 + 0.10(2.5))$ $\begin{cases} P = 600 \\ r = 0.10 \\ t = 2.5 \end{cases}$
$= 600(1 + 0.25)$
$= 600(1.25)$
$= 750$

20. (204) $Y = 0.2Q - 0.015Q^2$
$= 0.2(6) - 0.015(6)^2$
$= 0.2(6) - 0.015(36)$
$= 1.2 - 0.54 = 0.66$

EXERCISES 301, SET I (page 71)

1. Constants: 2, 4
Variables: x, y

2. Constants: 3, 7
Variables: a, b

3. Constants: 7, -8, 2

4. Constants: 3, -5, -2

5. One term.
No second term.

6. One term.
No second term.

7. Three terms.
Second term: $-5F$

8. Three terms.
Second term: $-2T$

9. Three terms.
Second term: $\frac{2x + y}{3xy}$

10. Three terms.
Second term: $\frac{5x - y}{7xy}$

11. 3
    y

12. 4
    T

13. 1, xy

14. 1, xy

15. 3, $3xy$, $3z$

16. 12, $12ab$, $12c$

17. Constants: 2, 3, -4, 5, 6
    Variables: x, y

18. Constants: -2, 3, 4, 5, 6
    Variables: x, y

19. Two terms.
    Second term: $-6u(2u + v^2)$

20. Two terms.
    Second term: $-2E(8E + F^2)$

21. One term.
    No second term.

22. One term.
    No second term.

23. 1, xy

24. -1, xy

EXERCISES 302, SET I (page 73)

1. $x^3 \cdot x^4 = x^{3+4} = x^7$

2. x^{11}

3. $y \cdot y^3 = y^{1+3} = y^4$

4. z^5

5. $m^2 \cdot m = m^{2+1} = m^3$

6. a^4

7. $10^2 \cdot 10^3 = 10^{2+3} = 10^5$

8. 10^7

9. $2 \cdot 2^3 \cdot 2^2 = 2^{1+3+2} = 2^6$

10. 3^6

11. $x \cdot x^3 \cdot x^4 = x^{1+3+4} = x^8$

12. y^9

13. $x^2 y^5$

14. $a^3 b^2$

15. $3^2 \cdot 5^3 = 9 \cdot 125 = 1125$

16. 72

17. $a^x \cdot a^w = a^{x+w}$

18. x^{a+b}

19. $x^y y^x$ (cannot be combined)

20. $a^b b^a$

21. $x^2 y^3 x^5 = x^{2+5} y^3 = x^7 y^3$

22. $z^7 w^2$

23. $a^2 b^3 a^5 = a^{2+5} b^3 = a^7 b^3$

24. $x^{12} y$

EXERCISES 303, SET I (page 75)

1. $(-2a)(4a^2) = -(2 \cdot 4)(a \cdot a^2)$
   $= -8a^3$

2. $-15x^4$

3. $(-5h^2)(-6h^3)$
   $= +(5 \cdot 6)(h^2 h^3) = 30h^5$

4. $48k^4$

5. $(-5x^3)^2 = (-5x^3)(-5x^3)$
   $= +(5 \cdot 5)(x^3 x^3) = 25x^6$

6. $49y^8$

7. $(-2a^3)(-4a)(3a^4)$
   $= +(2 \cdot 4 \cdot 3)(a^3 a a^4)$
   $= 24a^8$

8. $-48b^6$

9. $(-9m)(m^5)(-2m^2)$
   $= +(9 \cdot 2)(mm^5 m^2)$
   $= 18m^8$

10. $28n^7$

11. $-(5 \cdot 7)x^2 y = -35x^2 y$

12. $-12x^3 y$

13. $(-6m^3 n^2)(-4mn^2)$
    $= +(6 \cdot 4)(m^3 m)(n^2 n^2)$
    $= 24 m^4 n^4$

14. $-40h^6 k^4$

15. $-(2 \cdot 3)(x^{10} \cdot x^{12})(y^2 \cdot y^7)$
    $= -6x^{22} y^9$

16. $10a^{12} b^{15}$

17. $(3xy^2)^2 = (3xy^2)(3xy^2)$
    $= (3 \cdot 3)(x \cdot x)(y^2 \cdot y^2)$
    $= 9x^2 y^4$

18. $16x^4 y^6$

19. $-(5)(x^4)(y^5 \cdot y^4)(z \cdot z^7)$
    $= -5x^4 y^9 z^8$

20. $-21E^2 F^{11} G^{18}$

21. $-(2^3 \cdot 2^2)(R \cdot R^5)S^2 T^4$
    $= -32R^6 S^2 T^4$

22. $-243x^9 yz^5$

23. Because of the two negative factors, the answer is positive.
    $+(5 \cdot 4)(c^2 \cdot c^5)(d \cdot d)(e^3 \cdot e^2) = 20c^7 d^2 e^5$

24. $24m^4 n^7 r^5$

25. Because of the three negative factors, the answer is negative.
    $-(2 \cdot 3 \cdot 7)(x^2 \cdot x)(y^2 \cdot y)(z \cdot z) = -42x^3 y^3 z^2$

26. $420x^4 y^3 z^5$

27. $-(3 \cdot 5)(x \cdot x^2 \cdot x^3)(y \cdot y^2 \cdot y^3) = -15x^6 y^6$

28. $-6x^2 y^2 z^2$

29. $-(2 \cdot 5)(a \cdot a)(b \cdot b)(c \cdot c) = -10a^2 b^2 c^2$

30. $+6x^3 y^3 z^3$

31. $(5 \cdot 2)(x^2 \cdot x)(y \cdot y)(z^3 \cdot z) = 10x^3 y^2 z^4$

32. $6a^5 b^7$

33. $-(5 \cdot 7)(x^2 \cdot x^5 \cdot x)(y^2 \cdot y^3 \cdot y)(z \cdot z \cdot z^5)$
    $= -35x^8 y^6 z^7$

34. $-32R^9 S^7 T^{13}$

35. Because of the three negative factors, the answer is negative.
    $-(3 \cdot 7)(h^2 \cdot h^4)(k^1 \cdot k^5)(m^3 \cdot m^1) = -21h^6 k^6 m^4$

36. $-48k^3 m^3 n^3$

EXERCISES 304, SET I (page 79)

1. $5(a + 6)$
   $5a + 30$

2. $4x + 40$

3. $7(x + y)$
   $7x + 7y$

4. $5m + 5n$

5. $3(m - 4)$
   $(3)(m) + (3)(-4)$
   $3m - 12$

6. $3a - 15$

7. $4(x - y)$
   $(4)(x) + (4)(-y)$
   $4x - 4y$

8. $9m - 9n$

9. $a(6 + x)$
   $(a)(6) + (a)(x)$
   $6a + ax$

10. $7b + by$

11. $-2(x - 3)$
    $(-2)(x) + (-2)(-3)$
    $-2x + 6$

12. $-3x + 15$

13. $-3(2x^2 - 4x + 5)$
    $= (-3)(2x^2) + (-3)(-4x) + (-3)(5)$
    $= -6x^2 + 12x - 15$

14. $-15x^2 + 10x + 35$

15. $4x(3x^2 - 6)$
    $= (4x)(3x^2) + (4x)(-6)$
    $= 12x^3 - 24x$

16. $15x^3 - 30x$

17. $-2x(5x^2 + 3x - 4)$
    $= (-2x)(5x^2) + (-2x)(3x) + (-2x)(-4)$
    $= -10x^3 - 6x^2 + 8x$

18. $-8x^3 + 20x^2 - 12x$

19. $(x - 4)6$
    $= (x)(6) + (-4)(6)$
    $= 6x - 24$

20. $-15 + 10x$

21. $(y^2 - 4y + 3)7$
    $= (y^2)(7) + (-4y)(7) + (3)(7)$
    $= 7y^2 - 28y + 21$

22. $63 - 7z + 14z^2$

23. $(2x^2 - 3x + 5)4x$
    $= (2x^2)(4x) + (-3x)(4x) + (5)(4x)$
    $= 8x^3 - 12x^2 + 20x$

24. $15w^3 + 10w^2 - 40w$

25. $x(xy - 3)$
    $(x)(xy) + (x)(-3)$
    $x^2y - 3x$

26. $a^2b - 4a$

27. $3a(ab - 2a^2)$
    $(3a)(ab) + (3a)(-2a^2)$
    $3a^2b - 6a^3$

28. $12x^2 - 8xy^2$

29. $(-2x + 4x^2y)(-3y)$
    $(-2x)(-3y) + (4x^2y)(-3y)$
    $6xy - 12x^2y^2$

30. $6az - 4a^2z^2$

31. $-2xy(x^2y - y^2x - y - 5)$
    $(-2xy)(x^2y) + (-2xy)(-y^2x) + (-2xy)(-y) + (-2xy)(-5)$
    $-2x^3y^2 + 2x^2y^3 + 2xy^2 + 10xy$

32. $-24ab + 3a^3b + 3ab^3 - 3a^2b^2$

33. $-3(x - 2y + 2)$
    $(-3)(x) + (-3)(-2y) + (-3)(2)$
    $-3x + 6y - 6$

34. $-2x + 6y - 8$

35. $(3x^3 - 2x^2y + y^3)(-2xy)$
    $(3x^3)(-2xy) + (-2x^2y)(-2xy) + (y^3)(-2xy)$
    $-6x^4y + 4x^3y^2 - 2xy^4$

36. $-8yz^4 + 2y^2z^3 + 2y^4z$

37. $(2xy^2z - 7x^2z^2)(-5xz^3)$
    $(2xy^2z)(-5xz^3) + (-7x^2z^2)(-5xz^3)$
    $-10x^2y^2z^4 + 35x^3z^5$

38. $-9a^3bc^4 + 12a^2b^3c^3$

39. $(5x^2y^3z - 2xz^3 + y^4)(-4xz^2)$
    $(5x^2y^3z)(-4xz^2) + (-2xz^3)(-4xz^2) + (y^4)(-4xz^2)$
    $-20x^3y^3z^3 + 8x^2z^5 - 4xy^4z^2$

40. $-12x^3y^3z^2 + 6xy^3z^3 + 8x^2y^2z^4$

EXERCISES 305, SET I (page 83)

1. $8 + (a - b) = 8 + a - b$. When the parentheses are preceded by a + sign, the enclosed terms are unchanged.

2. $7 + m - n$

3. $5 - (x - y) = 5 - x + y$. When the parentheses are preceded by a - sign, change the sign of each enclosed term.

4. $6 - a + b$

5. $12 - 3(m - n) = 12 - 3m + 3n$
(Using the Distributive Rule.)

6. $14 - 5x + 5y$

7. $R - S - 8$ 8. $x - y - 2$

9. $10 - 2(\boxed{+}a - b)$
    $= 10 - 2a + 2b$ (Using the Distributive Rule.)

10. $12 - 5x + 10y$

11. $2(\boxed{+}x - y) + 3$
    $= 2x - 2y + 3$ (Using the Distributive Rule.)

12. $4a - 8b + 5$

13. $2a - 3(\boxed{+}x - y)$
    $= 2a - 3x + 3y$ (Using the Distributive Rule.)

14. $5x - 2a + 2b$

15. $a - [\boxed{+}x - (\boxed{+}b - c)]$
    $= a - [\boxed{+}x - b + c]$ (Removing innermost grouping symbols first.)
    $= a - x + b - c$

16. $a - x - b + c$

17. $4 - 2[\boxed{+}a - 3(\boxed{+}x - y)]$
    $4 - 2[\boxed{+}a - 3x + 3y]$
    $4 - 2a + 6x - 6y$

18. $8 - 3x + 18a - 6b$

19. $3(a - 2x) - 2(y - 3b)$
    $3a - 6x - 2y + 6b$

20. $4x - 2b - 3y + 15a$

21. $-10[-2(\boxed{+}x - 3y) + a] - b$
    $-10[-2x + 6y + a] - b$
    $20x - 60y - 10a - b$

22. $30x - 15y - 5a - c$

23. $(a - b) - \{[\boxed{+}x - (\boxed{+}3 - y)] - R\}$
    $(a - b) - \{[\boxed{+}x - 3 \boxed{+}y] - R\}$
    $(a - b) - \{\boxed{+}x - 3 + y - R\}$
    $a - b - x + 3 - y + R$

24. $x - y - a + c - 5 + b$

EXERCISES 306, SET I (page 85)

1. $15x - 3x = (15 - 3)x$
        $= 12x$

2. $3a$

3. $5a - 12a = (5 - 12)a$
          $= -7a$

4. $-14x$

5. $2a - 5a + 6a$
    $= (2 - 5 + 6)a$
    $= 3a$

6. $4y$

7. $5x - 8x + x$
    $= (5 - 8 + 1)x$
    $= -2x$

8. $-a$

9. $3x + 2y - 3x$
   $= 3x - 3x + 2y$
   $= (3 - 3)x + 2y$
   $= 0x + 2y$
   $= \quad 2y$

10. $4a$

11. $4y + y - 10y$
   $= (4 + 1 - 10)y$
   $= \qquad -5y$

12. $-3x$

13. $3mn - 5mn + 2mn$
   $= (3 - 5 + 2)mn$
   $= \quad (0)mn$
   $= \qquad 0$

14. 0

15. $2xy - 5yx + xy$
   $= 2xy - 5xy + xy$
   $= (2 - 5 + 1)xy$
   $= \qquad -2xy$

16. $4mn$

17. $8x^2y - 2x^2y$
   $= (8 - 2)x^2y$
   $= \quad 6x^2y$

18. $7ab^2$

19. $a^2b - 3a^2b$
   $= (1 - 3)a^2b$
   $= \quad -2a^2b$

20. $-4x^2y^2$

21. $5ab + 2c - 2ba$
   $= 5ab - 2ab + 2c$
   $= (5 - 2)ab + 2c$
   $= 3ab + 2c$

22. $3xy - 3z$

23. $5xyz^2 - 2xyz^2 - 4xyz^2$
   $= (5 - 2 - 4)xyz^2$
   $= \qquad -xyz^2$

24. $2a^2bc$

25. $5u - 2u + 10v$
   $= (5 - 2)u + 10v$
   $= \qquad 3u + 10v$

26. $4w + 5v$

27. $8x - 2y - 4x$
   $= 8x - 4x - 2y$
   $= (8 - 4)x - 2y$
   $= \qquad 4x - 2y$

28. $11x - 8y$

29. $7x^2y - 2xy^2 - 4x^2y$
   $= 7x^2y - 4x^2y - 2xy^2$
   $= (7 - 4)x^2y - 2xy^2$
   $= \qquad 3x^2y - 2xy^2$

30. $2xy^2 - 5x^2y$

31. $5x^2 - 3x + 7 - 2x^2 + 8x - 9$
   $= (5x^2 - 2x^2) + (-3x + 8x) + (7 - 9)$
   $= 3x^2 + 5x - 2$

32. $-2y^2 + 2y + 1$

33. 12.67 sec $+ 9.08$ sec $- 6.73$ sec
   $= (12.67 + 9.08 - 6.73)$ sec $= 15.02$ sec

34. 83.00 ft

EXERCISES 307, SET I (page 88)

1. $x - 3(x + y)$
   $x - 3x - 3y$
   $\quad -2x - 3y$

2. $-y - 2z$

3. $2a - 4(a - b)$
   $2a - 4a + 4b$
   $\quad -2a + 4b$

4. $c + 2d$

5. $u(u^2 + 2u + 4) - 2(u^2 + 2u + 4)$
   $u^3 + \underline{2u^2} + \underline{4u} - \underline{2u^2} - \underline{4u} - 8$
   $u^3 - 8$

6. $x^3 + 27$

7. $x^2(x^2 + y^2) - y^2(x^2 + y^2)$
   $x^4 + \underline{x^2y^2} - \underline{x^2y^2} - y^4$
   $x^4 - y^4$

8. $w^4 - 16$

9. $2x(3x^2 - 5x + 1) - 4x(2x^2 - 3x - 5)$
   $\underline{6x^3} - \underline{10x^2} + \underline{2x} - \underline{8x^3} + \underline{12x^2} + \underline{20x}$
   $-2x^3 + 2x^2 + 22x$

10. $6x^3 - 4x^2 - 11x$

11. $-3(a - 2b) + 2(a - 3b)$
   $-3a + 6b + 2a - 6b$
   $-a$

12. $2m - 2n$

13. $-5(2x - 3y) - 10(x + 5y)$
   $-10x + 15y - 10x - 50y$
   $-20x - 35y$

14. $-36s + 60t$

15. $x^2y(3xy^2 - y) - 2xy^2(4x - x^2y)$
   $\underline{3x^3y^3} - \underline{x^2y^2} - \underline{8x^2y^2} + \underline{2x^3y^3}$
   $5x^3y^3 - 9x^2y^2$

16. $-4a^2b^2 + 2a^2b^3$

17. $2h(3h^2 - k) - k(h - 3k^3)$
   $6h^3 - 2hk - hk + 3k^4$
   $6h^3 - 3hk + 3k^4$

18. $11xy^2 - 14x^2$

19. $3f(2f^2 - 4g) - g(2f - g^2)$
   $6f^3 - 12fg - 2fg + g^3$
   $6f^3 - 14fg + g^3$

20. $3ab^2 - 7ab$

21. $2x - [3a + (4x - 5a)]$
   $2x - [3a + 4x - 5a]$
   $2x - [-2a + 4x]$
   $2x + 2a - 4x$
   $2a - 2x$

22. $-c - y$

23. $5x + [-(2x - 10) + 7]$
   $5x + [-2x + 10 + 7]$
   $5x - 2x + 10 + 7$
   $3x + 17$

24. $x + 9$

25. $25 - 2[3g - 5(2g - 7)]$
   $25 - 2[3g - 10g + 35]$
   $25 - 2[-7g + 35]$
   $25 + 14g - 70$
   $14g - 45$

26. $66h - 200$

27. $-2\{-3[-5(-4 - 3z) - 2z] + 30z\}$
   $-2\{-3[20 + 15z - 2z] + 30z\}$
   $-2\{-60 - 45z + 6z + 30z\}$
   $-2\{-60 - 9z\}$
   $120 + 18z$

28. $138z + 90$

REVIEW EXERCISES 308, SET I (page 90)

1. Constants: 12, -7
   Variables: x, y

2. Constants: 4, 2, 3
   Variables: x, y

3. (a) 3
   (b) $2ab$

4. (a) 2
   (b) $-y^3$

5. (a) 2
   (b) $-2(x^2 + y^2)$

6. (a) 2
   (b) $5mn$

7. (a) 5
   (b) $5x^2$

8. (a) 10
   (b) $10y^2$

9. $m^2 m^3 = m^{2+3} = m^5$

10. p^9

11. x^4

12. y^8

13. 2^3

14. 10^4

15. $-20p^4$

16. $-56m^3$

17. $-63x^{12}y^8$

18. $-54x^8 y^8$

19. $40a^5 b^{10} c^3$

20. $44p^2 q^{17} r^4$

21. $100e^6 f^{10} g^5$

22. $200h^9 j^{10} k^5$

23. $x - 2(x - y)$
$x - 2x + 2y$
$-x + 2y$

24. $-2m + 3n$

25. $2x(3x^2 - x) - x^2(3x - 4)$
$6x^3 - 2x^2 - 3x^3 + 4x^2$
$3x^3 + 2x^2$

26. $-2y^3 - 9y^2$

27. $2m^2 n(3mn^2 - 2n) - 5mn^2(2m - 3m^2 n)$
$6m^3 n^3 - \underline{4m^2 n^2} - \underline{10m^2 n^2} + \underline{15m^3 n^3}$
$21m^3 n^3 - 14m^2 n^2$

28. $-26x^2 y^2 + 9x^2 y^3$

29. Constants: 4, 5
Variables: u, v

30. Constants: 2, 3, −5
Variables: x, y

31. (a) 2
(b) 4

32. (a) 2
(b) $-2(x^3 + 1)$

33. $10^2 \cdot 10 \cdot 10^5 = 10^{2+1+5} = 10^8$

34. 3^6

35. r^{17}

36. x^{18}

37. $x^{a+2a} = x^{3a}$

38. x^{7y}

39. $10^a \cdot 10^b = 10^{a+b}$

40. 5^{x+y}

41. 4^{1+x}

42. 10^{1+y}

43. $2x(4x^2 + 6xy + 9y^2) - 3y(4x^2 + 6xy + 9y^2)$
$8x^3 + \underline{12x^2 y} + \underline{18xy^2} - \underline{12x^2 y} - \underline{18xy^2} - 27y^3$
$8x^3 - 27y^3$

44. $64v^3 + 27w^3$

45. $4(2m - 3n) - \{5[4m - 2(m - 3n)] - 10n\}$
$8m - 12n - \{5[4m - 2m + 6n] - 10n\}$
$8m - 12n - \{5[2m + 6n] - 10n\}$
$8m - 12n - \{10m + 30n - 10n\}$
$\underline{8m} - \underline{12n} - \underline{10m} - \underline{30n} + \underline{10n}$
$-2m - 32n$

46. $42a - 10b$

47. $-5\{-2[-3(4 - 2x) - 7x] - 3x\} - 15x$
$-5\{-2[-12 + 6x - 7x] - 3x\} - 15x$
$-5\{24 - 12x + 14x - 3x\} - 15x$
$-5\{24 - x\} - 15x$
$-120 + 5x - 15x$
$-120 - 10x$

48. $-280 - 28x$

CUMULATIVE REVIEW EXERCISES:
CHAPTERS 1 and 2 (page 92)

1. $\dfrac{14 - 23}{-8 + 11} = \dfrac{-9}{3} = -3$

2. 12

3. $-4^2 + (-4)^2 = -16 + 16 = 0$

4. 0

5. $6(-3) - 4\sqrt{36}$
$= 6(-3) - 4(6)$
$= -18 - 24 = -42$

6. −28

7. $\dfrac{0}{-11} = 0$

8. −25

9. $A = P(1 + rt)$
$= 1200[1 + 0.15(4)]$
$= 1200[1 + 0.6]$
$= 1200[1.6] = 1920$

10. $\doteq 1256$

CHAPTER THREE DIAGNOSTIC TEST (page 93)

Following each problem number is the textbook section reference (in parentheses) where that kind of problem is discussed.

1. (301) (a) 3
(b) 2
(c) 5

2. (302; 303) $(-2x)(3x^4)$
$-(2 \cdot 3)(xx^4)$
$-6x^5$

3. (303) $(-3xy)(5x^3 y)(-2xy^4)$
Because two factors are negative, the answer is positive.
$(3 \cdot 5 \cdot 2)(xx^3 x)(yyy^4) = 30x^5 y^6$

4. (304) $2(x - 3y)$
$(2)x + (2)(-3y)$
$2x - 6y$

5. (304) $(x - 4)(-5)$
$x(-5) + (-4)(-5)$
$-5x + 20$

6. (304) $2xy^2(x^2 - 3y - 4)$
$2xy^2(x^2) + 2xy^2(-3y) + 2xy^2(-4)$
$2x^3 y^2 - 6xy^3 - 8xy^2$

7. (305) $5 - (x - y)$
$5 - x + y$

8. (305) $h - k + (m - n)$
$h - k + m - n$

9. (305) $-2[-4(3c - d) + a] - b$
$-2[-12c + 4d + a] - b$
$24c - 8d - 2a - b$

10. (306) $4x - 3x + 5x$
$(4 - 3 + 5)x = 6x$

11. (306) $8mn - nm + 3nm$
$(8 - 1 + 3)mn = 10mn$

12. (306) $6p - 7q + 2p$
$6p + 2p - 7q$
$8p - 7q$

13. (306) $\underline{2a} - \underline{5b} - \underline{7} - 3b + \underline{4} - \underline{5a}$
$2a - 5a - 5b - 3b - 7 + 4$
$-3a - 8b - 3$

14. (307) $5x - 3(y - x)$
$5x - 3y + 3x$
$5x + 3x - 3y$
$8x - 3y$

15. (307) $4(a - 2b) - 2(a - 3b)$
$\underline{4a} - \underline{8b} - \underline{2a} + \underline{6b}$
$2a - 2b$

16. (307) $3h(2k^2 - 5h) - h(2h - 3k^2)$
$\underline{6hk^2} - \underline{15h^2} - \underline{2h^2} + \underline{3hk^2}$
$9hk^2 - 17h^2$

17. (307) $ef^2(2e - ef) - 3ef(2ef - ef^2)$
$\underline{2e^2 f^2} - \underline{e^2 f^3} - \underline{6e^2 f^2} + \underline{3e^2 f^3}$
$-4e^2 f^2 + 2e^2 f^3$

18. (307) $x(x^2 + 2x + 4) - 2(x^2 + 2x + 4)$
$x^3 + 2x^2 + 4x - 2x^2 - 4x - 8$
$x^3 - 8$

19. (307) $7m - [5n + (4m - 3n)]$
$7m - [5n + 4m - 3n]$
$7m - 5n - 4m + 3n$
$3m - 2n$

20. (307) $25 - \{-3x - [5x - (7 - 2x)]\}$
$25 - \{-3x - [5x - 7 + 2x]\}$
$25 - \{-3x - 5x + 7 - 2x\}$
$25 + 3x + 5x - 7 + 2x$
$18 + 10x$

EXERCISES 402, SET I (page 100)

1. $\begin{aligned} x + 5 &= 8 \\ -5 \quad &-5 \\ \hline x \quad &= 3 \end{aligned}$ Check: $x + 5 = 8$
$3 + 5 = 8$
$8 = 8$

2. 5

3. $\begin{aligned} x - 3 &= 4 \\ +3 \quad &+3 \\ \hline x \quad &= 7 \end{aligned}$ Check: $x - 3 = 4$
$7 - 3 = 4$
$4 = 4$

4. 9

5. $\begin{aligned} 3 + x &= -4 \\ -3 \quad &-3 \\ \hline x &= -7 \end{aligned}$ Check: $3 + x = -4$
$3 + (-7) = -4$
$-4 = -4$

6. -7

7. $\begin{aligned} x + 4 &= 21 \\ -4 \quad &-4 \\ \hline x \quad &= 17 \end{aligned}$ Check: $x + 4 = 21$
$17 + 4 = 21$
$21 = 21$

8. 9

9. $\begin{aligned} x - 35 &= 7 \\ +35 \quad &+35 \\ \hline x \quad &= 42 \end{aligned}$ Check: $x - 35 = 7$
$42 - 35 = 7$
$7 = 7$

10. 51

11. $\begin{aligned} 9 &= x + 5 \\ -5 \quad &\quad -5 \\ \hline 4 &= x \end{aligned}$ Check: $9 = x + 5$
$9 = 4 + 5$
$9 = 9$

12. 3

13. $\begin{aligned} 12 &= x - 11 \\ +11 \quad &\quad +11 \\ \hline 23 &= x \end{aligned}$ Check: $12 = x - 11$
$12 = 23 - 11$
$12 = 12$

14. 29

15. $\begin{aligned} -17 + x &= 28 \\ +17 \quad\quad &+17 \\ \hline x &= 45 \end{aligned}$ Check: $-17 + x = 28$
$-17 + 45 = 28$
$28 = 28$

16. 47

17. $\begin{aligned} -28 &= -15 + x \\ +15 \quad &+15 \\ \hline -13 &= \quad\quad x \end{aligned}$ Check: $-28 = -15 + x$
$-28 = -15 + (-13)$
$-28 = -28$

18. -29

19. $\begin{aligned} x + \tfrac{1}{2} &= 2\tfrac{1}{2} \\ -\tfrac{1}{2} \quad &-\tfrac{1}{2} \\ \hline x \quad &= 2 \end{aligned}$ Check: $x + \tfrac{1}{2} = 2\tfrac{1}{2}$
$2 + \tfrac{1}{2} = 2\tfrac{1}{2}$
$2\tfrac{1}{2} = 2\tfrac{1}{2}$

20. 5

21. $\begin{aligned} 5.6 + x &= 2.8 \\ -5.6 \quad\quad &-5.6 \\ \hline x &= -2.8 \end{aligned}$ Check: $5.6 + x = 2.8$
$5.6 + (-2.8) = 2.8$
$2.8 = 2.8$

22. -0.08

23. $\begin{aligned} 7.84 &= x - 3.98 \\ +3.98 \quad &\quad +3.98 \\ \hline 11.82 &= x \end{aligned}$ Check: $7.84 = x - 3.98$
$7.84 = 11.82 - 3.98$
$7.84 = 7.84$

24. 7.07

EXERCISES 403, SET I (page 103)

1. $\begin{aligned} 2x &= 8 \\ \tfrac{2x}{2} &= \tfrac{8}{2} \\ x &= 4 \end{aligned}$ Check: $2x = 8$
$2(4) = 8$
$8 = 8$

2. 5

3. $\begin{aligned} 21 &= 7x \\ \tfrac{21}{7} &= \tfrac{7x}{7} \\ 3 &= x \end{aligned}$ Check: $21 = 7x$
$21 = 7(3)$
$21 = 21$

4. 7

5. $\begin{aligned} 11x &= 33 \\ \tfrac{11x}{11} &= \tfrac{33}{11} \\ x &= 3 \end{aligned}$ Check: $11x = 33$
$11(3) = 33$
$33 = 33$

6. 4

7. $\begin{aligned} 4x + 1 &= 9 \\ -1 \quad &-1 \\ \hline 4x \quad &= 8 \\ \tfrac{4x}{4} &= \tfrac{8}{4} \\ x &= 2 \end{aligned}$ Check: $4x + 1 = 9$
$4(2) + 1 = 9$
$8 + 1 = 9$
$9 = 9$

8. 2

9. $\begin{aligned} 6x - 2 &= 10 \\ +2 \quad &+2 \\ \hline 6x \quad &= 12 \\ \tfrac{6x}{6} &= \tfrac{12}{6} \\ x &= 2 \end{aligned}$ Check: $6x - 2 = 10$
$6(2) - 2 = 10$
$12 - 2 = 10$
$10 = 10$

10. 1

11. $\begin{aligned} 2x - 15 &= 11 \\ +15 \quad &+15 \\ \hline 2x \quad &= 26 \\ \tfrac{2x}{2} &= \tfrac{26}{2} \\ x &= 13 \end{aligned}$ Check: $2x - 15 = 11$
$2(13) - 15 = 11$
$26 - 15 = 11$
$11 = 11$

12. 6

13. $\begin{aligned} 4x + 2 &= -14 \\ -2 \quad &-2 \\ \hline 4x \quad &= -16 \\ \tfrac{4x}{4} &= \tfrac{-16}{4} \\ x &= -4 \end{aligned}$ 14. -3

15. $\begin{aligned} 14 &= 9x - 13 \\ +13 \quad &\quad +13 \\ \hline 27 &= 9x \\ \tfrac{27}{9} &= \tfrac{9x}{9} \\ 3 &= x \end{aligned}$ 16. 5

17.
$$12x + 17 = 65$$
$$\underline{-17 \quad -17}$$
$$12x = 48$$

$$\frac{12x}{12} = \frac{48}{12}$$

$$x = 4$$

18. 2

19.
$$8x - 23 = 31$$
$$\underline{+23 \quad +23}$$
$$8x = 54$$

$$\frac{8x}{8} = \frac{54}{8}$$

$$x = 6\frac{3}{4}$$

20. $10\frac{1}{3}$

21.
$$14 - 4x = -28 \quad 8$$
$$\underline{-14 \qquad -14 \quad 4}$$
$$-4x = -42 \quad 2$$

$$\frac{-4x}{-4} = \frac{-42}{-4}$$

$$x = 10\frac{1}{2}$$

22. $10\frac{1}{3}$

23.
$$8 = 25 - 3x$$
$$\underline{-25 \quad -25}$$
$$-17 = -3x$$

$$\frac{-17}{-3} = \frac{-3x}{-3}$$

$$5\frac{2}{3} = x$$

24. $8\frac{1}{2}$

25.
$$-73 = 24x + 31$$
$$\underline{-31 \qquad -31}$$
$$-104 = 24x$$

$$\frac{-104}{24} = \frac{24x}{24}$$

$$-4\frac{1}{3} = x$$

26. $-2\frac{1}{2}$

27.
$$18x - 4.8 = 6$$
$$\underline{+4.8 \quad +4.8}$$
$$18x = 10.8$$

$$\frac{18x}{18} = \frac{10.8}{18}$$

$$x = 0.6$$

28. $1.03\frac{1}{3}$

29.
$$2.5x - 3.8 = -7.9$$
$$\underline{+3.8 \quad +3.8}$$
$$2.5x = -4.1$$

$$\frac{2.5x}{2.5} = \frac{-4.1}{2.5}$$

$$x = -1.64$$

30. -0.0667

EXERCISES 404, SET I (page 107)

1.
$$\frac{x}{3} = 4$$

$$3\left(\frac{x}{3}\right) = 3(4)$$

$$x = 12$$

Check:
$$\frac{x}{3} = 4$$

$$\frac{12}{3} = 4$$

$$4 = 4$$

2. 15

3.
$$\frac{x}{5} = -2$$

$$5\left(\frac{x}{5}\right) = 5(-2)$$

$$x = -10$$

Check:
$$\frac{x}{5} = -2$$

$$\frac{-10}{5} = -2$$

$$-2 = -2$$

4. -24

5.
$$4 - \frac{x}{7} = 0$$
$$\underline{-4 \qquad -4}$$
$$-\frac{x}{7} = -4$$

$$7\left(-\frac{x}{7}\right) = 7(-4)$$

$$-x = -28$$

$$x = 28$$

Check:
$$4 - \frac{x}{7} = 0$$

$$4 - \frac{28}{7} = 0$$

$$4 - 4 = 0$$

6. 24

7.
$$-13 = \frac{x}{9}$$

$$9(-13) = 9\left(\frac{x}{9}\right)$$

$$-117 = x$$

8. -120

9.
$$\frac{x}{10} = 3.14$$

$$10\left(\frac{x}{10}\right) = 10(3.14)$$

$$x = 31.4$$

10. 39

11.
$$\frac{x}{4} + 6 = 9$$
$$\underline{\phantom{\frac{x}{4}}-6 \quad -6}$$
$$\frac{x}{4} = 3$$

$$4\left(\frac{x}{4}\right) = 4(3)$$

$$x = 12$$

12. 25

13.
$$\frac{x}{10} - 5 = 13$$
$$\underline{\phantom{\frac{x}{10}}+5 \quad +5}$$
$$\frac{x}{10} = 18$$

$$10\left(\frac{x}{10}\right) = 10(18)$$

$$x = 180$$

14. 320

15.
$$-14 = \frac{x}{6} - 7$$
$$\underline{+7 \qquad +7}$$
$$-7 = \frac{x}{6}$$

$$6(-7) = 6\left(\frac{x}{6}\right)$$

$$-42 = x$$

16. -88

17.
$$7 = \frac{2x}{5} + 3$$
$$\underline{-3 \qquad -3}$$
$$4 = \frac{2x}{5}$$

$$5(4) = 5\left(\frac{2x}{5}\right)$$

$$20 = 2x$$

$$\frac{20}{2} = \frac{2x}{2}$$

$$10 = x$$

18. 4

19.
$$4 - \frac{7x}{5} = 11$$
$$\underline{-4 \qquad -4}$$
$$-\frac{7x}{5} = 7$$

$$5\left(-\frac{7x}{5}\right) = 5(7)$$

20. -45

$$-7x = 35$$

$$\frac{-7x}{-7} = \frac{35}{-7}$$

$$x = -5$$

21.
$$\begin{array}{rcl} -24 + \dfrac{5x}{8} &=& 41 \\ +24 & & +24 \end{array}$$
$$\frac{5x}{8} = 65$$

$$8\left(\frac{5x}{8}\right) = 8(65)$$

$$5x = 8(65)$$

$$\frac{5x}{5} = \frac{8(\overset{13}{\cancel{65}})}{\cancel{5}}$$

$$x = 8(13) = 104$$

22. 20

23.
$$\begin{array}{rcl} 41 &=& 25 - \dfrac{4x}{5} \\ -25 & & -25 \end{array}$$
$$16 = -\frac{4x}{5}$$

$$5(16) = \cancel{5}\left(\frac{-4x}{\cancel{5}}\right)$$

$$5(16) = -4x$$

$$\frac{5(16)}{-4} = \frac{-4x}{-4}$$

$$-20 = x$$

24. -35

EXERCISES 405A, SET I (page 109)

1.
$$\begin{array}{rcl} 3x + 5 &=& 14 \\ -5 & & -5 \end{array}$$
$$3x = 9$$

$$\frac{3x}{3} = \frac{9}{3}$$

$$x = 3$$

2. 3

3.
$$\begin{array}{rcl} 9x - 7 &=& 20 \\ +7 & & +7 \end{array}$$
$$9x = 27$$

$$\frac{9x}{9} = \frac{27}{9}$$

$$x = 3$$

4. 7

5.
$$\begin{array}{rcl} 2x - 7 &=& x \\ -x & & -x \end{array}$$
$$\begin{array}{rcl} x - 7 &=& 0 \\ +7 & & +7 \end{array}$$
$$x = 7$$

6. 2

7.
$$\begin{array}{rcl} 5x &=& 3x - 4 \\ -3x & & -3x \end{array}$$
$$2x = -4$$

$$\frac{2x}{2} = \frac{-4}{2}$$

$$x = -2$$

8. -3

9.
$$\begin{array}{rcl} 9 - 2x &=& x \\ +2x & & +2x \end{array}$$
$$9 = 3x$$

$$\frac{9}{3} = \frac{3x}{3}$$

$$3 = x \quad or \quad x = 3$$

10. 1

11.
$$\begin{array}{rcl} 3x - 4 &=& 2x + 5 \\ -2x & & -2x \end{array}$$
$$\begin{array}{rcl} x - 4 &=& 5 \\ +4 & & +4 \end{array}$$
$$x = 9$$

12. 6

13.
$$\begin{array}{rcl} 6x + 7 &=& 3 + 8x \\ -6x & & -6x \end{array}$$
$$\begin{array}{rcl} 7 &=& 3 + 2x \\ -3 & & -3 \end{array}$$
$$\frac{4}{2} = \frac{2x}{2}$$

$$2 = x \quad or \quad x = 2$$

14. -7

15.
$$\begin{array}{rcl} 7x - 8 &=& 8 - 9x \\ +9x & & +9x \end{array}$$
$$\begin{array}{rcl} 16x - 8 &=& 8 \\ +8 & & +8 \end{array}$$
$$16x = 16$$

$$\frac{16x}{16} = \frac{16}{16}$$

$$x = 1$$

16. 1

17.
$$3x - 7 - x = 15 - 2x - 6$$
$$\begin{array}{rcl} 2x - 7 &=& 9 - 2x \\ +2x & & +2x \end{array}$$
$$\begin{array}{rcl} 4x - 7 &=& 9 \\ +7 & & +7 \end{array}$$
$$4x = 16$$

$$\frac{4x}{4} = \frac{16}{4}$$

$$x = 4$$

18. -3

19.
$$8x - 13 + 3x = 12 + 5x - 7$$
$$\begin{array}{rcl} 11x - 13 &=& 5 + 5x \\ -5x & & -5x \end{array}$$
$$\begin{array}{rcl} 6x - 13 &=& 5 \\ +13 & & +13 \end{array}$$
$$6x = 18$$

$$\frac{6x}{6} = \frac{18}{6}$$

$$x = 3$$

20. 2

21.
$$7 - 9x - 12 = 3x + 5 - 8x$$
$$\begin{array}{rcl} -9x - 5 &=& -5x + 5 \\ +9x & & +9x \end{array}$$
$$\begin{array}{rcl} -5 &=& 4x + 5 \\ -5 & & -5 \end{array}$$
$$-10 = 4x$$

$$\frac{-10}{4} = \frac{4x}{4}$$

$$-\frac{5}{2} = x \quad or \quad x = -2\frac{1}{2}$$

22. $-1\frac{1}{3}$

23.
$$\begin{array}{rcl} 7.84 - 1.15x &=& 2.45 \\ -7.84 & & -7.84 \end{array}$$
$$-1.15x = -5.39$$

$$\frac{-1.15x}{-1.15} = \frac{-5.39}{-1.15}$$

$$x \doteq 4.69$$

24. $\doteq 0.662$

1. $5x - 3(2 + 3x) = 6$
$5x - 6 - 9x = 6$
$-4x = 12$

$$\frac{-4x}{-4} = \frac{12}{-4}$$

$x = -3$

2. -18

3. $6x + 2(3 - 8x) = -14$
$6x + 6 - 16x = -14$
$-10x = -20$

$$\frac{-10x}{-10} = \frac{-20}{-10}$$

$x = 2$

4. 2

5. $7x + 5 = 3(3x + 5)$
$7x + 5 = 9x + 15$
$-10 = 2x$
$-5 = x$

6. -2

7. $9 - 4x = 5(9 - 8x)$
$9 - 4x = 45 - 40x$
$36x = 36$
$x = 1$

8. 2

9. $3y - 2(2y - 7) = 2(3 + y) - 4$
$3y - 4y + 14 = 6 + 2y - 4$
$-y + 14 = 2 + 2y$
$-3y = -12$
$y = 4$

10. 1

11. $6(3 - 4x) + 12 = 10x - 2(5 - 3x)$
$18 - 24x + 12 = 10x - 10 + 6x$
$30 - 24x = 16x - 10$
$40 = 40x$
$1 = x$

12. 1

13. $2(3x - 6) - 3(5x + 4) = 5(7x - 8)$
$6x - 12 - 15x - 12 = 35x - 40$
$-9x - 24 = 35x - 40$
$16 = 44x$

$$\frac{16}{44} = x$$

$$\frac{4}{11} = x$$

14. $\frac{1}{18}$

15. $6(5 - 4h) = 3(4h - 2) - 7(6 + 8h)$
$30 - 24h = 12h - 6 - 42 - 56h$
$30 - 24h = -48 - 44h$
$20h = -78$

$$h = -3\frac{9}{10}$$

16. $8\frac{1}{2}$

17. $2[3 - 5(x - 4)] = 10 - 5x$
$2[3 - 5x + 20] = 10 - 5x$
$2[23 - 5x] = 10 - 5x$
$46 - 10x = 10 - 5x$
$36 = 5x$

$$7\frac{1}{5} = x$$

18. 16

19. $3[2h - 6] = 2\{2(3 - h) - 5\}$
$6h - 18 = 2\{6 - 2h - 5\}$
$6h - 18 = 2\{1 - 2h\}$
$6h - 18 = 2 - 4h$
$10h = 20$
$h = 2$

20. $\frac{7}{10}$

21. $5(3 - 2x) - 10 = 4x + [-(2x - 5) + 15]$
$15 - 10x - 10 = 4x + [-2x + 5 + 15]$
$15 - 10x - 10 = 4x - 2x + 20$
$-15 = 12x$

$$-\frac{15}{12} = x$$

$$-1\frac{1}{4} = x$$

22. -1

23. $9 - 3(2x - 7) - 9x = 5x - 2[6x - (4 - x) - 20]$
$9 - 6x + 21 - 9x = 5x - 2[6x - 4 + x - 20]$
$9 - 6x + 21 - 9x = 5x - 2[7x - 24]$
$9 - 6x + 21 - 9x = 5x - 14x + 48$
$-6x = 18$
$x = -3$

24. 21

25. $-2\{5 - [6 - 3(4 - x)] - 2x\} = 13 - [-(2x - 1)]$
$-2\{5 - [6 - 12 + 3x] - 2x\} = 13 - [-2x + 1]$
$-2\{5 - 6 + 12 - 3x - 2x\} = 13 + 2x - 1$
$-2\{11 - 5x\} = 12 + 2x$
$-22 + 10x = 12 + 2x$
$8x = 34$

$$x = \frac{34}{8}$$

$$x = 4\frac{1}{4}$$

26. 10

27. $5.073x - 2.937(8.622 + 7.153x) = 6.208$
$5.073x - 25.322814 - 21.008361x = 6.208$
$-15.935361x = 31.530814$
$x \doteq -1.979$

28. $\doteq 0.5023$

29. $8.23x - 4.07(6.75x - 5.59) = 3.84(9.18 - x) - 2.67$
$8.23x - 27.4725x + 22.7513 = 35.2512 - 3.84x - 2.67$
$-19.2425x + 22.7513 = 32.5812 - 3.84x$
$-15.4025x = 9.8299$
$x = -0.6382015907$
$x \doteq -0.638$

30. $\doteq 1.011$

EXERCISES 406, SET I (page 115)

1. $x + 3 = 8$
$$\frac{-3 \quad -3}{x \quad = \quad 5}$$
Conditional

2. -2; Conditional

3. $2x + 5 = 7 + 2x$
$$\frac{-2x \quad\quad -2x}{5 \neq 7}$$
No solution

4. No solution

5. $6 + 4x = 4x + 6$
$$\frac{-4x \quad\quad -4x}{6 \quad = \quad 6}$$

Identity

6. Identity

7. $5x - 2(4 - x) = 6$
$5x - 8 + 2x = 6$
$7x = 14$
$x = 2$
Conditional

8. 2; Conditional

9. $6x - 3(5 + 2x) = -15$
$6x - 15 - 6x = -15$

Identity $-15 = -15$

10. Identity

11. $4x - 2(6 + 2x) = -15$
     $4x - 12 - 4x = -15$
     $0 \neq -3$
     No solution

12. No solution

13. $7(2 - 5x) - 32 = 10x - 3(6 + 15x)$
     $14 - 35x - 32 = 10x - 18 - 45x$
     $- 35x - 18 = -35x - 18$
     Identity

14. $\dfrac{34}{41}$; Conditional

15. $2(2x - 5) - 3(4 - x) = 7x - 20$
     $4x - 10 - 12 + 3x = 7x - 20$
     $-22 \neq -20$
     No solution

16. Identity

17. $2[3 - 4(5 - x)] = 2(3x - 11)$
     $2[3 - 20 + 4x] = 6x - 22$
     $6 - 40 + 8x = 6x - 22$
     $2x = 12$
     $x = 6$
     Conditional

18. No solution

19. $460.2x - 23.6(19.5x - 51.4) = 1213.04$
     $460.2x - 460.2x + 1213.04 = 1213.04$
     $1213.04 = 1213.04$
     Identity

20. $\doteq 2.42$ Conditional

REVIEW EXERCISES 407, SET I (page 117)

1. $3x - 5 = 4$
    $3x = 9$

    $\dfrac{3x}{3} = \dfrac{9}{3}$

    $x = 3$

2. 4

3. $17 - 5x = 2$
    $-5x = -15$

    $\dfrac{-5x}{-5} = \dfrac{-15}{-5}$

    $x = 3$

4. 2

5. $2 = 20 - 9x$
    $-18 = -9x$

    $\dfrac{-18}{-9} = \dfrac{-9x}{-9}$

    $2 = x$

6. 3

7. $\begin{aligned}2x + 1 &= 2x + 7\\ -2x & -2x \\ \hline 1 &\neq 7\end{aligned}$
    No solution

8. No solution

9. $7.5 = \dfrac{A}{10}$

    $10(7.5) = 10\left(\dfrac{A}{10}\right)$

    $75 = A$

10. 16

11. $\begin{aligned}\dfrac{C}{7} - 15 &= 13\\ + 15 & + 15\\ \hline \dfrac{C}{7} &= 28\end{aligned}$

    $7\left(\dfrac{C}{7}\right) = 7(28)$

    $C = 196$

12. 180

13. $7 - 2(M - 4) = 5$
     $7 - 2M + 8 = 5$
     $-2M + 15 = 5$
     $-2M = -10$

     $\dfrac{-2M}{-2} = \dfrac{-10}{-2}$

     $M = 5$

14. 4

15. $10 - 4(2 - 3x) = 2 + 12x$
     $10 - 8 + 12x = 2 + 12x$
     $2 + 12x = 2 + 12x$

     Identity

16. Identity

17. $6R - 8 = 6(2 - 3R)$

     $\begin{aligned}6R - 8 &= 12 - 18R\\ + 18R & + 18R\\ \hline 24R - 8 &= 12\\ + 8 & + 8\\ \hline 24R &= 20\end{aligned}$

     $\dfrac{24R}{24} = \dfrac{20}{24}$

     $R = \dfrac{5}{6}$

18. $1\dfrac{5}{7}$

19. $\begin{aligned}56T - 18 &= 7(8T - 4)\\ 56T - 18 &= 56T - 28\\ - 56T & - 56T\\ \hline -18 &\neq -28\end{aligned}$
     No solution

20. No solution

21. $15(4 - 5V) = 16(4 - 6V) + 10$
     $60 - 75V = 64 - 96V + 10$
     $60 - 75V = 74 - 96V$
     $21V = 14$

     $\dfrac{21V}{21} = \dfrac{14}{21}$

     $V = \dfrac{2}{3}$

22. $1\dfrac{2}{3}$

23. $9 - 3(x - 2) = 3(5 - x)$
     $9 - 3x + 6 = 15 - 3x$
     $15 - 3x = 15 - 3x$

     Identity

24. Identity

25. $5x - 7(4 - 2x) + 8 = 10 - 9(11 - x)$
     $5x - 28 + 14x + 8 = 10 - 99 + 9x$
     $19x - 20 = -89 + 9x$
     $10x = -69$
     $x = -6.9$

26. -8.3

27. $2[-7y - 3(5 - 4y) + 10] = 10y - 12$
     $2[-7y - 15 + 12y + 10] = 10y - 12$
     $2[5y - 5] = 10y - 12$
     $10y - 10 = 10y - 12$
     $-10 \neq -12$
     No solution

28. No solution

29. $4[-24 - 6(3x - 5) + 22x] = 0$
     $4[-24 - 18x + 30 + 22x] = 0$
     $4[6 + 4x] = 0$
     $24 + 16x = 0$
     $16x = -24$

     $x = -1\dfrac{1}{2}$

30. 1

1. $\dfrac{-7}{0}$ Not possible

2. 10

3. $\quad 7\sqrt{16} - 5(-4)$
$= 7(4) - 5(-4)$
$= 28 + 20 = 48$

4. 37

5. $V = \dfrac{4}{3}\pi R^3$
$\doteq \dfrac{4}{\cancel{3}}(3.14)\overset{3}{(\cancel{9})}(9)(9)$
$\doteq 4(3.14)(3)(9)(9)$
$\doteq 3052.08$

6. 3630

7. $\quad 15x - [9y - (7x - 10y)]$
$= 15x - [9y - 7x + 10y]$
$= 15x - 9y + 7x - 10y$
$= 22x - 19y$

8. $-14a - 57b$

9. $\quad x(2x^2 - 5x + 12) - 6(3x^2 + 2x - 5)$
$= 2x^3 \underset{\sim}{- 5x^2} + 12x \underset{\sim}{- 18x^2} - 12x + 30$
$= 2x^3 - 23x^2 + 30$

10. $10h^2k^2 - 3h^2k^3$

CHAPTER FOUR DIAGNOSTIC TEST (page 119)

Following each problem number is the textbook section reference (in parentheses) where that kind of problem is discussed.

1. (402) $\quad\begin{aligned} x - 3 &= 7 \\ \underline{+ 3} \quad &\underline{+ 3} \\ x \quad &= 10 \end{aligned}$

2. (402) $\quad\begin{aligned} 10 &= x + 4 \\ \underline{- 4} \quad &\underline{\quad - 4} \\ 6 &= x \end{aligned}$

3. (403) $\quad\begin{aligned} 3x + 2 &= 14 \\ \underline{\quad - 2} \quad &\underline{- 2} \\ 3x \quad &= 12 \\ \dfrac{3x}{3} &= \dfrac{12}{3} \\ x &= 4 \end{aligned}$ Check: $\begin{aligned} 3x + 2 &\overset{?}{=} 14 \\ 3(4) + 2 &\overset{?}{=} 14 \\ 12 + 2 &\overset{?}{=} 14 \\ 14 &= 14 \end{aligned}$

4. (403) $\quad\begin{aligned} 15 - 2x &= 7 \\ \underline{- 15} \quad\quad &\underline{\quad - 15} \\ -2x &= -8 \\ \dfrac{-2x}{-2} &= \dfrac{-8}{-2} \\ x &= 4 \end{aligned}$

5. (404) $\quad\begin{aligned} \dfrac{x}{4} &= 3.8 \\ \dfrac{\cancel{4}}{1}\left(\dfrac{x}{\cancel{4}}\right) &= 4(3.8) \\ x &= 15.2 \end{aligned}$

6. (404) $\quad\begin{aligned} -5 &= \dfrac{x}{7} \\ 7(-5) &= \dfrac{\cancel{7}}{1}\left(\dfrac{x}{\cancel{7}}\right) \\ -35 &= x \end{aligned}$

7. (404) $\quad\begin{aligned} \dfrac{x}{5} - 3 &= 2 \\ \underline{+ 3} \quad &\underline{+ 3} \\ \dfrac{x}{5} \quad &= 5 \\ \dfrac{\cancel{5}}{1}\left(\dfrac{x}{\cancel{5}}\right) &= 5(5) \\ x &= 25 \end{aligned}$

8. (404) $\quad\begin{aligned} 100 - \dfrac{10x}{7} &= -50 \\ \underline{- 100} \quad\quad &\underline{\quad - 100} \\ -\dfrac{10x}{7} &= -150 \end{aligned}$

$\dfrac{\cancel{7}}{1}\left(\dfrac{-10x}{\cancel{7}}\right) = 7(-150)$
$-10x = -1050$
$\dfrac{-10x}{-10} = \dfrac{-1050}{-10}$
$x = 105$

9. (405) $\quad\begin{aligned} 4x + 5 &= 17 - 2x \\ 6x &= 12 \\ \dfrac{6x}{6} &= \dfrac{12}{6} \\ x &= 2 \end{aligned}$

10. (405) $\quad\begin{aligned} 3z - 21 + 5z &= 4 - 6z + 17 \\ 8z - 21 &= 21 - 6z \\ 14z &= 42 \\ \dfrac{14z}{14} &= \dfrac{42}{14} \\ z &= 3 \end{aligned}$

11. (405) $\quad\begin{aligned} 6k - 3(4 - 5k) &= 9 \\ 6k - 12 + 15k &= 9 \\ 21k - 12 &= 9 \\ 21k &= 21 \\ \dfrac{21k}{21} &= \dfrac{21}{21} \\ k &= 1 \end{aligned}$

$\quad$ Check: $\quad\begin{aligned} 6k - 3(4 - 5k) &= 9 \\ 6(1) - 3(4 - 5(1)) &\overset{?}{=} 9 \\ 6 - 3(4 - 5) &\overset{?}{=} 9 \\ 6 - 3(-1) &\overset{?}{=} 9 \\ 6 + 3 &= 9 \end{aligned}$

12. (406) $\quad\begin{aligned} 6x - 2(3x - 5) &= 10 \\ 6x - 6x + 10 &= 10 \\ 10 &= 10 \end{aligned}$
$\quad$ Identity

13. (405) $\quad\begin{aligned} 2m - 4(3m - 2) &= 5(6 + m) - 7 \\ 2m - 12m + 8 &= 30 + 5m - 7 \\ -10m + 8 &= 23 + 5m \\ -15m &= 15 \\ \dfrac{-15m}{-15} &= \dfrac{15}{-15} \\ m &= -1 \end{aligned}$

14. (406) $\quad\begin{aligned} 2(3x + 5) &= 14 + 3(2x - 1) \\ 6x + 10 &= 14 + 6x - 3 \\ 6x + 10 &= 11 + 6x \\ 10 &\neq 11 \end{aligned}$
$\quad$ No solution

15. (405) $\quad\begin{aligned} 3[7 - 6(y - 2)] &= -3 + 2y \\ 3[7 - 6y + 12] &= -3 + 2y \\ 3[19 - 6y] &= -3 + 2y \\ 57 - 18y &= -3 + 2y \\ 60 &= 20y \\ \dfrac{60}{20} &= \dfrac{20y}{20} \\ 3 &= y \end{aligned}$

EXERCISES 501A, SET I (page 123)

1. $x + 10$
2. $A + B$
3. $A - 5$
4. $B - C$
5. $6z$
6. AB
7. $x - UV$
8. $PQ - x$
9. $C - D$
10. $A - 10$
11. $5x^2$
12. $10x^3$

13. $(A + B)^2$ 14. $\left(\dfrac{A}{B}\right)^2$ 15. $\dfrac{x + 7}{y}$

16. $\dfrac{T}{x + 9}$ 17. $x(y - 6)$ 18. $x + 40 = w$

EXERCISES 501B, SET I (page 125)

1. Fred's salary is the unknown. Let S represent Fred's salary. Then $S + 75$ is the algebraic expression for "Fred's salary plus seventy-five dollars."
2. $S - 42$
3. The number of children is the unknown. Let N represent the number of children. Then $N - 2$ is the algebraic expression for "two less than the number of children in Mr. Moore's family."
4. $N + 2$
5. Joyce's age is the unknown. Let x represent Joyce's age. Then $4x$ is the algebraic expression for "four times Joyce's age."
6. $\dfrac{x}{4}$ or $\dfrac{1}{4}x$
7. The cost of a record is the unknown. Let C represent the cost of a record (in cents). Then $20C + 89$ is the algebraic expression for "twenty times the cost of a record increased by eighty-nine cents."
8. $5C - 17$
9. The cost of a hamburger is the unknown. let C represent the cost of a hamburger. Then $\dfrac{1}{5}C$ or $\dfrac{C}{5}$ is the algebraic expression for "one-fifth the cost of a hamburger."
10. $\dfrac{L}{8}$
11. Let x = speed of car. Then $5x + 100$ is the algebraic expression for "five times the speed of the car plus one hundred miles per hour."
12. $2x - 40$

13. Let x = the unknown. Then x^2 = the square of the unknown, and $5x^2 - 10$ is the algebraic expression that represents "ten less than five times the square of the unknown."
14. $4x^3 + 8$
15. First method: Let W = width.
    Then $W + 12$ = length.
    Second method: Let L = length.
    Then $L - 12$ = width.
16. $\begin{cases} B = \text{base} \\ B - 7 = \text{altitude, or} \end{cases}$
    $\begin{cases} A = \text{altitude} \\ A + 7 = \text{base} \end{cases}$
17. x = unknown number. Then $50 - \dfrac{7}{x}$ represents the statement in the problem.
18. $15 + \dfrac{x}{9}$
19. Let L = length of rectangle. Then $2L + 11$ represents the statement in the problem.
20. $D - 1$
21. If W = Walter's weight, then $320 - W$ = Carlos' weight.
    If C = Carlos' weight, then $320 - C$ = Walter's weight.
22. T, $224 - T$, or L, $224 - L$
23. Let w = weight in kilograms. Then $2.2w$ represents the statement in the problem.
24. $0.62D$
25. Let x = the unknown number. Then $\dfrac{8 + x}{x^2}$ represents the statement.
26. $\dfrac{x^2 + 11}{x}$
27. Let C = Centigrade temperature. Then $32 + \dfrac{9}{5}C$ represents the statement.
28. $\dfrac{5}{9}(F - 32)$

EXERCISES 502, SET I (page 128)

1. Thirteen more than twice an unknown number is twenty-five.

   $13 \quad + \quad 2x \quad = \quad 25$

2. $25 + 3x = 34$

3. Five times an unknown number decreased by eight is twenty-two.

   $5 \quad \cdot \quad x \quad - \quad 8 \quad = \quad 22$

4. Four times an unknown number decreased by five is fifteen.

   $4 \quad \cdot \quad x \quad - \quad 5 \quad = \quad 15$

5. Seven minus an unknown number is equal to the unknown number plus one.

   $7 \quad - \quad x \quad = \quad x \quad + \quad 1$

6. Six plus an unknown number is equal to twelve decreased by the unknown number.

   $6 \quad + \quad x \quad = \quad 12 \quad - \quad x$

7. One-fifth of an unknown number is four.

   $\dfrac{1}{5} \quad \cdot \quad x \quad = \quad 4$

8. $\dfrac{x}{12} = 6$

9. When four is subtracted from one-half of an unknown number, the result is six.

   $\dfrac{1}{2}x \quad - \quad 4 \qquad = \qquad 6$

10. $\frac{1}{3}x - 5 = 4$

11. Twice the sum of five and an unknown number is equal to twenty-six.   12. $4(9 + x) = 18$

    2 · (5 + x) = 26

13. When the sum of an unknown number and itself is multiplied by three, the result is twenty-four.

    (x + x) · 3 = 24

14. $5(x + x) = 40$

15. When the sum of six and twice an unknown number is divided by two, the result is seven.

    (6 + $2x$) ÷ 2 = 7

    or $\frac{6 + 2x}{2} = 7$

16. $\frac{8 + x}{3} = 4$

17. When the sum of two and eight times an unknown number is divided by seven, the quotient equals the unknown number.

    (2 + $8x$) ÷ 7 = x

    or $\frac{2 + 8x}{7} = x$

18. $\frac{9 + 5x}{20} = x$

19. When one is subtracted from nineteen times an unknown number and the result is divided by eighteen, the quotient equals twice the unknown number.

    ($19x$ - 1) ÷ 18 = $2x$

    or $\frac{19x - 1}{18} = 2x$

20. $\frac{8 - 15x}{13} = 4x$

EXERCISES 503, SET I (page 131)

1. Thirteen more than twice an unknown number is twenty-five. $13 + 2x = 25$ 2. 3
                                                                   $2x = 12$
   13 + $2x$ = 25 $x = 6$

3. Five times an unknown number, decreased by eight, is twenty-two. $5x - 8 = 22$ 4. 5
                                                                        $5x = 30$
   5 · x - 8 = 22 $x = 6$

5. Seven minus an unknown number is equal to the unknown number plus one.   6. 3

   7 - x = x + 1

                7 - x = x + 1
                    6 = $2x$
                    3 = x

7. When four is subtracted from one-half of an unknown number, the result is six.   8. 27

   $\frac{1}{2}x$ - 4 = 6

                $\frac{1}{2}x - 4 = 6$
                $\phantom{\frac{1}{2}x} + 4 \quad + 4$
                $\frac{1}{2}x \quad = 10$

$$2\left(\frac{1}{2}x\right) = 2(10)$$
$$x = 20$$

9. | Twice | the sum of five and an unknown number | is equal to | twenty-six. |

 2 · (5 + x) = 26

$$2(5 + x) = 26$$
$$10 + 2x = 26$$
$$2x = 16$$
$$x = 8$$

10. -4

11. When | twice the sum of four and an unknown number | is added to | the unknown number | the result is | the same as when ten is added to the unknown number. |

 2(4 + x)   + x = x + 10

$$2(4 + x) + x = x + 10$$
$$8 + 2x + x = x + 10$$
$$2x = 2$$
$$x = 1$$

12. 5

13. | Three times the sum of eight and twice an unknown number | is equal to | four times the sum of three times the unknown number and eight. |

 3(8 + 2x)   =   4(3x + 8)

$$3(8 + 2x) = 4(3x + 8)$$
$$24 + 6x = 12x + 32$$
$$-6x = 8$$
$$\frac{-6x}{-6} = \frac{8}{-6}$$
$$x = -1\frac{1}{3}$$

14. $\frac{10}{11}$

15. When | three times the sum of four and an unknown number | is subtracted from | ten times the unknown number | the result is equal to | five times the sum of nine and twice the unknown number. |

 10x −   3(4 + x)   =   5(9 + 2x)

$$10x - 3(4 + x) = 5(9 + 2x)$$
$$10x - 12 - 3x = 45 + 10x$$
$$-3x = 57$$
$$x = -19$$

16. $-2\frac{1}{2}$

17. $8.66x - 5.75(6.94 + x) = 4.69(8.55 + 3.48x)$
    $x \doteq -5.97$

18. $\doteq -32.6$

EXERCISES 504A, SET I (page 134)

1. | number of nickels | · | value of each nickel | = | total value |

 7 · (5) = 35¢

2. $2.75

3. | number of 50-cent coins | · | value of each coin | = | total value |

 9 · (50) = 450¢
 = $4.50

4. $1.20

5. | number of quarters | · | value of each quarter | = | total value |

 x · (25) = 25x

6. 5y¢

7. | cost of adult tickets | + | cost of children's tickets | = | total cost |

 7(1.50) + 5(0.75) = 14.25
 10.50 + 3.75 = $14.25

8. $21.25

9.

cost of adult tickets	+	cost of children's tickets	=	total cost

$3.5x$ + $1.9y$ = $3.5x + 1.9y$

10. $2.75x + 1.50y$

11.

cost of 25¢ stamps	+	cost of 6¢ stamps	=	total cost

$25x$ + $6y$ = $25x + 6y$

12. $4x + 2y$

13.

cost of cashew nuts	+	cost of peanuts	=	total cost

$1.19x$ + $0.85y$ = $1.19x + 0.85y$

14. $1.95x + 1.25y$

EXERCISES 504B, SET I (page 136)

1. Let D = the number of dimes.
Then $13 - D$ = the number of nickels.
Each dime is worth 10¢. Therefore, D dimes are worth $10D$¢. Each nickel is worth 5¢. Therefore, $13 - D$ nickels are worth $5(13 - D)$¢.

The amount of money in dimes	+	the amount of money in nickels	is	95¢.

$10D$ + $5(13 - D)$ = 95

$$10D + 5(13 - D) = 95$$
$$10D + 65 - 5D = 95$$
$$5D = 30$$
$$D = 6 \quad \text{(number of dimes)}$$
$$\text{Then } 13 - D = 13 - 6 = 7 \text{ nickels.}$$

2. 5 nickels, 6 dimes

3. Let N = the number of nickels.
Then $12 - N$ = the number of quarters.
Each nickel is worth 5¢. Therefore, N nickels are worth $5N$¢.
Each quarter is worth 25¢. Therefore, $12 - N$ quarters are worth $25(12 - N)$¢.

The amount of money in nickels	+	the amount of money in quarters	is	220¢.

$5N$ + $25(12 - N)$ = 220

$$5N + 25(12 - N) = 220$$
$$5N + 300 - 25N = 220$$
$$-20N = -80$$
$$N = 4 \quad \text{(number of nickels)}$$
$$\text{Then } 12 - N = 12 - 4 = 8 \text{ quarters.}$$

4. 10 nickels, 8 quarters

5. Let x = number of nickels.
Then $x + 4$ = number of quarters (because there are 4 more quarters than nickels).
And $3x$ = number of dimes (because there are 3 times as many dimes as nickels).

Amount of money in nickels	+	amount in quarters	+	amount in dimes	=	400¢.

$5x$ + $25(x + 4)$ + $10(3x)$ = 400

$$5x + 25(x + 4) + 10(3x) = 400$$
$$5x + 25x + 100 + 30x = 400$$
$$60x = 300$$
$$x = 5 \quad \text{(number of nickels)}$$
$$x + 4 = 5 + 4 = 9 \quad \text{(number of quarters)}$$
$$3x = 3(5) = 15 \quad \text{(number of dimes)}$$

6. 2 nickels, 9 dimes, 18 quarters

7. Let x = number of quarters.
    Then $x - 3$ = number of dimes (because there are 3 fewer dimes than quarters).
    And $2x - 3$ = number of nickels (because there are as many nickels as dimes and quarters together).

Amount of money in quarters	+	amount in dimes	+	amount in nickels	=	225¢
$25x$	+	$10(x - 3)$	+	$5(2x - 3)$	=	225

$$25x + 10(x - 3) + 5(2x - 3) = 225$$
$$25x + 10x - 30 + 10x - 15 = 225$$
$$45x = 270$$
$$x = 6 \quad \text{(number of quarters)}$$
$$x - 3 = 6 - 3 = 3 \quad \text{(number of dimes)}$$
$$2x - 3 = 12 - 3 = 9 \quad \text{(number of nickels)}$$

8. 7 pennies, 12 nickels, 19 dimes

9. Let x = number of box seats sold.
    Then $5x$ = number of balcony seats sold.
    This leaves $1080 - x - 5x = 1080 - 6x$ for the number of orchestra seats.

The value of box seats	+	value of balcony seats	+	value of orchestra seats	=	total value
$10x$	+	$4(5x)$	+	$7(1080 - 6x)$	=	6600

$$10x + 4(5x) + 7(1080 - 6x) = 6600$$
$$10x + 20x + 7560 - 42x = 6600$$
$$-12x = -960$$
$$x = 80 \quad \text{(box seats)}$$
$$5x = 5(80) = 400 \quad \text{(balcony seats)}$$
$$1080 - 6x = 1080 - 6(80) = 600 \quad \text{(orchestra seats)}$$

10. 4400 box seats; 17,600 reserved seats; 35,200 general seats

11. Let x = number of 12-cent stamps.
     Then $2x$ = number of 10-cent stamps.

     This leaves $60 - x - 2x = 60 - 3x$ for the number of 2-cent stamps.

Value of 12¢ stamps	+	value of 10¢ stamps	+	value of 2¢ stamps	=	amount spent
$12x$	+	$10(2x)$	+	$2(60 - 3x)$	=	380¢

$$12x + 10(2x) + 2(60 - 3x) = 380$$
$$12x + 20x + 120 - 6x = 380$$
$$26x = 260$$
$$x = 10 \quad \text{(12-cent stamps)}$$
$$2x = 2(10) = 20 \quad \text{(10-cent stamps)}$$
$$60 - 3x = 60 - 3(10) = 30 \quad \text{(2-cent stamps)}$$

12. Ten 8-cent stamps, thirty 6-cent stamps, sixty 12-cent stamps

EXERCISES 505, SET I (page 140)

1. Two numbers are in the ratio of 3 : 4.

    3 : 4

    $3x$: $4x$

    Let $4x$ = larger number
    and $3x$ = smaller number.

    Their sum is 35.

    $$3x + 4x = 35$$
    $$7x = 35$$
    $$x = 5$$
    $$\text{smaller number} = 3x = 15$$
    $$\text{larger number} = 4x = 20$$

2. 91, 39

3. Length and width are in the ratio of 9 : 4.

    9 : 4

    $9x$: $4x$

    Let $4x$ = width
    and $9x$ = length.

3.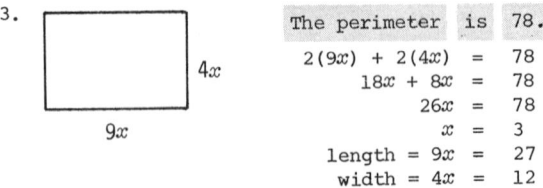

    The perimeter is 78.

    $$2(9x) + 2(4x) = 78$$
    $$18x + 8x = 78$$
    $$26x = 78$$
    $$x = 3$$
    $$\text{length} = 9x = 27$$
    $$\text{width} = 4x = 12$$

4. 28, 8

5. Food + Rent + Clothing = 300
    $$4x + 5x + 1x = 300$$
    $$10x = 300$$
    $$x = 30$$

    Food/month = $4x$ = 120 $\Rightarrow$ per year = 1440

Rent/month $= 5x = 150 \Rightarrow$ per year $= 1800$
Clothing/month $= 1x = 30 \Rightarrow$ per year $= 360$

6. 2700, 675, 1350/year

7. $6x + 5x = 88$
$11x = 88$
$x = 8$
$6x = 48$
$5x = 40$

8. 22, 77

9. $4x + 5x + 6x = 90$
$15x = 90$
$x = 6$
$4x = 24$
$5x = 30$
$6x = 36$

10. 20, 24, 28

11. $2x + 3x + 4x = 27{,}000$
$9x = 27{,}000$
$x = 3000$
$\begin{cases} 2x = 6000 \\ 3x = 9000 \\ 4x = 12{,}000 \end{cases}$

12. 75,000; 15,000; 60,000

13. $1 : 2\frac{1}{2} : 4$
$1x : 2\frac{1}{2}x : 4x$

Let $4x =$ cu yd of gravel
$2\frac{1}{2}x =$ cu yd of sand
and $1x =$ cu yd of cement

$4x = 5$
$x = \frac{5}{4} = 1\frac{1}{4}$ cu yd of cement
$2\frac{1}{2}x = \frac{5}{2}\left(\frac{5}{4}\right) = \frac{25}{8} = 3\frac{1}{8}$ cu yd of sand

14. 519 seafood dinners

EXERCISES 506A, SET I (page 145)

1. $\frac{3}{5}, \frac{6}{10}$
$3(10) \overset{?}{=} 5(6)$
$30 = 30$
Proportion

2. Proportion

3. $\frac{2}{3}, \frac{5}{7}$
$2(7) \overset{?}{=} 3(5)$
$14 \neq 15$
Not a proportion

4. Not a proportion

5. $\frac{6}{9}, \frac{4}{6}$
$6(6) \overset{?}{=} 9(4)$
$36 = 36$
Proportion

6. Proportion

7. $\frac{8}{14} = \frac{16}{x}$
(a) first term $= 8$
(b) second term $= 14$
(c) third term $= 16$
(d) fourth term $= x$
(e) means $= 14, 16$
(f) extremes $= 8, x$

8. (a) 3   (b) 5   (c) x
(d) 20   (e) 5, x (f) 3, 20

9. $\frac{x}{4} = \frac{2}{3}$
$3x = 2(4) = 8$
$x = \frac{8}{3} = 2\frac{2}{3}$

10. $7\frac{1}{2}$

11. $\frac{8}{x} = \frac{4}{5}$
$4x = 8(5) = 40$
$x = 10$

12. $2\frac{2}{3}$

13. $\frac{4}{7} = \frac{x}{21}$
$7x = 4(21)$
$x = \frac{4(21)}{7} = 12$

14. $11\frac{1}{4}$

15. $\frac{100}{x} = \frac{\cancel{40}}{\cancel{30}} = \frac{4}{3}$
$4x = 300$
$x = 75$

16. 24

17. $\frac{x}{100} = \frac{\overset{3}{\cancel{75}}}{\underset{5}{\cancel{125}}} = \frac{3}{5}$
$5x = 300$
$x = 60$

18. 36

19. $\frac{x + 1}{x - 1} = \frac{3}{2}$
$2(x + 1) = 3(x - 1)$
$2x + 2 = 3x - 3$
$5 = x$

20. 4

21. $\frac{2x + 7}{9} = \frac{2x + 3}{5}$
$5(2x + 7) = 9(2x + 3)$
$10x + 35 = 18x + 27$
$8 = 8x$
$1 = x$

22. -2

23. $\frac{5x - 10}{10} = \frac{3x - 5}{7}$
$7(5x - 10) = 10(3x - 5)$
$35x - 70 = 30x - 50$
$5x = 20$
$x = 4$

24. $2\frac{2}{7}$

25. $\frac{2.78x - 8.91}{14.73x + 22.85} = \frac{35.64}{57.26}$
$57.26(2.78x - 8.91) = 35.64(14.73x + 22.85)$
$159.1828x - 510.1866 = 524.9772x + 814.374$
$-365.7944x = 1324.5606$
$x \doteq -3.62$

26. $\doteq 7.02$

EXERCISES 506B, SET I (page 148)

1. $\frac{\frac{3}{4}}{6} = \frac{P}{16}$
$6P = \frac{3}{\cancel{4}} \cdot \frac{\overset{4}{\cancel{16}}}{1} = 12$
$\frac{\cancel{6}P}{\cancel{6}} = \frac{12}{6} = 2$

2. $2\frac{1}{2}$

3. $\dfrac{A}{9} = \dfrac{3\frac{1}{3}}{5}$ 4. 1

$5A = 9 \cdot 3\frac{1}{3}$

$5A = \dfrac{9}{1} \cdot \dfrac{10}{3} = 30$

$\dfrac{5A}{5} = \dfrac{30}{5} = 6$

5. $\dfrac{7.7}{B} = \dfrac{3.5}{5}$ 6. 22.96

$0.7B = 7.7$

$\dfrac{0.7B}{0.7} = \dfrac{7.7}{0.7} = 11$

7. $\dfrac{P}{100} = \dfrac{\frac{3}{2}}{15}$ 8. 4

$15P = \dfrac{100}{1} \cdot \dfrac{3}{2}$

$15P = 150$

$P = 10$

9. $\dfrac{12\frac{1}{2}}{100} = \dfrac{A}{48}$ 10. 54

$100A = 12\frac{1}{2} \cdot 48$

$100A = \dfrac{25}{2} \cdot \dfrac{48}{1}$

$\dfrac{100A}{100} = \dfrac{25(24)}{100} = 6$

11. $\dfrac{2.54}{1} = \dfrac{x}{7.5}$ 12. $\doteq$ 25.64

$x = 2.54(7.5)$

$x = 19.05$

EXERCISES 506C, SET I (page 152)

1. $\dfrac{3 \text{ gals}}{2 \text{ rooms}} = \dfrac{x \text{ gals}}{20 \text{ rooms}}$ 2. 7.5 days

$\dfrac{3}{2} = \dfrac{x}{20}$

$2x = 3(20) = 60$
$x = 30$ gals

3. $\dfrac{6 \text{ ft height}}{4 \text{ ft shadow}} = \dfrac{x \text{ ft height}}{20 \text{ ft shadow}}$ 4. 50 houses

$\dfrac{6}{4} = \dfrac{x}{20}$

$2x = 3(20) = 60$
$x = 30$ ft height

5. $\dfrac{1 \text{ in}}{8 \text{ ft}} = \dfrac{2\frac{1}{2} \text{ in}}{x \text{ ft}}$ 6. $750

$\dfrac{1}{8} = \dfrac{2\frac{1}{2}}{x}$

$x = 8\left(2\frac{1}{2}\right) = \dfrac{8}{1} \cdot \dfrac{5}{2} = 20$ ft

$\dfrac{1 \text{ in}}{8 \text{ ft}} = \dfrac{3 \text{ in}}{y \text{ ft}}$

$\dfrac{1}{8} = \dfrac{3}{y}$

$y = 8(3) = 24$ ft

7. $\dfrac{3000 \text{ invested}}{180 \text{ earned}} = \dfrac{x \text{ invested}}{540 \text{ earned}}$ 8. 21 jars

$\dfrac{3000}{180} = \dfrac{x}{540}$

$3x = 50(540)$

$x = \dfrac{50(540)}{3} = \$9000$

9. $\dfrac{6 \text{ earth}}{1 \text{ moon}} = \dfrac{150 \text{ earth}}{x \text{ moon}}$ 10. 78.4 lb

$\dfrac{6}{1} = \dfrac{150}{x}$

$6x = 150$

$x = \dfrac{150}{6} = 25$ lb

11. $\dfrac{21 \text{ lead}}{5 \text{ aluminum}} = \dfrac{x \text{ lead}}{150 \text{ aluminum}}$ 12. 7.5 lb

$\dfrac{21}{5} = \dfrac{x}{150}$

$5x = 21(150)$

$x = \dfrac{21(150)}{5} = 630$ lb

13. $10 - 6\frac{1}{2} = 3\frac{1}{2}$ hr   14. $1875

$\dfrac{26 \text{ chains}}{6\frac{1}{2} \text{ hr}} = \dfrac{x \text{ chains}}{3\frac{1}{2} \text{ hr}}$

$6\frac{1}{2}x = 26\left(3\frac{1}{2}\right)$

$\dfrac{13}{2}x = 26\left(\dfrac{7}{2}\right)$

$\dfrac{13x}{2} = \dfrac{91}{1}$

$13x = 2(91) = 182$

$\dfrac{13x}{13} = \dfrac{182}{13}$

$x = 14$ chains

15. $\dfrac{3420 \text{ dollars}}{9 \text{ steers}} = \dfrac{x \text{ dollars}}{16 \text{ steers}}$ 16. $45 per hog
     45¢ per kg

$9x = 16(3420)$

$\dfrac{9x}{9} = \dfrac{54720}{9}$

$x = \$6080$

EXERCISES 507, SET I (page 159)

1. (15)$_A$ is (30%)$_P$ of (what number?)$_B$

$\dfrac{15}{B} = \dfrac{30}{100}$

$3 \cdot B = 150$

$B = \dfrac{150}{3} = 50$

2. 80

3. (115)$_A$ is (what %)$_P$ of (250?)$_B$

$\dfrac{115}{250} = \dfrac{P}{100}$

$$250 \cdot P = 11{,}500$$

$$P = \frac{11{,}500}{250} = 46$$

4. $146\frac{2}{3}\%$

5. (What A) is (25% P) of (40? B)

$$\frac{A}{40} = \frac{\overset{1}{\cancel{25}}}{\underset{4}{\cancel{100}}}$$

$$4 \cdot A = 40$$

$$A = \frac{40}{4} = 10$$

6. 29.25

7. (15% P) of (what number B) is (127.5? A)

$$\frac{127.5}{B} = \frac{15}{100}$$

$$15 \cdot B = 12{,}750$$

$$B = \frac{12{,}750}{15} = 850$$

8. 800

9. (What % P) of (8 B) is ($17?$ A)

$$\frac{17}{8} = \frac{P}{100}$$

$$8 \cdot P = 1700$$

$$P = \frac{1700}{8} = 212.5$$

10. 200%

11. (63% P) of (48 B) is (what number? A)

$$\frac{A}{48} = \frac{63}{100}$$

$$100 \cdot A = 48 \times 63$$

$$A = \frac{48 \times 63}{100} = 30.24$$

12. 42.63

13. (750 A) is (125% P) of (what number? B)

$$\frac{750}{B} = \frac{\overset{5}{\cancel{125}}}{\underset{4}{\cancel{100}}}$$

$$5 \cdot B = 4 \times 750$$

$$B = \frac{4 \times \overset{150}{\cancel{750}}}{\underset{1}{\cancel{5}}} = 600$$

14. 250

15. (23 A) is (what % P) of (16 B)

$$\frac{23}{16} = \frac{P}{100}$$

$$16 \cdot P = 2300$$

$$P = \frac{2300}{16} = 143.75$$

16. $\doteq 247.8\%$

17. (What A) is (200% P) of (12 B)

$$\frac{A}{12} = \frac{\overset{2}{\cancel{200}}}{\underset{1}{\cancel{100}}}$$

$$A = 24$$

18. 27

19. (15% P) of (what number B) is (37.5? A)

$$\frac{37.5}{B} = \frac{15}{100}$$

$$15B = 37.5(100)$$

$$B = \frac{3750}{15} = 250$$

20. \$36.45

21. $P = 66\frac{2}{3}$
    $A = 42$
    B is unknown.

$$\frac{42}{B} = \frac{66\frac{2}{3}}{100}$$

$$66\frac{2}{3} \cdot B = 4200$$

$$B = \frac{4200}{66\frac{2}{3}} = 4200 \div 66\frac{2}{3}$$

$$= \frac{4200}{1} \div \frac{200}{3}$$

$$B = \frac{\overset{21}{\cancel{4200}}}{1} \cdot \frac{3}{\underset{1}{\cancel{200}}} = 63$$

22. 216

23. $P = 80$
    $A = 68$
    B is unknown.

$$\frac{68}{B} = \frac{80}{100}$$

$$8 \cdot B = 680$$

$$B = \frac{680}{8} = 85$$

24. 32,200

25. $A = 7$
    $B = 42$
    P is unknown.

$$\frac{\overset{1}{\cancel{7}}}{\underset{6}{\cancel{42}}} = \frac{P}{100}$$

$$6 \cdot P = 100$$

$$P = \frac{100}{6} = 16\frac{2}{3}$$

26. \$25.30

27. P is unknown.
    $A = 54$
    $B = 210$

$$\frac{\overset{9}{\cancel{54}}}{\underset{35}{\cancel{210}}} = \frac{P}{100}$$

$$35 \cdot P = 900$$

$$P = \frac{900}{35} \doteq 25.7$$

28. 11%

29. (Markup A) = (35% P) of (cost B)
    $B = 125$

$$\frac{A}{125} = \frac{\overset{7}{\cancel{35}}}{\underset{20}{\cancel{100}}}$$

$$20A = 7(125)$$

$$A = \frac{7(125)}{20} = 43.75 \text{ (Markup)}$$

$$S = C + M$$

$$= 125 + 43.75 = \$168.75$$

30. $86.40

31.

$$\frac{A}{460} = \frac{5.85}{100} = \frac{0.0585}{1}$$

$$A = 460(0.0585) = \$26.91$$

32. $20,881.58

33. Total weight of steers = 15 × 1027 = 15,405 lb
   Total weight of heiffers = 18 × 956 = 17,208 lb
   If 3% of the weight is lost in shipping, then
   97% of the weight remains at time of sale.

   Money from sale of steers
   $= 0.97 \times 15,405 \times 0.84 \qquad = 12,551.9940$
   Money from sale of heiffers
   $= 0.97 \times 17,208 \times 0.78 \qquad = \underline{13,019.5728}$
   $= 25,571.5668$
   Amount of check = $25,571.57

34. $\doteq 38.6\%$

EXERCISES 508A, SET I (page 164)

1. Condition 1 $\begin{cases} x_1 = -2 \\ y_1 = -14 \end{cases}$ Condition 2 $\begin{cases} x_2 = 4 \\ y_2 = ? \end{cases}$

   $$\frac{y_1}{y_2} = \frac{x_1}{x_2} \Rightarrow \frac{-14}{y_2} = \frac{\overset{-1}{\cancel{-2}}}{\underset{2}{\cancel{4}}}$$

   $$(-1)y_2 = (-14)(2)$$

   $$y_2 = 28$$

2. −30

3. Condition 1 $\begin{cases} x_1 = -3 \\ y_1 = -9 \end{cases}$ Condition 2 $\begin{cases} x_2 = ? \\ y_2 = -12 \end{cases}$

   $$\frac{y_1}{y_2} = \frac{x_1}{x_2} \Rightarrow \frac{\overset{3}{\cancel{-9}}}{\underset{4}{\cancel{-12}}} = \frac{-3}{x_2}$$

   $$3x_2 = -3(4)$$

   $$x_2 = -4$$

4. 9

5. Condition 1 $\begin{cases} x_1 = -2 \\ y_1 = -20 \end{cases}$ Condition 2 $\begin{cases} x_2 = 5 \\ y_2 = ? \end{cases}$

   $$\frac{y_1}{y_2} = \frac{x_1^2}{x_2^2} \Rightarrow \frac{-20}{y_2} = \frac{(-2)^2}{(5)^2} = \frac{4}{25}$$

   $$4y_2 = -20(25)$$

   $$y_2 = -125$$

6. 1000

7. Condition 1 $\begin{cases} F_1 = 5 \\ s_1 = 3 \end{cases}$ Condition 2 $\begin{cases} F_2 = 2 \\ s_2 = ? \end{cases}$

   $$\frac{s_1}{s_2} = \frac{F_1}{F_2} \Rightarrow \frac{3}{s_2} = \frac{5}{2}$$

   $$5s_2 = 3(2)$$

   $$s_2 = \frac{6}{5} = 1\frac{1}{5} \text{ in}$$

8. 25.98 psi

9. Condition 1 $\begin{cases} t_1 = 2 \\ s_1 = 64 \end{cases}$ Condition 2 $\begin{cases} t_2 = 3 \\ s_2 = ? \end{cases}$

   $$\frac{s_1}{s_2} = \frac{t_1^2}{t_2^2} \Rightarrow \frac{64}{s_2} = \frac{(2)^2}{(3)^2} = \frac{4}{9}$$

   $$4s_2 = 64(9)$$

   $$s_2 = \frac{\overset{16}{\cancel{64}}(9)}{\underset{1}{\cancel{4}}} = 144 \text{ ft}$$

10. 900 lb $6\frac{2}{3}$ cd

EXERCISES 508B, SET I (page 167)

1. Condition 1 $\begin{cases} x_1 = 5 \\ y_1 = 3 \end{cases}$ Condition 2 $\begin{cases} x_2 = -10 \\ y_2 = ? \end{cases}$

   $$\frac{y_1}{y_2} = \frac{x_2}{x_1} \Rightarrow \frac{3}{y_2} = \frac{\overset{-2}{\cancel{-10}}}{\underset{1}{\cancel{5}}}$$

   $$-2y_2 = 1(3)$$

   $$y_2 = -\frac{3}{2}$$

2. −12

3. Condition 1 $\begin{cases} x_1 = -2 \\ y_1 = 3 \end{cases}$ Condition 2 $\begin{cases} x_2 = ? \\ y_2 = -1 \end{cases}$

   $$\frac{y_1}{y_2} = \frac{x_2}{x_1} \Rightarrow \frac{3}{-1} = \frac{x_2}{-2}$$

   $$-1x_2 = 3(-2)$$

   $$x_2 = 6$$

4. 4

5. Condition 1 $\begin{cases} d_1 = -4 \\ F_1 = 3 \end{cases}$ Condition 2 $\begin{cases} d_2 = 8 \\ F_2 = ? \end{cases}$

   $$\frac{F_1}{F_2} = \frac{d_2^2}{d_1^2} \Rightarrow \frac{3}{F_2} = \frac{(8)^2}{(-4)^2} = \frac{\overset{4}{\cancel{64}}}{\underset{1}{\cancel{16}}}$$

   $$4F_2 = 1(3)$$

   $$F_2 = \frac{3}{4}$$

6. $\frac{3}{2}$

7. Condition 1 $\begin{cases} P_1 = 250 \\ V_1 = 1600 \end{cases}$ Condition 2 $\begin{cases} P_2 = 400 \\ V_2 = ? \end{cases}$

   $$\frac{V_1}{V_2} = \frac{P_2}{P_1} \Rightarrow \frac{1600}{V_2} = \frac{\overset{8}{\cancel{400}}}{\underset{5}{\cancel{250}}}$$

   $$8V_2 = 1600(5)$$

   $$V_2 = \frac{\overset{200}{\cancel{1600}}(5)}{\underset{}{\cancel{8}}} = 1000 \text{ cc}$$

8. $17\frac{7}{9}$ lb

9. Condition 1 $\begin{cases} d_1 = 50 \\ I_1 = 75 \end{cases}$ Condition 2 $\begin{cases} d_2 = 150 \\ I_2 = ? \end{cases}$

   $$\frac{I_1}{I_2} = \frac{d_2^2}{d_1^2} \Rightarrow \frac{75}{I_2} = \frac{(150)^2}{(50)^2} = \frac{9}{1}$$

$$9I_2 = 75(1)$$
$$I_2 = \frac{75}{9} = 8\frac{1}{3} \text{ db}$$

10. $6\frac{2}{3}$ cd

REVIEW EXERCISES 509, SET I (page 170)

1. $6x$ = the first number
    $7x$ = the second number

    $$6x + 7x = 52$$
    $$13x = 52$$
    $$x = 4$$
    $$6x = 6(4) = 24 \quad \text{first number}$$
    $$7x = 7(4) = 28 \quad \text{second number}$$

2. 88; 72

3. $$\frac{A}{B} = \frac{P}{100}$$
    $$\frac{A}{275} = \frac{35}{100}$$
    $$100A = 35(275)$$
    $$A = \frac{35(275)}{100}$$
    $$A = \$96.25$$

4. $1102.50

5. $$\frac{A}{B} = \frac{P}{100}$$
    $$\frac{77.5}{B} = \frac{31}{100}$$
    $$100(77.5) = 31B$$
    $$\frac{(100)(77.5)}{31} = B$$
    $$B = \$250$$

6. 244

7. $$\frac{A}{B} = \frac{P}{100}$$
    $$\frac{7}{8} = \frac{P}{100}$$
    $$7(100) = 8P$$
    $$\frac{700}{8} = P$$
    $$87.5 = P$$

8. 37.5%

9. $$\frac{A}{B} = \frac{P}{100}$$
    $$\frac{A}{180} = \frac{4\frac{1}{2}}{100}$$
    $$100A = 4\frac{1}{2}(180)$$
    $$A = \frac{4\frac{1}{2}(180)}{100} = \$8.10 \quad \text{(amount of raise)}$$
    New rent = 180 + 8.10 = \$188.10

10. \$92.25

11. Let the numbers be $3x$, $4x$, and $5x$.
    Then $3x + 4x + 5x = 108$
    $$12x = 108$$
    $$x = 9$$
    Therefore, the sides are:
    $$3(x) = 3(9) = 27$$
    $$4(x) = 4(9) = 36$$
    $$5(x) = 5(9) = 45$$

12. 9, 15

13. $$\frac{y_1}{y_2} = \frac{x_1}{x_2}$$
    $$\frac{-6}{y_2} = \frac{2}{4}$$
    $$2y_2 = -24$$
    $$y_2 = -12$$

14. +4

15. $$\frac{y_1}{y_2} = \frac{x_2^2}{x_1^2}$$
    $$\frac{2}{y} = \frac{2^2}{(-3)^2}$$
    $$4y = +18$$
    $$y = +\frac{9}{2}$$

16. 36

17. $$\frac{P}{100} = \frac{7\frac{1}{2}}{45}$$
    $$45P = 7\frac{1}{2}(100)$$
    $$P = \frac{\frac{15}{2}(100)}{45}$$
    $$P = 16\frac{2}{3}$$

18. 288

19. Leona has 15 coins.

    Let x = number of nickels $\Rightarrow$ having value = $5x$
    $15 - x$ = number of quarters $\Rightarrow$ having value = $25(15 - x)$.

value of nickels	+	value of quarters	=	total value of \$1.75
$5x$	+	$25(15 - x)$	=	175

    $$5x + 25(15 - x) = 175$$
    $$5x + 375 - 25x = 175$$
    $$-20x = -200$$
    $$x = 10 \quad \text{(nickels)}$$
    $$15 - x = 5 \quad \text{(quarters)}$$

20. 15 dimes
    7 halves

21. **There were twice as many 12¢ stamps as 10¢ stamps**

Let x = number of 10-cent stamps $\Rightarrow$ having value = $10x$,
then $2x$ = number of 12-cent stamps $\Rightarrow$ having vlaue = $12(2x)$.

and twice as many 2¢ stamps as 12¢ stamps.

$2x$ = number of 12-cent stamps
then $2(2x)$ = number of 2-cent stamps $\Rightarrow$ having value = $2(4x)$.

value of 10¢ stamps	+	value of 12¢ stamps	+	value of 2¢ stamps	=	total value, $2.10
$10x$	+	$12(2x)$	+	$2(4x)$	=	210

$$10x + 12(2x) + 2(4x) = 210$$
$$10x + 24x + 8x = 210$$
$$42x = 210$$
$$x = 5 \quad \text{(10-cent stamps)}$$
$$2x = 10 \quad \text{(12-cent stamps)}$$
$$4x = 20 \quad \text{(2-cent stamps)}$$

22. 10 (2-cent stamps)
20 (8-cent stamps)
80 (1-cent stamps)

23. Let x = number of box seats.
Then $x + 300$ = number of balcony seats (300 more balcony seats than box seats).
And $2(x + 300)$ = number of orchestra seats (three times as many orchestra seats as balcony seats).

value of box seats	+	value of balcony seats	+	value of orchestra seats	=	total value, 11,250
$12x$	+	$5(x + 300)$	+	$8(2x + 600)$	=	11,250

$$12x + 5(x + 300) + 8(2x + 600) = 11,250$$
$$12x + 5x + 1500 + 16x + 4800 = 11,250$$
$$33x = 4950$$
$$x = 150 \quad \text{(box seats)}$$
$$x + 300 = 150 + 300 = 450 \quad \text{(balcony seats)}$$
$$2(x + 300) = 2x + 600 = 2(150) + 600 = 900 \quad \text{(orchestra seats)}$$

24. 1000 box seats; 5500 reserved seats; 22,000 general seats

25. $$\frac{A}{B} = \frac{P}{100}$$

$$\frac{A}{1800} = \frac{\overset{6}{\cancel{24}}}{\underset{25}{\cancel{100}}}$$

$$25A = 6(1800)$$

$$A = \frac{6(1800)}{25}$$

$$A = \quad 432$$
$$\underline{\quad - 256}$$
$$176 \quad \text{more students}$$

26. Needs $348 more

27. Let $2x$, $5x$, $3x$, and $4x$ equal the number of each kind of record played, respectively.

Then $2x + 5x + 3x + 4x = 126$
$$14x = 126$$
$$x = 9$$

$2x = 2(9) = 18$ folk records
$5x = 5(9) = 45$ rock records
$3x = 3(9) = 27$ country records
$4x = 4(9) = 36$ Latino records

28. 30 travel
90 drama
60 comedy
15 wildlife
45 game

CUMULATIVE REVIEW EXERCISES:
CHAPTERS 1-4 (page 172)

1. Cannot be determined   2. 98

3. $46 - 2\{4 - [3(5 - 8) - 10]\}$
$46 - 2\{4 - [3(-3) - 10]\}$
$46 - 2\{4 - [-9 - 10]\}$
$46 - 2\{4 - [-19]\}$
$46 - 2\{23\}$
$46 - 46 = 0$

4. 45

5. $S = 4\pi R^2$
$\doteq 4(3.14)5^2$
$\doteq 4(3.14)25$
$\doteq 4(25)3.14$
$\doteq 100(3.14) = 314$

6. $4\frac{1}{4}$

7. $\frac{-11}{1} = \frac{x}{3}$
$x = (-11)(3) = -33$

8. $\frac{3}{4}$

9. $4(2y - 5) = 16 + 3(6y - 2)$
$8y - 20 = 16 + 18y - 6$
$8y - 20 = 18y + 10$
$-30 = 10y$
$-3 = y$

10. 1

CHAPTER FIVE DIAGNOSTIC TEST (page 172)

Following each problem number is the textbook section reference (in parentheses) where that kind of problem is discussed.

1. (507) $\frac{A}{B} = \frac{P}{100}$

$\frac{28}{B} = \frac{42}{100}$

$42B = 2800$

2. (507) $\frac{A}{B} = \frac{P}{100}$

$\frac{17}{20} = \frac{P}{100}$

$20P = 1700$

$$\frac{\cancel{42}B}{\cancel{42}} = \frac{2800}{42} \qquad\qquad \frac{\cancel{20}P}{\cancel{20}} = \frac{\cancel{1700}}{\cancel{20}}$$

$$B = 66\frac{2}{3} \doteq 67 \qquad\qquad P = 85$$

3. (507)

$$\boxed{\text{Markup} \atop A} = \boxed{5\% \atop P} \text{ of } \boxed{\text{cost.} \atop B} \; \$12.50$$

$$\frac{A}{12.50} = \frac{\overset{1}{\cancel{5}}}{\underset{20}{\cancel{100}}}$$

$$20A = 12.50$$

$$A = \frac{12.50}{20} \doteq 0.63 \quad \text{Markup}$$

$$S = C + M$$

$$= 12.50 + 0.63 = \$13.13$$

4. (503) $\boxed{\text{When sixteen}}$ $\boxed{\text{is added to}}$ $\boxed{\text{three}}$ $\boxed{\text{times}}$ $\boxed{\text{an unknown number}}$ $\boxed{\text{the sum is}}$ $\boxed{37.}$

$$16 \qquad + \qquad 3 \qquad \cdot \qquad x \qquad\qquad = \qquad 37$$

$$16 + 3x = 37$$
$$3x = 21$$
$$x = 7$$

5. (505) $\boxed{\text{The ratio of strawberries to cherries}}$ $\boxed{\text{is}}$ $\boxed{\text{3 to 5.}}$

$$\frac{\text{Pts of strawberries}}{\text{Pts of cherries}} = \frac{3x}{5x} = \frac{3}{5}$$

$$3x + 5x = 48$$
$$8x = 48$$
$$x = 6$$

$$3x = 18 \text{ pts of strawberries}$$
$$5x = \underline{30} \text{ pts of cherries}$$
$$48 \text{ (check)}$$

6. (504) Let $\quad x$ = number of nickels $\Rightarrow$ amount of money in nickels = $5x$

then $25 - x$ = number of dimes $\Rightarrow$ amount of money in dimes $= 10(25 - x)$.

$\boxed{\text{amount of money in nickels}}$ + $\boxed{\text{amount of money in dimes}}$ = $\boxed{165\text{¢}.}$

$$5x \qquad\qquad + \qquad\qquad 10(25 - x) \qquad\qquad = \qquad 165$$

$$5x + 250 - 10x = 165$$
$$-5x = -85$$
$$x = 17 \quad \text{(nickels)} = 17(5) = \quad 85\text{¢}$$
$$25 - x = 8 \quad \text{(dimes)} \;\; = 8(10) = \underline{\quad 80\text{¢}}$$
$$165\text{¢} \text{ (Check)}$$

7. (503)

$\boxed{\text{When}}$ $\boxed{\text{four}}$ $\boxed{\text{is subtracted from}}$ $\boxed{\text{five times an unknown number}}$ $\boxed{\text{the result is}}$ $\boxed{\text{the same as when six}}$ $\boxed{\text{is added to}}$ $\boxed{\text{three times the unknown number.}}$

$$5x - 4 = 6 + 3x$$
$$2x = 10$$
$$x = 5$$

8. (506) $\dfrac{\text{6-ft height}}{3\frac{1}{2}\text{-ft shadow}} = \dfrac{x\text{-ft height}}{21\text{-ft shadow}}$

$$\frac{6}{3\frac{1}{2}} = \frac{x}{21}$$

$$3\frac{1}{2}x = 6(21)$$

$$\frac{3\frac{1}{2}x}{3\frac{1}{2}} = \frac{6(21)}{3\frac{1}{2}} = \frac{6(21)}{1} \div \frac{7}{2}$$

$$x = \frac{6(\overset{3}{\cancel{21}})}{1} \cdot \frac{2}{\cancel{7}} = 36$$

9. (508) Condition 1 $\begin{cases} x_1 = -4 \\ y_1 = 3 \end{cases}$

Condition 2 $\begin{cases} x_2 = \dfrac{4}{5} \\ y_2 = \; ? \end{cases}$

$$\frac{y_1}{y_2} = \frac{x_2}{x_1} \Rightarrow \frac{3}{y_2} = \frac{\frac{4}{5}}{-4}$$

$$\frac{4}{5}y_2 = 3(-4) = -12$$

$$4y_2 = (-12)(5)$$

$$y_2 = \frac{(-12)(5)}{4} = -15$$

10. (508) Condition 1 $\begin{cases} d_1 = 40 \\ p_1 = 17.32 \end{cases}$

Condition 2 $\begin{cases} d_2 = 70 \\ p_2 = ? \end{cases}$

$$\frac{p_1}{p_2} = \frac{d_1}{d_2} \Rightarrow \frac{17.32}{p_2} = \frac{4\cancel{0}}{7\cancel{0}}$$

$$4p_2 = 7(17.32)$$

$$p_2 = \frac{7(17.32)}{4} = 30.31 \text{ psi}$$

EXERCISES 601, SET I   (page 178)

1. $x^5 \cdot x^8 = x^{5+8} = x^{13}$ 2. H^7

3. $(y^2)^5 = y^{2 \cdot 5} = y^{10}$ 4. N^{12}

5. $\frac{x^7}{x^2} = x^{7-2} = x^5$ 6. y^2

7. $a \cdot a^4 = a^{1+4} = a^5$ 8. B^8

9. $(x^4)^7 = x^{4 \cdot 7} = x^{28}$ 10. v^{24}

11. $\frac{a^5}{a} = a^{5-1} = a^4$ 12. b^6

13. $\frac{z^5}{z^4} = z^{5-4} = z^1 = z$ 14. x

15. $10^2 \cdot 10^5 = 10^{2+5} = 10^7$ 16. 5^5

17. $(10^2)^3 = 10^{2 \cdot 3} = 10^6$ 18. 10^{14}

19. $\frac{10^{11}}{10} = 10^{11-1} = 10^{10}$ 20. 5^5

21. $x^2 y^3$ cannot be simplified because the bases are different.   22. $a^4 b$

23. $\frac{6x^2}{2x} = \frac{\cancel{6}^3}{\cancel{2}} \cdot \frac{x^2}{x} = \frac{3}{1} \cdot \frac{x}{1} = 3x$ 24. $3y^2$

25. $\frac{a^3}{b^2}$ cannot be simplified because the bases are different.   26. $\frac{x^5}{y^3}$

27. $\frac{10x^4}{5x^3} = \frac{\cancel{10}^2}{\cancel{5}} \cdot \frac{x^4}{x^3} = \frac{2}{1} \cdot \frac{x}{1} = 2x$ 28. $\frac{5y^3}{3}$

29. $\frac{12h^4 k^3}{8h^2 k} = \frac{12}{8} \cdot \frac{h^4}{h^2} \cdot \frac{k^3}{k} = \frac{3}{2} \cdot \frac{h^2}{1} \cdot \frac{k^2}{1} = \frac{3h^2 k^2}{2}$

30. $\frac{4a^4 b}{3}$

31. $3^2 \cdot 5^3 = 9 \cdot 125 = 1125$ 32. 144

33. $2^1 \cdot 2^3 \cdot 2^2 = 2^{1+3+2} = 2^6 = 64$ 34. 729

35. $x^1 \cdot x^3 \cdot x^4 = x^{1+3+4} = x^8$ 36. y^9

37. $x^2 y^3 x^5 = x^{2+5} y^3 = x^7 y^3$ 38. $z^7 w^2$

39. $a^1 b^3 a^5 = a^{1+5} b^3 = a^6 b^3$ 40. $x^{12} y$

41. $5^{2a} \cdot 5^{4a} = 5^{2a+4a} = 5^{6a}$ 42. 6^{3x}

43. $\frac{x^{5a}}{x^{3a}} = x^{5a-3a} = x^{2a}$ 44. M^{4x}

45. Same form See Example 3(i)   46. Same form

EXERCISES 602, SET I   (page 185)

1. $x^{-4} = \frac{1}{x^4}$ 2. $\frac{1}{y^7}$ 3. $\frac{1}{a^{-4}} = a^4$ 4. b^5

5. $r^{-4} s t^{-2} = \frac{r^{-4}}{1} \cdot \frac{s}{1} \cdot \frac{t^{-2}}{1} = \frac{1}{r^4} \cdot \frac{s}{1} \cdot \frac{1}{t^2} = \frac{s}{r^4 t^2}$

6. $\frac{t}{r^5 s^3}$ 7. $x^{-2} y^3 = \frac{x^{-2}}{1} \cdot \frac{y^3}{1} = \frac{1}{x^2} \cdot \frac{y^3}{1} = \frac{y^3}{x^2}$

8. $\frac{x^3}{y^2}$ 9. $\frac{h^2}{k^{-4}} = \frac{h^2}{1} \cdot \frac{1}{k^{-4}} = \frac{h^2}{1} \cdot \frac{k^4}{1} = h^2 k^4$

10. $m^3 n^2$ 11. $\frac{x^{-4}}{y} = \frac{x^{-4}}{1} \cdot \frac{1}{y} = \frac{1}{x^4} \cdot \frac{1}{y} = \frac{1}{x^4 y}$

12. $\frac{1}{a^5 b}$ 13. $ab^{-2} c^0 = \frac{a}{1} \cdot \frac{b^{-2}}{1} \cdot \frac{c^0}{1} = \frac{a}{1} \cdot \frac{1}{b^2} \cdot \frac{1}{1} = \frac{a}{b^2}$

14. $\frac{z}{x^3}$ 15. $x^{-3} \cdot x^4 = x^{-3+4} = x^1 = x$

16. y^4 17. $10^3 \cdot 10^{-2} = 10^{3-2} = 10^1 = 10$

18. $\frac{1}{2}$ 19. $(x^2)^{-4} = x^{2(-4)} = x^{-8} = \frac{1}{x^8}$

20. $\frac{1}{z^6}$ 21. $(a^{-2})^3 = a^{-2(3)} = a^{-6} = \frac{1}{a^6}$

22. $\frac{1}{b^{10}}$ 23. $\frac{y^{-2}}{y^5} = y^{(-2)-(5)} = y^{-7} = \frac{1}{y^7}$ 24. $\frac{1}{z^4}$

25. $\frac{10^2}{10^{-5}} = 10^{2-(-5)} = 10^7$ 26. 2^5

27. $x^4 x^0 x^{-3} = x^{4+0-3} = x^1 = x$ 28. y^3

29. $\frac{1}{x^{+2}} = \frac{x^{-2}}{1} = x^{-2}$ 30. y^{-3}

31. $\frac{h}{k} = \frac{h}{1} \cdot \frac{1}{k} = \frac{h}{1} \cdot \frac{k^{-1}}{1} = hk^{-1}$ 32. mn^{-1}

33. $\frac{x^2}{yz^5} = \frac{x^2}{1} \cdot \frac{1}{y} \cdot \frac{1}{z^5} = \frac{x^2}{1} \cdot \frac{y^{-1}}{1} \cdot \frac{z^{-5}}{1} = x^2 y^{-1} z^{-5}$

34. $a^3 b^{-2} c^{-1}$

35. $10^4 \cdot 10^{-2} = 10^{4-2} = 10^2 = 100$ 36. 3

37. $10^{-4} = \frac{1}{10^4} = \frac{1}{10,000}$ 38. $\frac{1}{8}$

39. $5^0 \cdot 7^2 = 1 \cdot 49 = 49$ 40. 64

41. $\frac{10^0}{10^2} = \frac{1}{100}$ 42. 25

43. $\frac{10^{-3} \cdot 10^2}{10^5} = 10^{-3+2-5} = 10^{-6} = \frac{1}{10^6} = \frac{1}{1,000,000}$

44. $\frac{1}{8}$ 45. $(10^2)^{-1} = 10^{2(-1)} = 10^{-2} = \frac{1}{10^2} = \frac{1}{100}$

46. $\frac{1}{64}$ 47. $\frac{a^3 b^0}{c^{-2}} = \frac{a^3}{1} \cdot \frac{b^0}{1} \cdot \frac{1}{c^{-2}} = \frac{a^3}{1} \cdot \frac{1}{1} \cdot \frac{c^2}{1} = a^3 c^2$

48. $e^2 f^3$

49. $\frac{p^4 r^{-1}}{t^{-2}} = \frac{p^4}{1} \cdot \frac{r^{-1}}{1} \cdot \frac{1}{t^{-2}} = \frac{p^4}{1} \cdot \frac{1}{r^1} \cdot \frac{t^2}{1} = \frac{p^4 t^2}{r}$

50. $\frac{u^5 w^3}{v^2}$

51. $\frac{8x^{-3}}{12x} = \frac{\cancel{8}^2}{\cancel{12}_3} \cdot \frac{x^{-3}}{x} = \frac{2}{3} \cdot \frac{x^{-3-1}}{1} = \frac{2}{3} \cdot \frac{x^{-4}}{1} = \frac{2}{3} \cdot \frac{1}{x^4} = \frac{2}{3x^4}$

52. $\frac{3}{2y^3}$

53. $\dfrac{20h^{-2}}{35h^{-4}} = \dfrac{\cancel{20}^{4}}{\cancel{35}_{7}} \cdot \dfrac{h^{-2}}{h^{-4}} = \dfrac{4}{7} \cdot \dfrac{h^{(-2)-(-4)}}{1} = \dfrac{4}{7} \cdot \dfrac{h^2}{1} = \dfrac{4h^2}{7}$

54. $\dfrac{5k^3}{4}$

55. $\dfrac{7x^{-3}y}{14y^{-2}} = \dfrac{\cancel{7}^{1}}{\cancel{14}_{2}} \cdot \dfrac{x^{-3}}{1} \cdot \dfrac{y}{y^{-2}} = \dfrac{1}{2} \cdot \dfrac{1}{x^3} \cdot \dfrac{y^{1-(-2)}}{1}$

$= \dfrac{1}{2} \cdot \dfrac{1}{x^3} \cdot \dfrac{y^3}{1} = \dfrac{y^3}{2x^3}$

56. $\dfrac{3p}{2m^2}$

57. $\dfrac{15m^0 n^{-2}}{5m^{-3}n^4} = \dfrac{\cancel{15}^{3}}{\cancel{5}_{1}} \cdot \dfrac{m^0}{m^{-3}} \cdot \dfrac{n^{-2}}{n^4} = \dfrac{3}{1} \cdot \dfrac{m^{0-(-3)}}{1} \cdot \dfrac{n^{-2-4}}{1}$

$= \dfrac{3}{1} \cdot \dfrac{m^3}{1} \cdot \dfrac{n^{-6}}{1} = \dfrac{3}{1} \cdot \dfrac{m^3}{1} \cdot \dfrac{1}{n^6} = \dfrac{3m^3}{n^6}$

58. $\dfrac{7x^2 y}{6}$

59. $x^{3m} \cdot x^{-m} = x^{3m-m} = x^{2m}$

60. y^{3n}

61. $(x^{3b})^{-2} = x^{3b(-2)} = x^{-6b} = \dfrac{1}{x^{6b}}$

62. $\dfrac{1}{y^{6a}}$

63. $\dfrac{x^{2a}}{x^{-5a}} = x^{2a-(-5a)} = x^{7a}$

64. a^{8x}

65. $\dfrac{x + y^{-1}}{y} = \dfrac{x + \frac{1}{y}}{y}$

66. $\dfrac{\frac{1}{a} - b}{b}$

EXERCISES 603, SET I   (page 189)

1. $3(-2)^3 = 3(-8) = -24$

2. 18

3. $(2 \cdot 3)^2 = 2^2 \cdot 3^2 = 4 \cdot 9 = 36$

4. 144

5. $\dfrac{(-4)^2}{-4^2} = \dfrac{16}{-16} = -1$

6. -1

7. $(a^2 b^3)^2 = a^{2 \cdot 2} b^{3 \cdot 2} = a^4 b^6$

8. $x^{12} y^{15}$

9. $(2^1 z^3)^2 = 2^{1 \cdot 2} z^{3 \cdot 2} = 2^2 z^6 = 4z^6$

10. $27w^6$

11. $(m^{-2}n)^4 = m^{(-2)4} n^{1 \cdot 4} = m^{-8} n^4 = \dfrac{n^4}{m^8}$

12. $\dfrac{r^5}{p^{15}}$

13. $(x^{-2}y^3)^{-4} = x^{(-2)(-4)} y^{3(-4)}$

$= x^8 y^{-12} = \dfrac{x^8}{y^{12}}$

14. $\dfrac{w^6}{z^8}$

15. $\left(\dfrac{xy^4}{z^2}\right)^2 = \dfrac{x^{1 \cdot 2} y^{4 \cdot 2}}{z^{2 \cdot 2}} = \dfrac{x^2 y^8}{z^4}$

16. $\dfrac{a^9 b^3}{c^6}$

17. $\left(\dfrac{M^{-2}}{N^3}\right)^4 = \dfrac{M^{(-2)4}}{N^{3 \cdot 4}} = \dfrac{M^{-8}}{N^{12}} = \dfrac{1}{M^8 N^{12}}$

18. $R^{15} S^{12}$

19. $\left(\dfrac{a^2 b^{-4}}{b^{-5}}\right)^2 = (a^2 b^{5-4})^2$

$= a^{2 \cdot 2} b^{1 \cdot 2} = a^4 b^2$

20. $x^3 y^6$

21. $\left(\dfrac{10^2 \cdot 10^{-1}}{10^{-2}}\right)^2 = (10^{2-1+2})^2$

$= (10^3)^2 = 10^{3 \cdot 2} = 10^6$

22. 10^3

23. $\left(\dfrac{mn^{-1}}{m^3}\right)^{-2} = (m^{1-3}n^{-1})^{-2}$

$= m^{(-2)(-2)} n^{(-1)(-2)} = m^4 n^2$

24. $a^3 b^6$

25. $\left(\dfrac{x^4}{x^{-1}y^{-2}}\right)^{-1} = (x^{4+1}y^2)^{-1}$

$= x^{5(-1)} y^{2(-1)} = x^{-5} y^{-2}$

$= \dfrac{1}{x^5 y^2}$

26. $\dfrac{1}{x^5 y^4}$

27. $\left(\dfrac{2s^{-3}}{4st^2}\right)^{-2} = (2^1 s^{-3-1} t^{-2})^{-2}$

$= 2^{1(-2)} s^{-4(-2)} t^{-2(-2)}$

$= 2^{-2} s^8 t^4 = \dfrac{s^8 t^4}{2^2} = \dfrac{s^8 t^4}{4}$

28. $\dfrac{u^{10} v^6}{4}$

29. $(10^0 k^{-4})^{-2} = k^{(-4)(-2)} = k^8$

30. z^{10}

31. $(x^3 + y^4)^5$

32. $(a^5 - b^2)^6$

Cannot be simplified by rules of exponents. Rule 2 or Rule 6 *cannot* be used here because the + sign means that x^3 and y^4 are *not* factors.

Cannot be simplified by rules of exponents.

33. $\left(\dfrac{r^7 s^8}{r^9 s^6}\right)^0 = 1$

34. 1

35. $\left(\dfrac{6m^{-4}p}{3m^{-2}}\right)^{-1} = (3^1 4^{-1} m^{-4+2} p^1)^{-1}$

$= 3^{1(-1)} 4^{-1(-1)} m^{-2(-1)} p^{1(-1)}$

$= 3^{-1} 4^1 m^2 p^{-1} = \dfrac{4m^2}{3p}$

36. $\dfrac{6x^2}{5y}$

REVIEW EXERCISES 604, SET I   (page 190)

1. $x^4 \cdot x^7 = x^{4+7} = x^{11}$

2. y^8

3. $a^5 \cdot a^{-3} = a^{5-3} = a^2$

4. b^2

5. $c^{-5} d^0 = \dfrac{1}{c^5}$

6. $\dfrac{1}{f^6}$

7. $\dfrac{p^5}{p^2} = p^{5-2} = p^3$

8. r^2

9. $\dfrac{x^{-4}}{x^5} = x^{-4-5} = x^{-9} = \dfrac{1}{x^9}$

10. $\dfrac{1}{z^7}$

11. $\dfrac{m^0}{m^{-3}} = m^3$

12. $\dfrac{1}{n^6}$

13. $\dfrac{10^6}{10^2} = 10^{6-2} = 10^4 = 10,000$

14. $10^2 = 100$

15. $\dfrac{10^4}{10^{-3}} = 10^{4-(-3)} = 10^7 = 10,000,000$

16. 10^9

17. $(x^2)^5 = x^{2 \cdot 5} = x^{10}$

18. y^{12}

19. $(p^{-3})^5 = p^{(-3)5} = p^{-15} = \dfrac{1}{p^{15}}$

20. $\dfrac{1}{r^{14}}$

21. $(m^{-4})^{-2} = m^{(-4)(-2)} = m^8$

22. n^{15}

23. $(h^0)^{-4} = h^{0(-4)} = h^0 = 1$

24. 1

25. $(x^2 y^3)^4 = x^8 y^{12}$

26. $w^6 z^8$

27. $(p^{-1} r^3)^{-2} = p^{(-1)(-2)} r^{3(-2)}$

$= p^2 r^{-6} = \dfrac{p^2}{r^6}$

28. $\dfrac{t^3}{s^{12}}$

29. $(2a^3)^4 = 2^4 a^{12} = 16a^{12}$

30. $27b^6$

31. $(-2x^4)^2 = (-2)^2 x^8 = 4x^8$

32. $25y^6$

33. $(-4b^{-2})^3 = (-4)^3 b^{-6} = \dfrac{-64}{b^6}$

34. $\dfrac{-125}{a^{12}}$

35. $(-10)^{-1} = \dfrac{1}{(-10)^1} = -\dfrac{1}{10}$

36. $-\dfrac{1}{1000}$

37. $\left(\dfrac{x^2 y^3}{z^4}\right)^5 = \dfrac{x^{10} y^{15}}{z^{20}}$

38. $\dfrac{x^{24} y^8}{z^{20}}$

39. $\left(\dfrac{x^{-3}}{y^0 z^2}\right)^{-4} = \dfrac{x^{12}}{z^{-8}} = x^{12} z^8$

40. $a^{20} b^{15}$

41. $\dfrac{x^2}{y^3} = \dfrac{x^2}{1} \cdot \dfrac{y^{-3}}{1} = x^2 y^{-3}$

42. $a^3 b^{-2}$

43. $\dfrac{m^2}{n^{-3}} = \dfrac{m^2}{1} \cdot \dfrac{n^3}{1} = m^2 n^3$

44. $w^3 z^5$

45. $4^{-2} = \dfrac{1}{4^2} = \dfrac{1}{16}$

46. $\dfrac{1}{27}$

47. $(10^{-1})^3 = 10^{(-1)3} = 10^{-3}$

$\quad = \dfrac{1}{10^3} = \dfrac{1}{1000}$

48. $\dfrac{1}{10,000}$

49. $\dfrac{2^0}{2^{-3}} = \dfrac{2^3}{1} = 8$

50. $\dfrac{1}{25}$

51. $8^0 \cdot 10^{-2} = \dfrac{1}{10^2} = \dfrac{1}{100}$

52. 9

53. $\dfrac{(-8)^2}{-8^2} = \dfrac{(-8)(-8)}{-(8)(8)} = \dfrac{64}{-64} = -1$

54. -1

55. $\left(\dfrac{10^{-3} \cdot 10}{10^{-2}}\right)^5 = (10^{2-3+1})^5$

$\quad = (10^0)^5 = 1$

56. 1

57. $\left(\dfrac{u^{-5}}{v^2 w^{-4}}\right)^3 = \dfrac{u^{-15}}{v^6 w^{-12}} = \dfrac{w^{12}}{u^{15} v^6}$

58. $\dfrac{t^{12}}{r^{24} s^{20}}$

59. $(5a^3 b^{-4})^{-2} = 5^{-2} a^{-6} b^8$

$\quad = \dfrac{b^8}{25a^6}$

60. $\dfrac{c^{12}}{81d^{20}}$

61. $\left(\dfrac{4h^2}{ij^{-2}}\right)^{-3} = \dfrac{4^{-3} h^{-6}}{i^{-3} j^6} = \dfrac{i^3}{4^3 h^6 j^6}$

$\quad = \dfrac{i^3}{64 h^6 j^6}$

62. $\dfrac{25 k^4 n^2}{m^2}$

63. $\left(\dfrac{x^{10} y^5}{x^5 y}\right)^3 = (x^5 y^4)^3 = x^{15} y^{12}$

64. $a^{16} b^{12}$

65. $\left(\dfrac{6x^{-5} y^8}{3x^3 y^{-4}}\right)^0 = 1$

66. 1

67. $(a^2 + b^3)^3$

Cannot be simplified by rules of exponents. Rule 2 or Rule 6 *cannot* be used here because the + sign means that a^2 and b^3 are *not* factors.

68. $(m^4 - n^5)^4$

Cannot be simplified by rules of exponents.

69. $x^{3d} \cdot x^d = x^{3a+d} = x^{4d}$

70. y^{4e}

71. $(x^{4a})^{-2} = x^{(4a)(-2)} = x^{-8a}$

$\quad = \dfrac{1}{x^{8a}}$

72. $\dfrac{1}{y^{9b}}$

73. $\dfrac{6^{2x}}{6^{-x}} = 6^{2x+x} = 6^{3x}$

74. 5^{4a}

75. $\dfrac{a^{-3} b^2}{10c^{-4}} = \dfrac{10^{-1}}{1} \cdot \dfrac{a^{-3}}{1} \cdot \dfrac{b^2}{1} \cdot \dfrac{c^4}{1}$

$\quad = 10^{-1} a^{-3} b^2 c^4$

76. $10^{-2} u^{-4} v^3 w^5$

CUMULATIVE REVIEW EXERCISES: CHAPTERS 1-5 (page 193)

1. $F = \dfrac{9}{5} C + 32$

$\quad = \dfrac{9}{5}(-20) + 32$

$\quad F = -36 + 32 = -4$

2. -13

3. $5[11 - 2(6 - 9)] - 4(13 - 5)$
   $5[11 - 2(-3)] - 4(13 - 5)$
   $5[11 + 6] - 4(13 - 5)$
   $5[17] - 4(8)$
   $\quad 85 - 32 = 53$

4. $6x^3 - 4x + 24$

5. $3 \quad : \quad 5 \quad : \quad 7$
   $3x \quad : \quad 5x \quad : \quad 7x$

   The perimeter is 75.

   $3x + 5x + 7x = 75$
   $\qquad\qquad 15x = 75$
   $\qquad\qquad\quad x = 5$
   $\qquad\quad 3x = 3(5) = 15$
   $\qquad\quad 5x = 5(5) = 25$
   $\qquad\quad 7x = 7(5) = 35$

   Therefore, the sides of the triangle are 15, 25, and 35.

6. 88%

7. Markup A = 40% P of cost B

   $\dfrac{A}{B} = \dfrac{P}{100}$ $\qquad$ A = markup
   $\qquad\qquad\qquad\qquad$ B = cost = 125
   $\dfrac{A}{125} = \dfrac{\overset{2}{\cancel{40}}}{\underset{5}{\cancel{100}}}$ $\qquad$ P = 40

   $\quad 5A = 2(125) = 250$

   $\quad \dfrac{5A}{5} = \dfrac{250}{5}$

   $\qquad A = 50$ markup

   Selling price = cost + markup
   $\qquad\qquad\quad = 125 + 50 = \$175$

8. 4 adult
   5 children

9. $\dfrac{\text{girl}}{}$ $\qquad$ $\dfrac{\text{tree}}{}$

   $\dfrac{5 \text{ ft height}}{4 \text{ ft shadow}} = \dfrac{x \text{ ft height}}{24 \text{ ft shadow}}$

   $\qquad 4x = 5(24) = 120$

   $\qquad \dfrac{4x}{4} = \dfrac{120}{4}$

   $\qquad\quad x = 30$ ft tree

10. $266\dfrac{2}{3}$ ft

CHAPTER SIX DIAGNOSTIC TEST (page 193)

Following each problem number is the textbook section reference (in parentheses) where that kind of problem is discussed.

1. (601) $x^3 \cdot x^4 = x^{3+4} = x^7$

2. (601) $(x^2)^3 = x^{2 \cdot 3} = x^6$

3. (601) $\dfrac{x^5}{x^2} = x^{5-2} = x^3$

4. (602) $x^{-4} = \dfrac{1}{x^4}$

5. (602) $x^2 y^{-3} = \dfrac{x^2}{1} \cdot \dfrac{1}{y^3} = \dfrac{x^2}{y^3}$

6. (602) $\dfrac{a^{-3}}{b} = \dfrac{a^{-3}}{1} \cdot \dfrac{1}{b} = \dfrac{1}{a^3} \cdot \dfrac{1}{b} = \dfrac{1}{a^3 b}$

7. (601) $\dfrac{x^{5a}}{x^{3a}} = x^{5a-3a} = x^{2a}$

8. (602) $(4^{3x})^0 = 1$

9. (603) $(x^2 y^4)^3 = x^{2 \cdot 3} y^{4 \cdot 3} = x^6 y^{12}$

10. (603) $(a^{-3} b)^2 = a^{-3 \cdot 2} b^{1 \cdot 2} = a^{-6} b^2 = \dfrac{1}{a^6} \cdot \dfrac{b^2}{1} = \dfrac{b^2}{a^6}$

11. (603) $\left(\dfrac{p^3}{q^2}\right)^2 = \dfrac{p^{3\cdot2}}{q^{2\cdot2}} = \dfrac{p^6}{q^4}$ 12. (603) $\left(\dfrac{m^2}{n}\right)^0 = 1$

13. (603) $\left(\dfrac{x}{y^2}\right)^{-3} = \dfrac{x^{1(-3)}}{y^{2(-3)}} = \dfrac{x^{-3}}{y^{-6}} = \dfrac{1}{x^3} \cdot \dfrac{y^6}{1} = \dfrac{y^6}{x^3}$

14. (603) $\left(\dfrac{4x^{-2}}{2x^{-3}}\right)^{-1} = (2x^{-2-(-3)})^{-1} = (2^1 x^1)^{-1}$

$\qquad = 2^{1(-1)}x^{1(-1)} = 2^{-1}x^{-1}$

$\qquad = \dfrac{1}{2^1} \cdot \dfrac{1}{x^1} = \dfrac{1}{2x}$

15. (602) $\dfrac{1}{x^{-2}} = x^2$ 16. (602) $\dfrac{a^3}{b} = \dfrac{a^3}{1} \cdot \dfrac{b^{-1}}{1} = a^3 b^{-1}$

17. (602) $\dfrac{h^{-2}}{k^{-3}h^{-4}} = k^3 h^{-2-(-4)} = k^3 h^2$

18. (603) $2^3 \cdot 2^2 = 2^{3+2} = 2^5 = 32$

19. (603) $10^{-4} \cdot 10^2 = 10^{-2} = \dfrac{1}{10^2} = \dfrac{1}{100}$

20. (603) $5^{-2} = \dfrac{1}{5^2} = \dfrac{1}{25}$

21. (603) $(2^{-3})^2 = 2^{(-3)2} = 2^{-6} = \dfrac{1}{2^6} = \dfrac{1}{64}$

22. (603) $(4^{-2})^{-1} = 4^{(-2)(-1)} = 4^2 = 16$

23. (603) $\dfrac{10^{-3}}{10^{-4}} = 10^{-3-(-4)} = 10^1$

24. (603) $\dfrac{-3^2}{(-3)^2} = \dfrac{-(3)(3)}{(-3)(-3)} = \dfrac{-9}{9} = -1$

25. (603) $(5^0)^2 = 1^2 = 1$

EXERCISES 701, SET I (page 200)

1. 3 terms
2 variables

2. 3 terms
2 variables

3. 1 term
2 variables

4. 1 term
3 variables

5. 2 terms
2 variables

6. 2 terms
2 variables

7. 2nd degree
1st degree

8. 3rd degree
1st degree

9. 6th degree
3rd degree

10. 3rd degree
3rd degree

11. 4th degree
2nd degree

12. 3rd degree
2nd degree

13. $8x^5 + 7x^3 - 4x - 5$

14. $-3y^5 - 2y^3 + 4y^2 + 10$

15. 4 terms
3 variables

16. 3 terms
3 variables

17. Not a polynomial because exponents are not positive integers.

18. Not a polynomial

19. 2nd degree
2nd degree

20. 3rd degree
2nd degree

21. $xy^3 + 8xy^2 - 4x^2y$

22. $x^4y^2 + 3x^3y - 3xy^3$

EXERCISES 702, Set I (page 203)

1. $(2m^2 - m + 4) + (3m^2 + m - 5) = \underset{\sim}{2m^2} - \underline{m} + \underline{\underline{4}} + \underset{\sim}{3m^2} + \underline{m} - \underline{\underline{5}} = 5m^2 - 1$

2. $11n^2 + 2n + 3$

3. $(2x^3 - 4) + (4x^2 + 8x) + (-9x + 7) = 2x^3 - \underline{4} + 4x^2 + \underline{8x} - \underline{9x} + \underline{7} = 2x^3 + 4x^2 - x + 3$

4. $9z^2 + 9$

5. $(6a - 5a^2 + 6) + (4a^2 + 6 - 3a) = \underline{6a} - \underset{\sim}{5a^2} + \underline{\underline{6}} + \underset{\sim}{4a^2} + \underline{\underline{6}} - \underline{3a} = -a^2 + 3a + 12$

6. $11b^2 + 3$

7. $\begin{aligned} 17a^3 \qquad\quad + 4a - 9 \\ \underline{ 8a^2 - 6a + 9} \\ 17a^3 + 8a^2 - 2a \end{aligned}$

8. $-20b^4 + b^3 + 5b^2 - 1$

9. $\underline{7} - \underset{\sim}{8v^3} + \underline{\underline{9v^2}} + \underline{4v} + \underset{\sim}{9v^3} - \underline{\underline{8v^2}} + \underline{4v} + \underline{6} = v^3 + v^2 + 8v + 13$

10. $w^3 + 8w^2 + 33$

11. $\begin{aligned} 14x^2y^3 - 11xy^2 + 8xy \\ -9x^2y^3 + 6xy^2 - 3xy \\ \underline{7x^2y^3 - 4xy^2 - 5xy} \\ 12x^2y^3 - 9xy^2 \end{aligned}$

12. $9a^2b + 2ab^2 - 10ab$

13. $\underline{3x^4} + \underline{\underline{2x^3}} - \underline{5} + \underline{2x^4} + \underline{\underline{4x^3}} + \underline{8} = 5x^4 + 6x^3 + 3$

14. $9y^3 + 2y^2 - 1$

15. $(7m^8 - 4m^4) + (m^5 + 4m^4) + (8m^8 - m^5) = \underline{7m^8} - \underline{\underline{4m^4}} + \underline{m^5} + \underline{\underline{4m^4}} + \underline{8m^8} - \underline{m^5} = 15m^8$

16. $-h^6 + 17h$

17. $(6r^3t + 14r^2t - 11) + (r^3t - 8r^2t + 19) + (-6r^2t + 8)$

$= \underset{\sim}{6r^3t} + \underline{14r^2t} - \underline{\underline{11}} + \underset{\sim}{r^3t} - \underline{8r^2t} + \underline{\underline{19}} - \underline{6r^2t} + \underline{\underline{8}} = 7r^3t + 16$

18. $4m^2n^2 + 11$

19.
$$\begin{array}{r}
4m^3n^3 \qquad\qquad - 10mn \\
- 10m^2n^2 - 15mn \\
\underline{5m^3n^3 - 8m^2n^2 + 20mn} \\
9m^3n^3 - 18m^2n^2 - 5mn
\end{array}$$

20. $-5h^2k^2 - 32hk^2 + 9hk$

21. Remove parentheses, then combine like terms. $16x^2y + \underrightarrow{4xy} + \underrightarrow{5x^2y} - \underrightarrow{6xy} + \underrightarrow{4xy} - \underrightarrow{5x^2y} = 16x^2y + 2xy$

22. $y^3 + 5xy + 8$

23. $\underrightarrow{7.239x^2} - \underrightarrow{4.028x} + \underrightarrow{6.025} - \underrightarrow{2.846x^2} + \underrightarrow{8.096x} + \underrightarrow{5.307} = 4.393x^2 + 4.068x + 11.512$

24. $37.528x^2 + 6.15x - 52.64$

EXERCISES 703, SET I (page 206)

1. $(3x^2 + 4x - 10) - (5x^2 - 3x + 7) = \underrightarrow{3x^2} + \underrightarrow{4x} - \underrightarrow{10} - \underrightarrow{5x^2} + \underrightarrow{3x} - \underrightarrow{7} = -2x^2 + 7x - 17$

2. $-a^2 - 7a + 14$

3. $(8b^2 + 2b - 14) - (-5b^2 + 4b + 8) = \underrightarrow{8b^2} + \underrightarrow{2b} - \underrightarrow{14} + \underrightarrow{5b^2} - \underrightarrow{4b} - \underrightarrow{8} = 13b^2 - 2b - 22$

4. $19c^2 + 5c + 1$

5. $(4a^2 + 6 - 3a) - (5a + 3a^2 - 4) = \underrightarrow{4a^2} + \underrightarrow{6} - \underrightarrow{3a} - \underrightarrow{5a} - \underrightarrow{3a^2} + \underrightarrow{4} = a^2 - 8a + 10$

6. $2b^2 - 9b + 17$

7.
$$\begin{array}{r}
15x^3 - 4x^2 \qquad\quad + 12 \\
\underline{8x^3 \qquad\quad + 9x - 5} \\
7x^3 - 4x^2 - 9x + 17
\end{array}$$

8. $-7y^3 - 28y^2 + 19y - 24$

9. $(7x^2y^2 - 3x^2y + xy + 7) - (3x^2y^2 + 7x^2y - 5xy + 4)$

$= \underrightarrow{7x^2y^2} - \underrightarrow{3x^2y} + \underrightarrow{xy} + \underrightarrow{7} - \underrightarrow{3x^2y^2} - \underrightarrow{7x^2y} + \underrightarrow{5xy} - \underrightarrow{4} = 4x^2y^2 - 10x^2y + 6xy + 3$

10. $-x^2y^2 + 4x^2y - 5xy - 13$

11. $(x^2 + 4) - [x^2 - 5 - 3x^2 - 1] = \underrightarrow{x^2} + \underrightarrow{4} - \underrightarrow{x^2} + \underrightarrow{5} + \underrightarrow{3x^2} + \underrightarrow{1} = 3x^2 + 10$

12. $6x^2 - 7$

13. $(5x^2 - 2x + 1) + (-4x^2 + 6x - 8) - (2x^2 - 4x + 3)$

$= \underrightarrow{5x^2} - \underrightarrow{2x} + \underrightarrow{1} - \underrightarrow{4x^2} + \underrightarrow{6x} - \underrightarrow{8} - \underrightarrow{2x^2} + \underrightarrow{4x} - \underrightarrow{3} = -x^2 + 8x - 10$

14. $-4y$

15. $(11a^2 + 9a - 14) + (-6a^3 + 17a) - (10a^3 - 8a + 12)$

$= 11a^2 + \underrightarrow{9a} - \underrightarrow{14} - \underrightarrow{6a^3} + \underrightarrow{17a} - \underrightarrow{10a^3} + \underrightarrow{8a} - \underrightarrow{12} = -16a^3 + 11a^2 + 34a - 26$

16. $-24b^3 + 31b^2 + 4b - 17$

17. $[(5 + xy^2 + x^3y) + (-6 - 3xy^2 + 4x^3y)] - [(x^3y + 3xy^2 - 4) + (2x^3y - xy^2 + 5)]$

$= [\underrightarrow{5} + \underrightarrow{xy^2} + \underrightarrow{x^3y} + \underrightarrow{-6} - \underrightarrow{3xy^2} + \underrightarrow{4x^3y}] - [\underrightarrow{x^3y} + \underrightarrow{3xy^2} - \underrightarrow{4} + \underrightarrow{2x^3y} - \underrightarrow{xy^2} + \underrightarrow{5}]$

$= [-1 - 2xy^2 + 5x^3y] - [3x^3y + 2xy^2 + 1] = \underrightarrow{-1} - \underrightarrow{2xy^2} + \underrightarrow{5x^3y} - \underrightarrow{3x^3y} - \underrightarrow{2xy^2} - \underrightarrow{1} = -2 - 4xy^2 + 2x^3y$

18. $6m^2n + 6$

19. $\underrightarrow{12.62x^2} - \underrightarrow{8.905x} - \underrightarrow{16.08} - \underrightarrow{7.625x^2} - \underrightarrow{11.94x} + \underrightarrow{18.54} = 4.995x^2 - 20.845x + 2.46$

20. $8.8x^2 + 30.51x - 23.466$

EXERCISES 704A, SET I (page 208)

1. $2x(3x^2 + 7) = (2x)(3x^2) + (2x)(7) = 6x^3 + 14x$

2. $12y^4 - 6y$

3. $(5a^2 - b^2)2a = (5a^2)(2a) + (-b^2)(2a) = 10a^3 - 2ab^2$

4. $21c^3 - 3cd^2$

5. $-3z^2(5z^3 - 4z^2 + 2z - 8) = (-3z^2)(5z^3) + (-3z^2)(-4z^2) + (-3z^2)(2z) + (-3z^2)(-8)$

$= -15z^5 + 12z^4 - 6z^3 + 24z^2$

6. $-8m^6 + 12m^5 - 4m^4 + 20m^3$

7. $(-3x^2y + xy^2 - 4y^3)(-2xy) = (-3x^2y)(-2xy) + (xy^2)(-2xy) + (-4y^3)(-2xy) = 6x^3y^2 - 2x^2y^3 + 8xy^4$

8. $12x^2y^3 + 3x^3y^2 - 9x^4y$

9. $(-10x^8y - x^4y^5 + 5xy)(2x^2yz)$
   $= (-10x^8y)(2x^2yz) + (-x^4y^5)(2x^2yz) + (5xy)(2x^2yz) = -20x^{10}y^2z - 2x^6y^6z + 10x^3y^2z$

10. $40x^{11}y^6z^2 - 15x^9y^5z^2 - 10x^2y^3z^2$

11. $(8a^2b^3c - 3ab^2 - 4bc^3)(-3a^2b^3c^4)$
    $= (8a^2b^3c)(-3a^2b^3c^4) + (-3ab^2)(-3a^2b^3c^4) + (-4bc^3)(-3a^2b^3c^4) = -24a^4b^6c^5 + 9a^3b^5c^4 + 12a^2b^4c^7$

12. $-18x^3y^3z^6 + 4x^2y^5z^3 + 6xy^3z^7$

13. $5xy^2z(15x^{10}z^8 - 10y^5z^4 - 2xz^3)$
    $= (5xy^2z)(15x^{10}z^8) + (5xy^2z)(-10y^5z^4) + (5xy^2z)(-2xz^3) = 75x^{11}y^2z^9 - 50xy^7z^5 - 10x^2y^2z^4$

14. $30a^{13}b^3c - 15ab^{12}c^5 - 9a^5b^2c^2$

15. $(5.732x)(2.508x^2) + (5.732x)(-7.37) \doteq 14.376x^3 - 42.245x$ 16. $-4315.83a^3 + 1386.645a^2$

EXERCISES 704B, SET I   (page 211)

1. $(x + 3)(x - 2)$
   $= (x + 3)(x) + (x + 3)(-2)$ Distributive rule.
   $= x^2 + 3x - 2x - 6$ Distributive rule.
   $= x^2 + x - 6$ Combining like terms.

2. $a^2 - a - 12$

3. $(2y + 5)(y - 4)$
   $= (2y + 5)(y) + (2y + 5)(-4)$ Distributive rule.
   $= 2y^2 + 5y - 8y - 20$ Distributive rule.
   $= 2y^2 - 3y - 20$ Combining like terms.

4. $3z^2 + 13z - 10$

5.
$$
\begin{array}{r}
2x^2 \quad\; - 5 \\
x \;+ 2 \\
\hline
4x^2 \qquad - 10 \\
2x^3 \qquad - 5x \\
\hline
2x^3 + 4x^2 - 5x - 10
\end{array}
$$

6. $3y^3 - 6y^2 - 2y + 4$

7.
$$
\begin{array}{r}
x + y \\
a - b \\
\hline
- bx - by \\
ax + ay \\
\hline
ax + ay - bx - by
\end{array}
$$

8. $ax - ay + bx - by$

9.
$$
\begin{array}{r}
z^2 - 4z + 16 \\
z + 4 \\
\hline
4z^2 - 16z + 64 \\
z^3 - 4z^2 + 16z \\
\hline
z^3 \qquad\qquad + 64
\end{array}
$$

10. $a^3 - 125$

11.
$$
\begin{array}{r}
-3z^3 + z^2 - 5z + 4 \\
-z + 4 \\
\hline
-12z^3 + 4z^2 - 20z + 16 \\
3z^4 - z^3 + 5z^2 - 4z \\
\hline
3z^4 - 13z^3 + 9z^2 - 24z + 16
\end{array}
$$

12. $v^4 - 4v^3 + 5v + 6$

13. $(x + 4)^2 = (x + 4)(x + 4)$
$$
\begin{array}{r}
x + 4 \\
x + 4 \\
\hline
4x + 16 \\
x^2 + 4x \\
\hline
x^2 + 8x + 16
\end{array}
$$

14. $x^2 - 10x + 25$

15. $(x + y)^2(x - y)^2$
$$
\begin{array}{r}
(x^2 + 2xy + y^2)(x^2 - 2xy + y^2) \\
x^2 + 2xy + y^2 \\
x^2 - 2xy + y^2 \\
\hline
x^2y^2 + 2xy^3 + y^4 \\
- 2x^3y - 4x^2y^2 - 2xy^3 \\
x^4 + 2x^3y + x^2y^2 \\
\hline
x^4 \qquad - 2x^2y^2 \qquad + y^4
\end{array}
$$

16. $x^4 - 8x^2 + 16$

17. $(x + 2)^3 = \underbrace{(x + 2)(x + 2)}(x + 2)$

   First find
   $(x + 2)^2$

$$
\begin{array}{r}
x + 2 \\
x + 2 \\
\hline
2x + 4 \\
x^2 + 2x \\
\hline
x^2 + 4x + 4
\end{array}
\qquad
\begin{array}{r}
x^2 + 4x + 4 \\
x + 2 \\
\hline
2x^2 + 8x + 8 \\
x^3 + 4x^2 + 4x \\
\hline
x^3 + 6x^2 + 12x + 8
\end{array}
$$

18. $x^3 + 9x^2 + 27x + 27$

19.
$$
\begin{array}{r}
x^2 - xy + y^2 \\
x + y \\
\hline
x^2y - xy^2 + y^3 \\
x^3 - x^2y + xy^2 \\
\hline
x^3 \qquad\qquad + y^3
\end{array}
\qquad
\begin{array}{r}
x^2 + xy + y^2 \\
x - y \\
\hline
- x^2y - xy^2 - y^3 \\
x^3 + x^2y + xy^2 \\
\hline
x^3 \qquad\qquad - y^3
\end{array}
$$

   This shows that
   $[(x + y)(x^2 - xy + y^2)][(x - y)(x^2 + xy + y^2)]$
   $= [x^3 + y^3][x^3 - y^3]$

   Then
$$
\begin{array}{r}
x^3 + y^3 \\
x^3 - y^3 \\
\hline
- x^3y^3 - y^6 \\
x^6 + x^3y^3 \\
\hline
x^6 \qquad - y^6
\end{array}
$$

20. $a^6 - 1$

1. $\dfrac{3x + 6}{3} = \dfrac{3x}{3} + \dfrac{6}{3} = x + 2$

2. $2x + 3$

3. $\dfrac{4 + 8x}{4} = \dfrac{4}{4} + \dfrac{8x}{4} = 1 + 2x$

4. $1 - 2x$

5. $\dfrac{6x - 8y}{2} = \dfrac{6x}{2} + \dfrac{-8y}{2} = 3x - 4y$

6. $x - 2y$

7. $\dfrac{2x^2 + 3x}{x} = \dfrac{2x^2}{x} + \dfrac{3x}{x} = 2x + 3$

8. $4y - 3$

9. $\dfrac{15x^3 - 5x^2}{5x^2} = \dfrac{15x^3}{5x^2} + \dfrac{-5x^2}{5x^2} = 3x - 1$

10. $2y^2 - 1$

11. $\dfrac{3a^2b - ab}{ab} = \dfrac{3a^2b}{ab} + \dfrac{-ab}{ab} = 3a - 1$

12. $5n - 1$

13. $\dfrac{5x^3 - 4x^2 + 10}{-5x^2}$

$= \dfrac{5x^3}{-5x^2} + \dfrac{-4x^2}{-5x^2} + \dfrac{10}{-5x^2}$

$= -x + \dfrac{4}{5} - \dfrac{2}{x^2}$

14. $-y + \dfrac{5}{7} - \dfrac{2}{y^2}$

15. $\dfrac{-15x^2y^2z^2 - 30xyz}{-5xyz}$

$= \dfrac{-15x^2y^2z^2}{-5xyz} + \dfrac{-30xyz}{-5xyz}$

$= 3xyz + 6$

16. $3abc + 2$

17. $\dfrac{13x^3y^2 - 26xy^3 + 39xy}{13x^2y^2}$

$= \dfrac{13x^3y^2}{13x^2y^2} + \dfrac{-26xy^3}{13x^2y^2} + \dfrac{39xy}{13x^2y^2}$

$= x - \dfrac{2y}{x} + \dfrac{3}{xy}$

18. $3n - 5m - \dfrac{2}{mn}$

19. $\dfrac{42.63x^5}{9.07x} + \dfrac{-72.48x^3}{9.07x} + \dfrac{18.45x}{9.07x}$

$\doteq 4.700x^4 - 7.991x^2 + 2.034$

20. $\doteq 1.934x^3 + 2.208x - 1.622$

1.
```
          x + 3
x + 2 | x² + 5x + 6
        x² + 2x
        ───────
             3x + 6
             3x + 6
             ──────
                  0
```

2. $x + 2$

3.
```
          x + 3
x - 4 | x² - x - 12
        x² - 4x
        ───────
            3x - 12
            3x - 12
            ───────
                  0
```

4. $x - 4$

5.
```
          2x + 3
3x - 2 | 6x² + 5x - 6
         6x² - 4x
         ───────
              9x - 6
              9x - 6
              ──────
                   0
```

6. $4x + 5$

7.
```
          3v + 8 R 66
5v - 7 | 15v² + 19v + 10
         15v² - 21v
         ─────────
               40v + 10
               40v - 56
               ────────
                     66
```

8. $5v - 7$ R 52

9.
```
            4x² + 8x + 8 R -6
-x + 2 | -4x³      + 8x + 10
         -4x³ + 8x²
         ─────────
              - 8x² + 8x
              - 8x² + 16x
              ───────────
                    - 8x + 10
                    - 8x + 16
                    ─────────
                          - 6
```

10. $x^2 + 3x - 3$ R -6

11.
```
           3a - 2b R 7b²
2a + 3b | 6a² + 5ab + b²
          6a² + 9ab
          ────────
             - 4ab + b²
             - 4ab - 6b²
             ──────────
                    7b²
```

12. $2a + 3b$ R $5b^2$

13.
```
          a² + 2a + 4
a - 2 | a³ + 0a² + 0a - 8
        a³ - 2a²
        ───────
             2a² + 0a
             2a² - 4a
             ───────
                  4a - 8
                  4a - 8
                  ──────
                       0
```

14. $c^2 + 3c + 9$

15.
```
             x² + x - 1 R 3
x² + x - 1 | x⁴ + 2x³ - x² - 2x + 4
             x⁴ + x³ - x²
             ───────────
                   x³ + 0x² - 2x
                   x³ + x² - x
                   ───────────
                      - x² - x + 4
                      - x² - x + 1
                      ───────────
                               3
```

16. $x^2 - x + 1$ R 6

1. 2 terms
    3 variables

2. 2 terms
    3 variables

3. 3rd degree
    3rd degree

4. 4th degree
    1st degree

5. Not a polynomial,
    because $\dfrac{3}{u + v}$ is not
    of the form ax^n.

6. Not a polynomial

7. $3x^4 + 7x^2 + x - 6$

8. $y^3 + 3xy^2 + 3x^2y + x^3$

9. $(5x^2y + 3xy^2 - 4y^3) + (2xy^2 + 4y^3 + 3x^2y)$

$= \underline{5x^2y} + \underline{3xy^2} - \underline{4y^3} + \underline{2xy^2} + \underline{4y^3} + \underline{3x^2y}$

$= 8x^2y + 5xy^2$

10. $9a^3 - 3ab^2 + 5$

11. $(5x^2y + 3xy^2 - 4 + y^2) - (8 - 4x^2y + 2xy^2 - y^2)$

$= \underline{5x^2y} + \underline{3xy^2} - \underline{4} + \underline{y^2} - \underline{8} + \underline{4x^2y} - \underline{2xy^2} + \underline{y^2}$

$= 9x^2y + xy^2 + 2y^2 - 12$

12. $4a^2b + 9ab^2 + 4a - 8$

13. $(7a^2 - 3ab + 5 - b^2) - (6 - 3a^2 + 2ab + 2b^2)$

$= \underline{7a^2} - \underline{3ab} + \underline{5} - \underline{b^2} - \underline{6} + \underline{3a^2} - \underline{2ab} - \underline{2b^2}$

$= 10a^2 - 5ab - 3b^2 - 1$

14. $-6y^3 - 36y^2 + 40y + 6$

15. $\dfrac{8x + 2}{2} = \dfrac{8x}{2} + \dfrac{2}{2} = 4x + 1$ 16. $2 - y$

17. $15m^3n - 20m^3n^3$

18. $-20x^3y^3 + 12xy^3$

19. $x^2 + 2x - 35$

20. $x^3 - 8$

21. $6a^2 - 2a - 20$

22. $15b^2 + 7b - 2$ 23.
$$
\begin{array}{r}
a + b + 4 \\
a + b + 4 \\
\hline
4a + 4b + 16 \\
ab + 4b + b^2 \\
a^2 + ab + 4a \\
\hline
a^2 + 2ab + 8a + 8b + 16 + b^2
\end{array}
$$

24. $x^2 + 2xy + y^2 + 6x + 6y + 9$

25. $x - 2y$

26. $3ab^2 - \dfrac{4b}{5} + 2$

27. $2x - 3 \overline{\smash{\big)}\,6x^2 - 9x + 10} \quad 3x + 0 \text{ R } 10$
$$
\begin{array}{r}
3x + 0 \text{ R } 10 \\
2x - 3 \, \overline{\smash{\big)}\, 6x^2 - 9x + 10} \\
\underline{6x^2 - 9x } \\
+ 10
\end{array}
$$

28. $2a + 5b$

29. $2 - 3y$

30. $a^2 - 1$

31. $(2m^2 - 5) - [(7 - m^2) - (4m^2 - 3)]$
$(2m^2 - 5) - [7 - m^2 - 4m^2 + 3]$
$(2m^2 - 5) - [10 - 5m^2]$
$2m^2 - 5 - 10 + 5m^2$
$7m^2 - 15$

32. $-14x^2 + 22x - 2$

33. $\underline{26.8x^2} - \underline{17.5x} - \underline{83.2} + \underline{65.9x} + \underline{68.1} - \underline{53.6x^2}$
$= -26.8x^2 + 48.4x - 15.1$

34. $\doteq -35.0x^2 + 11.3x$

CUMULATIVE REVIEW EXERCISES:
CHAPTERS 1-6 (page 219)

1. $-5^2 \cdot 4 - 15 \div 3\sqrt{25}$
$-25 \cdot 4 - 15 \div 3(5)$
$-25 \cdot 4 - 5 (5)$
$-100 - 25 = -125$

2. -22

3. $A = P(1 + i)^n$
$= 500(1 + 0.01)^2$
$= 500(1.01)^2$
$= 500(1.0201)$
$= 510.05$

4. $10^5 = 100,000$

5. $\dfrac{x^{3c}}{x^c} = x^{3c - c} = x^{2c}$

6. $\dfrac{8a^6}{b^3}$

7. $\left(\dfrac{\cancel{6}^{\,2} y^{-1}}{\cancel{3} y^3}\right)^2$
$= (2y^{-1-3})^2 = (2y^{-4})^2$
$= 2^2 y^{-8} = \dfrac{4}{y^8}$

8. $\dfrac{x^4}{9}$

9. $6(8 + 2x) - 2(11 + x) = 6$
$48 + 12x - 22 - 2x = 6$
$10x + 26 = 6$
$10x = -20$
$x = -2$

10. $\doteq 92\%$

CHAPTER SEVEN DIAGNOSTIC TEST (page 220)

Following each problem number is the textbook section reference (in parentheses) where that kind of problem is discussed.

1. (701) $x^2 - 4xy^2 + 5$

   (a) The first term is 2nd degree.
   (b) The polynomial is 3rd degree.
   (c) The numerical coefficient of the 2nd term is -4.

2. (702)
$$
\begin{array}{r}
-5x^3 + 2x^2 - 5 \\
7x^3 + 5x - 8 \\
3x^2 - 6x + 10 \\
\hline
2x^3 + 5x^2 - x - 3
\end{array}
$$

3. (702) $(3xy^2 - 4xy) + (12xy - 3xy^2) + (4xy + x^3)$
$\underline{3xy^2} - \underline{4xy} + \underline{12xy} - \underline{3xy^2} + \underline{4xy} + \underline{x^3}$
$= 12xy + x^3$

4. (703) $(-4z^2 - 5z + 10) - (10 - z + 2z^2)$
$= -4z^2 - 5z + \underline{10} - \underline{10} + \underline{z} - \underline{2z^2}$
$= -6z^2 - 4z$

5. (704) $-2ab(5a^2 - 3ab^2 + 4b)$
$= (-2ab)(5a^2) + (-2ab)(-3ab^2) + (-2ab)(4b)$
$= -10a^3b + 6a^2b^3 - 8ab^2$

6. (704)
$$
\begin{array}{r}
2x - 5 \\
3x + 4 \\
\hline
8x - 20 \\
6x^2 - 15x \\
\hline
6x^2 - 7x - 20
\end{array}
$$
7. (704)
$$
\begin{array}{r}
2y - 3 \\
2y - 3 \\
\hline
- 6y + 9 \\
4y^2 - 6y \\
\hline
4y^2 - 12y + 9
\end{array}
$$

8. (704)
$$
\begin{array}{r}
w^2 + 3w + 9 \\
w - 3 \\
\hline
- 3w^2 - 9w - 27 \\
w^3 + 3w^2 + 9w \\
\hline
w^3 - 27 = w^3 - 27
\end{array}
$$

9. (705) $\dfrac{6x^3 - 4x^2 + 8x}{2x} = \dfrac{6x^3}{2x} + \dfrac{-4x^2}{2x} + \dfrac{8x}{2x}$
$= 3x^2 - 2x + 4$

10. (705)
$$
\begin{array}{r}
5x + 3 \text{ R} -2 \\
2x - 1 \, \overline{\smash{\big)}\, 10x^2 + x - 5} \\
\underline{10x^2 - 5x } \\
6x - 5 \\
\underline{6x - 3} \\
- 2
\end{array}
$$

   or $5x + 3 - \dfrac{2}{2x - 1}$

1. $\left.\begin{array}{l} 1 \cdot 4 = 4 \\ 2 \cdot 2 = 4 \end{array}\right\} \Rightarrow \{1, 2, 4\}$ 2. $\{1, 3, 9\}$

3. $\left.\begin{array}{l} 1 \cdot 10 = 10 \\ 2 \cdot 5 = 10 \end{array}\right\} \Rightarrow \{1, 2, 5, 10\}$ 4. $\{1, 2, 7, 14\}$

5. $\left.\begin{array}{l} 1 \cdot 15 = 15 \\ 3 \cdot 5 = 15 \end{array}\right\} \Rightarrow \{1, 3, 5, 15\}$

6. $\{1, 2, 4, 8, 16\}$

7. $\left.\begin{array}{l} 1 \cdot 18 = 18 \\ 2 \cdot 9 = 18 \\ 3 \cdot 6 = 18 \end{array}\right\} \Rightarrow \{1, 2, 3, 6, 9, 18\}$

8. $\{1, 2, 4, 5, 10, 20\}$

9. $\left.\begin{array}{l} 1 \cdot 21 \\ 3 \cdot 7 \end{array}\right\} \Rightarrow \{1, 3, 7, 21\}$ 10. $\{1, 2, 11, 22\}$

11. $\left.\begin{array}{l} 1 \cdot 27 \\ 3 \cdot 9 \end{array}\right\} \Rightarrow \{1, 3, 9, 27\}$

12. $\{1, 2, 4, 7, 14, 28\}$

13. $\left.\begin{array}{l} 1 \cdot 33 \\ 3 \cdot 11 \end{array}\right\} \Rightarrow \{1, 3, 11, 33\}$ 14. $\{1, 2, 17, 34\}$

15. $\left.\begin{array}{l} 1 \cdot 44 \\ 2 \cdot 22 \\ 4 \cdot 11 \end{array}\right\} \Rightarrow \{1, 2, 4, 11, 22, 44\}$

16. $\{1, 3, 5, 9, 15, 45\}$ 17. $\{1, 5\} \Rightarrow P$

18. C 19. $\{1, 13\} \Rightarrow P$ 20. C

21. $\{1, 2, 3, 4, 6, 12\} \Rightarrow C$ 22. P

23. $\{1, 3, 7, 21\} \Rightarrow C$ 24. P

25. $\{1, 5, 11, 55\} \Rightarrow C$ 26. P

27. $\{1, 7, 49\} \Rightarrow C$ 28. P

29. $\{1, 3, 17, 51\} \Rightarrow C$ 30. C

31. $\{1, 3, 37, 111\} \Rightarrow C$ 32. P

33. $\begin{array}{r|l} 2 & 14 \\ \hline & 7 \end{array}$ 34. $15 = 3 \cdot 5$

$14 = 2 \cdot 7$

35. $\begin{array}{r|l} 3 & 21 \\ \hline & 7 \end{array}$ 36. $22 = 2 \cdot 11$

$21 = 3 \cdot 7$

37. $\begin{array}{r|l} 2 & 26 \\ \hline & 13 \end{array}$ 38. $27 = 3^3$

$26 = 2 \cdot 13$

39. 29 is prime   40. 31 is prime

41. $\begin{array}{r|l} 2 & 32 \\ 2 & 16 \\ 2 & 8 \\ 2 & 4 \\ \hline & 2 \end{array}$ 42. $33 = 3 \cdot 11$

$32 = 2^5$

43. $\begin{array}{r|l} 2 & 34 \\ \hline & 17 \end{array}$ 44. $35 = 5 \cdot 7$

$34 = 2 \cdot 17$

45. $\begin{array}{r|l} 2 & 84 \\ 2 & 42 \\ 3 & 21 \\ \hline & 7 \end{array}$ 46. $75 = 3 \cdot 5^2$

$84 = 2^2 \cdot 3 \cdot 7$

47. $\begin{array}{r|l} 2 & 144 \\ 2 & 72 \\ 2 & 36 \\ 2 & 18 \\ 3 & 9 \\ \hline & 3 \end{array}$ 48. $180 = 2^2 \cdot 3^2 \cdot 5$

$144 = 2^4 \cdot 3^2$

1. $2(x + 4)$ 2. $3x + 9$ 3. $5(a - 2)$
    $= 2x + 8$ $= 5a - 10$

4. $7b - 14$ 5. $2x + 8$ 6. $3(x + 3)$
                     $= 2(x + 4)$

7. $5a - 10$ 8. $7(b - 2)$ 9. $6y - 3$
    $= 5(a - 2)$ $= 3(2y - 1)$

10. $5(3z - 1)$ 11. $9x^2 + 3x$ 12. $4y(2y - 1)$
                          $= 3x(3x + 1)$

13. $10a^3 - 25a^2$ 14. $9b^2(3 - 2b^2)$
     $= 5a^2(2a - 5)$

15. Cannot be factored   16. Cannot be factored

17. $2a^2b + 4ab^2$ 18. $3mn^2(1 + 2m)$
     $= 2ab(a + 2b)$

19. $12c^3d^2 - 18c^2d^3$ 20. $15ab^3(1 - 3ab)$
     $= 6c^2d^2(2c - 3d)$

21. $4x^3 - 12x - 24x^2$ 22. $6y(3 - y - 5y^2)$
     $= 4x(x^2 - 3 - 6x)$

23. $3a(2a^2 - 5a + 4)$ 24. $15b^3 + 10b^2 - 30b$
     $= 6a^3 - 15a^2 + 12a$

25. $6x^2(3x^3 - 7x + 1)$ 26. $20y^6 + 12y^4 - 4y^2$
     $= 18x^5 - 42x^3 + 6x^2$

27. $24a^4 + 8a^2 - 40$ 28. $15(3b^3 - b^4 - 2)$
     $= 8(3a^4 + a^2 - 5)$

29. $-14x^8y^9 + 42x^5y^4 - 28xy^3$
     $= 14xy^3(-x^7y^6 + 3x^4y - 2)$

30. $7uv^5(-3u^6v^3 - 9 + 5u)$

31. Cannot be factored   32. Cannot be factored

33. $-44a^{14}b^7 - 33a^{10}b^5 + 22a^{11}b^4$
     $= 11a^{10}b^4(-4a^4b^3 - 3b + 2a)$

34. $13e^8f^5(-2f + e^2f^3 - 3e^4)$

35. $18u^{10}v^5 + 24 - 14u^{10}v^6$
     $= 2(9u^{10}v^5 + 12 - 7u^{10}v^6)$

36. $15(2a^3b^4 - 1 + 3a^8b^7)$

37. $18x^3y^4 - 12y^2z^3 - 48x^4y^3$
     $= 6y^2(3x^3y^2 - 2z^3 - 8x^4y)$

38. $8m^3(4m^2n^7 - 3m^5p^9 - 5n^6)$

1. $(x + 3)(x - 3) = (x)^2 - (3)^2 = x^2 - 9$

2. $z^2 - 16$

3. $(w - 6)(w + 6) = (w)^2 - (6)^2 = w^2 - 36$

4. $y^2 - 25$

5. $(5a + 4)(5a - 4) = (5a)^2 - (4)^2 = 25a^2 - 16$

6. $36a^2 - 25$

7. $(2u + 5v)(2u - 5v) = (2u)^2 - (5v)^2 = 4u^2 - 25v^2$

8. $9m^2 - 49n^2$

9. $(4b - 9c)(4b + 9c) = (4b)^2 - (9c)^2 = 16b^2 - 81c^2$

10. $49a^2 - 64b^2$

11. $(2x^2 - 9)(2x^2 + 9) = (2x^2)^2 - (9)^2 = 4x^4 - 81$

12. $100y^4 - 9$

13. $(1 + 8z^3)(1 - 8z^3) = (1)^2 - (8z^3)^2 = 1 - 64z^6$

14. $81v^8 - 1$

15. $(5xy + z)(5xy - z) = (5xy)^2 - (z)^2 = 25x^2y^2 - z^2$

16. $100a^2b^2 - c^2$

17. $(7mn + 2rs)(7mn - 2rs) = (7mn)^2 - (2rs)^2$
    $= 49m^2n^2 - 4r^2s^2$

18. $64h^2k^2 - 25e^2f^2$

EXERCISES 803B, SET I   (page 235)

1. $\sqrt{64} = 8$ because $(8)^2 = 64$ 2. 9

3. $\sqrt{4x^2} = 2x$ because $(2x)^2 = 4x^2$ 4. $3y$

5. $\sqrt{100a^8} = 10a^4$ because $(10a^4)^2 = 100a^8$ 6. $7b^3$

7. $\sqrt{m^4n^2} = m^2n$ because $(m^2n)^2 = m^4n^2$ 8. u^5v^3

9. $\sqrt{x^{10}y^4} = x^{10 \div 2}y^{4 \div 2} = x^5y^2$ 10. x^6y^4

11. $\sqrt{25a^4b^2} = 5a^{4 \div 2}b^{2 \div 2} = 5a^2b^1$ 12. $10b^2c$

13. $\sqrt{36e^8f^2} = 6e^{8 \div 2}f^{2 \div 2} = 6e^4f^1$ 14. $9h^6k^7$

15. $\sqrt{100a^{10}y^2} = 10a^{10 \div 2}y^{2 \div 2} = 10a^5y^1$

16. $11a^{12}b^2$

17. $\sqrt{9a^4b^2c^6} = 3a^{4 \div 2}b^{2 \div 2}c^{6 \div 2} = 3a^2b^1c^3$

18. $12x^4y^1z^3$

EXERCISES 803C, SET I   (page 237)

1. $m^2 - n^2 = (\sqrt{m^2} + \sqrt{n^2})(\sqrt{m^2} - \sqrt{n^2})$
   $= (m + n)(m - n)$

2. $(u + v)(u - v)$

3. $x^2 - 9 = (\sqrt{x^2} + \sqrt{9})(\sqrt{x^2} - \sqrt{9}) = (x + 3)(x - 3)$

4. $(x + 5)(x - 5)$

5. $a^2 - 1 = (\sqrt{a^2} + \sqrt{1})(\sqrt{a^2} - \sqrt{1}) = (a + 1)(a - 1)$

6. $(1 + b)(1 - b)$

7. $4c^2 - 1 = (\sqrt{4c^2} + \sqrt{1})(\sqrt{4c^2} - \sqrt{1})$
   $= (2c + 1)(2c - 1)$

8. $(4d + 1)(4d - 1)$

9. $16x^2 - 9y^2 = (\sqrt{16x^2} + \sqrt{9y^2})(\sqrt{16x^2} - \sqrt{9y^2})$
   $= (4x + 3y)(4x - 3y)$

10. $(5a + 2b)(5a - 2b)$

11. Cannot be factored   12. Cannot be factored

13. $49u^4 - 36v^4 = (\sqrt{49u^4} + \sqrt{36v^4})(\sqrt{49u^4} - \sqrt{36v^4})$
    $= (7u^2 + 6v^2)(7u^2 - 6v^2)$

14. $(9m^3 + 10n^2)(9m^3 - 10n^2)$

15. $x^6 - a^4 = (\sqrt{x^6} + \sqrt{a^4})(\sqrt{x^6} - \sqrt{a^4})$
    $= (x^3 + a^2)(x^3 - a^2)$

16. $(b + y^3)(b - y^3)$

17. $a^2b^2 - c^2d^2 = (\sqrt{a^2b^2} + \sqrt{c^2d^2})(\sqrt{a^2b^2} - \sqrt{c^2d^2})$
    $= (ab + cd)(ab - cd)$

18. $(mn + rs)(mn - rs)$

19. $49 - 25w^2z^2 = (\sqrt{49} + \sqrt{25w^2z^2})(\sqrt{49} - \sqrt{25w^2z^2})$
    $= (7 + 5wz)(7 - 5wz)$

20. $(6 + 5uv)(6 - 5uv)$

21. $4h^4k^4 - 1 = (\sqrt{4h^4k^4} + \sqrt{1})(\sqrt{4h^4k^4} - \sqrt{1})$
    $= (2h^2k^2 + 1)(2h^2k^2 - 1)$

22. $(3x^2y^2 + 1)(3x^2y^2 - 1)$

23. $81a^4b^6 - 16m^2n^8$
    $= (\sqrt{81a^4b^6} + \sqrt{16m^2n^8})(\sqrt{81a^4b^6} - \sqrt{16m^2n^8})$
    $= (9a^2b^3 + 4mn^4)(9a^2b^3 - 4mn^4)$

24. $(7c^4d^2 + 10e^3f)(7c^4d^2 - 10e^3f)$

EXERCISES 804A, SET I   (page 240)

1. $(x + 1)(x + 4)$ 2. $x^2 + 4x + 3$
   $\underset{4x}{\underset{1x}{\overbrace{}}}$
   $x^2 + 5x + 4$

3. $(a + 5)(a + 2)$ 4. $a^2 + 8a + 7$
   $\underset{2a}{\underset{5a}{\overbrace{}}}$
   $a^2 + 7a + 10$

5. $(m - 4)(m + 2)$ 6. $n^2 + 4n - 21$
   $\underset{+2m}{\underset{-4m}{\overbrace{}}}$
   $m^2 - 2m - 8$

7. $(y + 8)(y - 9)$ 8. $z^2 + 7z - 30$
   $\underset{-9y}{\underset{8y}{\overbrace{}}}$
   $y^2 - y - 72$

9. $(x + 3)^2 = (x)^2 + 2(x)(3) + (3)^2 = x^2 + 6x + 9$

10. $x^2 + 10x + 25$

11. $(b - 4)^2 = (b)^2 + 2(b)(-4) + (-4)^2 = b^2 - 8b + 16$

12. $b^2 - 12b + 36$

13. $(2a + 5b)(a + b)$ 14. $3c^2 + 5cd + 2d^2$
    $\underset{2ab}{\underset{5ab}{\overbrace{}}}$
    $2a^2 + 7ab + 5b^2$

15. $(4x - y)(2x + 7y)$ 16. $12x^2 + 7xy - 10y^2$
    $\underset{+28xy}{\underset{-2xy}{\overbrace{}}}$
    $8x^2 + 26xy - 7y^2$

17. $(7x - 10y)^2 = (7x)^2 - 2(7x)(10y) + (10y)^2$
    $= 49x^2 - 140xy + 100y^2$

18. $16u^2 - 72uv + 81v^2$

19. $(3x + 4)^2 = (3x)^2 + 2(3x)(4) + (4)^2$
    $= 9x^2 + 24x + 16$

20. $4x^2 + 20x + 25$

21. $(4c - 3d)(4c + 3d)$
    $= (4c)^2 - (3d)^2 = 16c^2 - 9d^2$

22. $25e^2 - 4f^2$

EXERCISES 804B, SET I   (page 244)

1. $x^2 + 6x + 8 = (x + 2)(x + 4)$ $8 = 1 \cdot 8$
   $\qquad +6 \quad = \quad +2 \; + \; +4$ $= 2 \cdot 4$

2. $(x + 1)(x + 8)$

3. $x^2 + 5x + 4 = (x + 1)(x + 4)$ $4 = 1 \cdot 4$
   $\qquad +5 \quad = \quad +1 \; + \; +4$ $= 2 \cdot 2$

4. $(x + 2)(x + 2) = (x + 2)^2$

5. $k^2 + 7k + 6 = (k + 1)(k + 6)$ $6 = 1 \cdot 6$
   $\qquad +7 \quad = \quad +1 \; + \; +6$ $= 2 \cdot 3$

6. $(k + 2)(k + 3)$

7. $u^2 + 7u + 10 = (u + 2)(u + 5)$ $10 = 1 \cdot 10$
   $+7 = +2 + +5$ $= 2 \cdot 5$

8. $(u + 1)(u + 10)$

9. Cannot be factored   10. Cannot be factored

11. $b^2 - 9b + 14 = (b - 2)(b - 7)$ $14 = 1 \cdot 14$
    $-9 = -2 + -7$ $= 2 \cdot 7$

12. $(b - 1)(b - 14)$

13. $z^2 - 9z + 20 = (z - 4)(z - 5)$ $20 = 1 \cdot 20$
    $-9 = -4 + -5$ $= 2 \cdot 10$
    $= 4 \cdot 5$

14. $(z - 2)(z - 10)$

15. $x^2 - 11x + 18 = (x - 2)(x - 9)$ $18 = 1 \cdot 18$
    $-11 = -2 + -9$ $= 2 \cdot 9$
    $= 3 \cdot 6$

16. $(x - 3)(x - 6)$

17. $x^2 + 9x - 10 = (x - 1)(x + 10)$ $10 = 1 \cdot 10$
    $+9 = -1 + +10$ $= 2 \cdot 5$

18. $(y + 2)(y - 5)$

19. $z^2 - 1z - 6 = (z + 2)(z - 3)$ $6 = 1 \cdot 6$
    $-1 = +2 + -3$ $= 2 \cdot 3$

20. $(m - 1)(m + 6)$

21. Cannot be factored   22. Cannot be factored

23. $u^4 + 12u^2 - 64 = (u^2 - 4)(u^2 + 16)$ $64 = 1 \cdot 64$
    $+12 = -4 + +16$ $= 2 \cdot 32$
    $= 4 \cdot 16$
    $= 8 \cdot 8$

    $= (u^2 - 4)(u^2 + 16)$

    $= (u + 2)(u - 2)(u^2 + 16)$

24. $(v^2 + 2)(v^2 - 32)$

25. $16 - 8v + v^2 = (4 - v)(4 - v) = (4 - v)^2$
    $-4v$
    $-4v$
    $-8v$

26. $(2 - v)(8 - v)$

27. $b^2 - 11bd - 60d^2 = (b + 4d)(b - 15d)$ $60 = 1 \cdot 60$
    $-11 = +4 + -15$ $= 2 \cdot 30$
    $= 3 \cdot 20$
    $= 4 \cdot 15$
    $= 6 \cdot 10$

28. $(c - 3x)(c + 20x)$

29. $r^2 - 13rs - 48s^2 = (r + 3s)(r - 16s)$ $48 = 1 \cdot 48$
    $-13 = +3 + -16$ $= 2 \cdot 24$
    $= 3 \cdot 16$
    $= 4 \cdot 12$
    $= 6 \cdot 8$

30. $(s - 2t)(s + 24t)$

EXERCISES 804C, SET I   (page 250)

1. $3 = 1 \cdot 3$ $2 = 1 \cdot 2$
   $(1x + 2)(3x + 1)$
   $+6x$
   $+1x$
   $+7x$

2. $(x + 1)(3x + 2)$

3. $5 = 1 \cdot 5$ $2 = 1 \cdot 2$
   $(1x + 1)(5x + 2)$
   $+5x$
   $+2x$
   $+7x$

4. $(x + 2)(5x + 1)$

5. $4 = 1 \cdot 4$ $3 = 1 \cdot 3$
   $= 2 \cdot 2$
   $(1x + 1)(4x + 3)$
   $+4x$
   $+3x$
   $+7x$

6. $(x + 3)(4x + 1)$

7. Cannot be factored   8. Cannot be factored

9. $5 = 1 \cdot 5$ $3 = 1 \cdot 3$
   $(1a - 3)(5a - 1)$
   $-15a$
   $- 1a$
   $-16a$

10. $(m - 1)(5m - 3)$

11. $3 = 1 \cdot 3$ $7 = 1 \cdot 7$
    $(1b - 7)(3b - 1)$
    $-21b$
    $- 1b$
    $-22b$

12. $(u - 1)(3u - 7)$

13. $5 = 1 \cdot 5$ $7 = 1 \cdot 7$
    $(1z - 7)(5z - 1)$
    $-35z$
    $- 1z$
    $-36z$

14. $(z - 1)(5z - 7)$

15. $3 = 1 \cdot 3$ $5 = 1 \cdot 5$
    $(1n + 5)(3n - 1)$
    $+15n$
    $- 1n$
    $+14n$

16. $(n + 1)(3n - 5)$

17. $5 = 1 \cdot 5$ $7 = 1 \cdot 7$
    $(1k - 7)(5k + 1)$
    $-35k$
    $+ 1k$
    $-34k$

18. $(k - 1)(5k + 7)$

19. $7 = 1 \cdot 7$ $6 = 1 \cdot 6$
    $= 2 \cdot 3$
    $(1x + 3y)(7x + 2y)$
    $+21xy$
    $+ 2xy$
    $+23xy$

20. $(a + 6b)(7a + b)$

21. $7 = \boxed{1 \cdot 7}$ $4 = \boxed{1 \cdot 4}$
$$= 2 \cdot 2$$

$$(1h - 1k)(7h - 4k)$$

22. $(h - 2k)(7h - 2k)$

23. Cannot be factored   24. Cannot be factored

25. $6 = 1 \cdot 6$ $5 = \boxed{1 \cdot 5}$
$$ = 2 \cdot 3$$

$$(3 - 1v)(2 - 5v)$$

26. $(1 - v)(6 - 5v)$

27. $6 = 1 \cdot 6$ $20 = 1 \cdot 20$
$$ = 2 \cdot 3 = 2 \cdot 10$$
$$ = \boxed{4 \cdot 5}$$

$$(2e^2 - 5)(3e^2 + 4)$$

28. $(5f^2 + 3)(2f^2 - 7)$

EXERCISES 805, SET I (page 253)

1. $am + bm + an + bn = m(a + b) + n(a + b)$
$$= (a + b)(m + n)$$

2. $(u + v)(c + d)$

3. $mx - nx - my + ny = x(m - n) - y(m - n)$
$$= (m - n)(x - y)$$

4. $(h - k)(a - b)$

5. $xy + x - y - 1 = x(y + 1) - 1(y + 1)$
$$= (y + 1)(x - 1)$$

6. $(a - 1)(d + 1)$

7. $3a^2 - 6ab + 2a - 4b = 3a(a - 2b) + 2(a - 2b)$
$$= (a - 2b)(3a + 2)$$

8. $(h - 3k)(2h + 5)$

9. $6e^2 - 2ef - 9e + 3f = 2e(3e - f) - 3(3e - f)$
$$= (3e - f)(2e - 3)$$

10. $(2m - n)(4m - 3)$

11. $h^2 - k^2 + 2h + 2k = (h + k)(h - k) + 2(h + k)$
$$= (h + k)(h - k + 2)$$

12. $(x + y)(x - y + 4)$

13. $x^3 + 3x^2 - 4x + 12 = x^2(x + 3) - 4(x - 3)$
Therefore, cannot be factored

14. Cannot be factored

15. $a^3 - 2a^2 - 4a + 8 = a^2(a - 2) - 4(a - 2)$
$$= (a - 2)(a^2 - 4)$$
$$= (a - 2)(a + 2)(a - 2)$$
$$= (a - 2)^2(a + 2)$$

16. $(x - 3)(x + 3)(x - 3) = (x - 3)^2(x + 3)$

17. $10xy - 15y + 8x - 12$
$5y(2x - 3) + 4(2x - 3)$
$(2x - 3)(5y + 4)$

18. $(7 + 3n)(5 - 6m)$

19. $y(a + b) - x(a + b) + y(c - d) - x(c - d)$
$(a + b)(y - x) + (c - d)(y - x)$
$(y - x)(a + b + c - d)$

20. $(a - b)(2y + 5 + x - z)$

EXERCISES 806, SET I   (page 255)

1. $3x^2 + 7x + 2$
$MP = 3 \cdot 2 = 6$

   $\boxed{1 \cdot 6}$ $\Rightarrow$ $(+1) + (+6) = +7$
   $2 \cdot 3$ $\underbrace{3x^2 + 1x}_{} + \underbrace{6x + 2}_{}$
$$x(3x + 1) + 2(3x + 1)$$
$$(3x + 1)(x + 2)$$

2. $(x + 1)(3x + 2)$

3. $5x^2 + 7x + 2$
$MP = 5 \cdot 2 = 10$

   $1 \cdot 10$
   $\boxed{2 \cdot 5}$ $\Rightarrow$ $(+2) + (+5) = +7$
$$\underbrace{5x^2 + 2x}_{} + \underbrace{5x + 2}_{}$$
$$x(5x + 2) + 1(5x + 2)$$
$$(5x + 2)(x + 1)$$

4. $(x + 2)(5x + 1)$

5. $4x^2 + 7x + 3$
$MP = 4 \cdot 3 = 12$

   $1 \cdot 12$
   $2 \cdot 6$
   $\boxed{3 \cdot 4}$ $\Rightarrow$ $(+3) + (+4) = +7$
$$\underbrace{4x^2 + 3x}_{} + \underbrace{4x + 3}_{}$$
$$x(4x + 3) + 1(4x + 3)$$
$$(4x + 3)(x + 1)$$

6. $(x + 3)(4x + 1)$

7. Cannot be factored

8. Cannot be factored

9. $5a^2 - 16a + 3$
$MP = 5 \cdot 3 = 15$

   $\boxed{1 \cdot 15}$ $\Rightarrow$ $(-1) + (-15) = -16$
   $3 \cdot 5$ $\underbrace{5a^2 - 1a}_{} - \underbrace{15a + 3}_{}$
$$a(5a - 1) - 3(5a - 1)$$
$$(5a - 1)(a - 3)$$

10. $(m - 1)(5m - 3)$

11. $3b^2 - 22b + 7$
$MP = 3 \cdot 7 = 21$

   $\boxed{1 \cdot 21}$ $\Rightarrow$ $(-1) + (-21) = -22$
   $3 \cdot 7$ $\underbrace{3b^2 - 1b}_{} - \underbrace{21b + 7}_{}$
$$b(3b - 1) - 7(3b - 1)$$
$$(3b - 1)(b - 7)$$

12. $(u - 1)(3u - 7)$

13. $5z^2 - 36z + 7$
$MP = 5 \cdot 7 = 35$

   $\boxed{1 \cdot 35}$ $\Rightarrow$ $(-1) + (-35) = -36$
   $5 \cdot 7$ $\underbrace{5z^2 - 1z}_{} - \underbrace{35z + 7}_{}$
$$z(5z - 1) - 7(5z - 1)$$
$$(5z - 1)(z - 7)$$

14. $(z - 1)(5z - 7)$

15. $3n^2 + 14n - 5$
$MP = 3(-5) = -15$
$\boxed{1 \cdot 15} \implies (-1) + (+15) = +14$
$3 \cdot 5 \qquad \underbrace{3n^2 - 1n} + \underbrace{15n - 5}$
$\qquad\qquad n(3n - 1) + 5(3n - 1)$
$\qquad\qquad (3n - 1)(n + 5)$

16. $(n + 1)(3n - 5)$

17. $5k^2 - 34k - 7$
$MP = 5(-7) = -35$
$\boxed{1 \cdot 35} \implies (+1) + (-35) = -34$
$5 \cdot 7 \qquad \underbrace{5k^2 + 1k} - \underbrace{35k - 7}$
$\qquad\qquad k(5k + 1) - 7(5k + 1)$
$\qquad\qquad (5k + 1)(k - 7)$

18. $(k - 1)(5k + 7)$

19. $7x^2 + 23xy + 6y^2$
$MP = 7 \cdot 6 = 42$
$1 \cdot 42$
$\boxed{2 \cdot 21} \implies (+2) + (+21) = +23$
$3 \cdot 14 \qquad \underbrace{7x^2 + 2xy} + \underbrace{21xy + 6y^2}$
$6 \cdot 7 \qquad x(7x + 2y) + 3y(7x + 2y)$
$\qquad\qquad (7x + 2y)(x + 3y)$

20. $(a + 6b)(7a + b)$

21. $7h^2 - 11hk + 4k^2$
$MP = 7 \cdot 4 = 28$
$1 \cdot 28$
$2 \cdot 14$
$\boxed{4 \cdot 7} \implies (-4) + (-7) = -11$
$\underbrace{7h^2 - 4hk} - \underbrace{7hk + 4k^2}$
$h(7h - 4k) - k(7h - 4k)$
$(7h - 4k)(h - k)$

22. $(h - 2k)(7h - 2k)$

23. Cannot be factored

24. Cannot be factored

25. $5v^2 - 17v + 6$
$MP = 5 \cdot 6 = 30$
$1 \cdot 30$
$\boxed{2 \cdot 15} \implies (-2) + (-15) = -17$
$3 \cdot 10 \qquad \underbrace{5v^2 - 2v} - \underbrace{15v + 6}$
$5 \cdot 6 \qquad v(5v - 2) - 3(5v - 2)$
$\qquad\qquad (5v - 2)(v - 3)$

26. $(v - 1)(5v - 6)$

27. $6e^4 - 7e^2 - 20$
$MP = 6(-20) = -120$
$1 \cdot 120$
$2 \cdot 60$
$3 \cdot 40$
$4 \cdot 30$
$5 \cdot 24$
$6 \cdot 20$
(continued)

$\boxed{8 \cdot 15} \implies (+8) + (-15) = -7$
$10 \cdot 12 \qquad \underbrace{6e^4 + 8e^2} - \underbrace{15e^2 - 20}$
$\qquad\qquad 2e^2(3e^2 + 4) - 5(3e^2 + 4)$
$\qquad\qquad (3e^2 + 4)(2e^2 - 5)$

28. $(5f^2 + 3)(2f^2 - 7)$

EXERCISES 807, SET I (page 256)

1. $2x^2 - 8y^2 = 2(x^2 - 4y^2)$
$\qquad = 2(\sqrt{x^2} + \sqrt{4y^2})(\sqrt{x^2} - \sqrt{4y^2})$
$\qquad = 2(x + 2y)(x - 2y)$

2. $3(x + 3y)(x - 3y)$

3. $5a^4 - 20b^2 = 5(a^4 - 4b^2)$
$\qquad = 5(\sqrt{a^4} + \sqrt{4b^2})(\sqrt{a^4} - \sqrt{4b^2})$
$\qquad = 5(a^2 + 2b)(a^2 - 2b)$

4. $6(m + 3n^2)(m - 3n^2)$

5. $x^4 - y^4 = (\sqrt{x^4} + \sqrt{y^4})(\sqrt{x^4} - \sqrt{y^4})$
$\qquad = (x^2 + y^2)(x^2 - y^2)$
$\qquad = (x^2 + y^2)(x + y)(x - y)$

6. $(a^2 + 4)(a + 2)(a - 2)$

7. $4v^2 + 14v - 8 = 2(2v^2 + 7v - 4)$
$\qquad = 2(v + 4)(2v - 1)$
$2 = \boxed{1 \cdot 2} \qquad\qquad 4 = \boxed{1 \cdot 4}$
$\qquad\qquad\qquad\qquad = 2 \cdot 2$
$\qquad 2(1v + 4)(2v - 1)$
$\qquad\qquad \underset{+8v}{\diagdown} \underset{-1v}{\diagup}$
$\qquad\qquad\qquad +7v$

8. $3(v - 5)(2v + 1)$

9. $8z^2 - 12z - 8 = 4(2z^2 - 3z - 2)$
$\qquad = 4(z - 2)(2z + 1)$
$2 = 1 \cdot 2 \qquad\qquad 2 = 1 \cdot 2$
$\qquad 4(1z - 2)(2z + 1)$
$\qquad\qquad \underset{-4z}{\diagdown} \underset{+1z}{\diagup}$
$\qquad\qquad\qquad -3z$

10. $3(2z - 3)(3z + 1)$

11. $12x^2 + 10x - 8 = 2(6x^2 + 5x - 4)$
$\qquad = 2(2x - 1)(3x + 4)$
$6 = 1 \cdot 6 \qquad\qquad 4 = \boxed{1 \cdot 4}$
$\quad = \boxed{2 \cdot 3} \qquad\qquad = 2 \cdot 2$
$\qquad 2(2x - 1)(3x + 4)$
$\qquad\qquad \underset{-3x}{\diagdown} \underset{+8x}{\diagup}$
$\qquad\qquad\qquad +5x$

12. $3(3x + 2)(5x - 4)$

13. $ab^2 - 2ab + a = a(b^2 - 2b + 1)$
$\qquad = a(b - 1)(b - 1) = a(b - 1)^2$

14. $a(u - 1)^2$

15. $x^4 - 81 = (\sqrt{x^4} + \sqrt{81})(\sqrt{x^4} - \sqrt{81})$
$\qquad = (x^2 + 9)(x^2 - 9)$
$\qquad = (x^2 + 9)(x + 3)(x - 3)$

16. $(4y^4 + z^2)(2y^2 + z)(2y^2 - z)$

17. $a^5b^2 - 4a^3b^4 = a^3b^2(a^2 - 4b^2)$
$\qquad = a^3b^2(a + 2b)(a - 2b)$

18. $x^2y^2(y + 10x)(y - 10x)$

19. $2ax^2 - 8a^3y^2 = 2a(x^2 - 4a^2y^2)$
$$= 2a(\sqrt{x^2} + \sqrt{4a^2y^2})(\sqrt{x^2} - \sqrt{4a^2y^2})$$
$$= 2a(x + 2ay)(x - 2ay)$$

20. $3b^2(x^2 + 2y)(x^2 - 2y)$

21. $2u^3 + 2u^2v - 12uv^2 = 2u(u^2 + uv - 6v^2)$
$$= 2u(u + 3v)(u - 2v)$$

22. $3m(m + 3n)(m - 4n)$

23. $8h^3 - 20h^2k + 12hk^2 = 4h(2h^2 - 5hk + 3k^2)$
$$= 4h(2h - 3k)(h - k)$$

24. $5k(h - 2k)(3h - k)$

25. $12 + 4x - 3x^2 - x^3 = 4(3 + x) - x^2(3 + x)$
$$= (3 + x)(4 - x^2)$$
$$= (3 + x)(2 + x)(2 - x)$$

26. $(5 - z)(3 + z)(3 - z)$

27. $6my - \underline{4nz} + 15mz - \underline{5zn}$
$6my - 9nz + 15mz$
$3(2my - 3nz + 5mz)$

28. $4(xy + mn)$

29. $6ac - 6bd + 6bc - 6ad$
$6[ac + bc - bd - ad]$
$6[c(a + b) - d(b + a)]$
$6(a + b)(c - d)$

30. $(2c + d)(5y - 3z)$

EXERCISES 808, SET I (page 261)

1. $(x - 5)(x + 4) = 0$

$x - 5 = 0 \mid x + 4 = 0$
$\quad x = 5 \mid \quad x = -4$

2. $-7, 2$

3. $3x(x - 4) = 0$

$3x = 0 \mid x - 4 = 0$
$\ x = 0 \mid \quad x = 4$

4. $0, -6$

5. $(x + 10)(2x - 3) = 0$

$x + 10 = 0 \mid 2x - 3 = 0$
$\quad x = -10 \mid \quad 2x = 3$
$\qquad\qquad x = \dfrac{3}{2} = 1\dfrac{1}{2}$

6. $8, -\dfrac{2}{3}$

7. $x^2 + 9x + 8 = 0$
$(x + 1)(x + 8) = 0$

$x + 1 = 0 \mid x + 8 = 0$
$\quad x = -1 \mid \quad x = -8$

8. $-2, -4$

9. $x^2 - x - 12 = 0$
$(x - 4)(x + 3) = 0$

$x - 4 = 0 \mid x + 3 = 0$
$\quad x = 4 \mid \quad x = -3$

10. $-4, 3$

11. $x^2 - 18 = 9x$
$x^2 - 9x - 18 = 0$

Cannot be factored

12. Cannot be factored

13. $6x^2 - 10x = 0$
$2x(3x - 5) = 0$

$2x = 0 \mid 3x - 5 = 0$
$\ x = 0 \mid \quad 3x = 5$
$\qquad\qquad x = \dfrac{5}{3}$

14. $0, \dfrac{7}{2}$

15. $24w = 4w^2$
$0 = 4w^2 - 24w$
$0 = 4w(w - 6)$

$4w = 0 \mid w - 6 = 0$
$\ w = 0 \mid \quad w = 6$

16. $0, 4$

17. $5a^2 = 16a - 3$
$5a^2 - 16a + 3 = 0$
$(1a - 3)(5a - 1) = 0$

$a - 3 = 0 \mid 5a - 1 = 0$
$\quad a = 3 \mid \quad 5a = 1$
$\qquad\qquad a = \dfrac{1}{5}$

18. $7, \dfrac{1}{3}$

19. $3u^2 = 2u + 5$
$3u^2 - 2u - 5 = 0$
$(1u + 1)(3u - 5) = 0$

$u + 1 = 0 \mid 3u - 5 = 0$
$\quad u = -1 \mid \quad 3u = 5$
$\qquad\qquad u = \dfrac{5}{3} = 1\dfrac{2}{3}$

20. $7, -\dfrac{1}{5}$

21. $(x - 2)(x - 3) = 2$
$x^2 - 5x + 6 = 2$
$x^2 - 5x + 4 = 0$
$(x - 1)(x - 4) = 0$

$x - 1 = 0 \mid x - 4 = 0$
$\quad x = 1 \mid \quad x = 4$

22. $2, 6$

23. $x(x - 4) = 12$
$x^2 - 4x = 12$
$x^2 - 4x - 12 = 0$
$(x - 6)(x + 2) = 0$

$x - 6 = 0 \mid x + 2 = 0$
$\quad x = 6 \mid \quad x = -2$

24. $-3, 5$

25. $4x(2x - 1)(3x + 7) = 0$

$4x = 0 \mid 2x - 1 = 0 \mid 3x + 7 = 0$
$\ x = 0 \mid \quad 2x = 1 \mid \quad 3x = -7$
$\qquad\quad x = \dfrac{1}{2} \mid \quad x = -\dfrac{7}{3} = -2\dfrac{1}{3}$

26. $0, \dfrac{3}{4}, \dfrac{6}{7}$

27. $2x^3 + x^2 = 3x$
$2x^3 + x^2 - 3x = 0$
$x(2x^2 + x - 3) = 0$
$x(1x - 1)(2x + 3) = 0$

$x = 0 \mid x - 1 = 0 \mid 2x + 3 = 0$
$\qquad\quad x = 1 \mid \quad 2x = -3$
$\qquad\qquad\qquad x = -\dfrac{3}{2} = -1\dfrac{1}{2}$

28. $0, -5, \dfrac{1}{2}$

29. $2a^3 - 10a^2 = 0$
$2a^2(a - 5) = 0$

$2a^2 = 0 \mid a - 5 = 0$
$\ a = 0 \mid \quad a = 5$

30. $0, 6$

31. $\dfrac{x + 2}{x + 1} = \dfrac{10}{x + 5}$

$(x + 2)(x + 5) = 10(x + 1)$

$x^2 + 7x + 10 = 10x + 10$

$x^2 - 3x = 0$

$x(x - 3) = 0$

$x = 0 \mid x - 3 = 0$
$\qquad\quad x = 3$

32. $6, -2$

EXERCISES 809, SET I (page 266)

1. Let x = small number ⎞ since their difference
   $x + 5$ = larger number ⎠ is 5.

   Their product is 14.

   $x(x + 5) = 14$ | If $x = 2$: $\ x = 2$⎞
   $x^2 + 5x = 14$ | $\qquad\qquad x + 5 = 7$⎠
   $x^2 + 5x - 14 = 0$ | If $x = -7$: $x = -7$⎞
   $(x + 7)(x - 2) = 0$ | $\qquad\qquad x + 5 = -2$⎠

   $x + 7 = 0 \mid x - 2 = 0$ | There are two answers:
   $\quad x = -7 \mid \quad x = 2$ | $\{2, 7\}$ and $\{-7, -2\}$

2. Two answers: $\{3,\ 9\}$ and $\{-9,\ -3\}$

3. Let $\quad x$ = one number
   then $12 - x$ = other number

   Their product is 35.

   $$x(12 - x) = 35$$
   $$12x - x^2 = 35$$
   $$0 = x^2 - 12x + 35$$
   $$0 = (x - 5)(x - 7)$$

$x - 5 = 0$	$x - 7 = 0$
$x = 5$	$x = 7$
$12 - x = 7$	$12 - x = 5$

   One answer: $\{5,\ 7\}$

4. $2,\ -6$

5. Let $\ x$ and $x + 1$ be the two
   consecutive numbers.
   Then $\quad x(x + 1)$ represents their product
   and $\ x + (x + 1)$ represents their sum.

   Their product | **is 11 more than** | **their sum**

   $$x(x + 1) = 11 + x + (x + 1)$$
   $$x^2 + x = 11 + 2x + 1$$
   $$x^2 - x - 12 = 0$$
   $$(x + 3)(x - 4) = 0$$

$x + 3 = 0$	$x - 4 = 0$
$x = -3$	$x = 4$
$x + 1 = -2$	$x + 1 = 5$

   Two answers: $\{4,\ 5\}$ and $\{-3,\ -2\}$

6. Two answers: $\{3,\ 4\}$ and $\{-2,\ -1\}$

7. Let $\ x - 1,\ x,\ x + 1$ be the integers
   Then $x(x - 1)$ is product of first two
   and $\ x(x + 1)$ is product of last two

   Product of first two | **plus** | **Product of last two** | **is 8**

   $$x(x - 1) + x(x + 1) = 8$$
   $$x^2 - x + x^2 + x = 8$$
   $$2x^2 - 8 = 0$$
   $$2(x^2 - 4) = 0$$
   $$2(x + 2)(x - 2) = 0$$

$2 \neq 0$	$x + 2 = 0$	$x - 2 = 0$
	$x = -2$	$x = 2$
	$x - 1 = -3$	$x - 1 = 1$
	$x + 1 = -1$	$x + 1 = 3$

   Two answers: $\{1,\ 2,\ 3\}$ and $\{-3,\ -2,\ -1\}$

8. Only one answer: $\{2,\ 3,\ 4\}$

9. Let $\ x - 2,\ x,\ x + 2$ be the integers
   Then $(x - 2)x$ is product of first two
   and $\ x(x + 2)$ is product of last two.

   Twice | **Product of first two** | **is 16 more than** | **product of last two**

   $$2 \cdot (x - 2)x = 16 + x(x + 2)$$
   $$2x^2 - 4x = 16 + x^2 + 2x$$
   $$x^2 - 6x - 16 = 0$$
   $$(x + 2)(x - 8) = 0$$

$x = -2$	$x = 8$
$x - 2 = -4$	$x - 2 = 6$
$x + 2 = 0$	$x + 2 = 10$

   Two answers: $\{-4,\ -2,\ 0\}$
   and $\{6,\ 8,\ 10\}$

10. Two answers: $\{5,\ 7,\ 9\}$
    and $\{-15,\ -13,\ -11\}$

11.

    Area $= LW = (W + 5)W$

    Its area is 84 sq ft.

    $$(W + 5)W = 84$$
    $$W^2 + 5W = 84$$
    $$W^2 + 5W - 84 = 0$$
    $$(W + 12)(W - 7) = 0$$

$W + 12 = 0$	$W - 7 = 0$	
$W = -12$	$W = 7$	width
no meaning	$W + 5 = 12$	length

12. length = 7, width = 4

13. **The area of the larger square** | **is** | **4 times as great as** | **the area of the smaller square.**

    $$x^2 = 4 \cdot (x - 3)^2$$

    $$x^2 = 4(x - 3)^2$$
    $$x^2 = 4(x^2 - 6x + 9)$$
    $$x^2 = 4x^2 - 24x + 36$$
    $$0 = 3x^2 - 24x + 36$$
    $$0 = 3(x^2 - 8x + 12)$$
    $$0 = 3(x - 2)(x - 6)$$

$x - 2 = 0$	$x - 6 = 0$	
$x = 2$	$x = 6$	side larger square
$x - 3 = -1$	$x - 3 = 3$	side smaller square
(not possible)		

14. Side smaller square = 2
    Side larger square = 6

15. Area $= LW = L(L - 5)$ **Its area is 14 sq cm.**

    $$L(L - 5) = 14$$
    $$L^2 - 5L = 14$$
    $$L^2 - 5L - 14 = 0$$
    $$(L - 7)(L + 2) = 0$$

$L - 7 = 0$	$L + 2 = 0$
length $= L = 7$	$L = -2$
width $= L - 5 = 2$	no meaning

16. side = 8

17. Let $\quad x$ = altitude
    then $x + 3$ = base
    Area $= \frac{1}{2}bh$

    $$20 = \frac{1}{2}(x + 3)x$$
    $$\frac{20}{1} = \frac{(x + 3)x}{2} \qquad \text{A proportion}$$
    $$1 \cdot (x + 3)x = 20(2)$$
    $$x^2 + 3x = 40$$
    $$x^2 + 3x - 40 = 0$$
    $$(x + 8)(x - 5) = 0$$

$x = -8$	$x = 5$	altitude
No meaning	$x + 3 = 8$	base

18. Two answers: $\begin{cases} \text{base} = 6 \\ \text{altitude} = 9 \end{cases}$

    and $\begin{cases} \text{base} = 9 \\ \text{altitude} = 6 \end{cases}$

19. $$\frac{x}{3} = \frac{6}{x + 7} \qquad \text{A proportion}$$
    $$x(x + 7) = 3(6)$$
    $$x^2 + 7x = 18$$
    $$x^2 + 7x - 18 = 0$$
    $$(x - 2)(x + 9) = 0$$

$x - 2 = 0$	$x + 9 = 0$
$x = 2$	$x = -9$
$x + 7 = 9$	$x + 7 = -2$

Two answers: one proportion is $\frac{2}{3} = \frac{6}{9}$

the other proportion is $\frac{-9}{3} = \frac{6}{-2}$

20. Two answers:

one proportion is $\frac{3}{-6} = \frac{-4}{8}$

the other proportion is $\frac{3}{4} = \frac{6}{8}$

REVIEW EXERCISES 810, SET I   (page 269)

1. $\begin{array}{r|l} 2 & 12 \\ 2 & 6 \\ & 3 \end{array}$ $12 = 2^2 \cdot 3$

2. $2^2 \cdot 5$

3. $\begin{array}{r|l} 2 & 36 \\ 2 & 18 \\ 3 & 9 \\ & 3 \end{array}$ $36 = 2^2 \cdot 3^2$

4. $2^3 \cdot 3$

5. Prime

6. Prime

7. $\begin{array}{r|l} 2 & 42 \\ 3 & 21 \\ & 7 \end{array}$ $42 = 2 \cdot 3 \cdot 7$

8. $2^2 \cdot 11$

9. $\begin{array}{r|l} 2 & 210 \\ 5 & 105 \\ 3 & 21 \\ & 7 \end{array}$ $210 = 2 \cdot 3 \cdot 5 \cdot 7$

10. $3 \cdot 37$

11. $(m - 2)(4m + 1)$

$4m^2 - 7m - 2$

12. $15u^2 - u - 2$

13. $(c - 2)(5c + 2)$

$5c^2 - 8c - 4$

14. $49x^2 - 25$

15. $(a - 5)^2 = (a)^2 - 2(a)(5) + (5)^2 = a^2 - 10a + 25$

16. $b^2 + 16b + 64$

17. $(5x - 4y)(7x - 2y)$

$35x^2 - 38xy + 8y^2$

18. $18m^2 - 39mn + 20n^2$

19. $8x - 4 = 4(2x - 1)$

20. $5(1 + 3a)$

21. $m^2 - 4 = (\sqrt{m^2} + \sqrt{4})(\sqrt{m^2} - \sqrt{4}) = (m + 2)(m - 2)$

22. $(5 + n)(5 - n)$

23. $x^2 + 10x + 21 = (x + 3)(x + 7)$ $21 = 1 \cdot 21$

$+10 = +3 + +7$ $= 3 \cdot 7$

24. $(y + 2)(y + 8)$

25. $2u^2 + 4u = 2u(u + 2)$

26. $3b(1 - 2b)$

27. $z^2 - 7z - 18 = (z + 2)(z - 9)$ $18 = 1 \cdot 18$

$-7 = +2 + -9$ $= 2 \cdot 9$

28. $(x + 3)(x - 10)$

29. $4 = 1 \cdot 4$ $6 = 1 \cdot 6$

$= 2 \cdot 2$ $= 2 \cdot 3$

$(1x - 6)(4x - 1)$

$-25x$

30. $(c - 4)(5c - 2)$

31. $9k^2 - 144$

$= 9(k^2 - 16) = 9(\sqrt{k^2} + \sqrt{16})(\sqrt{k^2} - \sqrt{16})$

$= 9(k + 4)(k - 4)$

32. $(10 + 9p)(10 - 9p)$

33. $8 - 2a^2 = 2(4 - a^2)$

$= 2(\sqrt{4} + \sqrt{a^2})(\sqrt{4} - \sqrt{a^2})$

$= 2(2 + a)(2 - a)$

34. $2(y + 3)(y - 3)$

35. $ab + 2b - a - 2$

$= b(a + 2) - (a + 2)$

$= (a + 2)(b - 1)$

36. $(m - 5)(n - 1)$

37. $(x - 5)(x + 3) = 0$

$x - 5 = 0 \,|\, x + 3 = 0$

$x = 5 \,|\, x = -3$

38. $-4, 7$

39. $x^2 - 5x - 14 = 0$

$(x - 7)(x + 2) = 0$

$x - 7 = 0 \,|\, x + 2 = 0$

$x = 7 \,|\, x = -2$

40. $8, -3$

41. $m^2 = 18 + 3m$

$m^2 - 3m - 18 = 0$

$(m - 6)(m + 3) = 0$

$m - 6 = 0 \,|\, m + 3 = 0$

$m = 6 \,|\, m = -3$

42. $10, -2$

43. $x^2 - 9 = 0$

$(x + 3)(x - 3) = 0$

$x + 3 = 0 \,|\, x - 3 = 0$

$x = -3 \,|\, x = 3$

44. $6, -6$

45. $3z^2 = 12z$

$3z^2 - 12z = 0$

$3z(z - 4) = 0$

$3z = 0 \,|\, z - 4 = 0$

$z = 0 \,|\, z = 4$

46. $0, 1\frac{2}{3}$

47. $6e^2 = 13e + 5$

$6e^2 - 13e - 5 = 0$

$(2e - 5)(3e + 1) = 0$

$2e - 5 = 0 \,|\, 3e + 1 = 0$

$2e = 5 \,|\, 3e = -1$

$e = \frac{5}{2} = 2\frac{1}{2} \,|\, e = -\frac{1}{3}$

48. $1\frac{2}{3}, 2\frac{1}{4}$

49. $3xy^2(4x^2y^2 - 5xy - 10)$

$= (3xy^2)(4x^2y^2) + (3xy^2)(-5xy) + (3xy^2)(-10)$

$= 12x^3y^4 - 15x^2y^3 - 30xy^2$

50. $10x^3y^4 - 15x^4y^2 - 20x^2y$

51. $4x(x^2 - y^2)(x^2 + y^2) = 4x(x^4 - y^4) = 4x^5 - 4xy^4$

52. $3a^5 - 75ab^2$

53. $15u^2v - 3uv = 3uv(5u - 1)$

54. $7ab(3b - 1)$

55. $4x^2y - 8xy^2 + 4xy$

$4xy(x - 2y + 1)$

56. $5ab(b - 2a - 1)$

57. $10 = 1 \cdot 10$ $24 = 1 \cdot 24$

$= 2 \cdot 5$ $= 2 \cdot 12$

$= 3 \cdot 8$

$= 4 \cdot 6$

$(2x + 3y)(5x - 8y)$

$- 1xy$

58. $(4x - 3y)(7x + 2y)$

59. $15a^2 + 15ab - 30b^2$
$15(a^2 + ab - 2b^2)$

$15(1a + 2b)(a - 1b)$

```
      ∠+2ab ∖
   └─── -1ab ───┘
        +1ab
```

60. $3(u - v)(9u + 11v)$

61. $6u^3v^2 - 9uv^3 - 12uv$
$= 3uv(2u^2v - 3v^2 - 4)$

62. $4x^2y^2(2x^3 - 3y^2 - 4)$

63. $x^2 - y^2 + x - y = (x + y)(x - y) + (x - y)$
$= (x - y)(x + y + 1)$

64. $(a - b)(a + b - 1)$

65.
$2u(u + 6)(u - 2) = 0$

$2u = 0 \mid u + 6 = 0 \mid u - 2 = 0$
$u = 0 \mid u = -6 \mid u = 2$

66. $0, 8, -9$

67. $68x^2 = 30x^3 + 30x$
$0 = 30x^3 - 68x^2 + 30x$
$0 = 2x(15x^2 - 34x + 15)$
$0 = 2x(3x - 5)(5x - 3)$

$2x = 0 \mid 3x - 5 = 0 \mid 5x - 3 = 0$
$x = 0 \mid 3x = 5 \mid 5x = 3$
$x = \dfrac{5}{3} \mid x = \dfrac{3}{5}$

68. $0, \dfrac{3}{2}, \dfrac{2}{3}$

69.
$$\dfrac{x - 2}{9} = \dfrac{4}{x + 7}$$
$(x - 2)(x + 7) = 36$
$x^2 + 5x - 14 = 36$
$x^2 + 5x - 50 = 0$
$(x + 10)(x - 5) = 0$

$x + 10 = 0 \mid x - 5 = 0$
$x = -10 \mid x = 5$

70. $6, -6$

71. smaller number $= x$ ⎫ because the difference
       larger number $= x + 3$ ⎭ of the numbers is 3.

Their product is 28.
$x(x + 3) \quad = \quad 28$

$x(x + 3) = 28$
$x^2 + 3x = 28$
$x^2 + 3x - 28 = 0$
$(x + 7)(x - 4) = 0$

$x + 7 = 0 \mid x - 4 = 0$
$x = -7 \mid x = 4$
$x + 3 = -4 \mid x + 3 = 7$

72. There are two answers: $\{-6, -9\}$ and $\{6, 9\}$.

73. Area $= LW = L(L - 3)$ Its area is 40.
$L(L - 3) \quad = \quad 40$

[rectangle labeled $L - 3$ and L]

$L(L - 3) = 40$
$L^2 - 3L = 40$
$L^2 - 3L - 40 = 0$
$(L - 8)(L + 5) = 0$

$L - 8 = 0 \mid L + 5 = 0$
length $= L = 8 \mid L = -5$ (not possible)
width $= L - 3 = 5$

74. large $= 8$, small $= 2$

75. Area $= x^2$
Perimeter $= 4x$

Area of square is 3 times its perimeter
$x^2 \qquad = \qquad 3 \quad \cdot \qquad 4x$

[square labeled x]

$x^2 = 3(4x)$
$x^2 = 12x$
$x^2 - 12x = 0$
$x(x - 12) = 0$

$x = 0 \mid x - 12 = 0$
(Not possible) $\mid x = 12$ (side)

76. width $= 4$, length $= 10$

77. Let x and $x + 1$ represent the integers

Their product is 1 more their
            than sum
$x(x + 1) \quad = \quad 1 + x + (x + 1)$
$x^2 + x \quad = \quad 1 + 2x + 1$
$x^2 - x - 2 = 0$
$(x - 2)(x + 1) = 0$
$x - 2 = 0 \mid x + 1 = 0$
$x = 2 \mid x = -1$
$x + 1 = 3 \mid x + 1 = 0$

Two answers: $\{2, 3\}$ and $\{0, -1\}$

78. Two answers: $\{5, 6\}$ and $\{-4, -3\}$

79. Let $x - 1$, x, and $x + 1$ be the integers.

Product of plus Product of is 18
first two   Last two
$(x - 1)x \quad + \quad x(x + 1) \quad = \quad 18$
$x^2 - x \quad + \quad x^2 + x \quad = \quad 18$
$ 2x^2 - 18 = 0$
$ 2(x^2 - 9) = 0$
$ 2(x + 3)(x - 3) = 0$

$2 \neq 0 \mid x + 3 = 0 \mid x - 3 = 0$
$x = -3 \mid x = 3$
$ x - 1 = -4 \mid x - 1 = 2$
$ x + 1 = -2 \mid x + 1 = 4$

Two answers: $\{2, 3, 4\}$ and $\{-4, -3, -2\}$

80. One answer: $\{1, 3, 5\}$

CUMULATIVE REVIEW EXERCISES:
CHAPTERS 1–7 (page 271)

1. $24 \div 2\sqrt{16} - 3^2 \cdot 5$
$24 \div 2(4) - 9 \cdot 5$
$12(4) - 9 \cdot 5$
$48 - 45 = 3$

2. $\dfrac{12}{5}$ or $2\dfrac{2}{5}$

3. $C = \dfrac{a}{a + 12} \cdot A$

$= \dfrac{8}{8 + 12} \cdot 35$

$= \dfrac{\overset{2}{\cancel{8}}}{\underset{\cancel{4}}{\cancel{20}}} \cdot \dfrac{\overset{7}{\cancel{35}}}{1} = 14$

4. $\dfrac{y^6}{9z^4}$

5. $\left(\dfrac{\overset{3}{\cancel{15x^2}}}{\underset{2}{\cancel{10x^3}}}\right)^3 = \left(\dfrac{3}{2x}\right)^3 = \dfrac{3^3}{2^3x^3} = \dfrac{27}{8x^3}$

6. 18%

7. $(2x^2 + 5x - 3) - (-4x^2 + 8x + 10) + (6x^2 + 3x - 8)$

$\underline{2x^2} + \underline{5x} - \underset{\sim}{3} + \underline{4x^2} - \underline{8x} - \underset{\sim}{10} + \underline{6x^2} + \underline{3x} - \underset{\sim}{8}$

$12x^2 - 21$

8. $3y^3 - 14y^2 + 13y - 20$

9. $\dfrac{12a^2 - 3a}{3a} = \dfrac{12a^2}{3a} - \dfrac{3a}{3a} = 4a - 1$

10. $4x + 5 \quad R -2 \text{ or } 4x + 5 - \dfrac{2}{2x - 3}$

CHAPTER EIGHT DIAGNOSTIC TEST (page 273)

Following each problem number is the textbook section reference (in parentheses) where that kind of problem is discussed.

1. (801) (a) $18 = 2 \cdot 9 = 3 \cdot 6$
       18 is composite because it has factors other than itself and 1.
    (b) $21 = 3 \cdot 7 \Rightarrow$ composite
    (c) $31 = 1 \cdot 31 \Rightarrow$ prime
       31 has no factors other than itself and 1.

2. (801) (a) $\left.\begin{array}{l} 1 \cdot 6 = 6 \\ 2 \cdot 3 = 6 \end{array}\right\} \Rightarrow \{1, 2, 3, 6\}$
    (b) $1 \cdot 13 = 13 \Rightarrow \{1, 13\}$

3. (801) $\begin{array}{c|c} 5 & 45 \\ 3 & 9 \\ & 3 \end{array}$ $\quad 45 = 3^2 \cdot 5$

4. (801) $\begin{array}{c|c} 2 & 160 \\ 2 & 80 \\ 2 & 40 \\ 2 & 20 \\ 2 & 10 \\ & 5 \end{array}$ $\quad 160 = 2^5 \cdot 5$

5. (803) $(2x - 3)(2x + 3) = (2x)^2 - (3)^2 = 4x^2 - 9$

6. (804) $(3y - 5)(4y + 7)$
       $-20y$
       $+21y$
       $12y^2 + 1y - 35$

7. (804) $(4a - 5b)^2 = (4a)^2 + 2(4a)(-5b) + (-5b)^2$
       $= 16a^2 - 40ab + 25b^2$

8. (802) $5x + 10 = 5(x + 2)$

9. (802) $3x^2 - 6x = 3x(x - 2)$

10. (803) $16x^2 - 49y^2$
       $= (\sqrt{16x^2} + \sqrt{49y^2})(\sqrt{16x^2} - \sqrt{49y^2})$
       $= (4x + 7y)(4x - 7y)$

11. (807) $2z^2 - 8 = 2(z^2 - 4)$
       $= 2(\sqrt{z^2} + \sqrt{4})(\sqrt{z^2} - \sqrt{4})$
       $= 2(z + 2)(z - 2)$

12. (804) $z^2 + 6z + 8 = (z + 2)(z + 4)$ $\qquad 8 = 1 \cdot 8$
       $+6 \quad = \quad +2 \quad + \quad +4$ $\qquad = 2 \cdot 4$

13. (804) $m^2 + 1m - 6 = (m - 2)(m + 3)$ $\qquad 6 = 1 \cdot 6$
       $+1 \quad = \quad -2 \quad + \quad +3$ $\qquad = 2 \cdot 3$

14. (804) $5 = 1 \cdot 5 \qquad\qquad\qquad 7 = 1 \cdot 7$
       $(1w - 1)(5w - 7)$
       $-5w$
       $-7w$
       $-12w$

15. (804) $3 = 1 \cdot 3 \qquad\qquad\qquad 5 = 1 \cdot 5$
       $(1v + 5)(3v - 1)$
       $+15v$
       $-1v$
       $+14v$

16. (805) $5n - mn - 5 + m = n(5 - m) - (5 - m)$
       $= (5 - m)(n - 1)$

17. (806) $6h^2k - 8hk^2 + 2k^3 = 2k(3h^2 - 4hk + k^2)$
       $= 2k(h - k)(3h - k)$

18. (808) $x^2 - 12x + 20 = 0$
       $(x - 2)(x - 10) = 0$
       $x - 2 = 0 \mid x - 10 = 0$
       $x = 2 \mid \quad x = 10$

19. (808) $3x^2 = 12x$
       $3x^2 - 12x = 0$
       $3x(x - 4) = 0$
       $3x = 0 \mid x - 4 = 0$
       $x = 0 \mid \quad x = 4$

20. (809) $\text{Area} = LW = (W + 3)W$ $\qquad$ Its area is 28
       $(W + 3)W = 28$

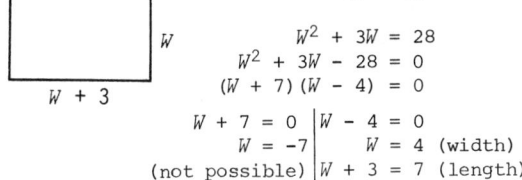

$W^2 + 3W = 28$
$W^2 + 3W - 28 = 0$
$(W + 7)(W - 4) = 0$
$W + 7 = 0 \mid W - 4 = 0$
$W = -7 \mid \quad W = 4 \text{ (width)}$
$\text{(not possible)} \mid W + 3 = 7 \text{ (length)}$

EXERCISES 901, SET I (page 279)

1. 2, because 2 would make the denominator zero.

2. -3 $\qquad\qquad$ 3. None $\qquad\qquad$ 4. None

5. 1 and -2 because either of these numbers make the denominator zero.

6. 0 and 2 $\qquad$ 7. -5 $\qquad$ 8. -2

9. y $\qquad\qquad$ 10. $x - 2$

11. $x - 5$ is the negative of $5 - x$. Therefore, the numerator must be changed to -7.

12. $x - 1$

13. -5, the sign of the numerator was changed, $y - 6 = -(6 - y)$ therefore, the sign of 5 must change.

14. $4 - x$ $\qquad$ 15. None $\qquad$ 16. None

17. $\dfrac{x^2 + 4}{x^2 - x - 2} = \dfrac{x^2 + 4}{(x - 2)(x + 1)}$
    Therefore, both 2 and (-1) must be excluded.

18. 2 and -2

EXERCISES 902, SET I (page 282)

1. $\dfrac{9}{12} = \dfrac{\cancel{3} \cdot 3}{\cancel{3} \cdot 4} = \dfrac{3}{4}$ $\qquad\qquad$ 2. $\dfrac{4}{7}$

3. $\dfrac{\overset{2}{\cancel{6}}ab^2}{\cancel{3}ab} = 2b$ $\qquad\qquad$ 4. $2m$

5. $\dfrac{\overset{2}{\cancel{4}x^2y}}{\cancel{2}xy} = 2x$　　　　6. $3x^2$

7. $\dfrac{5x - 10}{x - 2} = \dfrac{5\,\cancel{(x - 2)}}{\cancel{x - 2}} = 5$　　　　8. 3

9. $-\dfrac{5x - 6}{6 - 5x} = +\dfrac{5x - 6}{-(6 - 5x)} = \dfrac{5x - 6}{5x - 6} = 1$　　10. -1

11. $\dfrac{5x^2 + 30x}{10x^2 - 40x} = \dfrac{\overset{1}{\cancel{5}}x(x + 6)}{\underset{2}{\cancel{10}}x(x - 4)} = \dfrac{x + 6}{2(x - 4)}$　　12. $\dfrac{x}{3}$

13. $\dfrac{2 + 4}{4} = \dfrac{6}{4} = \dfrac{3}{2}$　　　　14. 4

It is incorrect to cancel the 4's.

15. Cannot be reduced　　16. Cannot be reduced

17. $\dfrac{x^2 - 1}{x + 1} = \dfrac{(x + 1)(x - 1)}{\cancel{(x + 1)}} = x - 1$　　18. $x + 2$

19. $\dfrac{6x^2 - x - 2}{10x^2 + 3x - 1} = \dfrac{(3x - 2)\cancel{(2x + 1)}}{(5x - 1)\cancel{(2x + 1)}} = \dfrac{3x - 2}{5x - 1}$

20. $\dfrac{2x - 3}{3x + 2}$

21. $\dfrac{x^2 - y^2}{(x + y)^2} = \dfrac{\cancel{(x + y)}(x - y)}{\cancel{(x + y)}(x + y)} = \dfrac{x - y}{x + y}$　　22. $\dfrac{a + 3b}{a - 3b}$

23. $\dfrac{2y^2 + xy - 6x^2}{3x^2 + xy - 2y^2} = \dfrac{(2y - 3x)(y + 2x)}{(3x - 2y)(x + y)}$

$\qquad = \dfrac{-\cancel{(3x - 2y)}(y + 2x)}{\cancel{(3x - 2y)}(x + y)} = -\dfrac{2x + y}{x + y}$

24. $-\dfrac{3x + 2y}{2x + 3y}$

25. $\dfrac{8x^2 - 2y^2}{2ax - ay + 2bx - by} = \dfrac{2(4x^2 - y^2)}{a(2x - y) + b(2x - y)}$

$\qquad = \dfrac{2(2x + y)\cancel{(2x - y)}}{\cancel{(2x - y)}(a + b)}$

$\qquad = \dfrac{2(2x + y)}{a + b}$

26. $\dfrac{3(x - 2y)}{a + b}$

27. $\dfrac{(-1)(z - 8)}{8 - z} = \dfrac{\overset{1}{\cancel{8 - z}}}{\underset{1}{\cancel{8 - z}}} = 1$

28. 1

29. $\dfrac{(-1)(a - 2b)(b - a)}{(2a + b)(a - b)}$

$\qquad = \dfrac{(a - 2b)\cancel{(a - b)}}{(2a + b)\cancel{(a - b)}} = \dfrac{a - 2b}{2a + b}$

30. $\dfrac{8}{3n + m}$

EXERCISES 903, SET I　(page 285)

1. $\dfrac{5}{6} \div \dfrac{5}{3} = \dfrac{\cancel{5}}{\cancel{6}} \cdot \dfrac{\cancel{3}}{\cancel{5}} = \dfrac{1}{2}$　　　2. $\dfrac{3}{14}$

3. $\dfrac{\cancel{4}a^3}{\cancel{3}b^2} \cdot \dfrac{\overset{2}{\cancel{10}}b}{\cancel{8}a^2} = \dfrac{a}{b}$　　　　4. c

5. $\dfrac{3x^2}{16} \div \dfrac{x}{8} = \dfrac{3x^2}{\underset{2}{\cancel{16}}} \cdot \dfrac{\cancel{8}}{x} = \dfrac{3x}{2}$　　6. $3y$

7. $\dfrac{\cancel{3}x^4y^2z}{\underset{\underset{2}{8}}{\cancel{18}xy}} \cdot \dfrac{\overset{5}{\cancel{15}}z}{x^3yz^2} = \dfrac{5x^4y^2z^2}{2x^4y^2z^2} = \dfrac{5}{2}$　　8. $\dfrac{9a^2b}{2c^2}$

9. $\dfrac{x}{\cancel{x + 2}} \cdot \dfrac{5\cancel{(x + 2)}}{x^3} = \dfrac{5}{x^2}$　　10. $\dfrac{2}{y}$

11. $\dfrac{b^3}{a + 3} \div \dfrac{4b^2}{2a + 6} = \dfrac{b^3}{\cancel{a + 3}} \cdot \dfrac{\overset{2}{\cancel{2}}\cancel{(a + 3)}}{\underset{2}{\cancel{4}}b^2} = \dfrac{b}{2}$　　12. $4n$

13. $\dfrac{a + 4}{a - 4} \div \dfrac{a^2 + 8a + 16}{a^2 - 16} = \dfrac{a + 4}{a - 4} \cdot \dfrac{a^2 - 16}{a^2 + 8a + 16}$

$\qquad = \dfrac{\cancel{a + 4}}{\cancel{a - 4}} \cdot \dfrac{\cancel{(a + 4)}\cancel{(a - 4)}}{\cancel{(a + 4)}\cancel{(a + 4)}} = 1$

14. $\dfrac{x}{3}$

15. $\dfrac{5}{z + 4} \cdot \dfrac{z^2 - 16}{(z - 4)^2} = \dfrac{5}{\cancel{z + 4}} \cdot \dfrac{\cancel{(z + 4)}\cancel{(z - 4)}}{(z - 4)\cancel{(z - 4)}} = \dfrac{5}{z - 4}$

16. $\dfrac{1}{3}$

17. $\dfrac{3a - 3b}{4c + 4d} \cdot \dfrac{2c + 2d}{b - a} = \dfrac{3\cancel{(a - b)}}{\underset{2}{\cancel{4}}\cancel{(c + d)}} \cdot \dfrac{\cancel{2}\cancel{(c + d)}}{(-1)\cancel{(a - b)}} = \dfrac{3}{-2}$

$\qquad = -1\tfrac{1}{2}$

18. $-\dfrac{1}{3}$

19. $\dfrac{4x - 8}{4} \cdot \dfrac{x + 2}{x^2 - 4} = \dfrac{\overset{1}{\cancel{4}}\cancel{(x - 2)}}{\underset{1}{\cancel{4}}} \cdot \dfrac{\overset{1}{\cancel{x + 2}}}{\cancel{(x + 2)}\cancel{(x - 2)}} = 1$

20. $\dfrac{2}{3}$

21. $\dfrac{4a + 4b}{ab^2} \div \dfrac{3a + 3b}{a^2b} = \dfrac{4\cancel{(a + b)}}{ab^2} \cdot \dfrac{a^2b}{3\cancel{(a + b)}} = \dfrac{4a}{3b}$

22. 1

23. $\dfrac{x - y}{9x + 9y} \div \dfrac{x^2 - y^2}{3x^2 + 6xy + 3y^2}$

$\qquad = \dfrac{\cancel{(x - y)}}{\underset{3}{\cancel{9}}\cancel{(x + y)}} \cdot \dfrac{\cancel{3}(x + y)(x + y)}{(x + y)\cancel{(x - y)}} = \dfrac{1}{3}$

24. $\dfrac{1}{2}$

25. $\dfrac{2x^3y + 2x^2y^2}{6x} \div \dfrac{x^2y^2 - xy^3}{y - x}$

$\qquad = \dfrac{\cancel{2}x^2y(x + y)}{\underset{3}{\cancel{6}}x} \cdot \dfrac{(-1)\cancel{(x - y)}}{xy^2\cancel{(x - y)}} = -\dfrac{x + y}{3y}$

26. -2

EXERCISES 904, SET I　(page 288)

1. $\dfrac{7}{a} + \dfrac{2}{a} = \dfrac{7 + 2}{a} = \dfrac{9}{a}$　　　2. $\dfrac{7}{b}$

3. $\dfrac{6}{x - y} - \dfrac{2}{x - y} = \dfrac{6 - 2}{x - y} = \dfrac{4}{x - y}$　　4. $\dfrac{6}{m + n}$

5. $\dfrac{2}{3a} + \dfrac{4}{3a} = \dfrac{2 + 4}{3a} = \dfrac{\overset{2}{\cancel{6}}}{\cancel{3}a} = \dfrac{2}{a}$　　6. $\dfrac{2}{z}$

7. $\dfrac{2y}{y + 1} + \dfrac{2}{y + 1} = \dfrac{2y + 2}{y + 1} = \dfrac{2\cancel{(y + 1)}}{\cancel{y + 1}} = 2$　　8. 3

9. $\dfrac{3}{x + 3} + \dfrac{x}{x + 3} = \dfrac{3 + x}{x + 3} = 1$　　10. 1

11. $\dfrac{x - 3}{y - 2} - \dfrac{x + 5}{y - 2} = \dfrac{x - 3 - x - 5}{y - 2}$　　12. $\dfrac{1}{a - b}$

$\qquad = -\dfrac{8}{y - 2}$

13. $\dfrac{a + 2}{2a + 1} - \dfrac{1 - a}{2a + 1} = \dfrac{a + 2 - 1 + a}{2a + 1}$

$= \dfrac{2a + 1}{2a + 1} = 1$

14. 1

15. $\dfrac{-x}{x - 2} - \dfrac{2}{2 - x} = \dfrac{-x}{x - 2} + \dfrac{2}{x - 2}$

$= \dfrac{-x + 2}{x - 2} = \dfrac{-(-x + 2)}{x - 2} = -\dfrac{x - 2}{x - 2} = -1$

16. 1

17. $\dfrac{-15w}{1 - 5w} - \dfrac{3}{5w - 1} = \dfrac{-15w}{1 - 5w} + \dfrac{3}{1 - 5w}$

$= \dfrac{3 - 15w}{1 - 5w} = \dfrac{3(1 - 5w)}{1 - 5w} = 3$

18. 5

19. $\dfrac{7z}{8z - 4} + \dfrac{6 - 5z}{4 - 8z} = \dfrac{7z}{8z - 4} + \dfrac{5z - 6}{8z - 4}$

$= \dfrac{12z - 6}{8z - 4} = \dfrac{\overset{3}{\cancel{6}}(2z - 1)}{\underset{2}{\cancel{4}}(2z - 1)} = \dfrac{3}{2}$

20. 2

EXERCISES 905, SET I   (page 292)

1. (1) The denominators are already factored.
   (2) 3, x all the different factors
   (3) 3^1, x^1 are the highest powers of each factor
   (4) LCD $= 3x$

2. $2y$

3. (1) $2^2 \cdot 3$, 2^2 denominators in factored form
   (2) 2, 3 all the different factors
   (3) 2^2, 3^1 are the highest powers of each factor
   (4) LCD $= 2^2 \cdot 3 = 12$

4. 9

5. (1) $5 \cdot x$, $2 \cdot x$ denominators in factored form
   (2) 2, 5, x all the different factors
   (3) 2^1, 5^1, x^1 are the highest power of each factor
   (4) LCD $= 2^1 \cdot 5^1 \cdot x^1 = 10x$

6. $12z$

7. (1) The denominators are already factored.
   (2) x is the only factor.
   (3) x^3 is the highest power of x in any denominator.
   (4) LCD $= x^3$

8. a^4

9. (1) $2^2 \cdot 3 \cdot u^3 \cdot v^2$; $2 \cdot 3^2 \cdot u \cdot v^3$ (denominators in factored form)
   (2) 2, 3, u, v (all the different factors)
   (3) 2^2, 3^2, u^3, v^3 (highest power of different factors)
   (4) LCD $= 2^2 \cdot 3^2 \cdot u^3 \cdot v^3 = 36u^3v^3$

10. $100x^3y^5$

11. (1) Denominators are already factored.
    (2) a, $(a + 3)$ are the different factors.
    (3) a, $(a + 3)$ highest powers of each factor.
    (4) LCD $= a(a + 3)$

12. $b(b - 5)$

13. (1) $2(x + 2)$, 2^2x (denominators in factored form)
    (2) 2, x, $(x + 2)$ are the different factors.
    (3) 2^2, x, $(x + 2)$ are the highest powers of each factor.
    (4) LCD $= 4x(x + 2)$

14. $3x(x + 2)$

15. (1) $2^2 \cdot z^2$, $(z + 1)^2$, $z + 1$ factored denominators
    (2) 2, z, $(z + 1)$ all the different factors
    (3) 2^2, z^2, $(z + 1)^2$ highest powers of each factor
    (4) LCD $= 4z^2(z + 1)^2$

16. $12x^3(x - 1)^2$

17. (1) $(x + 1)(x + 2)$, $(x + 1)^2$
    (2) $(x + 1)$, $(x + 2)$
    (3) $(x + 1)^2$, $(x + 2)$
    (4) LCD $= (x + 1)^2(x + 2)$

18. $(x - 4)(x + 3)^2$

19. (1) $2^2 \cdot 3 \cdot x^2(x + 2)$, $(x - 2)^2$, $(x + 2)(x - 2)$
    (2) 2, 3, x, $(x + 2)$, $(x - 2)$
    (3) 2^2, 3, x^2, $(x + 2)$, $(x - 2)^2$
    (4) LCD $= 12x^2(x + 2)(x - 2)^2$

20. $8y(y + 3)^2(y - 3)$

EXERCISES 906, SET I   (page 296)

1. LCD $= a^3$

$\dfrac{3}{a^2} + \dfrac{2}{a^3} = \dfrac{3}{a^2} \cdot \dfrac{a}{a} + \dfrac{2}{a^3} = \dfrac{3a}{a^3} + \dfrac{2}{a^3} = \dfrac{3a + 2}{a^3}$

2. $\dfrac{5u^2 + 4}{u^3}$

3. LCD $= 2x^2$

$\dfrac{1}{2} + \dfrac{3}{x} - \dfrac{5}{x^2} = \dfrac{1}{2} \cdot \dfrac{x^2}{x^2} + \dfrac{3}{x} \cdot \dfrac{2x}{2x} - \dfrac{5}{x^2} \cdot \dfrac{2}{2}$

$= \dfrac{x^2}{2x^2} + \dfrac{6x}{2x^2} - \dfrac{10}{2x^2} = \dfrac{x^2 + 6x - 10}{2x^2}$

4. $\dfrac{2y^2 - 3y + 12}{3y^2}$

5. LCD $= xy$

$\dfrac{2}{xy} - \dfrac{3}{y} = \dfrac{2}{xy} - \dfrac{3}{y} \cdot \dfrac{x}{x} = \dfrac{2}{xy} - \dfrac{3x}{xy} = \dfrac{2 - 3x}{xy}$

6. $\dfrac{5 - 4b}{ab}$

7. LCD $= x$

$\dfrac{5}{1} + \dfrac{2}{x} = \dfrac{5}{1} \cdot \dfrac{x}{x} + \dfrac{2}{x} = \dfrac{5x + 2}{x}$

8. $\dfrac{3y + 4}{y}$

9. First reduce $\dfrac{9}{6y}$ to $\dfrac{3}{2y}$.

LCD $= 4y^2$

$\dfrac{5}{4y^2} + \dfrac{3}{2y} \cdot \dfrac{2y}{2y} = \dfrac{5 + 6y}{4y^2}$

10. $\dfrac{8x + 3}{4x^2}$

11. LCD $= x$

$\dfrac{3x}{1} - \dfrac{3}{x} = \dfrac{3x}{1} \cdot \dfrac{x}{x} - \dfrac{3}{x} = \dfrac{3x^2 - 3}{x}$

12. $\dfrac{4y^2 - 5}{y}$

13. LCD $= a(a + 3)$

$\dfrac{3}{a} \cdot \dfrac{a + 3}{a + 3} + \dfrac{a}{a + 3} \cdot \dfrac{a}{a} = \dfrac{3a + 9}{a(a + 3)} + \dfrac{a^2}{a(a + 3)}$

$= \dfrac{3a + 9 + a^2}{a(a + 3)}$ or $\dfrac{a^2 + 3a + 9}{a(a + 3)}$

14. $\dfrac{b^2 + 5b - 25}{b(b - 5)}$

15. LCD $= 4x(x+2)$

$$\frac{x}{2x+4} + \frac{-5}{4x} = \frac{x}{2(x+2)} \cdot \boxed{\frac{2x}{2x}} + \frac{-5}{4x} \cdot \boxed{\frac{(x+2)}{(x+2)}}$$

$$= \frac{2x^2}{4x(x+2)} + \frac{-5x-10}{4x(x+2)}$$

$$= \frac{2x^2-5x-10}{4x(x+2)}$$

16. $\dfrac{8+4x-2x^2}{3x(x+2)}$

17. LCD $= x(x-2)$

$$\frac{x}{1} + \frac{2}{x} + \frac{-3}{x-2}$$

$$= \frac{x}{1} \cdot \boxed{\frac{x(x-2)}{x(x-2)}} + \frac{2}{x} \cdot \boxed{\frac{(x-2)}{(x-2)}} + \frac{-3}{x-2} \cdot \boxed{\frac{x}{x}}$$

$$= \frac{x^2(x-2)}{x(x-2)} + \frac{2(x-2)}{x(x-2)} + \frac{-3x}{x(x-2)}$$

$$= \frac{x^3 - 2x^2 + 2x - 4 - 3x}{x(x-2)}$$

$$= \frac{x^3 - 2x^2 - x - 4}{x(x-2)}$$

18. $\dfrac{m^3 + 4m^2 - m - 12}{m(m+4)}$

19. LCD $= b(a-b)$

$$\frac{a+b}{b} + \frac{b}{a-b} = \frac{a+b}{b} \cdot \boxed{\frac{a-b}{a-b}} + \frac{b}{a-b} \cdot \boxed{\frac{b}{b}}$$

$$= \frac{a^2-b^2}{b(a-b)} + \frac{b^2}{b(a-b)}$$

$$= \frac{a^2-b^2+b^2}{b(a-b)} = \frac{a^2}{b(a-b)}$$

20. $-\dfrac{y^2}{x(x+y)}$

21. LCD $= 6(e-1)$

$$\frac{3}{2e-2} - \frac{2}{3e-3} = \frac{3}{2(e-1)} \cdot \boxed{\frac{3}{3}} + \frac{-2}{3(e-1)} \cdot \boxed{\frac{2}{2}}$$

$$= \frac{9}{6(e-1)} + \frac{-4}{6(e-1)} = \frac{5}{6(e-1)}$$

22. $\dfrac{7}{15(f+2)}$

23. First change the sign of the last fraction and its denominator. Then we have

$$\frac{3}{m-2} + \frac{5}{m-2} = \frac{8}{m-2}$$

24. $\dfrac{9}{n-5}$

25. LCD $= (x-1)(x+1)$

$$\frac{x+1}{x-1} \cdot \boxed{\frac{x+1}{x+1}} + \frac{-(x-1)}{x+1} \cdot \boxed{\frac{x-1}{x-1}}$$

$$= \frac{x^2+2x+1}{(x-1)(x+1)} + \frac{-x^2+2x-1}{(x-1)(x+1)} = \frac{4x}{x^2-1}$$

26. $-\dfrac{20x}{x^2-25}$

27. LCD $= xy(x-y)$

$$\frac{y}{x(x-y)} \cdot \boxed{\frac{y}{y}} + \frac{-x}{y(x-y)} \cdot \boxed{\frac{x}{x}} = \frac{y^2-x^2}{xy(x-y)}$$

$$= -\frac{x^2-y^2}{xy(x-y)} = -\frac{(x+y)\cancel{(x-y)}}{xy\cancel{(x-y)}}$$

$$= -\frac{x+y}{xy}$$

28. $\dfrac{a+b}{ab}$

29. LCD $= (x-3)(x+3)$

$$\frac{2x}{x-3} \cdot \boxed{\frac{x+3}{x+3}} + \frac{-2x}{x+3} \cdot \boxed{\frac{x-3}{x-3}} + \frac{36}{(x+3)(x-3)}$$

$$= \frac{2x^2 + 6x - 2x^2 + 6x + 36}{(x-3)(x+3)} = \frac{12x+36}{(x-3)(x+3)}$$

$$= \frac{12\cancel{(x+3)}}{(x-3)\cancel{(x+3)}} = \frac{12}{x-3}$$

30. $\dfrac{8}{4-x}$

31. LCD $= (x+2)^2$

$$\frac{x}{x^2+4x+4} + \frac{1}{x+2} \cdot \boxed{\frac{x+2}{x+2}}$$

$$= \frac{x+x+2}{(x+2)^2} = \frac{2x+2}{(x+2)^2}$$

32. $\dfrac{5-3x}{(x-1)^2}$

EXERCISES 907, SET I   (page 301)

1. The LCD of secondary denominators is 8.

$$\frac{8}{8} \cdot \frac{\frac{3}{4} - \frac{1}{2}}{\frac{5}{8} + \frac{1}{4}} = \frac{8\left(\frac{3}{4}\right) + 8\left(-\frac{1}{2}\right)}{8\left(\frac{5}{8}\right) + 8\left(\frac{1}{4}\right)} = \frac{6-4}{5+2} = \frac{2}{7}$$

2. $\dfrac{9}{7} = 1\dfrac{2}{7}$

3. LCD of secondary denominators is 20.

$$\frac{20}{20} \cdot \frac{\frac{3}{5} + \frac{2}{1}}{\frac{2}{1} - \frac{3}{4}} = \frac{\overset{4}{20}\left(\frac{3}{5}\right) + 20\left(\frac{2}{1}\right)}{20(2) + \overset{5}{20}\left(-\frac{3}{4}\right)} = \frac{12+40}{40-15} = \frac{52}{25} = 2\frac{2}{25}$$

4. $1\dfrac{1}{82}$

5. LCD of secondary denominators is $9y^4$.   6. $6ab$

$$\frac{9y^4}{9y^4} \cdot \frac{\frac{5x^3}{3y^4}}{\frac{10x}{9y}} = \frac{15x^3}{10xy^3} = \frac{3x^2}{2y^3}$$

7. LCD $= 15a^3b^2$

$$\frac{15a^3b^2}{15a^3b^2} \cdot \frac{\frac{18cd^2}{5a^3b}}{\frac{12cd^2}{15ab^2}} = \frac{\frac{15a^3b^2}{1} \cdot \frac{18cd^2}{5a^3b}}{\frac{15a^3b^2}{1} \cdot \frac{12cd^2}{15ab^2}} = \frac{\overset{9}{\cancel{54}}bcd^2}{\underset{2}{\cancel{12}}a^2cd^2} = \frac{9b}{2a^2}$$

8. $\dfrac{2xz^2}{y}$

9. LCD $= 10$ 10. $1\dfrac{1}{2}$

$$\frac{10}{10} \cdot \frac{\left(\frac{x+3}{5}\right)}{\left(\frac{2x+6}{10}\right)} = \frac{2x+6}{2x+6} = 1$$

11. LCD $= b$ 12. $\dfrac{2y+x}{2y-x}$

$$\frac{b}{b} \cdot \frac{\left(\frac{a}{b}+1\right)}{\left(\frac{a}{b}-1\right)} = \frac{\cancel{b}\left(\frac{a}{\cancel{b}}\right) + b(1)}{\cancel{b}\left(\frac{a}{\cancel{b}}\right) - b(1)} = \frac{a+b}{a-b}$$

13. $LCD = d^2$

$$\dfrac{d^2}{d^2} \cdot \dfrac{\left(\frac{c}{d} + 2\right)}{\left(\frac{c^2}{d^2} - 4\right)} = \dfrac{d^2\left(\frac{c}{d}\right) + d^2(2)}{d^2\left(\frac{c^2}{d^2}\right) - d^2(4)} = \dfrac{cd + 2d^2}{c^2 - 4d^2}$$

$$= \dfrac{d(c + 2d)}{(c - 2d)(c + 2d)} = \dfrac{d}{c - 2d}$$

14. $\dfrac{x + y}{y}$

15. If we multiply by $\dfrac{x}{x}$ we get

$$\dfrac{x}{x} \cdot \dfrac{1}{1 - \frac{1}{x}} = \dfrac{x}{x(1) + x\left(-\frac{1}{x}\right)} = \dfrac{x}{x - 1}$$

16. $\dfrac{y}{y + 1}$

17. $LCD = y$

$$\dfrac{y}{y} \cdot \dfrac{x + \frac{1}{y}}{y} = \dfrac{y(x) + y\left(\frac{1}{y}\right)}{y(y)} = \dfrac{xy + 1}{y^2}$$

18. $\dfrac{1 - ab}{ab}$

19. $\dfrac{x + y^{-1}}{y} = \dfrac{y}{y} \cdot \left(\dfrac{x + \frac{1}{y}}{y}\right) = \dfrac{\frac{y}{1}\left(\frac{x}{1}\right) + \frac{y}{1}\left(\frac{1}{y}\right)}{\frac{y}{1}(y)} = \dfrac{xy + 1}{y^2}$

20. $\dfrac{1 - ab}{ab}$

21. $LCD = z$

$$\dfrac{z}{z} \cdot \dfrac{2 + \frac{3}{z}}{4 - \frac{5}{z}} = \dfrac{\left(\frac{z}{1}\right)\left(\frac{2}{1}\right) + \left(\frac{z}{1}\right)\left(\frac{3}{z}\right)}{\left(\frac{z}{1}\right)\frac{4}{1} + \left(\frac{z}{1}\right)\left(\frac{-5}{z}\right)} = \dfrac{2z + 3}{4z - 5}$$

22. $\dfrac{x + 2}{3x^2 + 4}$

23. $LCD = x^2 y^2$

$$\dfrac{x^2 y^2}{x^2 y^2} \cdot \dfrac{\frac{1}{x^2} - \frac{1}{y^2}}{\frac{1}{x} + \frac{1}{y}} = \dfrac{x^2 y^2\left(\frac{1}{x^2}\right) - x^2 y^2\left(\frac{1}{y^2}\right)}{x^2 y^2\left(\frac{1}{x}\right) + x^2 y^2\left(\frac{1}{y}\right)}$$

$$= \dfrac{y^2 - x^2}{xy^2 + x^2 y} = \dfrac{(y + x)(y - x)}{xy(y + x)} = \dfrac{y - x}{xy}$$

24. $\dfrac{a + 2}{2a}$

25. $\dfrac{x^{-2} - y^{-2}}{x^{-1} + y^{-1}} = \dfrac{\frac{x^2 y^2}{1}}{\frac{x^2 y^2}{1}} \cdot \dfrac{\frac{1}{x^2} - \frac{1}{y^2}}{\frac{1}{x} + \frac{1}{y}} = \dfrac{\frac{x^2 y^2}{1}\left(\frac{1}{x^2}\right) + \frac{x^2 y^2}{1}\left(-\frac{1}{y^2}\right)}{\frac{x^2 y^2}{1}\left(\frac{1}{x}\right) + \frac{x^2 y^2}{1}\left(\frac{1}{y}\right)}$

$$= \dfrac{y^2 - x^2}{xy^2 + x^2 y} = \dfrac{(y + x)(y - x)}{xy(y + x)} = \dfrac{y - x}{xy}$$

26. $\dfrac{a + 2}{2a}$

EXERCISES 908A, SET I (page 306)

1. $LCD = 12$
Multiply each term by 12.

$$(12)\dfrac{x}{3} + (12)\dfrac{x}{4} = (12)7$$

$$4x + 3x = 84$$
$$7x = 84$$
$$x = 12$$

2. 15

3. $\dfrac{10}{c} = \dfrac{2}{1}$ This is a proportion.

$2c = 10$ Product of means = product of extremes.

$c = 5$ Dividing both sides by 2.

4. $1\frac{1}{2}$

5. $LCD = 10$

$$(10)\dfrac{a}{2} + (10)\dfrac{-a}{5} = (10)6$$

$$5a - 2a = 60$$
$$3a = 60$$
$$a = 20$$

6. 63

7. $\dfrac{9}{2x} = \dfrac{3}{1}$ This is a proportion.

$6x = 9$ Product of means = product of extremes.

$x = \dfrac{9}{6} = \dfrac{3}{2}$ Dividing both sides by 6.

8. $\dfrac{2}{3}$

9. $LCD = 15$

$$(15)\dfrac{M - 2}{5} + (15)\dfrac{M}{3} = (15)\dfrac{1}{5}$$

$$3(M - 2) + 5M = 3$$
$$3M - 6 + 5M = 3$$
$$8M = 9$$
$$M = \dfrac{9}{8} = 1\frac{1}{8}$$

10. $-\dfrac{5}{9}$

11. $\dfrac{7}{x + 4} = \dfrac{3}{x}$ This is a proportion.

$7x = 3(x + 4)$ Product of means = product of extremes.

$7x = 3x + 12$ Distributive rule.
$4x = 12$
$x = 3$

12. 4

13. $\dfrac{3x}{x - 2} = \dfrac{5}{1}$ This is a proportion.

$5(x - 2) = 3x$ Product of means = product of extremes.

$5x - 10 = 3x$
$2x = 10$
$x = 5$

14. 3

15. $\dfrac{x}{x^2 + 1} = \dfrac{2}{1 + 2x}$ This is a proportion.

$x + 2x^2 = 2x^2 + 2$ Product of means = product of extremes.

$$\dfrac{-2x^2 \quad -2x^2}{x \quad = \quad 2}$$ Adding $-2x^2$ to both sides.

16. $\dfrac{2}{3}$

17. $LCD = 12$

$$(\overset{4}{\cancel{12}})\dfrac{2x - 1}{3} + (\overset{3}{\cancel{12}})\dfrac{3x}{4} = (\overset{2}{\cancel{12}})\dfrac{5}{6}$$

$$4(2x - 1) + 3(3x) = 10$$
$$8x - 4 + 9x = 10$$
$$17x = 14$$
$$x = \dfrac{14}{17}$$

18. $1\frac{1}{9}$

19. $LCD = 10$

$$(\overset{2}{\cancel{10}})\dfrac{2(m - 3)}{5} + (\overset{5}{\cancel{10}})\dfrac{(-3)(m + 2)}{2} = (10)\dfrac{7}{10}$$

$$4(m - 3) - 15(m + 2) = 7$$
$$4m - 12 - 15m - 30 = 7$$
$$-11m = 49$$
$$m = \dfrac{49}{-11} = -4\frac{5}{11}$$

20. $7\frac{4}{11}$

21. $LCD = x - 2$

$$\left(\dfrac{x - 2}{1}\right)\dfrac{x}{x - 2} = \left(\dfrac{x - 2}{1}\right)\dfrac{2}{x - 2} + \left(\dfrac{x - 2}{1}\right)(5)$$

$$x = 2 + 5x - 10$$
$$8 = 4x$$
$$x = 2 \text{ (Not a solution)}$$

Check: $\dfrac{x}{x-2} = \dfrac{2}{x-2} + 5$

$\dfrac{2}{2-2} \overset{?}{=} \dfrac{2}{2-2} + 5$

$\dfrac{2}{0} \overset{?}{=} \dfrac{2}{0} + 5$

↑ ↑ —— Not a real number. Therefore, 2 is not a solution.

22. No solution

EXERCISES 908B, SET I (page 309)

1. LCD = z

$(z)z + (\not z)\dfrac{1}{\not z} = (\not z)\dfrac{17}{\not z}$

$z^2 + 1 = 17$

$z^2 + 1 - 17 = 0$

$z^2 - 16 = 0$

$(z + 4)(z - 4) = 0$

$z + 4 = 0 \,\big|\, z - 4 = 0$

$z = -4 \,\big|\quad z = 4$

2. $-3, 3$

3. LCD = $2x^2$

$\left(\dfrac{2x^2}{1}\right)\dfrac{2}{x} + \left(\dfrac{2x^2}{1}\right)\left(-\dfrac{2}{x^2}\right) = \left(\dfrac{2x^2}{1}\right)\dfrac{1}{2}$

$4x - 4 = x^2$

$0 = x^2 - 4x + 4$

$0 = (x - 2)(x - 2)$

$x - 2 = 0 \,\big|\, x - 2 = 0$

$x = 2 \,\big|\quad x = 2$

4. $2, 4$

5. $\dfrac{x}{x + 1} = \dfrac{4x}{3x + 2}$ This is a proportion.

$4x(x + 1) = x(3x + 2)$ Product of means =
product of extremes.

$4x^2 + 4x = 3x^2 + 2x$

$x^2 + 2x = \qquad 0$

$x(x + 2) = 0$

$x = 0 \,\big|\, x + 2 = 0$

$\qquad\big|\, x = -2$

Check for $x = 0$: $\dfrac{(0)}{(0) + 1} = \dfrac{4(0)}{3(0) + 2}$

$\dfrac{0}{1} = \dfrac{0}{2}$

$0 = 0$ true

Check for $x = -2$: $\dfrac{(-2)}{(-2) + 1} = \dfrac{4(-2)}{3(-2) + 2}$

$\dfrac{-2}{-1} = \dfrac{-8}{-4}$

$2 = 2$ true

6. $0, 2$

7. LCD = $3(x + 1)(x - 1)$

$3(x + 1)(x - 1)\dfrac{1}{x - 1} + 3(x + 1)(x - 1)\dfrac{2}{x + 1}$

$= \not 3(x + 1)(x - 1)\dfrac{5}{\not 3}$

$3(x + 1) + 6(x - 1) = 5(x^2 - 1)$

$3x + 3 + 6x - 6 = 5x^2 - 5$

$0 = 5x^2 - 9x - 2$

$0 = (5x + 1)(x - 2)$

$5x + 1 = 0 \,\big|\, x - 2 = 0$

$x = -\dfrac{1}{5} \,\big|\quad x = 2$

8. $3, \dfrac{1}{21}$

9. LCD = $4(2x + 5)$

$\dfrac{4(2x + 5)}{1} \cdot \dfrac{3}{2x + 5} + \dfrac{4(2x + 5)}{1} \cdot \dfrac{x}{4} = \dfrac{4(2x + 5)}{1} \cdot \dfrac{3}{4}$

$4(3) + x(2x + 5) = 3(2x + 5)$

$12 + 2x^2 + 5x = 6x + 15$

$2x^2 - x - 3 = 0$

$(1x + 1)(2x - 3) = 0$

$x + 1 = 0 \,\big|\, 2x - 3 = 0$

$x = -1 \,\big|\quad 2x = 3$

$\qquad\big|\quad x = \dfrac{3}{2}$

10. $2, -\dfrac{19}{2}$

EXERCISES 909, SET I (page 311)

1. $2x + y = 4$

$2x = 4 - y$

$x = \dfrac{4 - y}{2}$

2. $y = \dfrac{6 - x}{3}$

3. $y - z = -8$

$-z = -8 - y$

$z = 8 + y$

4. $n = m + 5$

5. $2x - y = -4$

$-y = -2x - 4$

$y = 2x + 4$

6. $z = 3y + 5$

7. $2x - 3y = 6$

$2x = 3y + 6$

$x = \dfrac{3y + 6}{2}$

8. $x = \dfrac{2y + 6}{3}$

9. $2(x - 3y) = x + 4$

$2x - 6y = x + 4$

$x = 6y + 4$

10. $x = \dfrac{2y + 14}{7}$

11. $PV = k$

$\dfrac{\not P V}{\not P} = \dfrac{k}{P}$

$V = \dfrac{k}{P}$

12. $P = \dfrac{I}{rt}$

13. $\dfrac{S}{1} = \dfrac{a}{1 - r}$ This is a proportion.

$S(1 - r) = a$ Product of means =
product of extremes

$S - Sr = a$

$-Sr = a - S$

$\dfrac{-Sr}{-S} = \dfrac{a - S}{-S}$

$r = \dfrac{S - a}{S}$

14. $R = \dfrac{E - Ir}{I}$

15. LCD = 9

$9(C) = \dfrac{\not 9}{1}\left(\dfrac{5(F - 32)}{\not 9}\right)$

$9C = 5F - 160$

$9C + 160 = 5F$

$\dfrac{9C + 160}{5} = F$

16. $B = \dfrac{2A - hb}{h}$

17. LCD = Fuv

$$\frac{Fuv}{1}\left(\frac{1}{F}\right) = \frac{Fuv}{1}\left(\frac{1}{u}\right) + \frac{Fuv}{1}\left(\frac{1}{v}\right)$$

$$uv = Fv + Fu$$
$$uv - Fu = Fv$$
$$u(v - F) = Fv$$
$$\frac{u(v - F)}{v - F} = \frac{Fv}{v - F}$$
$$u = \frac{Fv}{v - F}$$

18. $R = \dfrac{rZ}{r - Z}$

19. Multiply by LCD = x

$$\frac{x}{1}\left(\frac{m + n}{x}\right) + \frac{x}{1}\left(\frac{-a}{1}\right) = \frac{x}{1}\left(\frac{m - n}{x}\right) + \frac{x}{1}\left(\frac{c}{1}\right)$$

$$m + n - ax = m - n + cx$$
$$2n = ax + cx \qquad \text{Collecting terms.}$$
$$2n = x(a + c) \qquad \text{Factoring } x \text{ from } ax + cx.$$
$$\frac{2n}{a + c} = \frac{x(a + c)}{a + c} \qquad \begin{array}{l}\text{Dividing both sides}\\ \text{by } a + c.\end{array}$$
$$\frac{2n}{a + c} = x$$

20. $x = \dfrac{2b}{c + h}$

EXERCISES 910, SET I   (page 315)

1. Let $\quad x$ = Speed of Malone car
$\quad\quad x + 9$ = Speed of King car

	d	=	r	$\cdot$	t	
Malone car			x		6	Leaves at 7 AM and is overtaken at 1 PM
King car			$x + 9$		5	Leaves at 8 AM and overtakes at 1 PM

	d	=	r	$\cdot$	t	
Malone car	$6x$		x		6	$d = r \cdot t$ $d = x \cdot 6 = 6x$
King car	$5(x + 9)$		$x + 9$		5	$d = r \cdot t$ $d = (x + 9)5$ $= 5(x + 9)$

Since both cars travel the same distance,
$$6x = 5(x + 9)$$
$$6x = 5x + 45$$

(a) $\quad x = 45$ mph $\quad$ Speed of Malone car
$$x + 9 = 45 + 9$$
$$= 54 \text{ mph} \quad \text{Speed of King car}$$

(b) $\quad 45 \times 6 = 54 \times 5$
$$= 270 \text{ miles} \quad \text{Distance traveled}$$

2. (a) Duran car 40 mph
$\quad\quad$ Silva car 50 mph
(b) 400 mi

3. Let x = Hours required to return from the lake
$\quad x + 3$ = Hours required to hike to the lake

	d	=	r	$\cdot$	t	
Going to lake	$2(x + 3)$		2		$x + 3$	$d = r \cdot t$ $d = 2(x + 3)$
Returning from lake	$5x$		5		x	$d = r \cdot t$ $d = 5x$

$$5x = 2(x + 3)$$
$$5x = 2x + 6$$
$$3x = 6$$
$$x = 2$$

(a) $\quad x + 3 = 5$ hr required to hike to lake
(b) $\quad d = rt$
$$= 2(5) = 10 \text{ miles} \quad \text{Distance to lake}$$

4. (a) 3 hr
(b) 6 mi

5. Let $\quad x$ = time for return trip
$100 + 20 = 120$ = speed with wind
$100 - 20 = 80$ = speed against wind

	d	=	r	$\cdot$	t	
With wind	$120x$		120		x	$d = r \cdot t$ $= 120 \cdot x$
Against Wind	$80(10 - x)$		80		$10 - x$	$d = r \cdot t$ $= 80(10 - x)$

distance with wind = distance against wind

$$120x = 80(10 - x)$$
$$120x = 800 - 80x$$
$$200x = 800$$
$$x = 4 \text{ hr}$$
$$\text{distance} = 120x = 120(4) = 480 \text{ mi}$$

6. 6 mi

7.

	English Toffee	Caramels	Mixture
Unit Cost	1.25	1.50	1.35
Amount	15	x	$15 + x$
Total Cost	$15(1.25)$	$1.50x$	$1.35(15 + x)$

$$15(1.25) + 1.50x = 1.35(15 + x) \qquad \text{LCD} = 100$$
$$15(125) + 150x = 135(15 + x)$$
$$1875 + 150x = 2025 + 135x$$
$$15x = 150$$
$$x = 10 \text{ lb of caramels}$$

8. $3.50

9.

	Ingredient A	Ingredient B	Mixture
Unit Cost	0.30	0.20	
Amount	x	$50 - x$	50
Total Cost	$0.30x$	$0.20(50 - x)$	14.50

Cost of ingredient A + Cost of ingredient B = Cost of mixture

$$0.30x + 0.20(50 - x) = 14.50$$
$$30x + 20(50 - x) = 1450$$
$$30x + 1000 - 20x = 1450$$
$$10x = 450$$
$$x = 45 \text{ lb Delicious}$$
$$50 - x = 50 - 45 = 5 \text{ lb Jonathan}$$

10. $1.03

11. Let $\quad x$ = amount invested at 15%
then $24{,}000 - x$ = amount invested at 18%

$$.15x + .18(24{,}000 - x) = 4{,}215 \qquad \text{LCD} = 100$$
$$15x + 18(24{,}000 - x) = 421{,}500$$
$$15x + 432{,}000 - 18x = 421{,}500$$
$$-3x = -10{,}500$$
$$x = 3{,}500 \text{ @ } 15\%$$
$$24{,}000 - x = 20{,}500 \text{ @ } 18\%$$

12. $15,500 @ 14%
     $11,800 @ 21%

13. | Amount of Sodium bromide in 25% solution | = | Amount of Sodium bromide in 40% solution |
     |---|---|---|

$$.25(x + 500) = .40(500)$$
$$25(x + 500) = 40(500)$$
$$25x + 12,500 = 20,000$$
$$25x = 7,500$$
$$x = 300 \text{ ml}$$

14. 6 ℓ

15. | Amount of acid in 50% solution | + | Amount of acid in 20% solution | = | Amount of acid in 25% solution |
     |---|---|---|---|---|

$$0.50(100) + 0.20(x) = 0.25(x + 100)$$
$$50(100) + 20x = 25(x + 100)$$
$$5,000 + 20x = 25x + 2,500$$
$$2,500 = 5x$$
$$500 = x$$
$$x = 500 \text{ cc of } 20\% \text{ solution}$$

16. 20 pints

17. Let n = numerator
     then $n + 6$ = denominator

     original fraction = $\dfrac{n}{n + 6}$

     $$\dfrac{n + 4}{n + 6 - 4} = \dfrac{11}{10} \qquad \text{A proportion}$$
     $$10(n + 4) = 11(n + 2)$$
     $$10n + 40 = 11n + 22$$
     $$18 = n$$

     original fraction = $\dfrac{n}{n + 6} = \dfrac{18}{18 + 6} = \dfrac{18}{24}$

18. $\dfrac{15}{30}$

19. Let n = number of nickels
     then $20 - n$ = number of dimes

Amount of money in nickels	+	Amount of money in dimes	=	165¢

     $$5n + 10(20 - n) = 165$$
     $$5n + 200 - 10n = 165$$
     $$-5n = -35$$
     $$n = 7$$
     $$20 - n = 13$$

     7 nickels and 13 dimes

20. 15 nickels
     6 dimes
     5 quarters

21. Let x = First integer
     $x + 1$ = Next consecutive integer

The sum of two consecutive integers	is	thirty-three.

     $$x + (x + 1) = 33$$
     $$x + x + 1 = 33$$
     $$2x = 32$$
     $$x = 16$$
     $$x + 1 = 17$$

     Therefore, the consecutive integers are 16 and 17

22. 33, 35, 37

23. Let x = Units digit
     $\dfrac{13 - x}{13}$ = Tens digit (Sum of the digits is 13)

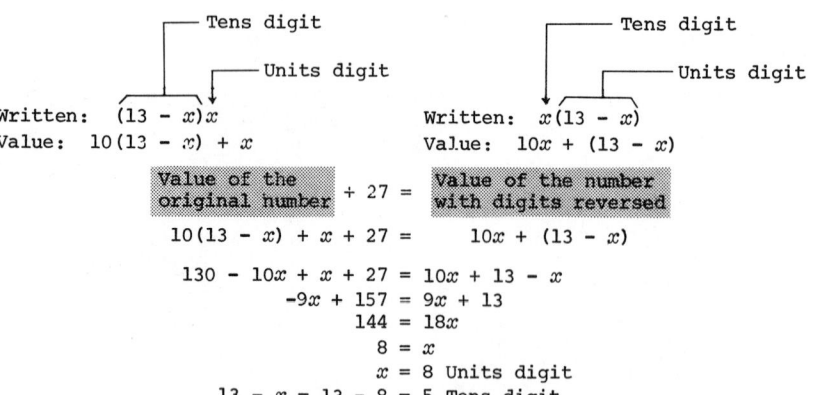

     Original number

     — Tens digit
     — Units digit
     Written: $(13 - x)x$
     Value: $10(13 - x) + x$

     Number with digits reversed

     — Tens digit
     — Units digit
     Written: $x(13 - x)$
     Value: $10x + (13 - x)$

Value of the original number	+ 27 =	Value of the number with digits reversed

     $$10(13 - x) + x + 27 = 10x + (13 - x)$$
     $$130 - 10x + x + 27 = 10x + 13 - x$$
     $$-9x + 157 = 9x + 13$$
     $$144 = 18x$$
     $$8 = x$$
     $$x = 8 \text{ Units digit}$$
     $$13 - x = 13 - 8 = 5 \text{ Tens digit}$$

     Therefore, the original number is 58. Check Sum of digits = 5 + 8 = 13

     Original number   58
     Increased by   27
                        85 Number with digits reversed

24. 52

25. The hour hand travels 1/12 as fast as the minute hand. Therefore, the minute hand gains 11/12 of a minute each minute. At 8 o'clock the hands are 40 min apart (see the figure). Therefore, the minute hand must gain 40 min on the hour hand before they will be together again. Let x equal the number of minutes required for the minute hand to overtake the hour hand. Then

$$x\left(\frac{11}{12}\right) = 40$$

$$11x = (12)(40) = 480$$

$$x = \frac{480}{11} = 43\frac{7}{11}$$

Therefore, the hands will be together at $8:43\frac{7}{11}$

26. $8:10\frac{10}{11}$

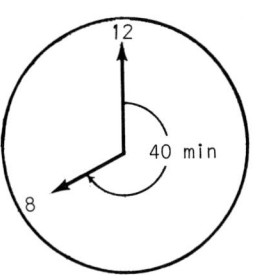

40 min

27. Let x = cost per cheap lens
$x + 23$ = cost per better lens.

$$\boxed{\text{Total cost of cheap lenses}} = \boxed{\text{Total cost of better lenses}}$$

$$18x = 15(x + 23)$$

$$18x = 15x + 345$$

$$3x = 345$$

$$x = \$115 \text{ for cheap lens}$$

$$x + 23 = \$138 \text{ for better lens}$$

28. $5.50, $8.25

REVIEW EXERCISES 911, SET I   (page 320)

1. -4 because when $x = -4$, $(x + 4) = 0$ and the denominator cannot be 0.

2. 0

3. $\dfrac{x - 1}{x^2 - 3x - 10} = \dfrac{x - 1}{(x - 5)(x + 2)}$

4. $+3$ and -3

5, and -2 must be excluded because either makes the denominator zero.

5. $\dfrac{x - 2}{2x^2 + x - 3} = \dfrac{x - 2}{(x - 1)(2x + 3)}$

Therefore, 1 and $-\dfrac{3}{2}$ must be excluded because they make the denominator zero.

6. $0, 1, -2$

7. $-\dfrac{2}{5} = \dfrac{-2}{5}$ The sign of the fraction and the numerator were changed.

8. $x - 6$

9. Sign of both the fraction and denominator were changed. Therefore, the numerator remains unchanged.

10. -4

11. $\dfrac{4x^3y}{2xy^2} = \dfrac{\cancel{2} \cdot 2 \cdot x^2 \cancel{xy}}{\cancel{2xy} \cdot y} = \dfrac{2x^2}{y}$

12. $\dfrac{2b}{a^2}$

13. $\dfrac{2 + 4m}{2} = \dfrac{\cancel{2}(1 + 2m)}{\cancel{2}} = 1 + 2m$

14. $1 - 2n$

15. $\dfrac{a^2 - 4}{a + 2} = \dfrac{(\cancel{a + 2})(a - 2)}{\cancel{a + 2}} = a - 2$

16. $3 + y$

17. $\dfrac{x + 3}{(x - 4)(\cancel{x + 3})} = \dfrac{1}{x - 4}$

18. $\dfrac{1}{x + 2}$

19. $\dfrac{a - b}{ax + ay - bx - by}$

$= \dfrac{a - b}{a(x + y) - b(x + y)} = \dfrac{\cancel{a - b}}{(x + y)\cancel{(a - b)}} = \dfrac{1}{x + y}$

20. $\dfrac{1}{a - b}$

21. $\dfrac{7}{z} - \dfrac{2}{z} = \dfrac{7 - 2}{z} = \dfrac{5}{z}$

22. $\dfrac{10}{k}$

23. LCD = $2x$

$\dfrac{2x}{2x} \cdot \dfrac{5}{1} - \dfrac{3}{2x} = \dfrac{10x}{2x} + \dfrac{-3}{2x} = \dfrac{10x - 3}{2x}$

24. $\dfrac{21x - 2}{3x}$

26. 1

25. $\dfrac{3x}{x + 1} - \dfrac{2x - 1}{x + 1} = \dfrac{3x}{x + 1} + \dfrac{-(2x - 1)}{x + 1}$

$= \dfrac{3x - 2x + 1}{x + 1} = \dfrac{x + 1}{x + 1} = 1$

27. $\dfrac{-5a^2}{3b} \div \dfrac{10a}{9b^2} = \dfrac{-\cancel{5}a^2}{\cancel{3}b} \cdot \dfrac{\cancel{9}b^2}{\cancel{10}a} = -\dfrac{3ab}{2}$

28. $-6x^2y^2$

29. $\dfrac{3x + 6}{6} \cdot \dfrac{2x^2}{4x + 8} = \dfrac{\cancel{3}(\cancel{x + 2})}{\cancel{6}} \cdot \dfrac{\cancel{2}x^2}{4(\cancel{x + 2})} = \dfrac{x^2}{4}$

30. x^3

31. LCD = 15

$\dfrac{3}{3} \cdot \dfrac{x + 4}{5} + \dfrac{5}{5} \cdot \dfrac{-(x - 2)}{3} = \dfrac{3x + 12 - 5x + 10}{15}$

$= \dfrac{-2x + 22}{15}$

32. $\dfrac{y - 17}{6}$

33. LCD = $(a - 1)(a + 2)$

$\dfrac{a + 2}{a + 2} \cdot \dfrac{a - 2}{a - 1} + \dfrac{a - 1}{a - 1} \cdot \dfrac{a + 1}{a + 2} = \dfrac{a^2 - 4 + a^2 - 1}{(a + 2)(a - 1)}$

$= \dfrac{2a^2 - 5}{(a + 2)(a - 1)}$

34. $\dfrac{-5}{(k - 2)(k - 3)}$

35. $\dfrac{2x^2 - 6x}{x + 2} \div \dfrac{x}{4x + 8} = \dfrac{2x(x - 3)}{\cancel{x + 2}} \cdot \dfrac{4(\cancel{x + 2})}{x}$

$= 8(x - 3)$

36. $8z$

37. LCD of secondary denominators = $9m^2$

$\dfrac{9m^2}{9m^2} \cdot \dfrac{\frac{5k^2}{3m^2}}{\frac{10k}{9m}} = \dfrac{\frac{9m^2}{1}\left(\frac{5k^2}{3m^2}\right)}{\frac{9m^2}{1}\left(\frac{10k}{9m}\right)} = \dfrac{15k^2}{10km} = \dfrac{3k}{2m}$

38. xy^3

39. LCD = y

$\dfrac{y}{y} \cdot \dfrac{\frac{x}{y} + 2}{\frac{x}{y} - 2} = \dfrac{(y)\frac{x}{y} + (y)2}{(y)\frac{x}{y} + (y)(-2)} = \dfrac{x + 2y}{x - 2y}$

40. $\dfrac{3b - a}{2b + a}$

41. $\dfrac{x^{-1} + 2}{x^{-1}} = \dfrac{\dfrac{1}{x} + 2}{\dfrac{1}{x}} = \dfrac{\dfrac{x}{1} \cdot \left(\dfrac{1}{x} + \dfrac{2}{1}\right)}{\dfrac{x}{1} \cdot \left(\dfrac{1}{x}\right)} = \dfrac{\dfrac{x}{1} \cdot \dfrac{1}{x} + \dfrac{x}{1} \cdot \dfrac{2}{1}}{\dfrac{x}{1} \cdot \dfrac{1}{x}}$

$= \dfrac{1 + 2x}{1} = 2x + 1$

42. $\dfrac{1}{3x + 1}$

43. LCD $= m$

$(m)\dfrac{6}{m} = (m)5$

$6 = 5m$

$\dfrac{6}{5} = m$

$m = 1\dfrac{1}{5}$

44. $m = \dfrac{7}{8}$

45. LCD $= 3$

$(3)\dfrac{2m}{3} + (3)(-m) = (3)1$

$2m - 3m = 3$

$-m = 3$

$m = -3$

46. 5

47. LCD $= 40$

$(40)\dfrac{z}{5} + (40)\dfrac{-z}{8} = (40)3$

$8z - 5z = 120$

$3z = 120$

$z = 40$

48. 20

49. $\dfrac{2x + 1}{3} = \dfrac{5x - 4}{2}$ This is a proportion.

$15x - 12 = 4x + 2$ Product of means = product of extremes.

$11x = 14$

$x = \dfrac{14}{11}$

50. $\dfrac{11}{9}$

51. LCD $= 2z$

$(2z)\dfrac{4}{2z} + (2z)\dfrac{2}{z} = (2z)1$

$4 + 4 = 2z$

$8 = 2z$

$z = 4$

52. $46\dfrac{2}{3}$

53. LCD $= 4x^2$

$\dfrac{4x^2}{1}\left(\dfrac{3}{x}\right) + \dfrac{4x^2}{1}\left(\dfrac{-8}{x^2}\right) = \dfrac{4x^2}{1}\left(\dfrac{1}{4}\right)$

$12x - 32 = x^2$

$0 = x^2 - 12x + 32$

$0 = (x - 4)(x - 8)$

$x - 4 = 0 \mid x - 8 = 0$

$x = 4 \mid x = 8$

54. $-2, \dfrac{4}{5}$

55. $3x - 4y = 12$

$3x = 4y + 12$

$x = \dfrac{4y + 12}{3}$

56. $y = \dfrac{2x - 14}{7}$

57. LCD $= n$

$(n)\dfrac{2m}{n} = (n)P$

$2m = nP$

$\dfrac{2m}{P} = n$

or $n = \dfrac{2m}{P}$

58. $t = \dfrac{rs}{5}$

59. $\dfrac{E}{1} = \dfrac{mv^2}{gr}$ This is a proportion.

$mv^2 = Egr$ Product of means = product of extremes.

$\dfrac{mv^2}{v^2} = \dfrac{Egr}{v^2}$ Dividing both sides by v^2.

$m = \dfrac{Egr}{v^2}$

60. $B = \dfrac{3V}{h}$

61. $\dfrac{F - 32}{C} = \dfrac{9}{5}$ This is a proportion.

$9C = 5(F - 32)$ Product of means = product of extremes.

$\dfrac{9C}{9} = \dfrac{5F - 160}{9}$

$C = \dfrac{5F - 160}{9}$ or $\dfrac{5}{9}(F - 32)$

62. $F = \dfrac{9C + 160}{5}$ or $F = \dfrac{9}{5}C + 32$

63. Let x = Speed returning from work

	d	=	r	$\cdot$	t
Going to work	$\dfrac{1}{2}(x + 10)$		$x + 10$		30 min $= \dfrac{1}{2}$ hr
Returning from work	$\dfrac{3}{4}(x)$		x		45 min $= \dfrac{3}{4}$ hr

Distance going to work = Distance returning from work

$\dfrac{1}{2}(x + 10) = \dfrac{3}{4}(x)$

$\dfrac{1}{2}x + 5 = \dfrac{3}{4}x$

$5 = \dfrac{1}{4}x$

$x = 20$ mph

Distance $= rt = 20\left(\dfrac{3}{4}\right) = 15$ mi

64. 5 mph

65. Let x = Pounds of 78¢ candy

$15 - x$ = Pounds of 99¢ candy

	78¢ candy	99¢ candy	Mixture, 85¢ candy
Unit Cost	78	99	85
Amount	x	$15 - x$	15
Total Cost	$78x$	$99(15 - x)$	$85(15)$

Cost of 78¢ candy + Cost of 99¢ candy = Cost of mixture

$78x + 99(15 - x) = 85(15)$

$78x + 1485 - 99x = 1275$

$-21x = -210$

$x = 10$ lb 78¢ candy

$15 - x = 15 - 10 = 5$ lb 99¢ candy

66. 12 lb 85¢ nuts, 18 lb 95¢ nuts

67. Let x = cc of water added

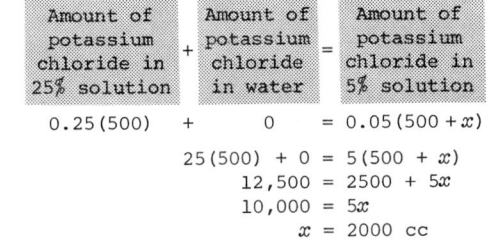

Amount of potassium chloride in 25% solution	+	Amount of potassium chloride in water	=	Amount of potassium chloride in 5% solution
0.25(500)	+	0	=	0.05(500 + x)

$$25(500) + 0 = 5(500 + x)$$
$$12{,}500 = 2500 + 5x$$
$$10{,}000 = 5x$$
$$x = 2000 \text{ cc}$$

68. 840 cc

CUMULATIVE REVIEW EXERCISES
CHAPTERS 1-8 (page 324)

1. $10 - (3\sqrt{4} - 5^2)$
$10 - (3 \cdot 2 - 25)$
$10 - (6 - 25)$
$10 - (-19) = 29$

2. $V = \dfrac{10}{9}$

3. $\left(\dfrac{\overset{3}{\cancel{24}}y^{-3}}{\cancel{8}y^{-1}}\right)^{-2} = (3y^{-2})^{-2}$
$= 3^{-2}y^4 = \dfrac{y^4}{3^2} = \dfrac{y^4}{9}$

4. $3x - 1$

5. $\begin{array}{r} 5z + 7 \quad \text{R } 18 \\ 3z - 2 \,\overline{)\,15z^2 + 11z + 4} \\ \underline{15z^2 - 10z} \\ 21z + 4 \\ \underline{21z - 14} \\ 18 \end{array}$

6. $(x + 6)(x - 7)$

7. $3w^2 - 48$
$3(w^2 - 16)$
$3(w + 4)(w - 4)$

8. $(5a - 3b)(4a + b)$

9. $\underbrace{3x^2 - 6x}\; - \underbrace{2xy + 4y}$
$3x(x - 2) - 2y(x - 2)$
$(x - 2)(3x - 2y)$

10. One answer: $\{-3, 8\}$

CHAPTER NINE DIAGNOSTIC TEST (page 325)

Following each problem number is the textbook section reference (in parentheses) where that kind of problem is discussed.

1.(a)(901) $\dfrac{3x}{x - 4}$; x cannot be 4 because that would make the denominator zero.

(b)(901) $\dfrac{5x + 4}{x^2 + 2x} = \dfrac{5x + 4}{x(x + 2)}$; x cannot be 0 or -2 because either value makes the denominator zero.

2. (901) (a) $-\dfrac{-4}{5} = +\dfrac{+4}{5}$

(b) $\dfrac{-3}{x - y} = \dfrac{+3}{-(x - y)} = \dfrac{+3}{y - x}$

3. (902) $\dfrac{\overset{2}{\cancel{8}}x^3y}{\underset{3}{\cancel{9}}x^2y^2} = \dfrac{2x}{3y}$

4. (902) $\dfrac{x^2 + 8x + 16}{x^2 - 16} = \dfrac{\cancel{(x + 4)}(x + 4)}{\cancel{(x + 4)}(x - 4)} = \dfrac{x + 4}{x - 4}$

5. (902) $\dfrac{6a^2 + 11ab - 10b^2}{6a^2b - 4ab^2} = \dfrac{(2a + 5b)\cancel{(3a - 2b)}}{2ab\cancel{(3a - 2b)}}$
$= \dfrac{2a + 5b}{2ab}$

6. (903) $\dfrac{a}{a + 2} \cdot \dfrac{4a + 8}{6a^2} = \dfrac{a}{\cancel{(a + 2)}} \cdot \dfrac{4\cancel{(a + 2)}}{\underset{3}{\cancel{6}}a^2} = \dfrac{2}{3a}$

7. (904) $\dfrac{3}{a - b} - \dfrac{2}{a - b} = \dfrac{3 - 2}{a - b} = \dfrac{1}{a - b}$

8. (906) $4 + \dfrac{2}{x} = \dfrac{4}{1} + \dfrac{2}{x} = \dfrac{4}{1} \cdot \dfrac{x}{x} + \dfrac{2}{x} = \dfrac{4x}{x} + \dfrac{2}{x}$
$= \dfrac{4x + 2}{x}$

9. (906) LCD = $b(b - 1)$;
$\dfrac{b + 1}{b} - \dfrac{b}{b - 1} = \dfrac{b + 1}{b} \cdot \dfrac{b - 1}{b - 1} - \dfrac{b}{b - 1} \cdot \dfrac{b}{b}$
$= \dfrac{(b + 1)(b - 1)}{b(b - 1)} - \dfrac{b^2}{b(b - 1)}$
$= \dfrac{(b + 1)(b - 1) - b^2}{b(b - 1)}$
$= \dfrac{b^2 - 1 - b^2}{b(b - 1)} = \dfrac{-1}{b(b - 1)}$
$= \dfrac{1}{b(1 - b)}$

10. (903) $\dfrac{2x}{x^2 - 9} \div \dfrac{4x^2}{x - 3} = \dfrac{2x}{(x + 3)\cancel{(x - 3)}} \cdot \dfrac{\cancel{(x - 3)}}{\underset{2}{\cancel{4}}x^2}$
$= \dfrac{1}{2x(x + 3)}$

11. (907) $\dfrac{\frac{9x^5}{10y}}{\frac{3x^2}{20y^3}} = \dfrac{9x^5}{10y} \div \dfrac{3x^2}{20y^3} = \dfrac{\overset{3}{\cancel{9}}x^5}{\cancel{10}y} \cdot \dfrac{\overset{2}{\cancel{20}}y^3}{\cancel{3}x^2} = 6x^3y^2$
(Method 2)

12. (907) $\dfrac{x}{x} \cdot \dfrac{4 + \frac{10}{x}}{2 + \frac{5}{x}} = \dfrac{x(4) + \frac{x}{1}\left(\frac{10}{x}\right)}{x(2) + \frac{x}{1}\left(\frac{5}{x}\right)} = \dfrac{4x + 10}{2x + 5}$
$= \dfrac{2\cancel{(2x + 5)}}{\cancel{(2x + 5)}} = 2$ (Method 1)

x is the LCD of the secondary denominators.

13. (908) $\dfrac{y}{3} - \dfrac{y}{4} = 1$; LCD = $3 \cdot 4 = 12$
$\dfrac{\overset{4}{\cancel{12}}}{1} \cdot \left(\dfrac{y}{\cancel{3}}\right) - \dfrac{\overset{3}{\cancel{12}}}{1} \cdot \left(\dfrac{y}{\cancel{4}}\right) = 12(1)$
$4y - 3y = 12$
$y = 12$

14. (908) $\dfrac{x - 2}{5} = \dfrac{x + 1}{2} + \dfrac{3}{5}$; LCD = $2 \cdot 5 = 10$
$\dfrac{\overset{2}{\cancel{10}}}{1} \cdot \dfrac{x - 2}{\cancel{5}} = \dfrac{\overset{5}{\cancel{10}}}{1} \cdot \dfrac{x + 1}{\cancel{2}} + \dfrac{\overset{2}{\cancel{10}}}{1} \cdot \dfrac{3}{\cancel{5}}$
$2(x - 2) = 5(x + 1) + 2 \cdot 3$
$2x - 4 = 5x + 5 + 6$
$-3x = 15$
$x = -5$

15. (908) $\dfrac{3}{a + 4} = \dfrac{5}{a}$ This is a proportion.

$5a + 20 = 3a$ Product of means = product of extremes.

$2a = -20$

$a = -10$

16. (908) $\dfrac{2x - 5}{x} = \dfrac{x - 2}{3}$ This is a proportion.

$6x - 15 = x^2 - 2x$ Product of means = product of extremes.

$0 = x^2 - 8x + 15$

$0 = (x - 3)(x - 5)$

$x = 3 \mid x = 5$

17. (909) $3x - 4y = 9$

$-4y = 9 - 3x$

$y = \dfrac{9 - 3x}{-4}$

$y = \dfrac{3x - 9}{4}$

18. (909) $\dfrac{PV}{T} = \dfrac{k}{1}$ This is a proportion.

$kT = PV$ Product of means = product of extremes.

$\dfrac{kT}{k} = \dfrac{PV}{k}$

$T = \dfrac{PV}{k}$

19. (909) $PM + Q = PN$

$PM - PN = -Q$

$P(M - N) = -Q$

$\dfrac{P(M - N)}{M - N} = \dfrac{-Q}{M - N}$

$P = \dfrac{Q}{N - M}$

20. (910) original fraction $= \dfrac{n}{n + 6}$

$\dfrac{n - 1}{n + 6 + 1} = \dfrac{1}{3}$

$\dfrac{n - 1}{n + 7} = \dfrac{1}{3}$ A proportion

$3(n - 1) = 1(n + 7)$

$3n - 3 = n + 7$

$2n = 10$

$n = 5$

$\dfrac{n}{n + 6} = \dfrac{5}{5 + 6} = \dfrac{5}{11}$ original fraction

EXERCISES 1001, SET I (page 333)

1. (a) (3, 1):   Start at the origin, move right 3 units, then move up 1 unit.

(b) (-4, -2):   Start at the origin, move left units, then down 2 units.

(c) (0, 3):   Start at the origin, move right 0 units, then up 3 units.

(d) (5, -4):   Start at the origin, move right 5 units, then down 4 units.

(e) (4, 0):   4 units to the right and 0 units up.

(f) (-2, 4):   Start at the origin, move left units, then up 4 units.

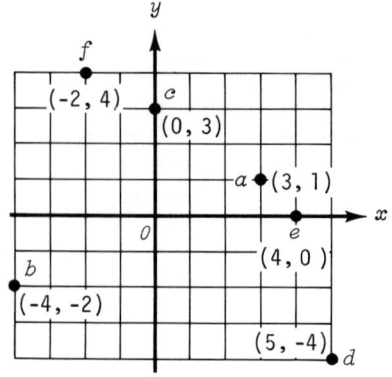

2.

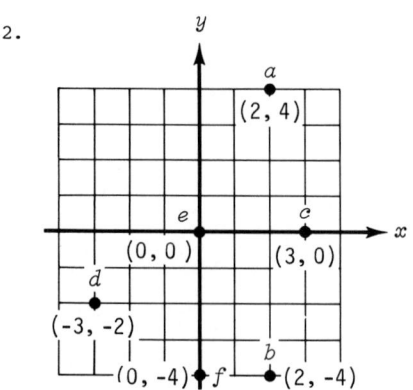

3. (a) (3, 0)
   (b) (0, 5)
   (c) (-5, 2)
   (d) (-4, -3)

4. (a) (4, 3)
   (b) (-6, 0)
   (c) (3, -4)
   (d) (0, -3)

5. (a) 5 because A is 5 units to the right.
   (b) -3 because C is 3 units to the left.
   (c) 3 because E is 3 units to the right.
   (d) 1 because F is 1 unit to the right.

6. (a) 5
   (b) -2
   (c) 0
   (d) -5

7. 0.   The y-coordinate is the distance up or down from the horizontal axis.

8. 0

9. (a) 1 because F is 1 unit to the right. Abscissa is the number of units to the right or left of the vertical axis.
   (b) 2 because C is 2 units above the horizontal axis.

10. (a) 5
    (b) -4

11.

12.

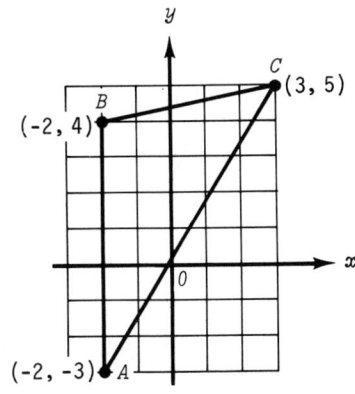

EXERCISES 1002, SET I   (page 342)

1. $x + y = 3$
    $\quad\quad y = 3 - x$

    Substitute three values for x and find the cor-
    responding values for y.

    If $x = 0$, $y = 3 - 0 = 3$
    If $x = 1$, $y = 3 - 1 = 2$
    If $x = 3$, $y = 3 - 3 = 0$

TABLE OF VALUES

x	y
0	3
1	2
3	0

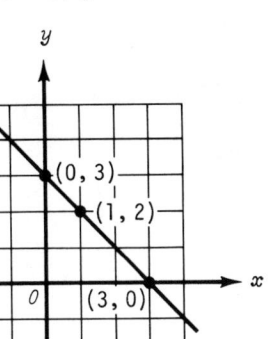

2.

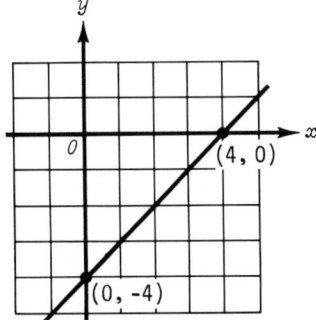

3. Using the intercept method, we get: $2x - 3y = 6$

    Set $y = 0$.   Then $x = 3$.
    Set $x = 0$.   Then $y = -2$.

    This gives the points (3, 0) and (0, -2).

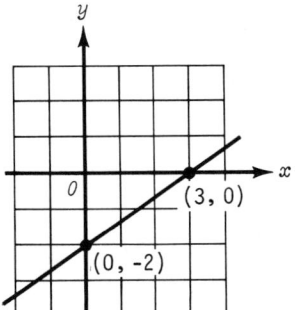

4.

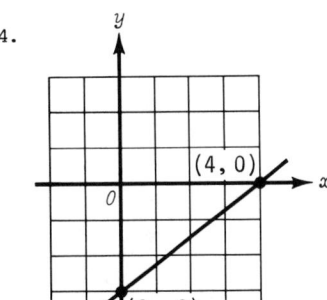

5. x can be any number but y is always 8.

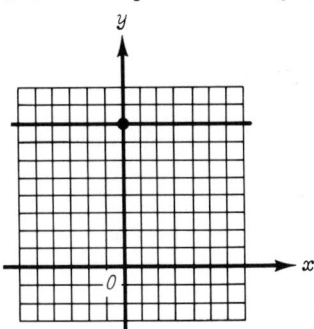

6.

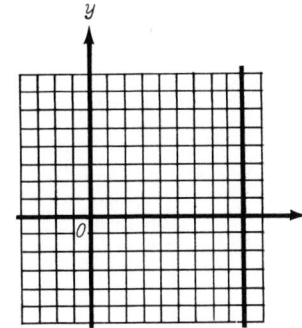

7. x is always -5. $x + 5 = 0$; $x = -5$.

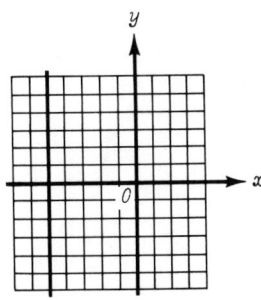

8.

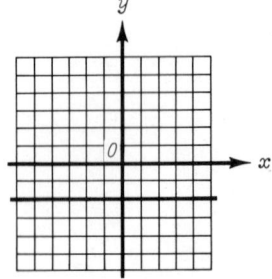

9. $3x = 5y + 15$

Set $y = 0$.
Then $3x = 15$
$x = 5$.

This gives point $(5, 0)$.

Set $x = 0$.
Then $5y = -15$
$y = -3$.

This gives point $(0, -3)$.

x	y
0	-3
5	0

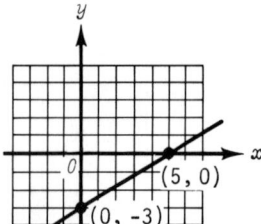

10.

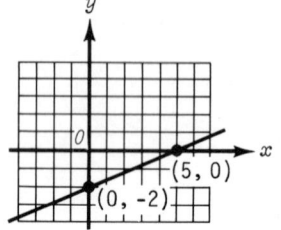

11. $x = -2y$

Set $y = 0$.
Then $x = 0$.

Set $y = 2$.
Then $x = -4$.

x	y
0	0
-4	2

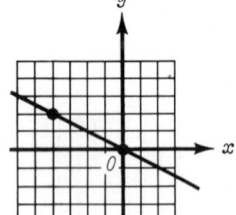

12.

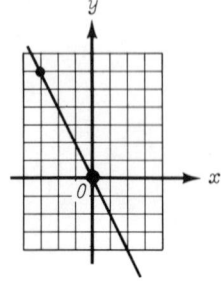

13. $4 - x = y$

Set $x = 0$.
Then $y = 4$.

Set $y = 0$.
Then $x = 4$.

x	y
0	4
4	0

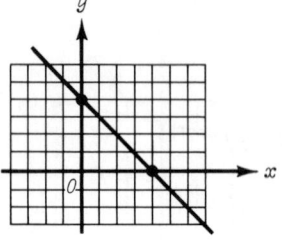

14.

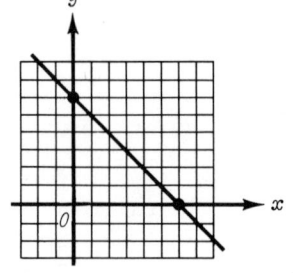

15. $y = x$

x	y
0	0
4	4
-3	-3

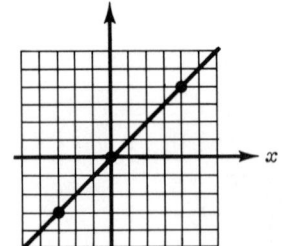

16.

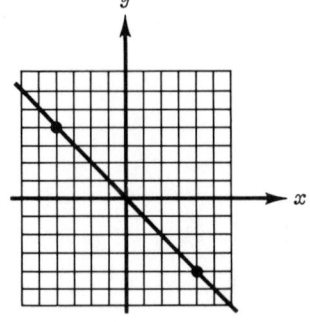

17. $x = \frac{2}{3}y + 4$

If we set $y = 0$, $x = 4$.

Set $y = 3$, $x = 6$.

x	y
4	0
6	3
0	-6

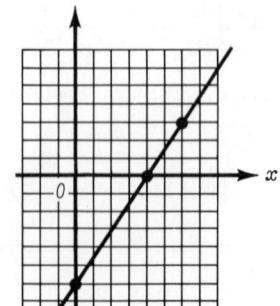

18.

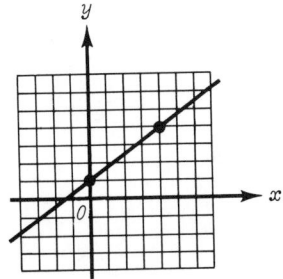

19. Find intercepts.
    $3x = 24 + 4y$

x	y
0	-6
8	0

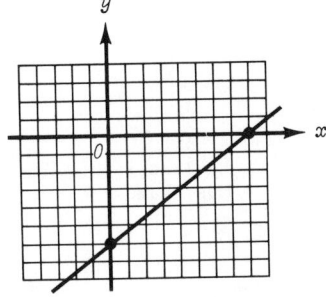

20.

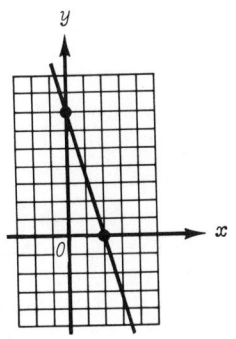

21. Set $x = 0$.
    Then $5y = 9(0) + 160$
    $5y = 160$
    $y = 32$

    Set $y = 0$.
    Then $5(0) = 9x + 160$
    $-160 = 9x$
    $-17\frac{7}{9} = x$

x	y
0	32
$-17\frac{7}{9}$	0

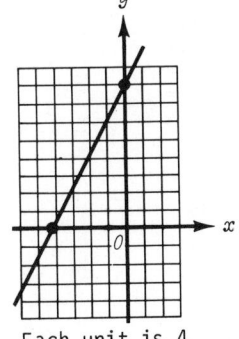

Each unit is 4

22.

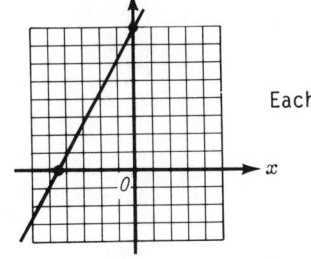

Each unit is 4.

23. (a) $x - y = 5$

x	y
0	-5
5	0

(b) $x + y = 1$

x	y
0	1
1	0

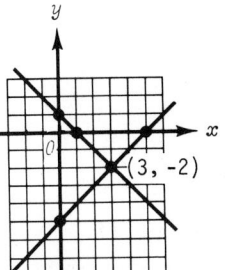

$(3, -2)$

24.

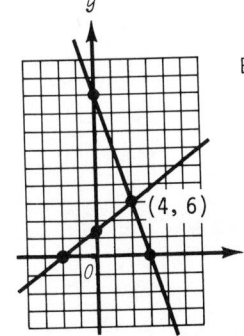

Each unit is 2.

$(4, 6)$

EXERCISES 1003A, SET I   (page 345)

1. (a) $y_2 - y_1 = (-9) - (8) = -17$
   (b) $x_2 - x_1 = (7) - (-4) = 11$

2. (a) 24   (b) -9

3. (a) $y_2 - y_1 = (-11) - (-14) = 3$
   (b) $x_2 - x_1 = (8) - (16) = -8$

4. (a) 30   (b) -8

5. $m = \dfrac{y_2 - y_1}{x_2 - x_1} = \dfrac{3 - 1}{7 - (-2)} = \dfrac{2}{9}$ 6. $\dfrac{5}{6}$

7. $m = \dfrac{y_2 - y_1}{x_2 - x_1} = \dfrac{-3 - (-1)}{5 - (-1)} = \dfrac{-2}{6} = -\dfrac{1}{3}$ 8. $-\dfrac{1}{2}$

9. $m = \dfrac{y_2 - y_1}{x_2 - x_1} = \dfrac{-3 - (-3)}{4 - (-5)} = \dfrac{0}{9} = 0$ 10. 0

11. $m = \dfrac{y_2 - y_1}{x_2 - x_1} = \dfrac{(-3) - (5)}{(8) - (-7)} = \dfrac{-8}{15}$

12. $-\dfrac{5}{17}$

13. $m = \dfrac{y_2 - y_1}{x_2 - x_1} = \dfrac{(-5) - (-15)}{(4) - (-6)} = \dfrac{10}{10} = 1$

14. -1

15. $m = \dfrac{y_2 - y_1}{x_2 - x_1} = \dfrac{(8) - (5)}{(-2) - (-2)} = \dfrac{3}{0}$

    Slope does not exist.

16. Does not exist

17. If $x = 0$: $2x - 3y = 6$
                $2(0) - 3y = 6$
                        $y = -2$

Therefore, $P_1 = (0, -2)$

If $y = 0$: $2x - 3y = 6$
            $2x - 3(0) = 6$
                    $x = 3$

Therefore, $P_2 = (3, 0)$

$m = \dfrac{y_2 - y_1}{x_2 - x_1} = \dfrac{(0) - (-2)}{(3) - (0)} = \dfrac{2}{3}$

18. $-\dfrac{1}{4}$

19. If $x = 0$: $4x + 5y = 20$
                $4(0) + 5y = 20$
                        $y = 4$

Therefore, $P_1 = (0, 4)$

If $y = 0$: $4x + 5y = 20$
            $4x + 5(0) = 20$
                    $x = 5$

Therefore, $P_2 = (5, 0)$

$m = \dfrac{y_2 - y_1}{x_2 - x_1} = \dfrac{(0) - (4)}{(5) - (0)} = \dfrac{-4}{5}$

20. $\dfrac{3}{5}$

EXERCISES 1003B, SET I   (page 350)

1. $3x = 2y - 4$ 2. $2x - 3y - 7 = 0$
   $3x - 2y + 4 = 0$

3. $y = -\dfrac{3}{4}x - 2$ 4. $3x + 5y + 20 = 0$
              $4y = -3x - 8$
   $3x + 4y + 8 = 0$

5. $2(3x + y) = 5(x - y) + 4$ 6. $4x - 9y + 5 = 0$
      $6x + 2y = 5x - 5y + 4$
   $x + 7y - 4 = 0$

7. $y - y_1 = m(x - x_1)$
      $y - 4 = \dfrac{1}{2}(x - 3)$
   $2y - 8 = x - 3$
          $0 = x - 2y + 5$ or $x - 2y + 5 = 0$

8. $x - 3y + 13 = 0$

9. $y - y_1 = m(x - x_1)$
      $y - (-2) = -\dfrac{2}{3}[x - (-1)]$
      $3(y + 2) = -2(x + 1)$
        $3y + 6 = -2x - 2$
   $2x + 3y + 8 = 0$

10. $5x + 4y + 22 = 0$

11. $y = mx + b$ 12. $2x - 7y - 14 = 0$
          $y = \dfrac{3}{4}x - 3$
        $4y = 3x - 12$
   $3x - 4y - 12 = 0$

13. $y = mx + b$ 14. $20x + 12y - 9 = 0$
          $y = -\dfrac{2}{5}x + \dfrac{1}{2}$

   LCD = 10

        $10y = -4x + 5$
   $4x + 10y - 5 = 0$

15. Use the two points to find the slope, then use m
     and one point to find the equation of the line.

$m = \dfrac{y_2 - y_1}{x_2 - x_1} = \dfrac{4 - (-1)}{2 - 4} = -\dfrac{5}{2}$

        $y - y_1 = m(x - x_1)$
         $y - 4 = -\dfrac{5}{2}(x - 2)$
        $2y - 8 = -5x + 10$
   $5x + 2y - 18 = 0$

16. $3x + 2y - 11 = 0$

17. $m = \dfrac{4 - 0}{3 - 0} = \dfrac{4}{3}$ 18. $5x - 2y = 0$
     $y - y_1 = m(x - x_1)$
      $y - 0 = \dfrac{4}{3}(x - 0)$
        $3y = 4x$
   $4x - 3y = 0$

19. Because the line is horizontal, every point on
     the line must have $y = 5$. Therefore, $y - 5 = 0$.

20. $x + 2 = 0$

21. $3x + 4y + 12 = 0$ 22. (a) $y = -\dfrac{2}{5}x + 3$
     Solve for y.

     (a) $4y = -3x - 12$ (b) $-\dfrac{2}{5}$
               $y = -\dfrac{3}{4}x - 3$
                                   (c) 3

     (b) $m = -\dfrac{3}{4}$

     (c) y-intercept = -3

23. $m = \dfrac{y_2 - y_1}{x_2 - x_1} = \dfrac{-2 - 3}{-4 - (-4)} = \dfrac{-5}{0}$

     Not a real number. m does not exist. (The line
     is vertical.)

24. Slope does not exist. (The line is vertical.)

EXERCISES 1004, SET I   (page 353)

1. $y = x^2$
    $y = (-2)^2 = 4$
    $y = (-1)^2 = 1$
    $y = 0^2 = 0$
    $y = 1^2 = 1$
    $y = 2^2 = 4$

x	y
-2	4
-1	1
0	0
1	1
2	4

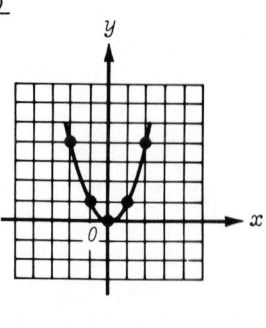

2.

x	y
-3	$2\frac{1}{4}$
-2	1
-1	$\frac{1}{4}$
0	0
1	$\frac{1}{4}$
2	1
3	$2\frac{1}{4}$

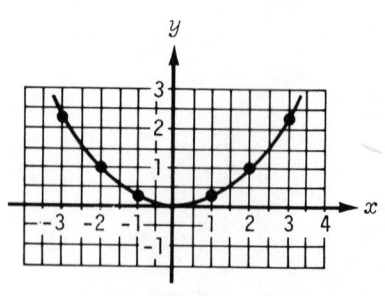

3. $y = x^2 - 2x$
$y = (-2)^2 - 2(-2)$
   $= 4 + 4 = 8$
$y = (-1)^2 - 2(-1)$
   $= 1 + 2 = 3$
$y = 0^2 - 2(0) = 0$
$y = 1^2 - 2(1) = -1$
$y = 2^2 - 2(2) = 0$
$y = 3^2 - 2(3) = 3$
$y = 4^2 - 2(4) = 8$

x	y
-2	8
-1	3
0	0
1	-1
2	0
3	3
4	8

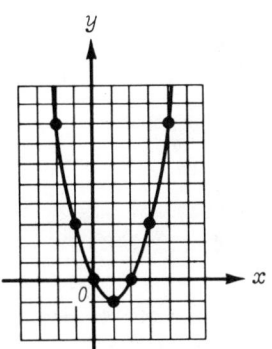

4.

x	y
-2	-10
-1	-4
0	0
1	2
2	2
3	0
4	-4

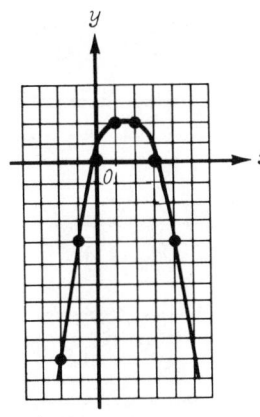

5. $y = 2x - x^2$
$y = 2(-2) - (-2)^2$
   $= -4 - 4 = -8$
$y = 2(-1) - (-1)^2$
   $= -2 - 1 = -3$
$y = 2(0) - 0^2 = 0$
$y = 2(1) - (1)^2$
   $= 2 - 1 = 1$
$y = 2(2) - (2)^2$
   $= 4 - 4 = 0$
$y = 2(3) - (3)^2$
   $= 6 - 9 = -3$
$y = 2(4) - (4)^2$
   $= 8 - 16 = -8$

x	y
-2	-8
-1	-3
0	0
1	1
2	0
3	-3
4	-8

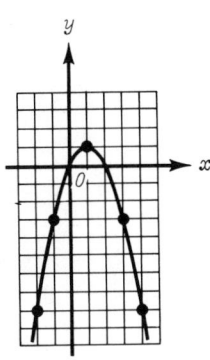

6.

x	y
-3	3
-2	0
-1	-1
0	0
1	3

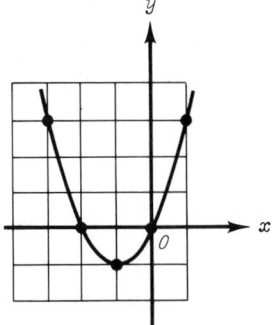

7. $y = x^3$
$y = (-2)^3 = -8$
$y = (-1)^3 = -1$
$y = 0^3 = 0$
$y = 1^3 = 1$
$y = 2^3 = 8$

x	y
-2	-8
-1	-1
0	0
1	1
2	8

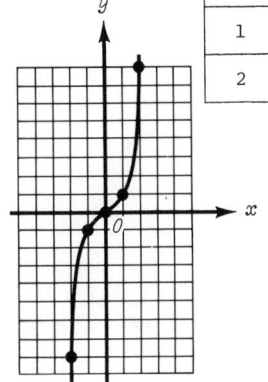
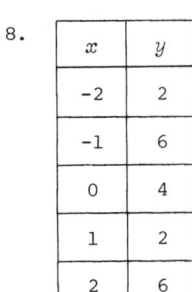

8.

x	y
-2	2
-1	6
0	4
1	2
2	6

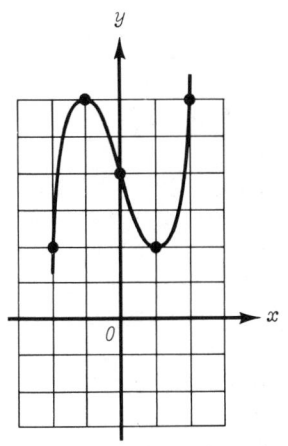

EXERCISES 1005A, SET I (page 359)

1. $x - 5 < 2$
$\underline{+ 5 \qquad +5}$
$x \quad < \quad 7$

2. $x < 11$

3. $5x + 4 \le 19$
$\underline{- 4 \qquad -4}$
$5x \quad \le \quad 15$
$\frac{\not5x}{\not5} \le \frac{15}{5}$
$x \le 3$

4. $x \le 3$

5. $6x + 7 > 3 + 8x$
$\quad\ 7 - 3 > 8x - 6x$
$\qquad\quad 4 > 2x$
$\qquad\quad \dfrac{4}{2} > \dfrac{2x}{2}$
$\qquad\quad 2 > x$ or $x < 2$

6. $x > -7$

7. $2x - 9 > 3(x - 2)$
$\quad 2x - 9 > 3x - 6$
$\ 2x - 3x > 9 - 6$
$\qquad\ -x > 3$
$\qquad\quad x < -3$

8. $x < -3$

9. $6(3 - 4x) + 12 \geq 10x - 2(5 - 3x)$
$\quad 18 - 24x + 12 \geq 10x - 10 + 6x$
$\quad 18 + 12 + 10 \geq 10x + 6x + 24x$
$\qquad\qquad\ 40 \geq 40x$
$\qquad\qquad\ 1 \geq x$

10. $x \leq 1$

11. $4(6 - 2x) \neq 5x - 2$
$\quad 24 - 8x \neq 5x - 2$
$\qquad\quad 26 \neq 13x$
$\qquad\qquad 2 \neq x$

12. $x \neq 4$

13. $2[3 - 5(x - 4)] < 10 - 5x$
$\quad 2[3 - 5x + 20] < 10 - 5x$
$\qquad 2[23 - 5x] < 10 - 5x$
$\qquad\ 46 - 10x < 10 - 5x$
$\qquad\ 46 - 10 < 10x - 5x$
$\qquad\qquad 36 < 5x$
$\qquad\qquad \dfrac{36}{5} < \dfrac{5x}{5}$
$\qquad\qquad 7\dfrac{1}{5} < x$

14. $x > 16$

15. LCD = 12
$\quad (12)\dfrac{x}{3} + (12)\dfrac{x}{4} > (12)7$
$\qquad\quad 4x + 3x > 84$
$\qquad\qquad\ 7x > 84$
$\qquad\qquad\ x > 12$

16. $x > 15$

17. LCD = 15
$\quad (15)\dfrac{y - 5}{3} \leq (15)\dfrac{y + 2}{5} + (15)\dfrac{1}{3}$
$\quad 5(y - 5) \leq 3(y + 2) + 5$
$\quad 5y - 25 \leq 3y + 6 + 5$
$\quad 5y - 25 \leq 3y + 11$
$\qquad\quad 2y \leq 36$
$\qquad\qquad y \leq 18$

18. $x \geq 6$

19. $12.85x - 15.49 \geq 22.06(9.66x - 12.74)$
$\quad 12.85x - 15.49 \geq 213.0996x - 281.0444$
$\qquad 265.5544 \geq 200.2496x$
$\qquad\quad 1.326 \geq x$ (approx.)

20. $x > -8.41$ (approx.)

EXERCISES 1005B, SET I (page 361)

1.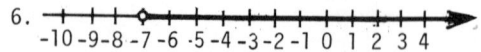

2.

3.

4.

5.

6.

7.

8.

9.

10

11.

12.

13. $7\dfrac{1}{5}$

14.

15.

16. 15

17.

18.

19. -1.326

20. -8.41

EXERCISES 1006, SET I (page 366)

1. $x + 2y < 4$

Change to $x + 2y = 4$ to
find boundary line.
Boundary line goes
through:

x	y
0	2
4	0

Boundary line is dashed
because equality sign
is not included with $<$.

Half-plane is the part that includes the origin
because $(0, 0)$ makes $x + 2y < 4$ true.

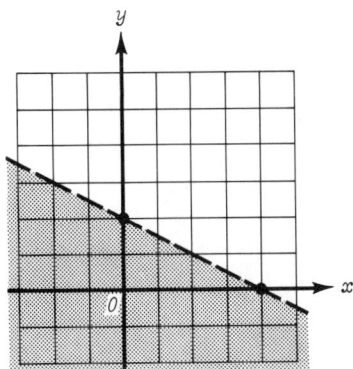

2.

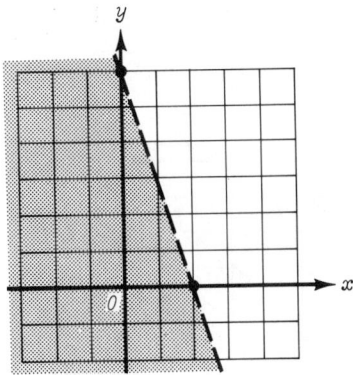

3. $2x - 3y > 6$

Boundary line is

$2x - 3y = 6$
$2(0) - 3y = 6$
$y = -2$
$2x - 3(0) = 6$
$x = 3$

Half-plane does not in-
clude the origin because

$2(0) - 3(0) \not> 6$
$0 \not> 6$

x	y
0	-2
3	0

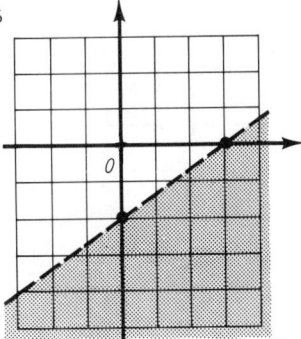

4.

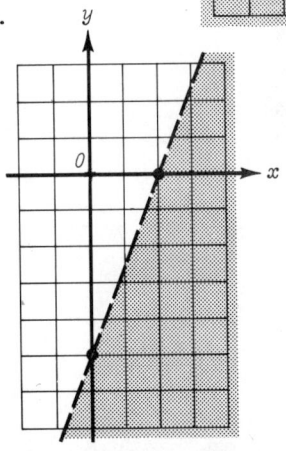

5. $x \geq -2$

All points to the right
and including the line
$x = -2$

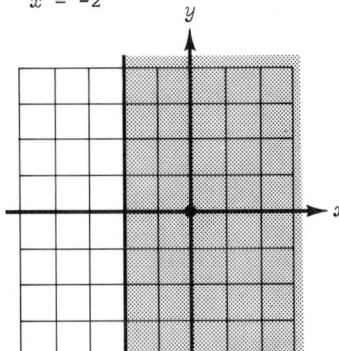

6.

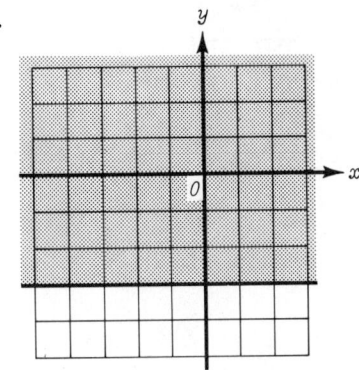

7. $3y - 4x \geq 12$

Boundary line:
$3y - 4x = 12$

$x = 0, \quad 3y = 12$
$y = 4$

$y = 0, \quad -4x = 12$
$x = -3$

x	y
0	4
-3	0

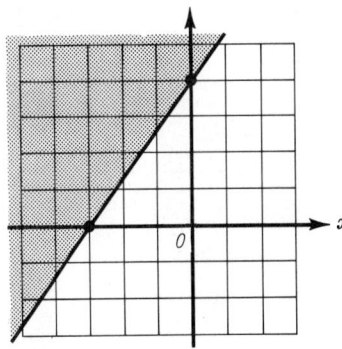

8.

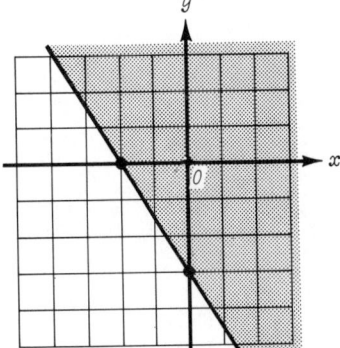

9. $x + y > 0$

Boundary line: $x + y = 0$

Intercepts:
(0, 0)

x	y
0	0
3	-3

Find one
other point.

Set $x = 3$.
Then
$3 + y = 0$
$\quad y = -3$.

The point (1, 1) makes $x + y > 0$. Therefore,
(1, 1) is in the correct half-plane.

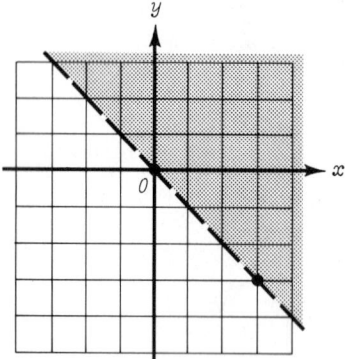

10.

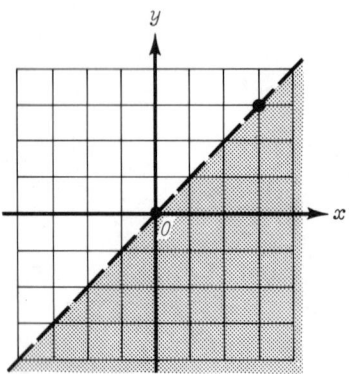

11. $3x - 4y \geq 10$

Boundary line:

$3x - 4y = 10$

$x = 0, \ y = \dfrac{10}{-4} = -2\dfrac{1}{2}$

$y = 0, \ x = \dfrac{10}{3} = 3\dfrac{1}{3}$

x	y
0	$-2\dfrac{1}{2}$
$3\dfrac{1}{3}$	0

The correct half-plane does not include the
origin.

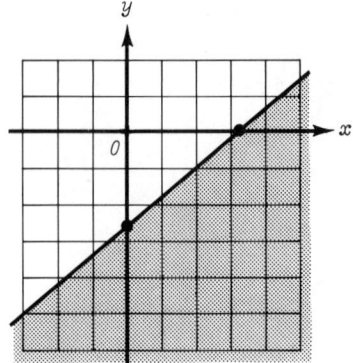

12.

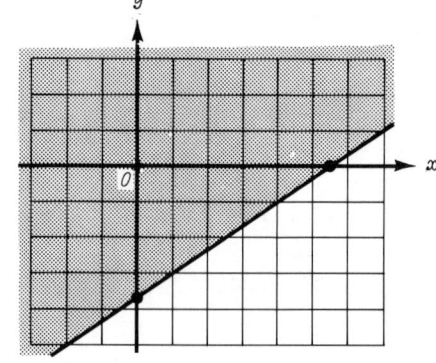

13. $2(x + 1) + 3 \leq 3(2x - 1)$
$\quad 2x + 2 + 3 \leq 6x - 3$
$\qquad 2x - 6x \leq -2 - 3 - 3$
$\qquad\quad -4x \leq -8$
$\qquad\quad\ \ 4x \geq 8$
$\qquad\quad\ \ \ x \geq 2$

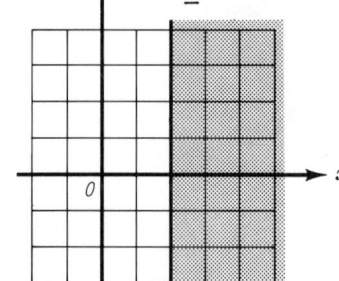

14.

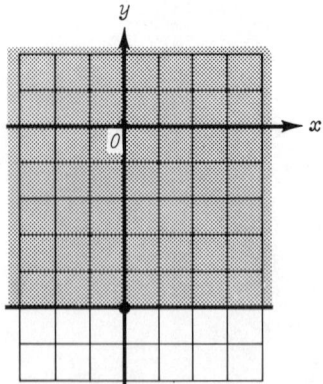

15. $\dfrac{x}{5} - \dfrac{y}{3} > 1$

LCD = 15

$15\left(\dfrac{x}{5}\right) + 15\left(-\dfrac{y}{3}\right) > 15(1)$
$\qquad\qquad 3x - 5y > 15$

Boundary line:
$3x - 5y = 15$

The point $(0, 0)$ does not make the inequality true.

x	y
0	-3
5	0

Therefore, the correct half-plane does not include the origin.

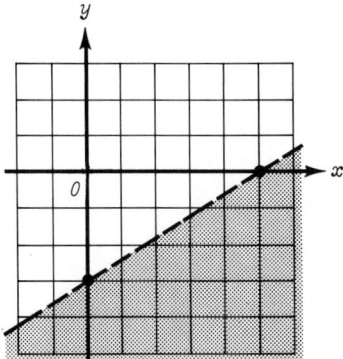

16.

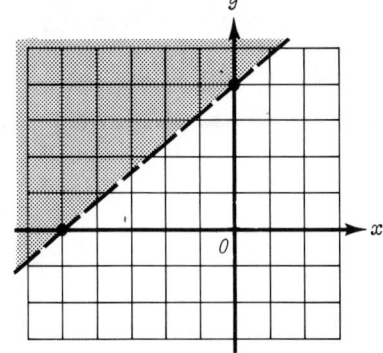

17. $\dfrac{2x + y}{3} - \dfrac{x - y}{2} \geq \dfrac{5}{6}$

LCD = 6

$\dfrac{2}{\cancel{6}}\left(\dfrac{2x + y}{\cancel{3}}\right) + \dfrac{3}{\cancel{6}}\left(\dfrac{-(x - y)}{\cancel{2}}\right) \geq \cancel{6}\left(\dfrac{5}{\cancel{6}}\right)$

$4x + 2y - 3x + 3y \geq 5$
$\qquad\qquad x + 5y \geq 5$

Boundary line:
$x + 5y = 5$

Correct half-plane does not include origin.

x	y
0	1
5	0

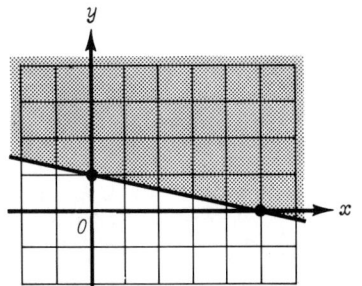

18.

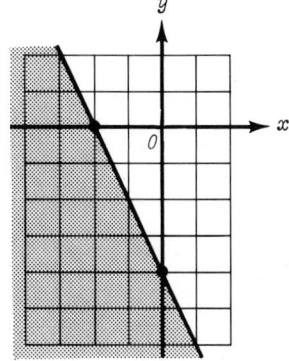

REVIEW EXERCISES 1007, SET I   (page 369)

1.

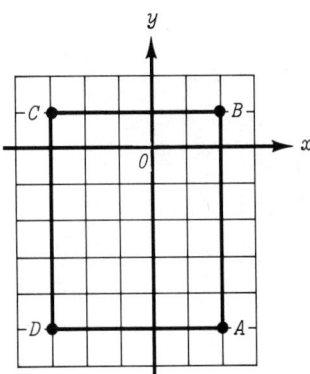

2.

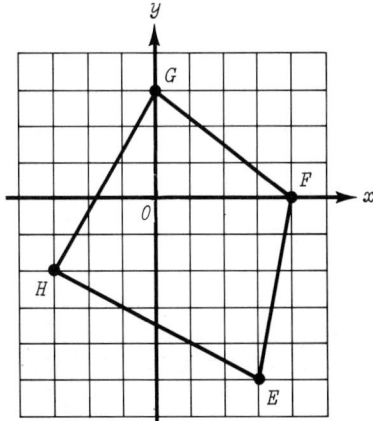

3.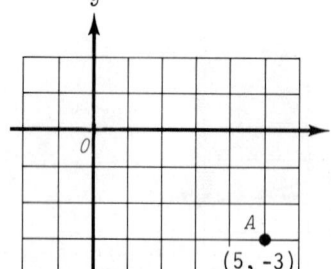

(a) abscissa = 5
(b) ordinate = -3
(c) y-coordinate = -3

4.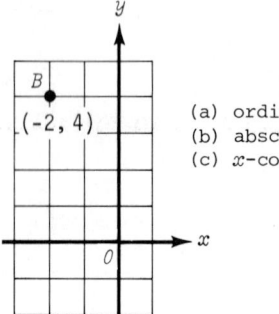

(a) ordinate = 4
(b) abscissa = -2
(c) x-coordinate = -2

5. $x - y = 5$

x	y
0	-5
5	0

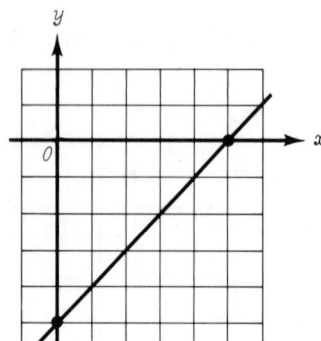

6.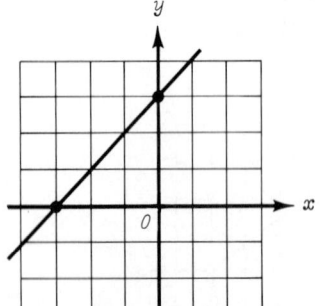

7. $x = y$

x	y
0	0
1	1
3	3

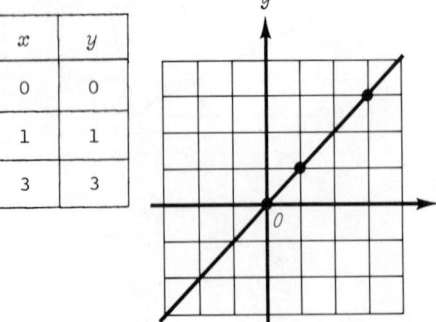

8.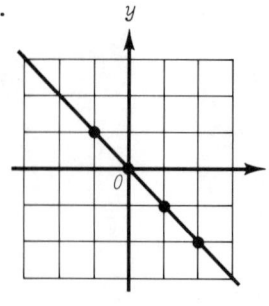

9.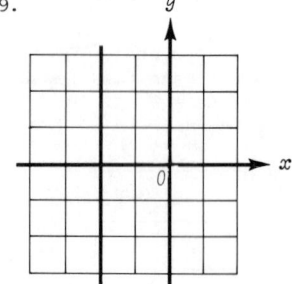

10.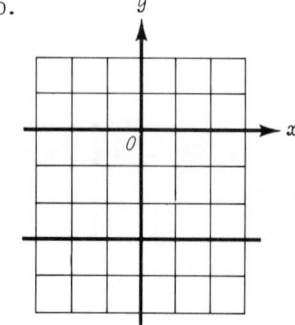

11. $4y - 5x = 20$

x	y
0	5
-4	0

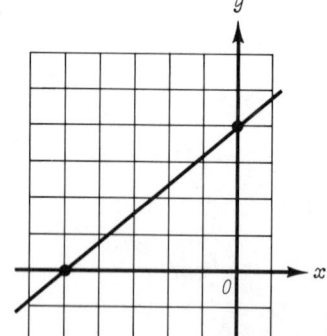

12.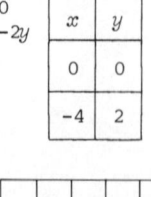

13. $x + 2y = 0$
    $x = -2y$

x	y
0	0
-4	2

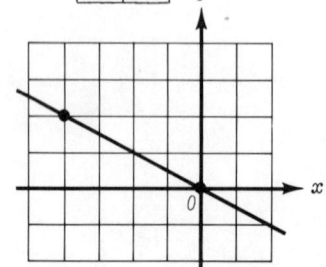

14.

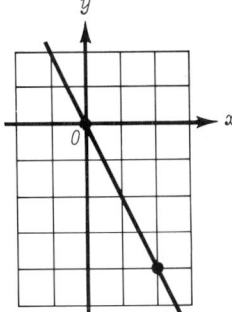

15. $y = \dfrac{x^2}{2}$

$y = \dfrac{(-4)^2}{2} = 8$

$y = \dfrac{(-2)^2}{2} = \dfrac{4}{2} = 2$

$y = \dfrac{(-1)^2}{2} = \dfrac{1}{2}$

$y = \dfrac{0^2}{2} = 0$

$y = \dfrac{1^2}{2} = \dfrac{1}{2}$

$y = \dfrac{2^2}{2} = \dfrac{4}{2} = 2$

$y = \dfrac{4^2}{2} = \dfrac{16}{2} = 8$

x	y
-4	8
-2	2
-1	$\frac{1}{2}$
0	0
1	$\frac{1}{2}$
2	2
4	8

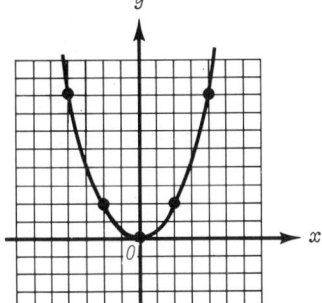

16.

x	y
-2	10
-1	4
0	0
1	-2
2	-2
3	0
4	4

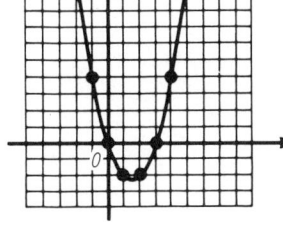

17. $m = \dfrac{y_2 - y_1}{x_2 - x_1}$

$= \dfrac{5 - (-6)}{-3 - 2}$

$= \dfrac{11}{-5} = -\dfrac{11}{5}$

18. $-\dfrac{9}{5}$

19. $y - y_1 = m(x - x_1)$

$y - (-5) = -\dfrac{2}{3}(x - 3)$

$3(y + 5) = -2(x - 3)$

$3y + 15 = -2x + 6$

$2x + 3y + 9 = 0$

20. $3x + 4y + 8 = 0$

21. $x + 7 > 2$

$\quad x > 2 - 7$

$\quad x > -5$

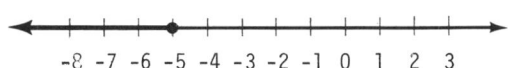

22. $x > -4$

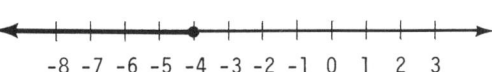

23. $x - 3 \le -8$

$\quad x \le 3 - 8$

$\quad x \le -5$

24. $x \le -4$

25. $2x - 5y > 10$

Boundary line:
$2x - 5y = 10$

x	y
0	-2
5	0

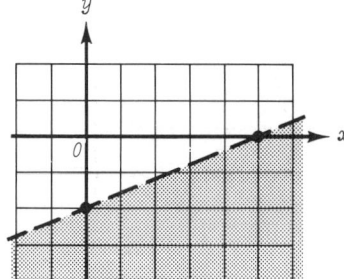

26.

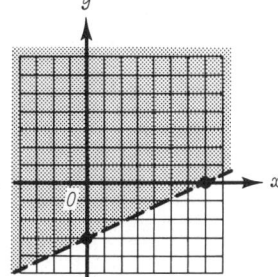

27. Boundary line:
$x = -4y$

x	y
0	0
-4	1

(-1, -1) makes the in-
equality true. There-
fore, correct half-
plane contains (-1, -1).

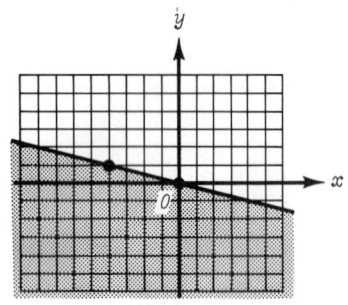

28.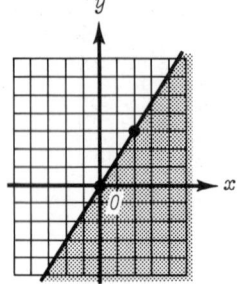

29. $x < 2$
Boundary line: $x = 2$

30.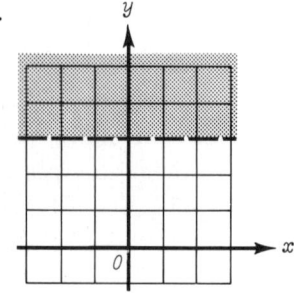

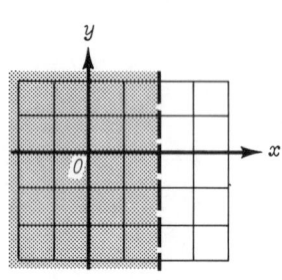

31. $y = x^3 - 3x$
$y = (-3)^3 - (3)(-3)$
$= -27 + 9 = -18$
$y = (-2)^3 - 3(-2)$
$= -8 + 6 = -2$
$y = (-1)^3 - 3(-1)$
$= -1 + 3 = 2$
$y = 0^3 - 3(0) = 0$
$y = 1^3 - 3(1) = -2$
$y = 2^3 - 3(2) = 2$
$y = 3^3 - 3(3) = 18$

x	y
-3	-18
-2	-2
-1	2
0	0
1	-2
2	2
3	18

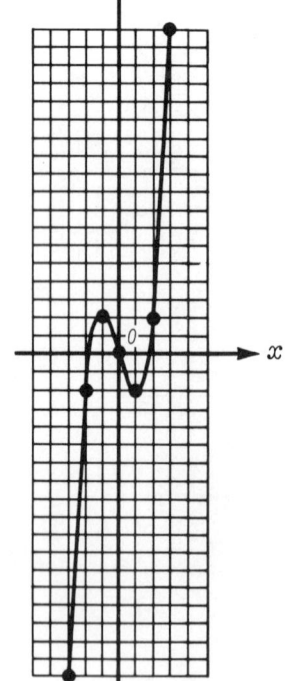

32.

x	y
-4	-18
-3	-2
-2	2
-1	0
0	-2
1	2
2	18

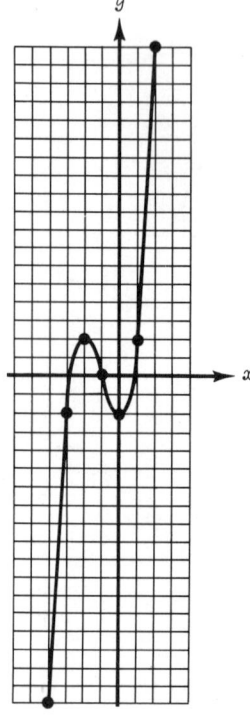

33. $y = mx + b$
$y = -\frac{1}{2}x + 6$
$2y = -x + 12$
$x + 2y - 12 = 0$

34. $x + 3y - 27 = 0$

35. First find m; then use m and one point to find the equation.
$m = \frac{y_2 - y_1}{x_2 - x_1} = \frac{-2 - 4}{1 - (-3)}$
$= \frac{-6}{4} = -\frac{3}{2}$
$y - y_1 = m(x - x_1)$
$y - (-2) = -\frac{3}{2}(x - 1)$
$2(y + 2) = -3(x - 1)$
$2y + 4 = -3x + 3$
$3x + 2y + 1 = 0$

36. $7x - 3y + 2 = 0$

37. LCD = 10
$\frac{10}{1}\left(\frac{2x}{5}\right) + \frac{10}{1}\left(-\frac{3y}{2}\right) = \frac{10}{1}(3)$
$4x - 15y = 30$
$-15y = -4x + 30$
$y = \frac{4}{15}x - 2$
$m = \frac{4}{15}$, y-intercept $= -2$

38. $m = \frac{4}{15}$, y-intercept $= -2$

39. $x + 2(x - y) = 6$
$x + 2x - 2y = 6$
$3x - 2y = 6$

x	y
0	-3
2	0

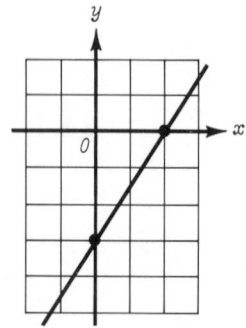

40.

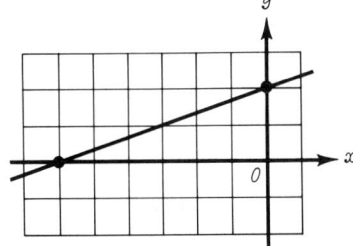

41. $\dfrac{2x + 3y}{5} - \dfrac{x - 3y}{4} = \dfrac{9}{10}$

LCD = 20

$$20\left(\dfrac{2x + 3y}{5}\right) + 20\left(\dfrac{-(x - 3y)}{4}\right) = 20\left(\dfrac{9}{10}\right)$$

$$4(2x + 3y) + 5(-x + 3y) = 2(9)$$
$$8x + 12y - 5x + 15y = 18$$
$$3x + 27y = 18$$
$$x + 9y = 6$$

x	y
0	$\frac{2}{3}$
6	0

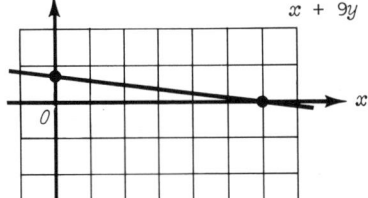

42.

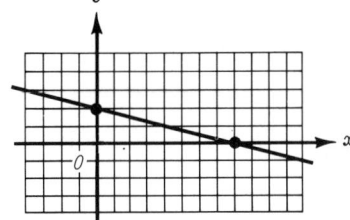

43. $2(x - 4) - 5 \geq 7 + 3(2x - 1)$
$2x - 8 - 5 \geq 7 + 6x - 3$
$2x - 6x \geq 7 - 3 + 8 + 5$
$-4x \geq 17$
$\dfrac{-4x}{-4} \leq \dfrac{17}{-4}$
$x \leq -4\frac{1}{4}$

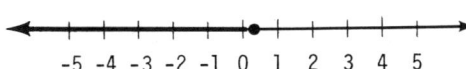

44. $x < \frac{1}{3}$

45. LCD = 30

$$(30)\dfrac{3z}{5} + (30)\dfrac{-2z}{3} < (30)\dfrac{1}{2}$$

$$18z - 20z < 15$$
$$-2z < 15$$
$$z > \dfrac{-15}{2}$$

$$z > -7\frac{1}{2}$$

46. $w > -3\frac{1}{2}$

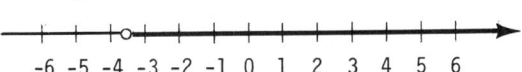

47. LCD = 6

$$6\left(\dfrac{x}{2}\right) + 6\left(\dfrac{-y}{6}\right) \geq 6(1)$$
$$3x - y \geq 6$$

x	y
0	-6
2	0

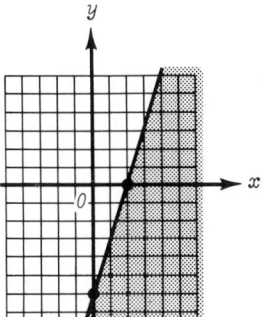

The correct half-plane does not include the origin.

48.

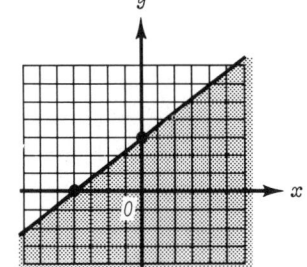

49. LCD = 6

$2(x - y) \leq 3(x - y)$
$2x - 2y \leq 3x - 3y$
$3y - 2y \leq 3x - 2x$
$y \leq x$

Boundary line:
$y = x$

x	y
0	0
5	5

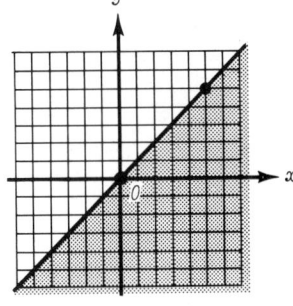

Correct half-plane includes (1, 0).

50.

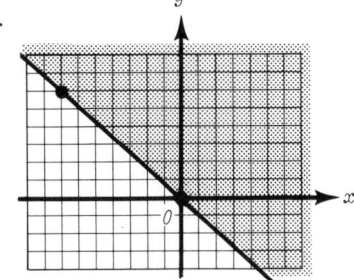

1. $A = \dfrac{h}{2}(B + b)$

$= \dfrac{5}{2}(11 + 7)$

$= \dfrac{5}{2}(\overset{9}{\cancel{18}}) = 45$

2. $\dfrac{9b^2}{49a^6}$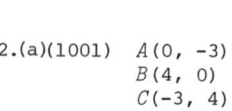

3. $\begin{array}{r} 2z + 3 \quad \text{R } 8 \\ 3z - 5 \overline{\smash{)}6z^2 - \quad z - 7} \\ \underline{6z^2 - 10z} \\ 9z - 7 \\ \underline{9z - 15} \\ 8 \end{array}$

4. $\dfrac{2x^2 + 1}{(x - 2)(x + 1)}$

5. $\dfrac{b + 1}{a^2 + ab} \div \dfrac{b^2 - b - 2}{a^3 - ab^2}$

$\dfrac{b + 1}{\cancel{a(a + b)}} \cdot \dfrac{\cancel{a}(a + b)(a - b)}{(b + 1)(b - 2)} = \dfrac{a - b}{b - 2}$

6. $\dfrac{xy - 2}{y}$

7. $\dfrac{2x - 4}{3} = \dfrac{4 - 6x}{5}$ A proportion

$5(2x - 4) = 3(4 - 6x)$
$10x - 20 = 12 - 18x$
$28x = 32$
$x = \dfrac{32}{28} = \dfrac{8}{7} \text{ or } 1\dfrac{1}{7}$

8. -6

9. $C = \dfrac{5}{2h} - \dfrac{h}{k}$ LCD $= 2hk$

$\dfrac{2hk}{1} \cdot \dfrac{C}{1} = \dfrac{2hk}{1} \cdot \dfrac{5}{2h} - \dfrac{2hk}{1} \cdot \dfrac{h}{k}$

$2hkC = 5k - 2h^2$
$2hkC - 5k = -2h^2$
$k(2hC - 5) = -2h^2$

$\dfrac{k(2hC - 5)}{2hC - 5} = \dfrac{-2h^2}{2hC - 5}$

$k = \dfrac{-2h^2}{2hC - 5} \text{ or } \dfrac{2h^2}{5 - 2hC}$

10. Two answers: $\left\{-\dfrac{1}{2} \text{ and } 3\dfrac{1}{2}\right\}$

or $\left\{\dfrac{1}{2} \text{ and } -3\dfrac{1}{2}\right\}$

CHAPTER TEN DIAGNOSTIC TEST (page 374)

Following each problem number is the textbook section reference (in parentheses) where that kind of problem is discussed.

1. (1001) (a) The ordinate of $P(2, -4)$ is the second number, -4.
(b) The y-coordinate of $P(2, -4)$ is the second number, -4.
(c) The abscissa of $P(2, -4)$ is the first number, 2.

2.(a)(1001) $A(0, -3)$
$B(4, 0)$
$C(-3, 4)$

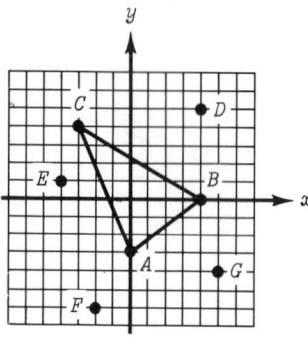

(b)(1001) $D(4, 5)$
$E(-4, 1)$
$F(-2, -6)$
$G(5, -4)$

3. (1002) For all points on this line, $x = -2$.

For all points on this line, $x = -2$

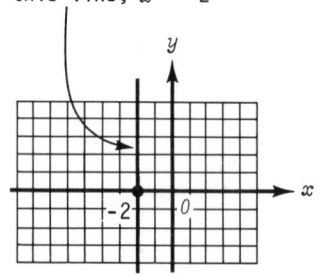

4. (1002) $x + y = 3$
If $x = 0$, $0 + y = 3$; therefore, the y-intercept is $(0, 3)$. If $y = 0$, $x + 0 = 3$; therefore, the x-intercept is $(3, 0)$.

Draw the line through $(0, 3)$ and $(3, 0)$.

x	y
0	3
3	0

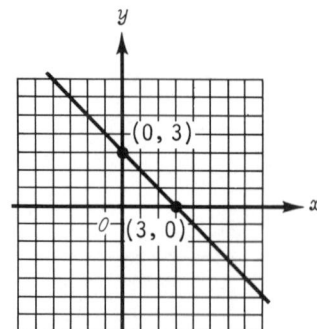

5. (1002) $2x - y = 4$
If $x = 0$, $2(0) - y = 4$
$y = -4$
If $y = 0$, $2x - 0 = 4$
$x = 2$

x	y
0	-4
2	0

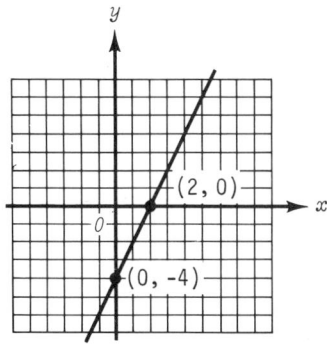

(2, 0)

0

(0, -4)

6. (1002) $4x + 5y = 18$

If $x = 0$, $4(0) + 5y = 18$

$$y = \frac{18}{5} = 3\frac{3}{5}$$

If $y = 0$, $4x + 5(0) = 18$

$$x = \frac{18}{4} = 4\frac{1}{2}$$

x	y
0	$3\frac{3}{5}$
$4\frac{1}{2}$	0

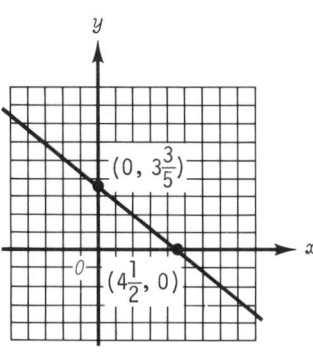

$(0, 3\frac{3}{5})$

0   $(4\frac{1}{2}, 0)$

7. (1004) $y = x^2 + x - 6$

$y = (-4)^2 + (-4) - 6 = 6$
$y = (-3)^2 + (-3) - 6 = 0$
$y = (-2)^2 + (-2) - 6 = -4$
$y = (-1)^2 + (-1) - 6 = -6$
$y = (0)^2 + (0) - 6 = -6$
$y = (1)^2 + (1) - 6 = -4$
$y = (2)^2 + (2) - 6 = 0$
$y = (3)^2 + (3) - 6 = 6$

x	y
-4	6
-3	0
-2	-4
-1	-6
0	-6
1	-4
2	0
3	6

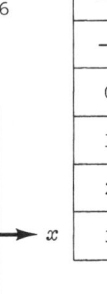

0

8. (1006) Boundary line: $3x - 2y \leq 6$

If $x = 0$, $3(0) - 2y = 6 \Rightarrow y = -3$
If $y = 0$, $3x - 2(0) = 6 \Rightarrow x = 2$

<u>Boundary line solid</u>, because equality included.

$$3x - 2y \leq 6$$

<u>Correct half-plane</u> includes (0, 0), because

$$3x - 2y \leq 6$$
$$3(0) - 2(0) \leq 6$$
$$0 \leq 6$$

is true.

x	y
0	-3
2	0

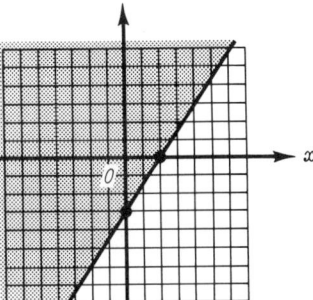

0

9. (1005)
$$\begin{array}{rcl} 5x - 2 & \leq & 10 - x \\ +x & & + x \\ \hline 6x - 2 & \leq & 10 \\ + 2 & & +2 \\ \hline 6x & \leq & 12 \\ \frac{6x}{6} & \leq & \frac{12}{6} \\ x & \leq & 2 \end{array}$$

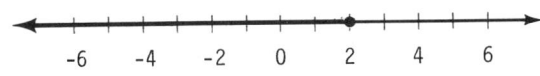

-6   -4   -2   0   2   4   6

10. (1003) $A(-4, 2)$, $B(1, -3)$

(a) $m = \dfrac{-3 - 2}{1 - (-4)} = \dfrac{-5}{5} = -1$

(b)
$$y - y_1 = m(x - x_1)$$
$$y - (-3) = -1(x - 1)$$
$$y + 3 = -x + 1$$
$$x + y + 2 = 0$$

<u>EXERCISES 1101, SET I</u>   (page 381)

1. (1) $2x + y = 6$
   (2) $2x - y = -2$

   (1) intercepts (0, 6), (3, 0)
   (2) intercepts (0, 2), (-1, 0)

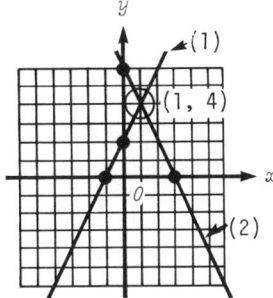

(1)

(1, 4)

0   x

(2)

2.

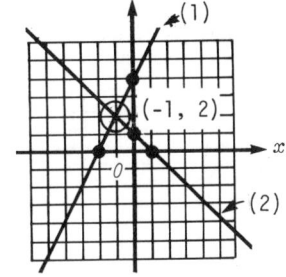

(1)

(-1, 2)

0

(2)

3. (1) $x - 2y = -6$
   (2) $4x + 3y = 20$

   (1) intercepts $(-6, 0)$, $(0, 3)$

   (2) intercepts $(5, 0)$, $(0, 6\frac{2}{3})$

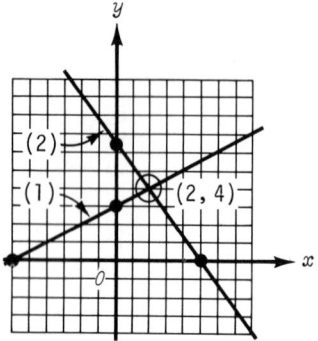

4.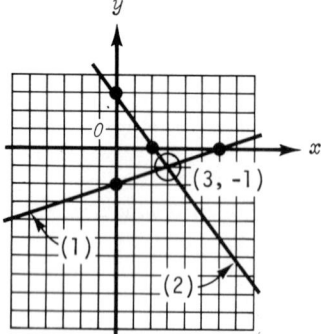

5. (1) $x + 2y = 0$
   (2) $x - 2y = -2$

   (1)

x	y
0	0
2	-1

   (2)

x	y
0	1
-2	0

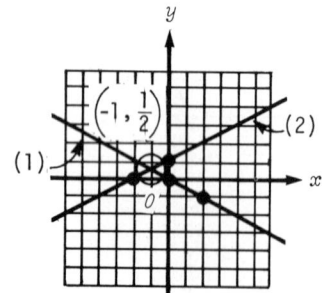

6.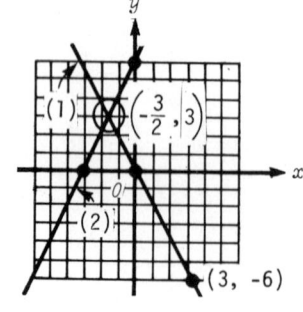

7. (1) $3x - 2y = -9$
   (2) $x + y = 2$

   (1) Intercepts $(-3, 0)$, $(0, 4\frac{1}{2})$

   (2) Intercepts $(2, 0)$, $(0, 2)$

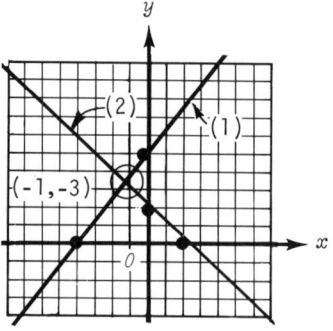

8.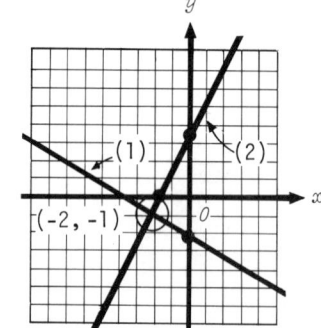

9. (1) $10x - 4y = 20$
   (2) $6y - 15x = -30$

   (1) intercepts $(2, 0)$, $(0, -5)$
   (2) intercepts $(2, 0)$, $(0, -5)$

   Since both lines have the same intercepts, they are the same line.

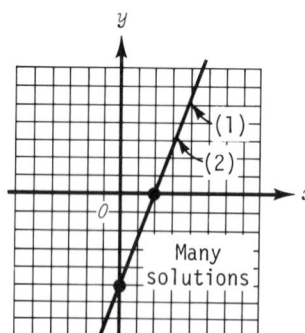

   Many solutions

10.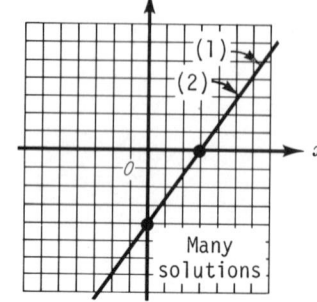

   Many solutions

11. (1) $2x - 4y = -2$
     (2) $-3x + 6y = 12$

(1)

x	y
-1	0
-3	-1
4	$\frac{5}{2}$

(2)

x	y
0	2
-4	0
3	$\frac{7}{2}$

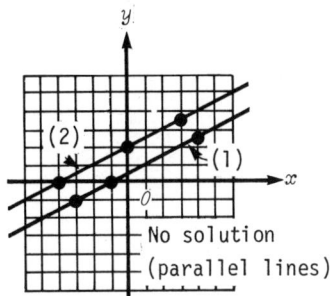

No solution
(parallel lines)

12.

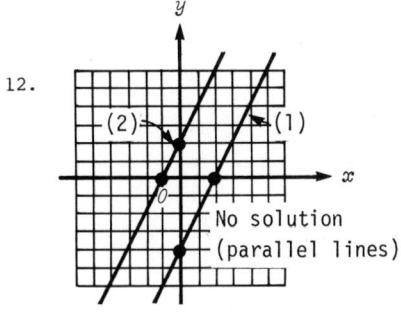

No solution
(parallel lines)

EXERCISES 1102, SET I (page 387)

1. (1) $2x - y = -4$
    (2) $\underline{x + y = -2}$
         $3x \quad\;\; = -6$
         $\quad\;\; x = -2$

    Substituting $x = -2$
    into equation (2),

    (2) $x + y = -2$
         $-2 + y = -2$
         $\quad\;\; y = 0$

    Solution: (-2, 0)

2. (2, 2)

3. (1) $x - 2y = 10$
         $\underline{x + y = 4}$
         $-3y = 6$
         $\quad y = -2$

    Substituting $y = -2$
    into equation (2),

    (2) $x + y = 4$
         $x - 2 = 4$
         $\quad x = 6$

    Solution: (6, -2)

4. (0, 1)

5. (1) $x - 3y = 6$
         $\underline{4x + 3y = 9}$
         $5x \quad\;\; = 15$
         $\quad\; x = 3$

    Substituting $x = 3$
    into equation (1),

    (1) $x - 3y = 6$
         $3 - 3y = 6$
         $\quad -3y = 3$
         $\quad\;\; y = -1$

    Solution: (3, -1)

6. (1, 0)

7. 2] $1x + 1y = 2$ $\Rightarrow$ $2x + 2y = 4$
    1] $3x - 2y = -9$ $\Rightarrow$ $\underline{3x - 2y = -9}$
         $5x \qquad\; = -5$
         $\quad\; x = -1$

8. (-2, -1)

    Substituting $x = -1$ into equa-
    tion (1),

    (1) $x + y = 2$
         $-1 + y = 2$
         $\quad\;\; y = 3$

    Solution: (-1, 3)

9. 1] $1x + 2y = 0$ $\Rightarrow$ $1x + 2y = 0$
    2] $2x - 1y = 0$ $\Rightarrow$ $\underline{4x - 2y = 0}$
         $5x \qquad\; = 0$
         $\quad\; x = 0$

10. (0, 0)

    Substituting $x = 0$ into equa-
    tion (2),

    (2) $2x - y = 0$
         $2(0) - y = 0$
         $\quad -y = 0$
         $\quad\;\; y = 0$

    Solution: (0, 0)

11. 3] $4x + 3y = 2$ $\Rightarrow$ $12x + 9y = 6$
     4] $3x + 5y = -4$ $\Rightarrow$ $\underline{12x + 20y = -16}$
          $-11y = 22$
          $\quad\; y = -2$

12. (3, -2)

    Substituting $y = -2$ into equation (1),

    (1) $4x + 3y = 2$
         $4x + 3(-2) = 2$
         $4x - 6 = 2$
         $4x = 8$
         $\quad x = 2$

    Solution: (2, -2)

13. 9] 3] $6x - 10y = 6$ $\Rightarrow$ $18x - 30y = 18$
     6] 2] $9x - 15y = -4$ $\Rightarrow$ $\underline{18x - 30y = -8}$
            $0 \neq 26$

    Inconsistent (no solution)

14. Inconsistent (no solution)

15. 2] $3x - 5y = -2$ $\Rightarrow$ $6x - 10y = -4$
     1] $-6x + 10y = 4$ $\Rightarrow$ $\underline{-6x + 10y = 4}$
          $0 = 0$

    Dependent (many solutions)

    Let $x = 0$ in equation (1).

    (1) $3x - 5y = -2$
         $3(0) - 5y = -2$
         $-5y = -2$
         $\quad y = \frac{2}{5}$

    One of the many solutions is $(0, \frac{2}{5})$.

16. Dependent (many solutions)

17. 82] $73x - 49y = 38$ $\Rightarrow$ $5986x - 4018y = 3116$
     49] $56x + 82y = 91$ $\Rightarrow$ $\underline{2744x + 4018y = 4459}$
           $8730x \qquad\qquad = 7575$
           $\quad x \doteq 0.86770$

     56] $73x - 49y = 38$ $\Rightarrow$ $4088x - 2744y = 2128$
     73] $56x + 82y = 91$ $\Rightarrow$ $\underline{4088x + 5986y = 6643}$
           $8730y = 4515$
           $\quad y \doteq 0.51718$

18. $\doteq$ (-2.35, -5.81)

1. (1) $2x - 3y = 1$
    (2) $x = y + 2$

    Substitute $y + 2$ in place of
    x in equation (1); we have

    (1) $2x - 3y = 1$
              $2(y + 2) - 3y = 1$
               $2y + 4 - 3y = 1$
                          $-y = -3$
                           $y = 3$

    Substitute $y = 3$ in $x = y + 2$

    $x = 3 + 2 = 5$

    Solution: (5, 3)

2.   (2, 7)

3. (1) $3x + 4y = 2$
    (2) $y = x - 3$

    Substituting $x - 3$ in place of
    y in equation (1); we have

    $3x + 4(x - 3) = 2$
    $3x + 4x - 12 = 2$
             $7x = 14$
              $x = 2$

    Substituting $x = 2$ in (2)

    $y = x - 3 = 2 - 3 = -1$

    Solution: (2, -1)

4.   (1, 3)

5. (1) $4x + y = 2 \Rightarrow y = 2 - 4x$
    (2) $7x + 3y = 1$

    Substitute $2 - 4x$ in place of y
    in equation (2):

    (2) $7x + 3y = 1$
            $7x + 3(2 - 4x) = 1$
            $7x + 6 - 12x = 1$
                      $-5x = -5$
                        $x = 1$

    Substitute $x = 1$ in

    $y = 2 - 4x$
    $y = 2 - 4(1) = -2$

    Solution: (1, -2)

6.   (3, -2)

7. (1) $4x - y = 3 \Rightarrow y = 4x - 3$
    (2) $8x - 2y = 6$

    Substitute $4x - 3$ in place of y in (2):

    (2) $8x - 2y = 6$
            $8x - 2(4x - 3) = 6$
             $8x - 8x + 6 = 6$
                        $6 = 6$
    Therefore, *any* ordered pair that satisfies (1)
    or (2) is a solution.
    Dependent (many solutions)

8. *Any* ordered pair that satisfies (1) or (2) is a
    solution.
    Dependent (many solutions)

9. (1) $x + 3 = 0 \Rightarrow x = -3$
    (2) $3x - 2y = 6$

    Substitute $x = -3$ into (2):
    (2) $3x - 2y = 6$
           $3(-3) - 2y = 6$
             $-9 - 2y = 6$
                  $-2y = 15$
                    $y = \frac{15}{-2} = -7\frac{1}{2}$

    Solution: $(-3, -7\frac{1}{2})$

10. $(-\frac{3}{5}, 4)$

11. (1) $8x + 4y = 7$
     (2) $3x + 6y = 6 \Rightarrow 3x = 6 - 6y$
                  $x = \frac{6 - 6y}{3} = 2 - 2y$

     Substitute $2 - 2y$ in (1) for x:

     (1) $8x + 4y = 7$
             $8(2 - 2y) + 4y = 7$
              $16 - 16y + 4y = 7$
                      $-12y = -9 \Rightarrow y = \frac{3}{4}$

     Substitute $y = \frac{3}{4}$ in $x = 2 - 2y$

                  $x = 2 - 2\left(\frac{3}{4}\right) = \frac{1}{2}$

     $\left(\frac{1}{2}, \frac{3}{4}\right)$ is the solution.

12. $\left(\frac{3}{5}, \frac{1}{4}\right)$

13. (1) $3x - 2y = 8$
     (2) $2y - 3x = 4 \Rightarrow 2y = 3x + 4$
                  $y = \frac{3x + 4}{2}$

     Substitute $\frac{3x + 4}{2}$ in (1) for y:

     (1) $3x - 2y = 8$
             $3x - 2\left(\frac{3x + 4}{2}\right) = 8$
             $3x - 3x - 4 = 8$
                       $-4 \neq 8$

     Inconsistent (no solution)

14. Inconsistent (no solution)

15. (1) $8x + 5y = 2$
     (2) $7x + 4y = 1 \Rightarrow 4y = 1 - 7x$
                  $y = \frac{1 - 7x}{4}$

     Substitute $\frac{1 - 7x}{4}$ in (1) for y:

                  $8x + 5\left(\frac{1 - 7x}{4}\right) = 2$

     $\frac{4}{1} \cdot \frac{8x}{1} + \frac{4}{1} \cdot \frac{5}{1}\left(\frac{1 - 7x}{4}\right) = \frac{4}{1} \cdot \frac{2}{1}$

                  $32x + 5 - 35x = 8$
                         $-3x = 3$
                           $x = \frac{3}{-3} = -1$

     Substitute $x = -1$ in $y = \frac{1 - 7x}{4}$

                  $y = \frac{1 - 7(-1)}{4} = \frac{8}{4} = 2$

     (-1, 2) is the solution

16. (4, 1)

17. (1) $4x + 4y = 3 \Rightarrow 4x = 3 - 4y$
     (2) $6x + 12y = -6$
                  $x = \frac{3 - 4y}{4}$

     Substitute $\frac{3 - 4y}{4}$ in (2) for x:

     (2) $6x + 12y = -6$
             $6\left(\frac{3 - 4y}{4}\right) + 12y = -6$

     LCD = 2

$$\frac{\cancel{2}}{1} \cdot 3\left(\frac{3 - 4y}{\cancel{2}}\right) + 2(12y) = 2(-6)$$

$$9 - 12y + 24y = -12$$
$$12y = -21$$
$$y = -\frac{21}{12} = -\frac{7}{4} = -1\frac{3}{4}$$

Substitute $y = -\frac{7}{4}$ in $x = \frac{3 - 4y}{4}$

$$x = \frac{3 - 4\left(-\frac{7}{4}\right)}{4} = \frac{3 + 7}{4} = \frac{10}{4} = 2\frac{1}{2}$$

Solution: $\left(2\frac{1}{2},\ -1\frac{3}{4}\right)$

18. $\left(2\frac{1}{2},\ -2\frac{1}{3}\right)$

19. 56] $44x + 75y = 63 \Rightarrow 2464x + 4200y = 3528$
    75] $91x - 56y = 28 \Rightarrow \underline{6825x - 4200y = 2100}$
    $9289x \qquad\qquad = 5628$
    $x \doteq 0.60588$

    91] $44x + 75y = 63 \Rightarrow 4004x + 6825y = 5733$
    44] $91x - 56y = 28 \Rightarrow \underline{4004x - 2464y = 1232}$
    $9289y = 4501$
    $y \doteq 0.48455$

    Solution $\doteq$ (0.60588, 0.48455)

20. $\doteq$ (1.69, 0.616)

EXERCISES 1104, SET I (page 396)

1. Let x = larger number
   y = smaller number

   (1) The sum of two numbers is 30.
   $x + y \qquad = 30$

   (2) Their difference is 12.
   $x - y \qquad = 12$

   Using addition-subtraction,

   (1) $x + y = 30$
       $\underline{x - y = 12}$
       $2x \qquad = 42$
       $x = 21$ (larger number)

   Substituting $x = 21$ into (1),

   (1) $x + y = 30$
       $21 + y = 30$
       $y = 9$ (smaller number)

2. {36, 14}

3. x = larger angle
   y = smaller angle

   (1) The sum of two angles is 90°.
   $x + y \qquad = 90$

   (2) Their difference is 40°.
   $x - y \qquad = 40$

   Using addition-subtraction,

   (1) $x + y = 90$
       $\underline{x - y = 40}$
       $2x \qquad = 130$
       $x = 65°$ (larger angle)

   Substituting $x = 65$ into (1),

   (1) $x + y = 90$
       $65 + y = 90$
       $y = 25°$ (smaller angle)

4. {125°, 55°}

5. x = smaller number
   y = larger number

   (1) Twice the smaller plus three times the larger is 34.
       $2x \quad + \quad 3y \quad = 34$

   (2) Five times the smaller minus twice the larger is 9.
       $5x \quad - \quad 2y \quad = 9$

   Using addition-subtraction:

   (1) 2] $2x + 3y = 34 \Rightarrow 4x + 6y = 68$
   (2) 3] $5x - 2y = 9 \Rightarrow \underline{15x - 6y = 27}$
   $19x \qquad = 95$
   $x = 5$ (smaller)

   Substituting $x = 5$ in (1),

   (1) $2x + 3y = 34$
       $2(5) + 3y = 34$
       $10 + 3y = 34$
       $3y = 24$
       $y = 8$ (larger)

6. {7, 4}

7. a = lb of almonds
   h = lb of hazel nuts

   (1) $a + h = 20 \Rightarrow a = 20 - h$
   (2) $85a + 140h = 1975$

   Substituting $20 - h$ in (2) for a,

   (2) $85a + 140h = 1975$
       $85(20 - h) + 140h = 1975$
       $1700 - 85h + 140h = 1975$
       $55h = 275$
       $h = 5$ (lb hazel nuts)

   Substituting $h = 5$ in $a = 20 - h$,

   $a = 20 - 5 = 15$ (lb almonds)

8. 30 lb grade A, 70 lb grade B.

9. x = no. of 10-cent stamps
   y = no. of 12-cent stamps

   (1) $x + y = 22 \Rightarrow x = 22 - y$
   (2) $10x + 12y = 236$

   Substitute $22 - y$ in (2) for x:

   (2) $10x + 12y = 236$
       $10(22 - y) + 12y = 236$
       $220 - 10y + 12y = 236$
       $2y = 16$
       $y = 8$ (12-cent stamps)

   Substitute $y = 8$ in $x = 22 - y$

   $x = 22 - 8 = 14$ (10-cent stamps)

10. 20 2-cent stamps, 30 10-cent stamps.

11.

$2W + 2L$ = Perimeter

(1) $2W + 2L = 19$
(2) $L = W + 1.5$

Substituting $W + 1.5$ in equation (1) for L, we get
$$2W + 2L = 19$$
$$2W + 2(W + 1.5) = 19$$
$$2W + 2W + 3 = 19$$
$$4W = 16$$
$$W = 4$$

(continued)

Substituting $W = 4$ in equation (2), we get

$L = W + 1.5$
$\quad = (4) + 1.5$
$\quad = 5.5 = 5$ ft 6 in

12. width = 5 ft
   length = 7 ft 6 in

13. Let n = numerator
   and d = denominator.

   Then

   (1)$\quad \dfrac{n}{d} = \dfrac{2}{3}$ and $\quad$ (2)$\quad \dfrac{n + 4}{d - 2} = \dfrac{6}{7}$

   $\qquad 2d = 3n \qquad\qquad\qquad 6(d - 2) = 7(n + 4)$

   $\qquad d = \dfrac{3n}{2} \qquad\qquad\qquad\, 6d - 12 = 7n + 28$

   $\qquad\qquad\qquad$ (3)$\qquad$ (3)$6d = 7n + 40$

   Substitute $\dfrac{3n}{2}$ for d in (3) $\Rightarrow 6\left(\dfrac{3n}{2}\right) = 7n + 40$

   $\qquad\qquad\qquad\qquad\qquad\qquad\qquad 9n = 7n + 40$
   $\qquad\qquad\qquad\qquad\qquad\qquad\qquad 2n = 40$
   $\qquad\qquad\qquad\qquad\qquad\qquad\qquad\; n = 20$

   Substitute $n = 20$ in $d = \dfrac{3n}{2}$

   $\qquad\qquad\qquad\qquad\quad = \dfrac{3(20)}{2}$
   $\qquad\qquad\qquad\qquad\quad = 30$

   Therefore, the original fraction is $\dfrac{20}{30}$.

14. $\dfrac{36}{48}$

15. t = cost of tie
   p = cost of pin

   (1) A tie and a pin cost $1.10.
   $\qquad t \quad + \quad p \quad = \quad 110$

   (2) The tie costs $1 more than the pin.
   $\qquad t \quad = \quad 100 \quad + \quad p$

   Substitute $100 + p$ in (1) for t:

   (1)$\qquad\qquad t + p = 110$
   $\qquad 100 + p + p = 110$
   $\qquad\qquad\qquad 2p = 10$
   $\qquad\qquad\qquad\; p = 5$ (pin)
   $\qquad\qquad\qquad\; t = 100 + p = 100 + 5 = 105$ (tie)

   Pin costs 5¢
   Tie costs $1.05

16. 7 on upper branch
   5 on lower branch

17. Let p = speed of plane in still air
   and w = speed of wind

	d	$=$	r	$\cdot$	t
Against wind	1200		$p - w$		.2.5
With wind	1200		$p + w$		2

   $t \cdot r = d$

   $2.5(p - w) = 1200 \Rightarrow$ (1) $p - w = \dfrac{1200}{2.5} = 480$

   $2(p + w) = 1200 \Rightarrow$ (2) $p + w = \dfrac{1200}{2} = 600$
   $\qquad\qquad\qquad\qquad\qquad\overline{\qquad\qquad\qquad\qquad\qquad\quad}$
   $\qquad\qquad\qquad\qquad\qquad\; 2p \qquad\qquad\quad = 1080$
   $\qquad\qquad\qquad\qquad\qquad\qquad\qquad\; p = 540$ mph

   Substitute $p = 540$ into (2): $\;p + w = 600$
   $\qquad\qquad\qquad\qquad\qquad\qquad\; 540 + w = 600$
   $\qquad\qquad\qquad\qquad\qquad\qquad\qquad\;\; w = 60$ mph

18. Jerry's average speed = 10 mph
   Wind's average speed = 5 mph

REVIEW EXERCISES 1105, SET I (page 399)

1. (1) $x + y = 6$
   (2) $x - y = 4$

   (1) intercepts (6, 0), (0, 6)
   (2) intercepts (4, 0), (0, -4)

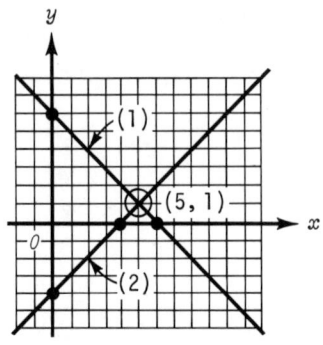

2.

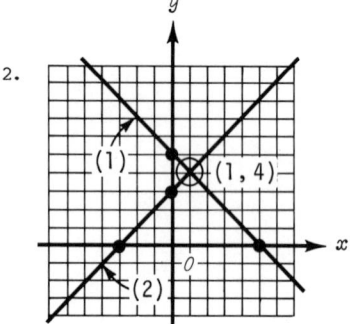

3. (1) $4x + 5y = 22$
   (2) $3x - 2y = 5$

   (1) intercepts $\left(5\frac{1}{2}, 0\right)$, $\left(0, 4\frac{2}{5}\right)$
   (2) intercepts $\left(1\frac{2}{3}, 0\right)$, $\left(0, -2\frac{1}{2}\right)$

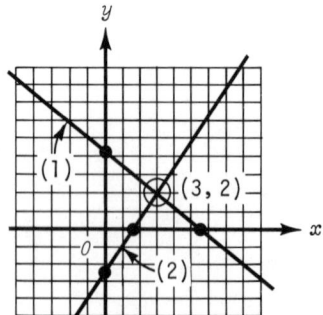

4.

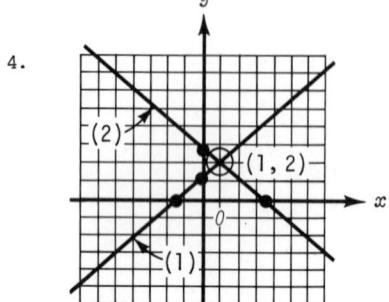

5. (1) $2x - 3y = 3$
    (2) $3y - 2x = 6$

    (1) intercepts $\left(1\frac{1}{2}, 0\right)$, $(0, -1)$
    (2) intercepts $(-3, 0)$, $(0, 2)$

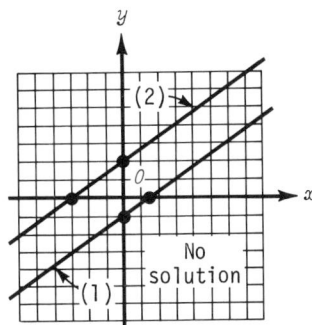

6.

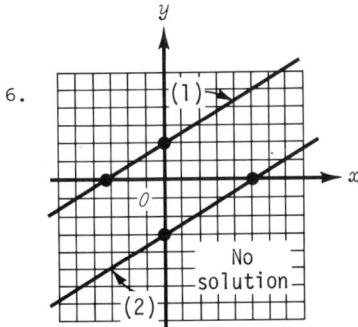

7. (1) $8x - 12y = 4$
    (2) $6x - 9y = 3$

    (1) intercepts $\left(\frac{1}{2}, 0\right)$, $\left(0, -\frac{1}{3}\right)$
    (2) intercepts $\left(\frac{1}{2}, 0\right)$, $\left(0, -\frac{1}{3}\right)$

    Since both lines have the same intercepts, they are the same line.
    Since the intercepts are so close together, we choose a third point. If $x = 5$, then $y = 3$.

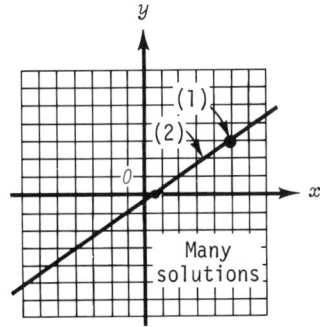

8.

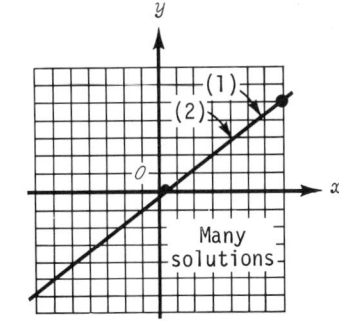

9. 3] $1x + 5y = 11 \Rightarrow 3x + 15y = 33$ 10. $(\smile, 2)$
    1] $3x + 4y = 11 \Rightarrow \underline{3x + 4y = 11}$
    $ 11y = 22$
    $ y = 2$

    Substituting $y = 2$ in (1):

    (1) $x + 5y = 11$
    $ x + 5(2) = 11$
    $ x + 10 = 11$
    $ x = 1$

    Solution: $(1, 2)$

11. 3] $4x - 8y = 4 \Rightarrow 12x - 24y = 12$
     4] $3x - 6y = 3 \Rightarrow \underline{12x - 24y = 12}$
     $ 0 = 0$

     Dependent (many solutions)

      Let $y = 0$ in (1):
     (1) $ 4x - 8y = 4$
     $ 4x - 8(0) = 4$
     $ 4x = 4$
     $ x = 1$

     One of many solutions is $(1, 0)$.

12. Dependent (many solutions)

13. (1) $3x - 5y = 15 \Rightarrow 3x - 5y = 15$
     (2) $5y - 3x = 8 \Rightarrow \underline{-3x + 5y = 8}$
     $ 0 \neq 23$

     Inconsistent (no solution)

14. Inconsistent (no solution)

15. (1) $4x - 16y = 4$
     (2) $3x - 12y = 3 \Rightarrow 3x = 12y + 3$
     $ x = \dfrac{12y + 3}{3} = 4y + 1$

     Substitute $4y + 1$ for x in (1):

     (1) $ 4x - 16y = 4$
     $ 4(4y + 1) - 16y = 4$
     $ 16y + 4 - 16y = 4$
     $ 4 = 4$

     Dependent (many solutions)

     Let $y = 0$ in (2):
     (2) $ 3x - 12y = 3$
     $ 3x - 12(0) = 3$
     $ 3x = 3$
     $ x = 1$

     One of the many solutions is $(1, 0)$.

16. Dependent (many solutions)

17. (1) $x = y + 2$ 18. $(4, 9)$
     (2) $4x - 5y = 3$

     Substitute $y + 2$ in place of x in (2):

     (2) $ 4x - 5y = 3$
     $ 4(y + 2) - 5y = 3$
     $ 4y + 8 - 5y = 3$
     $ -y = -5 \Rightarrow y = 5$

     Substitute $y = 5$ in $x = y + 2$
     $ x = 5 + 2 = 7$

     Solution: $(7, 5)$

19. (1) $4x + 6y = -9$
     (2) $2x - 8y = 23 \Rightarrow 2x = 8y + 23$
     $ x = \dfrac{8y + 23}{2}$

Substitute $\dfrac{8y + 23}{2}$ for x in (1):

(1) $4x + 6y = -9$

$$4\left(\dfrac{8y + 23}{\not{2}}\right) + 6y = -9$$

$$16y + 46 + 6y = -9$$

$$22y = -55$$

$$y = -\dfrac{5}{2}$$

Substitute $y = -\dfrac{5}{2}$ in $x = \dfrac{8y + 23}{2}$:

$$x = \dfrac{\overset{4}{\not{8}}\left(-\dfrac{5}{\not{2}}\right) + 23}{2} = \dfrac{-20 + 23}{2} = \dfrac{3}{2}$$

Solution: $\left(\dfrac{3}{2},\ -\dfrac{5}{2}\right)$ or $\left(1\dfrac{1}{2},\ -2\dfrac{1}{2}\right)$

20. $\left(-\dfrac{7}{2},\ \dfrac{9}{2}\right)$ or $\left(-3\dfrac{1}{2},\ 4\dfrac{1}{2}\right)$

21. 8] 2] $4x + 3y = 8 \Rightarrow 8x + 6y = 16$
     4] 1] $8x + 7y = 12 \Rightarrow \underline{8x + 7y = 12}$
     $ y = -4$

Substitute $y = -4$ in (1):

(1) $4x + 3y = 8$
     $4x + 3(-4) = 8$
     $4x - 12 = 8$
     $4x = 20$
     $x = 5$

Solution: (5, -4)

22. (-3, -2)

23. Let x = larger number
     y = smaller number

(1) The sum of two numbers is 84.
     $x + y = 84$

(2) Their difference is 22.
     $x - y = 22$

Using addition-subtraction,

(1) $x + y = 84$
(2) $\underline{x - y = 22}$
     $2x = 106$
     $x = 53$ (larger number)

Substitute $x = 53$ in (1):

(1) $x + y = 84$
     $53 + y = 84$
     $y = 31$ (smaller number)

24. {23, -17}

25. x = hours as tutor
     y = hours as waiter

(1) Brian worked at two jobs for a total of 32 hours.
     $x + y = 32$

(2) He received a total of $86.60.
     $220x + 310y = 8660$

(1) $x + y = 32 \Rightarrow x = 32 - y$

Substitute $32 - y$ in (2) for x:

(2) $220x + 310y = 8660$
     $220(32 - y) + 310y = 8660$
     $7040 - 220y + 310y = 8660$
     $90y = 1620$
     $y = 18$ hours

Substitute $y = 18$ in $x = 32 - y$:

$x = 32 - 18 = 14$ hours.

26. 10 hours as a lab assistant
     16 hours as clerk-typist

27. Let x = number of $10 rolls
     y = number of $8 rolls

(1) The total number of rolls is 80.
     $x + y = 80$

(2) The total amount paid for stamps is $7.30.
     $10x + 8y = 730¢$

(1) $x + y = 80 \Rightarrow x = 80 - y$

Substitute $80 - y$ in (2) for x:

(2) $10x + 8y = 730$
     $10(80 - y) + 8y = 730$
     $800 - 10y + 8y = 730$
     $-2y = -70$
     $y = 35$ ($8 rolls)

Substitute $y = 35$ in $x = 80 - y$:

$x = 80 - 35 = 45$ ($10 rolls)

28. 12 boxes letter size
     8 boxes legal size

CUMULATIVE REVIEW EXERCISES:
CHAPTERS 1-10 (page 401)

1. $\left(\dfrac{24w^{-2}z^4}{16w^{\frac{3}{2}}}\right)^{-3} = \left(\dfrac{3w^{-3}z^4}{2}\right)^{-3}$

    $= \dfrac{3^{-3}w^9z^{-12}}{2^{-3}} = \dfrac{2^3w^9}{3^3z^{12}} = \dfrac{8w^9}{27z^{12}}$

2. $1322.50

3. $\dfrac{2 + 5x}{6x - 1} = \dfrac{3}{4}$ A proportion

    $4(2 + 5x) = 3(6x - 1)$
    $8 + 20x = 18x - 3$
    $2x = -11$
    $x = -\dfrac{11}{2}$ or $-5\dfrac{1}{2}$

4. -5

5. $\dfrac{1 + a}{2 - 3a} + \dfrac{2 + a}{4a}$ LCD $= 4a(2 - 3a)$

    $\dfrac{1 + a}{2 - 3a} \cdot \dfrac{4a}{4a} + \dfrac{2 + a}{4a} \cdot \dfrac{2 - 3a}{2 - 3a}$

    $\dfrac{4a + 4a^2}{4a(2 - 3a)} + \dfrac{4 - 4a - 3a^2}{4a(2 - 3a)}$

    $\dfrac{4a + 4a^2 + 4 - 4a - 3a^2}{4a(2 - 3a)}$

    $\dfrac{a^2 + 4}{4a(2 - 3a)}$

6.

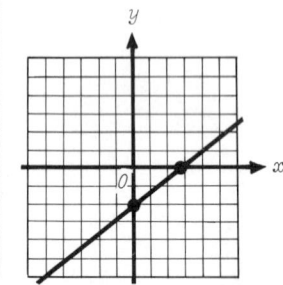

7. $4y = x^2 \Rightarrow y = \frac{1}{4}x^2$

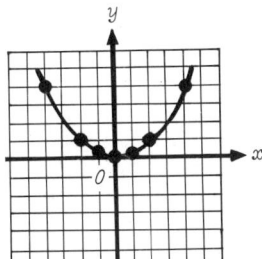

x	y
-4	4
-2	1
-1	$\frac{1}{4}$
0	0
1	$\frac{1}{4}$
2	1
4	4

8. $x \le 5$

9. $3x - 4y > 12$
   Boundary line: $\quad 3x - 4y = 12$
   Let $x = 0$: $\qquad 3(0) - 4y = 12$
   $\qquad\qquad\qquad\qquad\quad y = -3$

   $\qquad\qquad\qquad\quad 3x - 4y = 12$
   Let $y = 0$: $\qquad 3x - 4(0) = 12$
   $\qquad\qquad\qquad\qquad\quad x = 4$

x	y
0	-3
4	0

   Correct half plane does not include
   the origin because:

   $\qquad 3(0) - 4(0) \not> 12$
   $\qquad\qquad\qquad\quad 0 \not> 12$

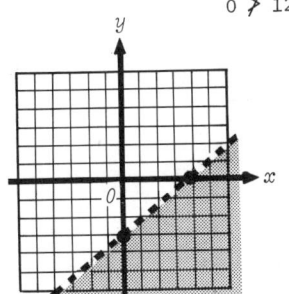

x	y
0	-3
4	0

10. $3x + 7y - 5 = 0$

CHAPTER ELEVEN DIAGNOSTIC TEST (page 402)

Following each problem number is the textbook section
reference (in parentheses) where that kind of problem
is discussed.

1. (1101) (1) $\quad 3x + 2y = 2$
   (2) $\qquad x - y = 4$

   (1) intercepts: $\left(\frac{2}{3}, 0\right)$, $(0, 1)$
   (2) intercepts: $(4, 0)$, $(0, -4)$

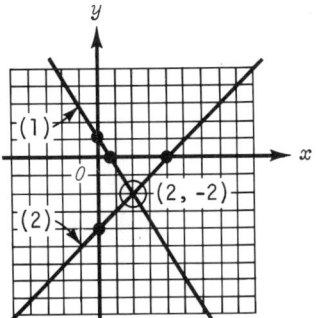

2. (1102) (1) $\quad 2x + y = 7$
   (2) $\quad \underline{3x - y = 3}$
   $\qquad\qquad 5x \quad\;\; = 10$
   $\qquad\qquad\quad\; x \;= 2$

   Substitute $x = 2$ into (1):

   (1) $\qquad 2x + y = 7$
   $\qquad\qquad 2(2) + y = 7$
   $\qquad\qquad\quad 4 + y = 7$
   $\qquad\qquad\qquad\quad y = 3$

   Solution: $(2, 3)$

3. (1102) 3] $3x - 4y = 1 \Rightarrow 9x - 12y = 3$
   4] $5x - 3y = 9 \Rightarrow \underline{20x - 12y = 36}$
   $\qquad\qquad\qquad\qquad\quad 11x \qquad\;\; = 33$
   $\qquad\qquad\qquad\qquad\qquad\quad x = 3$

   Substitute $x = 3$ into (1):

   (1) $\qquad 3x - 4y = 1$
   $\qquad\qquad 3(3) - 4y = 1$
   $\qquad\qquad\; 9 - 4y = 1$
   $\qquad\qquad\qquad -4y = -8$
   $\qquad\qquad\qquad\quad\; y = 2$

   Solution: $(3, 2)$

4. (1103) (1) $\quad 3x - 5y = 14$
   (2) $\quad x = y + 2$

   Substitute $y + 2$ in place of x in (1):

   (1) $\qquad\qquad 3x - 5y = 14$
   $\qquad\qquad 3(y + 2) - 5y = 14$
   $\qquad\qquad 3y + 6 - 5y = 14$
   $\qquad\qquad\qquad\quad -2y = 8$
   $\qquad\qquad\qquad\qquad\; y = -4$

   Substitute $y = -4$ in $x = y + 2$:

   $x = -4 + 2 = -2$

   Solution: $(-2, -4)$

5. (1103) (1) $\quad 3x + 4y = 1$
   (2) $\quad 2x - 5y = 16 \Rightarrow 2x = 5y + 16$
   $\qquad\qquad\qquad\qquad\qquad\quad x = \dfrac{5y + 16}{2}$

   Substitute $\dfrac{5y + 16}{2}$ for x in (1):

   (1) $\qquad\qquad 3x + 4y = 1$
   $\qquad\qquad 3\left(\dfrac{5y + 16}{2}\right) + 4y = 1$

   LCD = 2

   $\dfrac{2}{1} \cdot \dfrac{3}{1}\left(\dfrac{5y + 16}{2}\right) + 2 \cdot 4y = 2 \cdot 1$
   $\qquad\quad 15y + 48 + 8y = 2$
   $\qquad\qquad\qquad\quad 23y = -46$
   $\qquad\qquad\qquad\qquad y = -2$

Substitute $y = -2$ in $x = \dfrac{5y + 16}{2}$

$$x = \dfrac{5(-2) + 16}{2}$$

$$x = \dfrac{-10 + 16}{2} = \dfrac{6}{2} = 3$$

Solution: $(3, -2)$

6. (1102) $\begin{array}{l} 9] \\ 3] \end{array}$ $\begin{array}{l} 3] \\ 1] \end{array}$ $\begin{array}{l} 4x + 3y = 14 \Rightarrow 12x + 9y = 42 \\ 10x - 9y = 13 \Rightarrow \underline{10x - 9y = 13} \\ 22x = 55 \\ x = \dfrac{5}{2} \end{array}$

Substitute $x = \dfrac{5}{2}$ into (1):

(1) $\quad 4x + 3y = 14$

$$\overset{2}{\underset{1}{\cancel{4}}}\left(\dfrac{5}{\cancel{2}}\right) + 3y = 14$$

$$10 + 3y = 14$$

$$3y = 4$$

$$y = \dfrac{4}{3}$$

Solution: $\left(\dfrac{5}{2}, \dfrac{4}{3}\right)$

7. (1102)

(1) $\boxed{10}$ $\boxed{5}$ $6x - 9y = 2 \Rightarrow 30x - 45y = 10$

(2) $\boxed{6}$ $\boxed{3}$ $-10x + 15y = -5 \Rightarrow \underline{-30x + 45y = -15}$

$ 0 \neq -5$

Inconsistent (no solution)

8. (1104) Let x = larger number
$ y$ = smaller number

(1) The sum of two numbers is 18.
$ x + y = 18$

(2) Their difference is 42.
$ x - y = 42$

Using addition-subtraction:

(1) $\quad x + y = 18$
(2) $\quad \underline{x - y = 42}$
$ 2x = 60$
$ x = 30$ (larger number)

Substitute $x = 30$ in (1):

(1) $\quad x + y = 18$
$ 30 + y = 18$
$ y = -12$ (smaller number)

9. (1104)

Let x = number of classical records
$ y$ = number of pop records

(1)
Amount of money for classical records	+	Amount of money for pop records	=	Total amount spent
$299x$	+	$88y$	=	1953

(2)
Number of classical records	+	Number of pop records	=	Total records
x	+	y	=	15

Using substitution:

(1) $299x + 88y = 1953$
(2) $x + y = 15 \Rightarrow y = 15 - x$

Substitute $15 - x$ in place of y in (1):

$$299x + 88(15 - x) = 1953$$
$$299x + 1320 - 88x = 1953$$
$$211x + 1320 = 1953$$
$$211x = 633$$

Number of classical records = $x = 3$
Number of pop records = $y = 15 - x = 15 - 3 = 12$

10. (1104)

Length is 3 cm more than width.

(1) $\qquad L = 3 + W$
$ 2L + 2W = $ perimeter

(2) $\quad 2L + 2W = 102$

Substituting $3 + W$ for L in equation (2), we get

$$2L + 2W = 102$$
$$2(3 + W) + 2W = 102$$
$$6 + 2W + 2W = 102$$
$$4W = 96$$
$$W = 24$$

Substituting $W = 24$ in $\dot{L} = 3 + W$
$ = 3 + 24$
$ = 27$

Therefore, the dimensions are

length = 27 cm
width = 24 cm

EXERCISES 1201, SET I (page 408)

1. A rational number is any number that can be expressed in the form $\dfrac{a}{b}$, where a and b are integers and b is not zero. Therefore, $-5 = \dfrac{-5}{1}$; $\dfrac{3}{4}$; $2\dfrac{1}{2} = \dfrac{5}{2}$; $3.5 = \dfrac{7}{2}$; $\sqrt{4} = \dfrac{2}{1}$; and $3 = \dfrac{3}{1}$ are rational numbers.

2. $\sqrt{3}$
3. (a) 17
   (b) $x + 1$
4. (a) 15
   (b) $m - n$
5. 6, because $6^2 = 36$
6. 7
7. 49
8. 36
9. a
10. m^2
11. $a^2 b$
12. xy^2
13. $x - y$
14. $m + n$

EXERCISES 1202A, SET I (page 412)

1. 5
2. 10
3. 9
4. 8
5. $\sqrt{4x^2} = \sqrt{4}\ \sqrt{x^2}$
   $= 2x$
6. $3y$
7. $\sqrt{16z^4} = \sqrt{16}\ \sqrt{z^4}$
   $= 4z^2$
8. $5b^3$
9. $\sqrt{12} = \sqrt{4 \cdot 3} = \sqrt{4}\ \sqrt{3} = 2\sqrt{3}$
10. $2\sqrt{5}$
11. $\sqrt{18} = \sqrt{9 \cdot 2} = \sqrt{9}\ \sqrt{2} = 3\sqrt{2}$
12. $3\sqrt{5}$
13. $\sqrt{8} = \sqrt{4 \cdot 2} = \sqrt{4}\ \sqrt{2} = 2\sqrt{2}$
14. $4\sqrt{2}$
15. $\sqrt{x^3} = \sqrt{x^2 \cdot x} = \sqrt{x^2}\ \sqrt{x} = x\sqrt{x}$
16. $y^2\sqrt{y}$
17. $\sqrt{m^7} = \sqrt{m^6 \cdot m} = m^3\sqrt{m}$
18. $n^4\sqrt{n}$
19. $\sqrt{24} = \sqrt{4 \cdot 6} = \sqrt{4}\ \sqrt{6} = 2\sqrt{6}$
20. $3\sqrt{6}$
21. $\sqrt{6}\ \sqrt{6} = \sqrt{36} = 6$
22. 3
23. $\sqrt{4x}\ \sqrt{4x} = 4x$
24. $7y$
25. $\sqrt{a^2 b^3} = \sqrt{a^2 b^2 b} = \sqrt{a^2}\ \sqrt{b^2}\ \sqrt{b} = ab\sqrt{b}$
26. $c^2 d\sqrt{c}$
27. $\sqrt{40x^6 y^2} = \sqrt{4 \cdot 10 x^6 y^2} = \sqrt{4}\ \sqrt{10}\ \sqrt{x^6}\ \sqrt{y^2} = 2\sqrt{10}x^3 y$
28. $3\sqrt{15}a^3 b^4$

29. $\sqrt{60h^5k^4} = \sqrt{4 \cdot 15h^4hk^4} = 2h^2k^2\sqrt{15h}$

30. $3m^3n^3\sqrt{10m}$

31. First express 280 in prime factored form:

$$\begin{array}{r|l} 2 & 280 \\ 2 & 140 \\ 2 & 70 \\ 5 & 35 \\ & 7 \end{array} \quad 280 = 2^2 \cdot 2 \cdot 5 \cdot 7$$

$\sqrt{280y^5z^6} = \sqrt{2^2 \cdot 70 \cdot y^4 \cdot y \cdot z^6} = 2y^2z^3\sqrt{70y}$

32. $3g^4h^4\sqrt{30h}$

33. $\sqrt{500x^7y^9} = \sqrt{100 \cdot 5 \cdot x^6 \cdot x \cdot y^8 \cdot y} = 10x^3y^4\sqrt{5xy}$

34. $6x^5y^6\sqrt{6xy}$

35. $\sqrt{a+b}\,\sqrt{a+b} = a + b$

36. $m - n$

EXERCISES 1202B, SET I (page 414)

1. $\sqrt{\dfrac{9}{25}} = \dfrac{\sqrt{9}}{\sqrt{25}} = \dfrac{3}{5}$

2. $\dfrac{6}{7}$

3. $\sqrt{\dfrac{16}{25}} = \dfrac{\sqrt{16}}{\sqrt{25}} = \dfrac{4}{5}$

4. $\dfrac{9}{10}$

5. $\sqrt{\dfrac{y^4}{x^2}} = \dfrac{\sqrt{y^4}}{\sqrt{x^2}} = \dfrac{y^2}{x}$

6. $\dfrac{x^3}{v^4}$

7. $\sqrt{\dfrac{4x^2}{9}} = \dfrac{\sqrt{4x^2}}{\sqrt{9}} = \dfrac{2x}{3}$

8. $\dfrac{4a}{7}$

9. $\sqrt{\dfrac{2}{8k^2}} = \sqrt{\dfrac{1}{4k^2}} = \dfrac{\sqrt{1}}{\sqrt{4k^2}} = \dfrac{1}{2k}$

10. $\dfrac{m}{3}$

11. $\sqrt{\dfrac{4x^3y}{xy^3}} = \sqrt{\dfrac{4x^2}{y^2}} = \dfrac{\sqrt{4x^2}}{\sqrt{y^2}} = \dfrac{2x}{y}$

12. $\dfrac{x^2}{3y}$

13. $\dfrac{3}{\sqrt{7}}\,\dfrac{\sqrt{7}}{\sqrt{7}} = \dfrac{3\sqrt{7}}{7}$

14. $\dfrac{2\sqrt{3}}{3}$

15. $\dfrac{10}{\sqrt{5}}\,\dfrac{\sqrt{5}}{\sqrt{5}} = \dfrac{\overset{2}{10}\sqrt{5}}{\underset{1}{5}} = 2\sqrt{5}$

16. $7\sqrt{2}$

17. $\sqrt{\dfrac{m^2}{3}} = \dfrac{\sqrt{m^2}}{\sqrt{3}}\,\dfrac{\sqrt{3}}{\sqrt{3}} = \dfrac{m\sqrt{3}}{3}$

18. $\dfrac{k\sqrt{5}}{5}$

19. $\sqrt{\dfrac{x^5z^4}{36y^2}} = \dfrac{\sqrt{x^4xz^4}}{\sqrt{36y^2}} = \dfrac{x^2z^2\sqrt{x}}{6y}$

20. $\dfrac{ac^3\sqrt{a}}{5b}$

21. $\sqrt{\dfrac{3a^2b}{4b^3}} = \sqrt{\dfrac{3a^2}{4b^2}} = \dfrac{a\sqrt{3}}{2b}$

22. $\dfrac{v\sqrt{5}}{2}$

23. $\sqrt{\dfrac{b^2c^4}{16d^3}} = \dfrac{\sqrt{b^2c^4}}{\sqrt{16d^2d}} = \dfrac{bc^2}{4d\sqrt{d}}\,\dfrac{\sqrt{d}}{\sqrt{d}} = \dfrac{bc^2\sqrt{d}}{4d^2}$

24. $\dfrac{h^2k^4\sqrt{p}}{7p^3}$

25. $\sqrt{\dfrac{8m^2n}{2n^2}} = \sqrt{\dfrac{4m^2n}{n^2}} = \dfrac{2m\sqrt{n}}{n}$

26. $\dfrac{3y\sqrt{x}}{x}$

EXERCISES 1203A, SET I (page 416)

1. $\sqrt{3}\,\sqrt{3} = 3$

2. 7

3. $\sqrt{4}\,\sqrt{4} = 4$

4. 9

5. $\sqrt{3}\,\sqrt{12} = \sqrt{36} = 6$

6. 8

7. $\sqrt{9x}\,\sqrt{x} = \sqrt{9x^2} = 3x$

8. $5y$

9. $\sqrt{5}\,\sqrt{10}\,\sqrt{2} = \sqrt{5 \cdot 10 \cdot 2} = \sqrt{100} = 10$

10. 12

11. $\sqrt{5ab^2}\,\sqrt{20ab} = \sqrt{100a^2b^2b} = 10ab\sqrt{b}$

12. $9xy\sqrt{x}$

13. $\sqrt{2a}\,\sqrt{6}\,\sqrt{3a} = \sqrt{2a \cdot 6 \cdot 3a} = \sqrt{36a^2} = 6a$

14. $4h^2$

15. $5\sqrt{2x} \cdot \sqrt{8x^3} \cdot 2\sqrt{3x^5}$

$= (5 \cdot 2)\sqrt{2x \cdot 8x^3 \cdot 3x^5}$

$= 10\sqrt{48x^9}$

$= 10\sqrt{3 \cdot 16 \cdot x^8 \cdot x}$

$= 10 \cdot 4 \cdot x^4\sqrt{3x} = 40x^4\sqrt{3x}$

16. $72M^3\sqrt{2M}$

EXERCISES 1203B, SET I (page 418)

1. $\dfrac{\sqrt{20}}{\sqrt{5}} = \sqrt{\dfrac{20}{5}} = \sqrt{\dfrac{4}{1}} = 2$

2. $\dfrac{1}{2}$

3. $\dfrac{\sqrt{32}}{\sqrt{2}} = \sqrt{\dfrac{32}{2}} = \sqrt{\dfrac{16}{1}} = 4$

4. 7

5. $\dfrac{\sqrt{4}}{\sqrt{5}} = \dfrac{2}{\sqrt{5}}\,\dfrac{\sqrt{5}}{\sqrt{5}} = \dfrac{2\sqrt{5}}{5}$

6. $\dfrac{3\sqrt{7}}{7}$

7. $\dfrac{\sqrt{15x}}{\sqrt{5x}} = \sqrt{\dfrac{15x}{5x}} = \sqrt{3}$

8. $\sqrt{6}$

9. $\dfrac{\sqrt{72x^3y^2}}{\sqrt{2xy^2}} = \sqrt{\dfrac{72x^3y^2}{2xy^2}} = \sqrt{36x^2} = 6x$

10. $3y$

11. $\dfrac{\sqrt{x^4y}}{\sqrt{5y}} = \sqrt{\dfrac{x^4y}{5y}} = \dfrac{\sqrt{x^4}}{\sqrt{5}}\,\dfrac{\sqrt{5}}{\sqrt{5}} = \dfrac{x^2\sqrt{5}}{5}$

12. $\dfrac{m^3\sqrt{3}}{3}$

13. $\dfrac{4\sqrt{45m^3}}{3\sqrt{10m}} = \dfrac{4}{3}\sqrt{\dfrac{\overset{9}{45}m^3}{\underset{2}{10}m}}$

$= \dfrac{4}{3}\dfrac{\sqrt{9m^2}}{\sqrt{2}} = \dfrac{4 \cdot 3m}{3\sqrt{2}} \cdot \dfrac{\sqrt{2}}{\sqrt{2}}$

$= \dfrac{4m\sqrt{2}}{2} = 2m\sqrt{2}$

14. $4x\sqrt{6x}$

EXERCISES 1204, SET I (page 423)

1. $2\sqrt{3} + 5\sqrt{3} = (2 + 5)\sqrt{3} = 7\sqrt{3}$

2. $7\sqrt{2}$

3. $3\sqrt{x} - \sqrt{x} = (3 - 1)\sqrt{x} = 2\sqrt{x}$

4. $4\sqrt{a}$

5. $\dfrac{3}{2}\sqrt{2} - \dfrac{\sqrt{2}}{2} = \left(\dfrac{3}{2} - \dfrac{1}{2}\right)\sqrt{2} = \dfrac{2}{2}\sqrt{2} = \sqrt{2}$

6. $\sqrt{3}$

7. $5 \cdot 8\sqrt{5} + \sqrt{5} = 40\sqrt{5} + \sqrt{5}$

$= (40 + 1)\sqrt{5} = 41\sqrt{5}$

8. $13\sqrt{7}$

9. $\sqrt{25} + \sqrt{5} = 5 + \sqrt{5}$

10. $4 - \sqrt{6}$

11. $2\sqrt{3} + \sqrt{12} = 2\sqrt{3} + \sqrt{4 \cdot 3}$

$= 2\sqrt{3} + 2\sqrt{3} = 4\sqrt{3}$

12. $5\sqrt{2}$

13. $2\sqrt{50} - \sqrt{32} = 2\sqrt{25 \cdot 2} - \sqrt{16 \cdot 2}$

$= 2 \cdot 5\sqrt{2} - 4\sqrt{2}$

$= 10\sqrt{2} - 4\sqrt{2} = 6\sqrt{2}$

14. $3\sqrt{6}$

15. $3\sqrt{32} - \sqrt{8} = 3\sqrt{16 \cdot 2} - \sqrt{4 \cdot 2}$

$= 3 \cdot 4\sqrt{2} - 2\sqrt{2}$

$= 12\sqrt{2} - 2\sqrt{2} = 10\sqrt{2}$

16. $6\sqrt{3}$

17. $\sqrt{\dfrac{1}{2}} + \sqrt{8} = \dfrac{\sqrt{1}}{\sqrt{2}}\,\dfrac{\sqrt{2}}{\sqrt{2}} + \sqrt{4 \cdot 2}$

$= \dfrac{1}{2}\sqrt{2} + 2\sqrt{2} = \left(\dfrac{1}{2} + 2\right)\sqrt{2} = \dfrac{5\sqrt{2}}{2}$

18. $\dfrac{7\sqrt{3}}{3}$

19. $\sqrt{24} - \sqrt{\dfrac{2}{3}}$

$= \sqrt{4 \cdot 6} - \dfrac{\sqrt{2}}{\sqrt{3}} \cdot \dfrac{\sqrt{3}}{\sqrt{3}}$

$= 2\sqrt{6} - \dfrac{\sqrt{6}}{3}$

$= \left(2 - \dfrac{1}{3}\right)\sqrt{6} = \dfrac{5\sqrt{6}}{3}$

20. $\dfrac{13\sqrt{5}}{5}$

21. $10\sqrt{\dfrac{3}{5}} + \sqrt{60} = 10\dfrac{\sqrt{3}}{\sqrt{5}}\dfrac{\sqrt{5}}{\sqrt{5}} + \sqrt{4 \cdot 15}$

$= \dfrac{10\sqrt{15}}{5} + 2\sqrt{15}$

$= 2\sqrt{15} + 2\sqrt{15} = 4\sqrt{15}$

22. $6\sqrt{3}$

23. $\sqrt{\dfrac{25}{2}} - \dfrac{3}{\sqrt{2}} = \dfrac{\sqrt{25}}{\sqrt{2}} - \dfrac{3}{\sqrt{2}} = \dfrac{5-3}{\sqrt{2}} = \dfrac{2}{\sqrt{2}} = \dfrac{2}{\sqrt{2}} \cdot \dfrac{\sqrt{2}}{\sqrt{2}} = \dfrac{2\sqrt{2}}{2} = \sqrt{2}$

24. $\dfrac{7\sqrt{5}}{10}$

25. $3\sqrt{\dfrac{1}{6}} + \sqrt{12} - 5\sqrt{\dfrac{3}{2}}$

$= 3\dfrac{\sqrt{1}}{\sqrt{6}}\dfrac{\sqrt{6}}{\sqrt{6}} + \sqrt{4 \cdot 3} - 5\dfrac{\sqrt{3}}{\sqrt{2}}\dfrac{\sqrt{2}}{\sqrt{2}}$

$= \dfrac{3}{1} \cdot \dfrac{\sqrt{6}}{6} + \sqrt{4}\sqrt{3} - \dfrac{5}{1} \cdot \dfrac{\sqrt{6}}{2}$

$= \dfrac{1}{2}\sqrt{6} + 2\sqrt{3} - \dfrac{5}{2}\sqrt{6}$

$= \left(\dfrac{1}{2} - \dfrac{5}{2}\right)\sqrt{6} + 2\sqrt{3} = -2\sqrt{6} + 2\sqrt{3}$

26. $\sqrt{10} + 2\sqrt{5}$

27. $\sqrt{2}(\sqrt{2} + 1) = \sqrt{2}(\sqrt{2}) + \sqrt{2}(1) = 2 + \sqrt{2}$

28. $3 + \sqrt{3}$

29. $\sqrt{3}(2\sqrt{3} + 1) = \sqrt{3}(2\sqrt{3}) + \sqrt{3}(1) = 6 + \sqrt{3}$

30. $15 + \sqrt{5}$

31. $\sqrt{x}(\sqrt{x} - 3) = \sqrt{x}(\sqrt{x}) + \sqrt{x}(-3) = x - 3\sqrt{x}$

32. $4\sqrt{y} - y$

33. $(\sqrt{7} + 2)(\sqrt{7} + 3)$

$\sqrt{7}\sqrt{7} + 5\sqrt{7} + 2(3) = 7 + 5\sqrt{7} + 6 = 13 + 5\sqrt{7}$

34. $11 + 6\sqrt{3}$

35. $(\sqrt{8} - 3\sqrt{2})(\sqrt{8} + 2\sqrt{5})$

$= \sqrt{8}\sqrt{8} - 3\sqrt{2}\sqrt{8} + 2\sqrt{8}\sqrt{5} - 3\sqrt{2} \cdot 2\sqrt{5}$

$= 8 - 3\sqrt{16} + 2\sqrt{40} - 6\sqrt{10}$

$= 8 - 3(4) + 2\sqrt{4 \cdot 10} - 6\sqrt{10}$

$= 8 - 12 + 2 \cdot 2\sqrt{10} - 6\sqrt{10}$

$= -4 + 4\sqrt{10} - 6\sqrt{10}$

$= -4 - 2\sqrt{10}$

36. 0

37. $(\sqrt{2x} + 3)^2 = (\sqrt{2x} + 3)(\sqrt{2x} + 3)$

$(\sqrt{2x})^2 + 6\sqrt{2x} + (3)^2$

$= 2x + 6\sqrt{2x} + 9$

38. $-8\sqrt{7x} + 16$

39. $\dfrac{\sqrt{8} + \sqrt{18}}{\sqrt{2}} = \dfrac{\sqrt{8}}{\sqrt{2}} + \dfrac{\sqrt{18}}{\sqrt{2}} = \sqrt{\dfrac{8}{2}} + \sqrt{\dfrac{18}{2}}$

$= \sqrt{4} + \sqrt{9} = 2 + 3 = 5$

40. 5

41. $\dfrac{\sqrt{20} + 5\sqrt{10}}{\sqrt{5}} = \dfrac{\sqrt{20}}{\sqrt{5}} + \dfrac{5\sqrt{10}}{\sqrt{5}} = \sqrt{\dfrac{20}{5}} + 5\sqrt{\dfrac{10}{5}}$

$= \sqrt{4} + 5\sqrt{2} = 2 + 5\sqrt{2}$

42. $2 + \dfrac{\sqrt{21}}{3}$

43. (a) $2 - \sqrt{3}$
    (b) $2\sqrt{5} + 7$

44. (a) $3\sqrt{2} + 5$
    (b) $\sqrt{7} - 4$

45. $\dfrac{3}{\sqrt{2} - 1} = \dfrac{3}{\sqrt{2} - 1} \cdot \dfrac{\sqrt{2} + 1}{\sqrt{2} + 1}$

$= \dfrac{3(\sqrt{2} + 1)}{(\sqrt{2})^2 - 1^2} = \dfrac{3(\sqrt{2} + 1)}{2 - 1} = 3(\sqrt{2} + 1)$

46. $5(\sqrt{2} + 1)$

47. $\dfrac{6}{\sqrt{3} - \sqrt{2}}\dfrac{\sqrt{3} + \sqrt{2}}{\sqrt{3} + \sqrt{2}} = \dfrac{6(\sqrt{3} + \sqrt{2})}{(\sqrt{3})^2 - (\sqrt{2})^2}$

$= \dfrac{6(\sqrt{3} + \sqrt{2})}{3 - 2} = 6(\sqrt{3} + \sqrt{2})$

48. $-8(\sqrt{2} + \sqrt{3})$

49. $\dfrac{6}{\sqrt{5} + \sqrt{2}}\dfrac{\sqrt{5} - \sqrt{2}}{\sqrt{5} - \sqrt{2}} = \dfrac{6(\sqrt{5} - \sqrt{2})}{5 - 2} = \dfrac{\overset{2}{6}(\sqrt{5} - \sqrt{2})}{\cancel{3}}$

$= 2(\sqrt{5} - \sqrt{2})$

50. $2(\sqrt{7} - \sqrt{5})$

51. $\dfrac{x - 4}{\sqrt{x} + 2}\dfrac{\sqrt{x} - 2}{\sqrt{x} - 2} = \dfrac{(x - 4)(\sqrt{x} - 2)}{(x - 4)} = \sqrt{x} - 2$

52. $\sqrt{y} + 3$

53. $\dfrac{1}{3}\sqrt{7} - 2\sqrt{3} = \dfrac{1}{3}(2.646) - 2(1.732)$

$= 0.882 - 3.464$

$= -2.582$

$\doteq -2.58$

54. $\doteq 6.79$

55. $\dfrac{3 + 2\sqrt{11}}{6} = \dfrac{3 + 2(3.317)}{6}$

$= \dfrac{3 + 6.634}{6}$

$= \dfrac{9.634}{6} \doteq 1.61$

56. $\doteq -0.61$

EXERCISES 1205, SET I (page 428)

1. $\sqrt{x} = 5$
   $(\sqrt{x})^2 = 5^2$
   $x = 25$

   Check: $\sqrt{x} = 5$
   $\sqrt{25} = 5$
   $5 = 5$

2. 16

3. $\sqrt{2x} = 4$
   $(\sqrt{2x})^2 = 4^2$
   $2x = 16$
   $x = 8$

   Check: $\sqrt{2x} = 4$
   $\sqrt{2(8)} = 4$
   $\sqrt{16} = 4$
   $4 = 4$

4. 12

5. $\sqrt{x - 3} = 2$
   $(\sqrt{x - 3})^2 = 2^2$
   $x - 3 = 4$
   $x = 7$

6. 32

Check: $\sqrt{x-3}=2$
$\sqrt{7-3}=2$
$\sqrt{4}=2$
$2=2$

7. $\sqrt{2x+1}=9$
$(\sqrt{2x+1})^2=9^2$
$2x+1=81$
$2x=80$
$x=40$

8. 4

Check: $\sqrt{2x+1}=9$
$\sqrt{2\cdot40+1}=9$
$\sqrt{81}=9$
$9=9$

9. $\sqrt{3x+1}=5$
$(\sqrt{3x+1})^2=5^2$
$3x+1=25$
$3x=24$
$x=8$

10. 4

Check: $\sqrt{3x+1}=5$
$\sqrt{3\cdot8+1}=5$
$\sqrt{25}=5$
$5=5$

11. $\sqrt{x+1}=\sqrt{2x-7}$
$x+1=2x-7$
$8=x$

12. 3

Check: $\sqrt{x+1}=\sqrt{2x-7}$
$\sqrt{8+1}=\sqrt{2\cdot8-7}$
$\sqrt{9}=\sqrt{9}$
$3=3$

13. $(\sqrt{3x-2})^2=(x)^2$
$3x-2=x^2$
$0=x^2-3x+2$
$0=(x-2)(x-1)$

$x-2=0 \mid x-1=0$
$x=2 \mid \quad x=1$

14. 2, 3

Check: For $x=2$: $\mid$ For $x=1$:
$\sqrt{3x-2}=x$ $\mid$ $\sqrt{3x-2}=x$
$\sqrt{3(2)-2}=2$ $\mid$ $\sqrt{3(1)-2}=1$
$\sqrt{4}=2$ $\mid$ $\sqrt{1}=1$
$2=2$ $\mid$ $1=1$

15. $(\sqrt{4x-1})^2=(2x)^2$
$4x-1=4x^2$
$0=4x^2-4x+1$
$0=(2x-1)(2x-1)$
$2x-1=0$
$2x=1$
$x=\dfrac{1}{2}$

16. $\dfrac{1}{3}$

Check: $\sqrt{4x-1}=2x$
$\sqrt{4\left(\dfrac{1}{2}\right)-1}=2\left(\dfrac{1}{2}\right)$
$\sqrt{2-1}=1$
$1=1$

17. $\sqrt{x-3}+5=x$
$(\sqrt{x-3})^2=(x-5)^2$
$x-3=x^2-10x+25$
$0=x^2-11x+28$
$0=(x-4)(x-7)$

$x-4=0 \mid x-7=0$
$x=4 \mid \quad x=7$

18. 5

Check: For $x=7$: $\mid$ For $x=4$:
$\sqrt{x-3}+5 \overset{?}{=} x$ $\mid$ $\sqrt{x-3}+5 \overset{?}{=} x$
$\sqrt{7-3}+5 \overset{?}{=} 7$ $\mid$ $\sqrt{4-3}+5 \overset{?}{=} 4$
$\sqrt{4}+5 \overset{?}{=} 7$ $\mid$ $\sqrt{1}+5 \overset{?}{=} 4$
$2+5=7$ $\mid$ $1+5 \neq 4$
$7=7$ $\mid$

Therefore, 7 is $\mid$ Therefore, 4 is
a solution. $\mid$ *not* a solution.

19. $\sqrt{3.14x+6.75}=4.96$
$(\sqrt{3.14x+6.75})^2=(4.96)^2$
$3.14x+6.75=24.6016$
$3.14x=17.8516$
$x \doteq 5.69$

20. $\doteq 9.98$

EXERCISES 1206, SET I (page 432)

1. $x^2=(16)^2+(12)^2$
$x^2=256+144$
$x^2=400$
$x=\sqrt{400}=20$
$x=20$

2. 15

3. $x^2=6^2+2^2$
$x^2=36+4$
$x^2=40$
$x=\sqrt{40}=\sqrt{4\cdot10}=2\sqrt{10}$
$x=2\sqrt{10}$

4. $2\sqrt{5}$

5. $x^2=(\sqrt{5})^2+2^2$
$x^2=5+4$
$x^2=9$
$x=\sqrt{9}=3$

6. 4

7. $x^2=(\sqrt{6})^2+(\sqrt{3})^2$
$x^2=6+3$
$x^2=9$
$x \doteq \sqrt{9}=3$

8. 4

9. $5^2=x^2+3^2$
$25=x^2+9$
$16=x^2$
$\sqrt{16}=x$
$4=x$
$x=4$

10. 5

11. $(3\sqrt{3})^2=3^2+x^2$
$9\cdot3=9+x^2$
$27=9+x^2$
$x^2=18$
$x=\sqrt{18}=\sqrt{9\cdot2}=3\sqrt{2}$
$x=3\sqrt{2}$

12. $2\sqrt{2}$

13. $x^2=10^2+6^2$
$x^2=100+36$
$x^2=136$
$x=\sqrt{136}=\sqrt{4\cdot34}=2\sqrt{34}$
$x=2\sqrt{34}$

14. $4\sqrt{13}$

15. $(x+1)^2+(\sqrt{20})^2=(x+3)^2$
$x^2+2x+1+20=x^2+6x+9$
$12=4x$
$x=3$

16. 7

17. Draw a rectangle and write the information on the figure.

$(24)^2+W^2=(25)^2$
$576+W^2=625$
$W^2=49$
$W=\sqrt{49}$
$W=7$ cm

18. 9 in

19. Let x = One leg
    then $2x - 4$ = Other leg

$$(10)^2 = (2x - 4)^2 + x^2$$
$$100 = 4x^2 - 16x + 16 + x^2$$
$$0 = 5x^2 - 16x - 84$$
$$0 = (5x + 14)(x - 6)$$

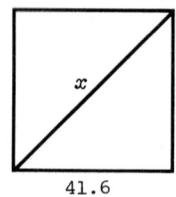

10   x

$2x - 4$

$5x + 14 = 0$ $x - 6 = 0$

$x = -\dfrac{14}{5}$ $x = 6$ m   One leg

Not a solution | $2x - 4 = 12 - 4$
                      = 8 m   Other leg

20. Width = 9 yd
    Length = 12 yd

21. Let x = length of diagonal

$$(x)^2 = (41.6)^2 + (41.6)^2$$
$$x^2 = 1730.56 + 1730.56$$
$$x^2 = 3461.12$$
$$x = \sqrt{3461.12}$$
$$x \doteq 58.8 \text{ cm}$$

x 41.6

41.6

22. $\doteq 2.66$ m

REVIEW EXERCISES 1207, SET I   (page 437)

1. (a) $\sqrt{3}$, $2\sqrt{5}$, $\sqrt{5}$, because they cannot be expressed as a fraction.
   (b) $2\sqrt{5}$ and $\sqrt{5}$

2. (a) $7\dfrac{3}{4}$, 5.8
   (b) $\sqrt{2}$ and $3\sqrt{2}$

3. (a) $9x$
   (b) $\dfrac{1}{2}$
   (c) $x - 5$

4. (a) $\dfrac{3}{5}$
   (b) $3x + 4$
   (c) $4x$

5. 9

6. 10   7. 3   8. 5   9. $2x$

10. $3y$ 11. $a + b$

12. $a - b$

13. $\sqrt{x^3} = \sqrt{x^2 \cdot x} = \sqrt{x^2}\sqrt{x} = x\sqrt{x}$

14. $y^2\sqrt{y}$

15. $\sqrt{16x^2y^4} = \sqrt{16}\sqrt{x^2}\sqrt{y^4} = 4xy^2$

16. $6a^2b$

17. $\sqrt{a^3b^3} = \sqrt{a^2ab^2b} = ab\sqrt{ab}$

18. $x^2y^2\sqrt{xy}$

19. $\sqrt{8}\sqrt{8} = \sqrt{8 \cdot 8} = \sqrt{64} = 8$

20. 11

21. $\sqrt{2}\sqrt{32} = \sqrt{64} = 8$

22. 6

23. $3\sqrt{5} + \sqrt{5} = (3 + 1)\sqrt{5} = 4\sqrt{5}$

24. $3\sqrt{2}$

25. $\sqrt{18} - \sqrt{8} = \sqrt{9 \cdot 2} - \sqrt{4 \cdot 2}$
    $= 3\sqrt{2} - 2\sqrt{2} = \sqrt{2}$

26. $\sqrt{3}$

27. $\dfrac{1}{\sqrt{5}} \cdot \dfrac{\sqrt{5}}{\sqrt{5}} = \dfrac{\sqrt{5}}{5}$

28. $\dfrac{\sqrt{7}}{7}$

29. $\dfrac{6}{\sqrt{3}} \cdot \dfrac{\sqrt{3}}{\sqrt{3}} = \dfrac{6\sqrt{3}}{3} = 2\sqrt{3}$

30. $2\sqrt{10}$

31. $\sqrt{8} - \sqrt{\dfrac{1}{2}} = \sqrt{4 \cdot 2} - \dfrac{\sqrt{1}}{\sqrt{2}} \cdot \dfrac{\sqrt{2}}{\sqrt{2}}$
    $= 2\sqrt{2} - \dfrac{\sqrt{2}}{2}$
    $= 2\sqrt{2} - \dfrac{1}{2}\sqrt{2} = \dfrac{3\sqrt{2}}{2}$

32. $\dfrac{8\sqrt{6}}{3}$

33. $\sqrt{x} = 4$
    $(\sqrt{x})^2 = 4^2$
    $x = 16$

34. $y = 9$

35. $(\sqrt{3a})^2 = 6^2$
    $3a = 36$
    $a = 12$

36. 25

37. $(\sqrt{2x - 1})^2 = 5^2$
    $2x - 1 = 25$
    $2x = 26$
    $x = 13$

38. $4\dfrac{2}{3}$

39. $(\sqrt{5a - 4})^2 = (\sqrt{3a + 2})^2$
    $5a - 4 = 3a + 2$
    $2a = 6$
    $a = 3$

40. 3

41. $(10)^2 = 8^2 + x^2$
    $100 = 64 + x^2$
    $36 = x^2$
    $\sqrt{36} = \sqrt{x^2}$
    $6 = x$

42. 16

43. $\sqrt{2}(\sqrt{8} + \sqrt{18}) = \sqrt{2}(\sqrt{8}) + \sqrt{2}(\sqrt{18})$
    $= \sqrt{16} + \sqrt{36}$
    $= 4 + 6 = 10$

44. 15

45. $(\sqrt{5} + 3)(\sqrt{5} - 3) = (\sqrt{5})^2 - 3^2$
    $= 5 - 9 = -4$

46. 23

47. $(2\sqrt{3} + 1)^2 = (2\sqrt{3} + 1)(2\sqrt{3} + 1)$
    $= (2\sqrt{3})^2 + 2(2\sqrt{3})(1) + (1)^2$
    $= 12 + 4\sqrt{3} + 1$
    $= 13 + 4\sqrt{3}$

48. $19 - 6\sqrt{2}$

49. $(3\sqrt{2} + 1)(2\sqrt{2} - 1)$

     $+2\sqrt{2}$
     $-3\sqrt{2}$

$(3\sqrt{2})(2\sqrt{2}) - 1\sqrt{2} + (1)(-1)$

$= \quad 12 \quad - \quad \sqrt{2} \quad - 1$

$= \quad\quad 11 - \sqrt{2}$

50. $44 + 2\sqrt{3}$

51. $\dfrac{8}{\sqrt{3} - 2} \cdot \dfrac{\sqrt{3} + 2}{\sqrt{3} + 2} = \dfrac{8(\sqrt{3} + 2)}{3 - 4}$
    $= -8(\sqrt{3} + 2)$

52. $6(\sqrt{5} - 2)$

53. $\dfrac{10}{\sqrt{6} - 2} \cdot \dfrac{\sqrt{6} + 2}{\sqrt{6} + 2} = \dfrac{10(\sqrt{6} + 2)}{6 - 4} = \dfrac{\overset{5}{\cancel{10}}(\sqrt{6} + 2)}{\cancel{2}}$
    $= 5(\sqrt{6} + 2)$

54. $4(3 + \sqrt{7})$

55. $x^2 = 5^2 + 5^2$
    $x^2 = 25 + 25 = 50$
    $\sqrt{x^2} = \sqrt{50} = \sqrt{25 \cdot 2} = 5\sqrt{2}$
    $x = 5\sqrt{2}$
    $x = 5(1.414) \doteq 7.07$ m

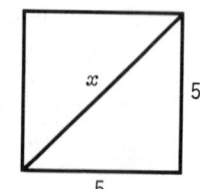

x 5

5

56. 5 in

57. $(\sqrt{7x - 6})^2 = (x)^2$
    $7x - 6 = x^2$
    $0 = x^2 - 7x + 6$
    $0 = (x - 6)(x - 1)$

    $x - 6 = 0$ | $x - 1 = 0$
    $x = 6$ | $x = 1$

58. 1, 8

59.
$$(\sqrt{2x + 7})^2 = (\sqrt{x} + 2)^2$$
$$2x + 7 = x + 4\sqrt{x} + 4$$
$$x + 3 = 4\sqrt{x}$$
$$(x + 3)^2 = (4\sqrt{x})^2$$
$$x^2 - 6x + 9 = 16x$$
$$x^2 - 10x + 9 = 0$$
$$(x - 9)(x - 1) = 0$$

$$x - 9 = 0 \mid x - 1 = 0$$
$$x = 9 \mid \quad x = 1$$

60. 4

CUMULATIVE REVIEW EXERCISES: CHAPTERS 1-11 (page 439)

1. $\left(\dfrac{\cancel{30}x^4 y^{-3}}{\cancel{12}y^{-1}}\right)^{-2} = \left(\dfrac{5x^4 y^{-2}}{2}\right)^{-2}$

$= \dfrac{5^{-2}x^{-8}y^4}{2^{-2}} = \dfrac{2^2 y^4}{5^2 x^8} = \dfrac{4y^4}{25x^8}$

2. $4(3 + h)(3 - h)$

3. $\dfrac{x^2 + x - 2}{x^2 - 1} \div \dfrac{x^2 - 2x - 8}{x^2 - 4x}$

$\dfrac{(\cancel{x - 1})(x + 2)}{(\cancel{x - 1})(x + 1)} \cdot \dfrac{x(\cancel{x - 4})}{(\cancel{x + 2})(\cancel{x - 4})} = \dfrac{x}{x + 1}$

4. $x \le 4$

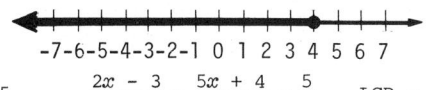

$-7\,{-}6\,{-}5\,{-}4\,{-}3\,{-}2\,{-}1\ 0\ 1\ 2\ 3\ 4\ 5\ 6\ 7$

5. $\dfrac{2x - 3}{2} = \dfrac{5x + 4}{6} - \dfrac{5}{3}$ LCD = 6

$\dfrac{\cancel{6}^3}{1} \cdot \dfrac{2x - 3}{\cancel{2}} = \dfrac{\cancel{6}^1}{1} \cdot \dfrac{5x + 4}{\cancel{6}} - \dfrac{\cancel{6}^2}{1} \cdot \dfrac{5}{\cancel{3}}$

$3(2x - 3) = 1(5x + 4) - 2(5)$
$6x - 9 = 5x + 4 - 10$
$x = 3$

6. $\dfrac{2x^2 - 7x - 10}{(x + 2)(x - 1)}$

7. (1) $4x - 3y = -9$
(2) $3y + x = -6$

(1) Intercepts: $\left(-2\tfrac{1}{4},\ 0\right),\ (0,\ 3)$

(2) Intercepts: $(-6,\ 0),\ (0,\ -2)$

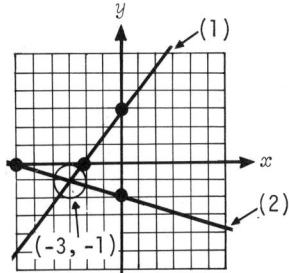

8. $(6, -5)$

9. (1) $2x - 5y = 2 \Rightarrow 2x = 5y + 2$
(2) $3x - 7y = 2 \quad x = \dfrac{5y + 2}{2}$

Substitute $\dfrac{5y + 2}{2}$ for x in (2)

(2) $\quad\quad 3x - 7y = 2$
$3\left(\dfrac{5y + 2}{2}\right) - 7y = 2$ LCD = 2

$\dfrac{\cancel{2}}{1} \cdot \dfrac{3}{1}\left(\dfrac{5y + 2}{\cancel{2}}\right) - \dfrac{\cancel{2}}{1} \cdot \dfrac{7y}{1} = \dfrac{2}{1} \cdot \dfrac{\cancel{2}}{1}$
$15y + 6 - 14y = 4$
$y = -2$

Substitute $y = -2$ in $x = \dfrac{5y + 2}{2}$

$x = \dfrac{5(-2) + 2}{2} = \dfrac{-10 + 2}{2} = \dfrac{-8}{2} = -4$

Solution: $(-4, -2)$

10. $-\dfrac{7}{2}$, 4

CHAPTER TWELVE DIAGNOSTIC TEST (page 441)

Following each problem number is the textbook section reference (in parentheses) where that kind of problem is discussed.

1. (1201) $\sqrt{3}, \sqrt{5}$ are irrational

$2\tfrac{1}{2} = \dfrac{5}{2}$ rational

$\sqrt{9} = 3 = \dfrac{3}{1}$ rational

$\dfrac{3}{4}$ rational

$-4 = \dfrac{-4}{1}$ rational

2. (1202) $\sqrt{9x^2} = 3x$

3. (1202) $\sqrt{18} = \sqrt{3^2 \cdot 2} = \sqrt{3^2}\,\sqrt{2} = 3\sqrt{2}$

$\begin{array}{r|l} 2 & 18 \\ 3 & \underline{9} \\ & 3 \end{array}$ $18 = 3^2 \cdot 2$

4. (1202) $\sqrt{x^4 y^3} = \sqrt{x^4 y^2 y^1} = x^2 y^1 \sqrt{y}$

5. (1202) $\sqrt{\dfrac{36}{49}} = \dfrac{\sqrt{36}}{\sqrt{49}} = \dfrac{6}{7}$

6. (1202) $\sqrt{\dfrac{18}{2m^2}} = \sqrt{\dfrac{9}{m^2}} = \dfrac{\sqrt{9}}{\sqrt{m^2}} = \dfrac{3}{m}$

7. (1203) $\sqrt{6}\,\sqrt{6} = \sqrt{6 \cdot 6} = \sqrt{6^2} = 6$

8. (1203) $\sqrt{2}\,\sqrt{18x^2} = \sqrt{2 \cdot 18x^2} = \sqrt{36x^2} = 6x$

9. (1204) $\sqrt{3}(2\sqrt{3} - 5) = (\sqrt{3})(2\sqrt{3}) + (\sqrt{3})(-5)$
$= 6 - 5\sqrt{3}$

10. (1204) $(\sqrt{7} + \sqrt{3})(\sqrt{7} - \sqrt{3}) = (\sqrt{7})^2 - (\sqrt{3})^2$
$= 7 - 3 = 4$

11. (1204)
$(5\sqrt{x} + 1)(5\sqrt{x} + 4)$
$+5\sqrt{x}$
$+20\sqrt{x}$

$= (5\sqrt{x})(5\sqrt{x}) + 25\sqrt{x} + (+1)(+4)$
$= \quad 25x \quad + 25\sqrt{x} + \quad 4$

12. (1203) $\dfrac{\sqrt{6}}{\sqrt{24}} = \sqrt{\dfrac{6}{24}} = \sqrt{\dfrac{1}{4}} = \dfrac{\sqrt{1}}{\sqrt{4}} = \dfrac{1}{2}$

13. (1203) $\dfrac{\sqrt{4}}{\sqrt{6}} = \dfrac{2}{\sqrt{6}} \cdot \dfrac{\sqrt{6}}{\sqrt{6}} = \dfrac{2\sqrt{6}}{6} = \dfrac{\sqrt{6}}{3}$

14. (1203) $\dfrac{\sqrt{15} - \sqrt{27}}{\sqrt{3}} = \dfrac{\sqrt{15}}{\sqrt{3}} - \dfrac{\sqrt{27}}{\sqrt{3}} = \sqrt{\dfrac{15}{3}} - \sqrt{\dfrac{27}{3}}$
$= \sqrt{5} - \sqrt{9} = \sqrt{5} - 3$

15. (1203) $\dfrac{\sqrt{a^6 b}}{\sqrt{2b}} = \sqrt{\dfrac{a^6 b}{2b}} = \sqrt{\dfrac{a^6}{2}} = \dfrac{\sqrt{a^6}}{\sqrt{2}} = \dfrac{a^3}{\sqrt{2}} \cdot \dfrac{\sqrt{2}}{\sqrt{2}}$
$= \dfrac{a^3\sqrt{2}}{2}$

16. (1203) $\dfrac{4}{1 + \sqrt{3}} \cdot \dfrac{1 - \sqrt{3}}{1 - \sqrt{3}} = \dfrac{4(1 - \sqrt{3})}{1 - 3} = \dfrac{4(1 - \sqrt{3})}{-2}$

$= -2(1 - \sqrt{3})$

17. (1204) $4\sqrt{x} - \sqrt{x} = (4 - 1)\sqrt{x} = 3\sqrt{x}$

18. (1204) $3\sqrt{2} - \sqrt{18}$

$= 3\sqrt{2} - \sqrt{3^2 \cdot 2}$

$= 3\sqrt{2} - 3\sqrt{2} = 0$

19. (1204) $\sqrt{27} + 3\sqrt{\dfrac{4}{3}} = \sqrt{3^2 \cdot 3} + \dfrac{3\sqrt{4}}{\sqrt{3}} \cdot \dfrac{\sqrt{3}}{\sqrt{3}}$

$= 3\sqrt{3} + \dfrac{\cancel{3} \cdot 2\sqrt{3}}{\cancel{3}} = 5\sqrt{3}$

20. (1205) $(x)^2 = (8)^2 + (6)^2$

$x^2 = 64 + 36 = 100$

$\sqrt{x^2} = \sqrt{100}$

$x = 10$

21. (1205) $(4)^2 = (\sqrt{11})^2 + (x)^2$

$16 = 11 + x^2$

$5 = x^2$

$\sqrt{5} = \sqrt{x^2} = x$

22. (1205) $(d)^2 = (6)^2 + (6)^2$

$d^2 = 36 + 36 = 72$

$\sqrt{d^2} = \sqrt{72}$

$d = \sqrt{36(2)} = 6\sqrt{2}$

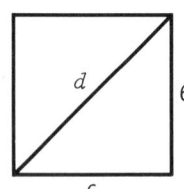

23. (1206) $(\sqrt{2x})^2 = (6)^2$ Check: $\sqrt{2x} \overset{?}{=} 6$

$2x = 36$ $\sqrt{2(18)} \overset{?}{=} 6$

$x = 18$ $\sqrt{36} = 6$

                       $6 = 6$

24. (1206) $(\sqrt{4x + 5})^2 = (5)^2$ Check: $\sqrt{4x + 5} \overset{?}{=} 5$

$4x + 5 = 25$ $\sqrt{4(5) + 5} \overset{?}{=} 5$

$4x = 20$ $\sqrt{25} = 5$

$x = 5$ $5 = 5$

25. (1206) $(\sqrt{5x - 6})^2 = (x)^2$

$5x - 6 = x^2$

$x^2 - 5x + 6 = 0$

$(x - 3)(x - 2) = 0$

$x - 3 = 0 \,|\, x - 2 = 0$

$x = 3 \quad\;\; x = 2$

Check: For $x = 3$:   For $x = 2$:

$\sqrt{5x - 6} \overset{?}{=} x$ $\sqrt{5x - 6} = x$

$\sqrt{5(3) - 6} \overset{?}{=} 3$ $\sqrt{5(2) - 6} = 2$

$\sqrt{9} = 3$ $\sqrt{4} = 2$

$3 = 3$ $2 = 2$

EXERCISES 1301, SET I   (page 447)

1. $2x^2 = 5x + 3$ $\begin{cases} a = 2 \\ b = -5 \\ c = -3 \end{cases}$

    $2x^2 - 5x - 3 = 0$

2. $3x^2 + 2x - 4 = 0$ $\begin{cases} a = 3 \\ b = 2 \\ c = -4 \end{cases}$

3. $6x^2 = x$ $\begin{cases} a = 6 \\ b = -1 \\ c = 0 \end{cases}$

    $6x^2 - 1x + 0 = 0$

4. $3x^2 - 2x + 0 = 0$ $\begin{cases} a = 3 \\ b = -2 \\ c = 0 \end{cases}$

5. $\dfrac{3x}{2} + 5 = x^2$ LCD = 2

$\dfrac{\cancel{2}}{1} \cdot \dfrac{3x}{\cancel{2}} + 2 \cdot 5 = 2 \cdot x^2$

      $3x + 10 = 2x^2$ $\begin{cases} a = 2 \\ b = -3 \\ c = -10 \end{cases}$

   $2x^2 - 3x - 10 = 0$

6. $3x^2 + 2x - 12 = 0$ $\begin{cases} a = 3 \\ b = 2 \\ c = -12 \end{cases}$

7. $x^2 - \dfrac{5x}{4} + \dfrac{2}{3} = 0$ LCD = 12

$12(x^2) - \dfrac{\overset{3}{\cancel{12}}}{1}\left(\dfrac{-5x}{\cancel{4}}\right) + \dfrac{\overset{4}{\cancel{12}}}{1}\left(\dfrac{2}{\cancel{3}}\right) = 12 \cdot 0$

$12x^2 - 15x + 8 = 0$ $\begin{cases} a = 12 \\ b = -15 \\ c = 8 \end{cases}$

8. $30x^2 + 9x - 5 = 0$ $\begin{cases} a = 30 \\ b = 9 \\ c = -5 \end{cases}$

9. $x(x - 3) = 4$ $\begin{cases} a = 1 \\ b = -3 \\ c = -4 \end{cases}$

     $x^2 - 3x = 4$

  $1x^2 - 3x - 4 = 0$

10. $2x^2 + 2x - 12 = 0$ $\begin{cases} a = 2 \\ b = 2 \\ c = -12 \end{cases}$

11. $3x(x + 1) = (x + 1)(x + 2)$

   $3x^2 + 3x = x^2 + 3x + 2$

  $2x^2 + 0x - 2 = 0$ $\begin{cases} a = 2 \\ b = 0 \\ c = -2 \end{cases}$

12. $3x^2 - 2x + 3 = 0$ $\begin{cases} a = 3 \\ b = -2 \\ c = 3 \end{cases}$

13. $8.63x = 5.91 - 3.82x^2$

  $3.82x^2 + 8.63x - 5.91 = 0$

                       $\begin{cases} a = 3.82 \\ b = 8.63 \\ c = -5.91 \end{cases}$

14. $16.8x^2 - 11.4x + 15.7 = 0$ $\begin{cases} a = 16.8 \\ b = -11.4 \\ c = 15.7 \end{cases}$

EXERCISES 1302, SET I   (page 451)

1. $x^2 + x - 6 = 0$ 2.   3, -2

   $(x + 3)(x - 2) = 0$

$x + 3 = 0 \,|\, x - 2 = 0$

$x = -3 \quad\;\; x = 2$

3. $x^2 + x - 12 = 0$ 4.   3, -5

   $(x + 4)(x - 3) = 0$

$x + 4 = 0 \,|\, x - 3 = 0$

$x = -4 \quad\;\; x = 3$

5. $2x^2 - x - 1 = 0$ 6. $\dfrac{1}{2}$, -1

   $(2x + 1)(x - 1) = 0$

$2x + 1 = 0 \,|\, x - 1 = 0$

$x = -\dfrac{1}{2} \,\Big|\; x = 1$

7. $\dfrac{x}{8} = \dfrac{2}{x}$ This is a proportion.

                Product of means =

         $x^2 = 16$ product of extremes.

      $x^2 - 16 = 0$

   $(x - 4)(x + 4) = 0$

$x - 4 = 0 \,|\, x + 4 = 0$

$x = 4 \quad\;\; x = -4$

8. 6, -6

9.
$$\frac{x+2}{3} = \frac{-1}{x-2}$$ This is a proportion.

$(x+2)(x-2) = 3(-1)$ Product of means = product of extremes.

$$x^2 - 4 = -3$$
$$x^2 - 1 = 0$$
$$(x+1)(x-1) = 0$$

$x+1 = 0 \mid x-1 = 0$
$x = -1 \mid x = 1$

10. 1, -1

11.
$$x^2 + 9x + 8 = 0$$
$$(x+1)(x+8) = 0$$

$x+1 = 0 \mid x+8 = 0$
$x = -1 \mid x = -8$

12. -1, -6

13.
$$2x^2 + 4x = 0$$
$$2x(x+2) = 0$$

$2x = 0 \mid x+2 = 0$
$x = 0 \mid x = -2$

14. 0, 3

15.
$$x^2 = x + 2$$
$$x^2 - x - 2 = 0$$
$$(x-2)(x+1) = 0$$

$x-2 = 0 \mid x+1 = 0$
$x = 2 \mid x = -1$

16. 3, -2

17. $\dfrac{x}{2} + \dfrac{2}{x} = \dfrac{5}{2}$ LCD = $2x$

$$\frac{2x}{1} \cdot \frac{x}{2} + \frac{2x}{1} \cdot \frac{2}{x} = \frac{2x}{1} \cdot \frac{5}{2}$$

$$x^2 + 4 = 5x$$
$$x^2 - 5x + 4 = 0$$
$$(x-1)(x-4) = 0$$

$x-1 = 0 \mid x-4 = 0$
$x = 1 \mid x = 4$

18. 1, 6

19. $\dfrac{x-1}{4} + \dfrac{6}{x+1} = 2$ LCD = $4(x+1)$

$$\frac{4(x+1)}{1} \cdot \frac{x-1}{4} + \frac{4(x+1)}{1} \cdot \frac{6}{(x+1)} = 4(x+1)2$$

$$(x+1)(x-1) + 24 = 8(x+1)$$
$$x^2 - 1 + 24 = 8x + 8$$
$$x^2 - 8x + 15 = 0$$
$$(x-3)(x-5) = 0$$

$x-3 = 0 \mid x-5 = 0$
$x = 3 \mid x = 5$

20. 2, 3

21.
$$\frac{2x^2}{1} = \frac{2-x}{3}$$ This is a proportion.

$3(2x^2) = 1(2-x)$ Product of means = product of extremes.

$$6x^2 = 2 - x$$
$$6x^2 + x - 2 = 0$$
$$(2x-1)(3x+2) = 0$$

$2x-1 = 0 \mid 3x+2 = 0$
$2x = 1 \mid 3x = -2$
$x = \dfrac{1}{2} \mid x = -\dfrac{2}{3}$

22. $1\dfrac{1}{2}$, $\dfrac{1}{4}$

23. Area is 24.

$$W(W+5) = 24$$
$$W^2 + 5W = 24$$
$$W^2 + 5W - 24 = 0$$
$$(W+8)(W-3) = 0$$

$W+8 = 0 \mid W-3 = 0$
$W = -8 \mid W = 3$ (width)
No meaning $\mid W+5 = 3+5$
$\mid \quad\quad = 8$ (length)

Area = $LW = W(W+5)$

24. Width: 7, Length: 11

25.
$$(10)^2 = (x+2)^2 + (x)^2$$
$$100 = x^2 + 4x + 4 + x^2$$
$$0 = 2x^2 + 4x - 96$$
$$x^2 + 2x - 48 = 0$$
$$(x+8)(x-6) = 0$$

$x+8 = 0 \mid x-6 = 0$
$x = -8 \mid x = 6$ (short leg)
No meaning $\mid x+2 = 8$ (long leg)

26. 12

27. Let $\quad x$ = 1st even integer
then $x+2$ = 2nd even integer

The product	is increased by 4	the result is	84
$x(x+2)$	$+ 4$	$=$	84

$$x^2 + 2x + 4 = 84$$
$$x^2 + 2x - 80 = 0$$
$$(x+10)(x-8) = 0$$

$x = -10 \mid x = 8$
$x+2 = -8 \mid x+2 = 10$

Two answers: -10 and -8, or 8 and 10

28. 40 mph

EXERCISES 1303, SET I   (page 456)

1.
$$8x^2 = 4x$$
$$8x^2 - 4x = 0$$
$$4x(2x-1) = 0$$

$4x = 0 \mid 2x-1 = 0$
$x = 0 \mid 2x = 1$
$\mid x = \dfrac{1}{2}$

2. 0, $\dfrac{1}{3}$

3.
$$x^2 - 9 = 0$$
$$x^2 = 9$$
$$x = \pm\sqrt{9}$$
$$x = \pm 3$$

4. 6, -6

5.
$$5x^2 = 4$$
$$x^2 = \frac{4}{5}$$
$$x = \pm\sqrt{\frac{4}{5}}$$
$$x = \pm\frac{2}{\sqrt{5}} = \pm\frac{2}{\sqrt{5}} \cdot \frac{\sqrt{5}}{\sqrt{5}}$$
$$x = \pm\frac{2\sqrt{5}}{5}$$

6. $\pm\dfrac{5\sqrt{3}}{3}$

7.
$$8 - 2x^2 = 0$$
$$2x^2 = 8$$
$$x^2 = 4$$
$$x = \pm\sqrt{4}$$
$$x = \pm 2$$

8. ± 3

9. $2(x + 3) = 6 + x(x + 2)$
$2x + 6 = 6 + x^2 + 2x$
$x^2 = 0$
$x = \pm\sqrt{0}$
$x = 0$

10. 0

11. $2x(3x - 4) = 2(3 - 4x)$
$6x^2 - 8x = 6 - 8x$
$6x^2 = 6$
$x^2 = 1$
$x = \pm\sqrt{1}$
$x = \pm 1$

12. $\pm\frac{1}{5}\sqrt{30}$

13. $x^2 = 8^2 + 4^2$
$x^2 = 64 + 16$
$x^2 = 80$
$x = \sqrt{80}$
$x = \sqrt{16 \cdot 5} = 4\sqrt{5}$
$ = 4(2.236) \doteq 8.94$

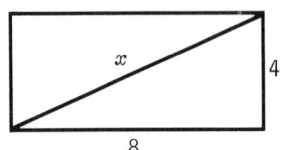

14. $\doteq 9.49$

15. Let x = Hours for Merwin;
Merwin does $\frac{1}{x}$ of the work each hour;

$x + 3$ = Hours for Mina;
Mina does $\frac{1}{x + 3}$ of the work each hour;

Mina works a total of 8 hr and Merwin works 3 hr to do the complete job:

| Work done by Mina | + | Work done by Merwin | = | Total work done | (the complete job) |

$8\left(\frac{1}{x + 3}\right) + 3\left(\frac{1}{x}\right) = 1$ LCD = $x(x + 3)$

$\frac{x(x + 3)}{1} \cdot \frac{8}{x + 3} + \frac{x(x + 3)}{1} \cdot \frac{3}{x} = \frac{x(x + 3)}{1} \cdot 1$

$8x + 3x + 9 = x^2 + 3x$
$x^2 - 8x - 9 = 0$
$(x + 1)(x - 9) = 0$

$x + 1 = 0 \quad | \quad x - 9 = 0$
$x = -1 \quad | \quad x = 9$ Hours for Merwin to do the job

No meaning $\quad | \quad x + 3 = 12$ Hours for Mina to do the job

16. $2\sqrt{5}$

EXERCISES 1304, SET I   (page 461)

1. $3x^2 - 1x - 2 = 0 \begin{cases} a = 3 \\ b = -1 \\ c = -2 \end{cases}$

$x = \frac{-(-1) \pm \sqrt{(-1)^2 - 4(3)(-2)}}{2(3)}$

$x = \frac{1 \pm \sqrt{1 + 24}}{6} = \frac{1 \pm \sqrt{25}}{6}$

$x = \frac{1 \pm 5}{6} = \begin{cases} \frac{1 + 5}{6} = \frac{6}{6} = 1 \\ \frac{1 - 5}{6} = \frac{-4}{6} = -\frac{2}{3} \end{cases}$

2. $\frac{1}{2}$, -2

3. $1x^2 - 4x + 1 = 0 \begin{cases} a = 1 \\ b = -4 \\ c = 1 \end{cases}$

$x = \frac{-(-4) \pm \sqrt{(-4)^2 - 4(1)(1)}}{2(1)}$

$x = \frac{4 \pm \sqrt{16 - 4}}{2(1)} = \frac{4 \pm \sqrt{12}}{2}$

$x = \frac{4 \pm 2\sqrt{3}}{2} = 2 \pm \sqrt{3}$

4. $2 \pm \sqrt{5}$

5. $\frac{x}{2} + \frac{2}{x} = \frac{5}{2}$ LCD = $2x$

$\frac{2x}{1} \cdot \frac{x}{2} + \frac{2x}{1} \cdot \frac{2}{x} = \frac{2x}{1} \cdot \frac{5}{2}$

$x^2 + 4 = 5x$

$1x^2 - 5x + 4 = 0 \begin{cases} a = 1 \\ b = -5 \\ c = 4 \end{cases}$

$x = \frac{-(-5) \pm \sqrt{(-5)^2 - 4(1)(4)}}{2(1)}$

$x = \frac{5 \pm \sqrt{25 - 16}}{2} = \frac{5 \pm \sqrt{9}}{2}$

$x = \frac{5 \pm 3}{2} = \begin{cases} \frac{5 + 3}{2} = \frac{8}{2} = 4 \\ \frac{5 - 3}{2} = \frac{2}{2} = 1 \end{cases}$

6. 1, 6

7. $2x^2 = 8x - 5$ $\begin{cases} a = 2 \\ b = -8 \\ c = 5 \end{cases}$
$2x^2 - 8x + 5 = 0$

$x = \frac{-(-8) \pm \sqrt{(-8)^2 - 4(2)(5)}}{2(2)}$

$x = \frac{8 \pm \sqrt{64 - 40}}{4} = \frac{8 \pm \sqrt{24}}{4} = \frac{8 \pm 2\sqrt{6}}{4}$

$x = \frac{2(4 \pm \sqrt{6})}{4} = \frac{4 \pm \sqrt{6}}{2}$

8. $\frac{3 \pm \sqrt{3}}{3}$

9. $\frac{1}{x} + \frac{x}{x - 1} = 3$ LCD = $x(x - 1)$

$\frac{x(x - 1)}{1} \cdot \frac{1}{x} + \frac{x(x - 1)}{1} \cdot \frac{x}{x - 1} = \frac{x(x - 1)}{1} \cdot \frac{3}{1}$

$(x - 1) + x^2 = 3x(x - 1)$
$x - 1 + x^2 = 3x^2 - 3x$
$0 = 2x^2 - 4x + 1$

$a = 2$
$b = -4$
$c = 1$

$x = \frac{-b \pm \sqrt{b^2 - 4ac}}{2a}$

$x = \frac{-(-4) \pm \sqrt{(-4)^2 - 4(2)(1)}}{2(2)}$

$= \frac{4 \pm \sqrt{16 - 8}}{4} = \frac{4 \pm \sqrt{8}}{4}$

$= \frac{4 \pm 2\sqrt{2}}{4} = \frac{2 \pm \sqrt{2}}{2}$

10. $\frac{-1 \pm \sqrt{11}}{5}$

11. Let x = the number
$x - \frac{1}{x} = \frac{2}{3}$ LCD = $3x$

$\frac{3x}{1} \cdot \frac{x}{1} - \frac{3x}{1} \cdot \frac{1}{x} = \frac{3x}{1} \cdot \frac{2}{3}$

$3x^2 - 3 = 2x$
$3x^2 - 2x - 3 = 0$ $\begin{cases} a = 3 \\ b = -2 \\ c = -3 \end{cases}$

$x = \frac{-b \pm \sqrt{b^2 - 4ac}}{2a}$

$= \frac{-(-2) \pm \sqrt{(-2)^2 - 4(3)(-3)}}{2(3)}$

$= \frac{2 \pm \sqrt{4 + 36}}{6} = \frac{2 \pm \sqrt{40}}{6}$

$= \frac{2 \pm 2\sqrt{10}}{6} = \frac{1 \pm \sqrt{10}}{3}$

Two answers: $\frac{1 + \sqrt{10}}{3}$ and $\frac{1 - \sqrt{10}}{3}$

12. $\dfrac{-5 \pm 3\sqrt{17}}{8}$

13. Area $= LW = (W + 2)W = 2$

$$W^2 + 2W = 2 \quad \begin{cases} a = 1 \\ b = 2 \\ c = -2 \end{cases}$$
$$1W^2 + 2W - 2 = 0$$

W

$W + 2$

$$W = \dfrac{-(2) \pm \sqrt{(2)^2 - 4(1)(-2)}}{2(1)} = \dfrac{-2 \pm \sqrt{4 + 8}}{2}$$

$$W = \dfrac{-2 \pm \sqrt{12}}{2} = \dfrac{-2 \pm 2\sqrt{3}}{2} = -1 \pm \sqrt{3}$$

$$W = -1 \pm \sqrt{3} = \begin{cases} -1 + \sqrt{3} \doteq -1 + 1.732 = 0.732 \\ -1 - \sqrt{3} \doteq -1 - 1.732 = -2.732 \end{cases}$$

When $W = 0.732$	When $W = -2.732$
Width $= W = 0.732$	Not possible
Length $= W + 2 = 2.732$	

14. 1.16, 5.16

15. $$4x^2 + 4x - 1 = 0 \quad \begin{cases} a = 4 \\ b = 4 \\ c = -1 \end{cases}$$

$$x = \dfrac{-(4) \pm \sqrt{(4)^2 - 4(4)(-1)}}{2(4)} = \dfrac{-4 \pm \sqrt{16 + 16}}{8}$$

$$= \dfrac{-4 \pm \sqrt{16 \cdot 2}}{8} = \dfrac{-4 \pm 4\sqrt{2}}{8} = \dfrac{4(-1 \pm \sqrt{2})}{8} = \dfrac{-1 \pm \sqrt{2}}{2}$$

$$\doteq \dfrac{-1 \pm 1.414}{2} = \begin{cases} \dfrac{0.414}{2} \doteq 0.21 \\ \dfrac{-2.414}{2} \doteq -1.21 \end{cases}$$

16. $\doteq 0.91$ and $\doteq -0.24$

17. $$3x^2 + 2x + 1 = 0 \quad \begin{cases} a = 3 \\ b = 2 \\ c = 1 \end{cases}$$

$$x = \dfrac{-(2) \pm \sqrt{(2)^2 - 4(3)(1)}}{2(3)}$$

$$x = \dfrac{-2 \pm \sqrt{4 - 12}}{6} = \dfrac{-2 \pm \sqrt{-8}}{6}$$

Solution is not a real number because radicand is negative.

18. Solution is not a real number because radicand is negative.

19. 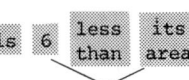 The perimeter of a square is 6 less than its area

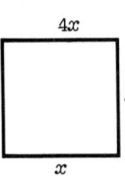

$4x$ $=$ $x^2 - 6$

x

x

Area $= x^2$
Perimeter $= 4x$

$$x^2 - 4x - 6 = 0 \quad \begin{cases} a = 1 \\ b = -4 \\ c = -6 \end{cases}$$

$$x = \dfrac{-(-4) \pm \sqrt{(-4)^2 - 4(1)(-6)}}{2(1)}$$

$$= \dfrac{4 \pm \sqrt{16 + 24}}{2} = \dfrac{4 \pm \sqrt{40}}{2}$$

$$= \dfrac{4 \pm 2\sqrt{10}}{2} = 2 \pm \sqrt{10} = \begin{cases} 2 + \sqrt{10} \doteq 2 + 3.162 \doteq 5.16 \text{ Side of square} \\ 2 - \sqrt{10} \doteq 2 - 3.162 \doteq -1.16 \text{ Not Possible} \end{cases}$$

20. $\doteq 4.45$

1. $$x^2 + x = 6$$
$$x^2 + x - 6 = 0$$
$$(x + 3)(x - 2) = 0$$
$$x + 3 = 0 \mid x - 2 = 0$$
$$x = -3 \mid \quad x = 2$$

2. 5, -2

3. $$x^2 - 25x = 0$$
$$x(x - 25) = 0$$
$$x = 0 \mid x - 25 = 0$$
$$\quad \mid \quad x = 25$$

4. 0, 49

5. $$x^2 - 2x - 4 = 0 \quad \begin{cases} a = 1 \\ b = -2 \\ c = -4 \end{cases}$$

$$x = \dfrac{-(-2) \pm \sqrt{(-2)^2 - 4(1)(-4)}}{2(1)}$$

$$x = \dfrac{2 \pm \sqrt{4 + 16}}{2} = \dfrac{2 \pm \sqrt{20}}{2}$$

$$x = \dfrac{2 \pm 2\sqrt{5}}{2} = 1 \pm \sqrt{5}$$

6. $2 \pm \sqrt{3}$

7. $$x^2 = 5x$$
$$x^2 - 5x = 0$$
$$x(x - 5) = 0$$
$$x = 0 \mid x - 5 = 0$$
$$\quad \mid \quad x = 5$$

8. 0, 7

9. $$\dfrac{2x}{3} = \dfrac{3}{8x}$$
$$16x^2 = 9$$
$$x^2 = \dfrac{9}{16}$$
$$x = \pm\sqrt{\dfrac{9}{16}}$$
$$x = \pm\dfrac{3}{4}$$

10. $\pm\dfrac{5}{6}$

11. $\dfrac{x + 2}{3} = \dfrac{1}{x - 2} + \dfrac{2}{3}$ LCD $= 3(x - 2)$

$$\dfrac{\cancel{3}(x - 2)}{1} \cdot \dfrac{(x + 2)}{\cancel{3}} = \dfrac{3\cancel{(x - 2)}}{1} \cdot \dfrac{1}{\cancel{(x - 2)}}$$
$$+ \dfrac{\cancel{3}(x - 2)}{1} \cdot \dfrac{2}{\cancel{3}}$$

$$(x - 2)(x + 2) = 3 + 2(x - 2)$$
$$x^2 - 4 = 3 + 2x - 4$$
$$x^2 - 2x - 3 = 0$$
$$(x - 3)(x + 1) = 0$$

$$x - 3 = 0 \mid x + 1 = 0$$
$$x = 3 \mid \quad x = -1$$

12. -4, 2

13. $5(x + 2) = x(x + 5)$
$$5x + 10 = x^2 + 5x$$
$$x^2 = 10$$
$$x = \pm\sqrt{10}$$
$$x = \pm\sqrt{10}$$

14. $\pm 2\sqrt{3}$

15. $\dfrac{2}{x} + \dfrac{x}{x + 1} = 5$ LCD $= x(x + 1)$

$$\dfrac{\cancel{x}(x + 1)}{1} \cdot \dfrac{2}{\cancel{x}} + \dfrac{x\cancel{(x + 1)}}{1} \cdot \dfrac{x}{\cancel{(x + 1)}} = \dfrac{x(x + 1)}{1} \cdot \dfrac{5}{1}$$

$$2(x + 1) + x^2 = 5x(x + 1)$$
$$2x + 2 + x^2 = 5x^2 + 5x$$

$$4x^2 + 3x - 2 = 0 \begin{cases} a = 4 \\ b = 3 \\ c = -2 \end{cases}$$

$$x = \dfrac{-(3) \pm \sqrt{(3)^2 - 4(4)(-2)}}{2(4)} = \dfrac{-3 \pm \sqrt{9 + 32}}{8}$$
$$= \dfrac{-3 \pm \sqrt{41}}{8}$$

16. $\dfrac{-1 \pm \sqrt{73}}{6}$

17. $3x^2 + 2x + 1 = 0 \begin{cases} a = 3 \\ b = 2 \\ c = 1 \end{cases}$

$$x = \dfrac{-(2) \pm \sqrt{(2)^2 - 4(3)(1)}}{2(3)}$$

$$x = \dfrac{-2 \pm \sqrt{4 - 12}}{6} \quad \text{Not a real number}$$

18. Not a real number

19. $(x + 5)(x - 2) = x(3 - 2x) + 2$
$$x^2 + 3x - 10 = 3x - 2x^2 + 2$$
$$3x^2 = 12$$
$$x^2 = 4$$
$$x = \pm\sqrt{4}$$
$$x = \pm 2$$

20. $\pm\dfrac{3\sqrt{5}}{5}$

21.

Area $= LW = (W + 4)W = 7 \begin{cases} a = 1 \\ b = 4 \\ c = -7 \end{cases}$
$$W^2 + 4W - 7 = 0$$

$$W = \dfrac{-(4) \pm \sqrt{(4)^2 - 4(1)(-7)}}{2(1)}$$

$$W = \dfrac{-4 \pm \sqrt{16 + 28}}{2} = \dfrac{-4 \pm \sqrt{44}}{2}$$

$$W = \dfrac{-4 \pm 2\sqrt{11}}{2} = -2 \pm \sqrt{11} \doteq \begin{cases} -2 + 3.317 = 1.317 \\ -2 - 3.317 = -5.317 \end{cases}$$

When $W = 1.317$ When $W = -5.317$

Width $= W = 1.317$ Not possible

Length $= W + 4 = 5.317$

22. $\doteq 6.87$, 0.87

CUMULATIVE REVIEW EXERCISES:
CHAPTERS 1–12 (page 464)

1. $\left(\dfrac{\overset{3}{\cancel{18}}s^{-1}t^{-3}}{\underset{2}{\cancel{12}s}}\right)^{-2} = \left(\dfrac{3s^{-2}t^{-3}}{2}\right)^{-2}$

$= \dfrac{3^{-2}s^4t^6}{2^{-2}} = \dfrac{2^2s^4t^6}{3^2} = \dfrac{4s^4t^6}{9}$

2. $9 - 2\sqrt{3}$

3. $\dfrac{x^2 + 3x}{2x^2 + 7x + 5} \div \dfrac{x^2 - 9}{x^2 - 2x - 3}$

$\dfrac{x(x + 3)}{(2x + 5)(x + 1)} \cdot \dfrac{(x + 1)(x - 3)}{(x + 3)(x - 3)}$

$= \dfrac{x}{2x + 5}$

4. $-\dfrac{3}{7}$

5. (1) $2]\ 3x + 4y = 3 \Rightarrow 6x + 8y = 6$
   (2) $3]\ 2x - 5y = 25 \Rightarrow \underline{6x - 15y = 75}$
   $$23y = -69$$
   $$y = -3$$

   Substitute $y = -3$ into (1):

   (1) $3x + 4y = 3$
   $$3x + 4(-3) = 3$$
   $$3x - 12 = 3$$
   $$3x = 15$$
   $$x = 5$$

   Solution: $(5, -3)$

6. $-\dfrac{2}{3}$

7. $\dfrac{14}{3 - \sqrt{2}} \cdot \dfrac{3 + \sqrt{2}}{3 + \sqrt{2}} = \dfrac{14(3 + \sqrt{2})}{9 - 2}$

$= \dfrac{\overset{2}{14}(3 + \sqrt{2})}{\cancel{7}} = 6 + 2\sqrt{2}$

8. $6\sqrt{2}$

9. $(\sqrt{5x + 3})^2 = (10x)^2$
$$5x + 3 = 100x^2$$
$$0 = 100x^2 - 5x - 3$$
$$0 = (20x + 3)(5x - 1)$$

$$20x + 3 = 0 \mid 5x - 1 = 0$$
$$20x = -3 \mid \quad 5x = 1$$
$$x = -\dfrac{3}{20} \mid \quad x = \dfrac{1}{5}$$

Check for $x = \dfrac{1}{5}$:

$$\sqrt{5\left(\dfrac{1}{5}\right) + 3} = 10\left(\dfrac{1}{5}\right)$$
$$\sqrt{1 + 3} \overset{?}{=} 2$$
$$\sqrt{4} = 2 \ \underline{\text{True}}$$

Check for $x = -\dfrac{3}{20}$:

$$\sqrt{5\left(-\dfrac{3}{20}\right) + 3} = 10\left(-\dfrac{3}{20}\right)$$
$$\sqrt{-\dfrac{3}{4} + 3} \overset{?}{=} -\dfrac{3}{2}$$
$$\sqrt{\dfrac{9}{4}} = -\dfrac{3}{2} \ \underline{\text{False}}$$

Only one answer: $\dfrac{1}{5}$

10. 6 cm

Following each problem number is the textbook section reference (in parentheses) where that kind of problem is discussed.

1. (1301)
$$5x + 3x^2 = 7$$
$$3x^2 + 5x - 7 = 0 \quad \begin{cases} a = 3 \\ b = 5 \\ c = -7 \end{cases}$$

2. (1301) $2(x + 1) = 3(2 - x^2)$
$$2x + 2 = 6 - 3x^2$$
$$3x^2 + 2x - 4 = 0 \quad \begin{cases} a = 3 \\ b = 2 \\ c = -4 \end{cases}$$

3. (1302)
$$x^2 + 3x = 10$$
$$x^2 + 3x - 10 = 0$$
$$(x + 5)(x - 2) = 0$$
$$x + 5 = 0 \quad | \quad x - 2 = 0$$
$$x = -5 \quad | \quad x = 2$$

4. (1302)
$$6x^2 = 5 - 7x$$
$$6x^2 + 7x - 5 = 0$$
$$(2x - 1)(3x + 5) = 0$$
$$2x - 1 = 0 \quad | \quad 3x + 5 = 0$$
$$2x = 1 \quad | \quad 3x = -5$$
$$x = \frac{1}{2} \quad | \quad x = -\frac{5}{3}$$

5. (1303)
$$3x^2 = 12x$$
$$3x^2 - 12x = 0$$
$$3x(x - 4) = 0$$
$$3x = 0 \quad | \quad x - 4 = 0$$
$$x = 0 \quad | \quad x = 4$$

6. (1303)
$$5x^2 = 20$$
$$x^2 = 4$$
$$x = \pm\sqrt{4}$$
$$x = \pm 2$$

7. (1303)
$$x(x - 4) = x$$
$$x^2 - 4x = x$$
$$x^2 - 5x = 0$$
$$x(x - 5) = 0$$
$$x = 0 \quad | \quad x - 5 = 0$$
$$\quad \quad | \quad x = 5$$

8. (1304)
$$2x^2 - 5x - 3 = 0 \quad \begin{cases} a = 2 \\ b = -5 \\ c = -3 \end{cases}$$
$$x = \frac{-(-5) \pm \sqrt{(-5)^2 - 4(2)(-3)}}{2(2)}$$
$$x = \frac{5 \pm \sqrt{25 + 24}}{4} = \frac{5 \pm \sqrt{49}}{4}$$
$$x = \frac{5 \pm 7}{4} = \begin{cases} \frac{5 + 7}{4} = \frac{12}{4} = 3 \\ \frac{5 - 7}{4} = \frac{-2}{4} = -\frac{1}{2} \end{cases}$$

9. (1304) $2(x + 1) = x^2$
$$2x + 2 = x^2$$
$$1x^2 - 2x - 2 = 0 \quad \begin{cases} a = 1 \\ b = -2 \\ c = -2 \end{cases}$$
$$x = \frac{-(-2) \pm \sqrt{(-2)^2 - 4(1)(-2)}}{2(1)}$$
$$x = \frac{2 \pm \sqrt{4 + 8}}{2} = \frac{2 \pm \sqrt{12}}{2}$$
$$x = \frac{2 \pm 2\sqrt{3}}{2} = 1 \pm \sqrt{3}$$

10. (1302)

$$\text{Area} = LW = (W + 5)W$$

Its area is 36.
$$(W + 5)W = 36 \quad \text{Equation used.}$$
$$W^2 + 5W = 36$$
$$W^2 + 5W - 36 = 0$$
$$(W + 9)(W - 4) = 0$$
$$W + 9 = 0 \quad | \quad W - 4 = 0$$
$$W = -9 \quad | \quad W = 4 \text{ (width)}$$
$$\text{Not possible} \quad | \quad W + 5 = 9 \text{ (length)}$$

APPENDIX EXERCISES 1 (page 471)

1. Yes, because it is a collection of objects or things.

2. Yes.

3. Yes, because they have exactly the same members. Writing a member more than once tells you no more than when you write it once—namely, that element is a member of the set.

4. {0, 1, 2}

5. { }. Since there are no digits greater than 9.

6. {0, 1, 2}

7. {10, 11, 12, ...}. This is the way we show the set of whole numbers greater than 9. It is an infinite set.

8. {5}

9. { }, since there are no whole numbers greater than 4 and at the same time less than 5.

10. {0, 1, 2, 3}

11. 2, a, 3. Because of the way the set is written we know that these are its elements.

12. 0, 1, 2, 3, 4, 5, 6, 7, 8, 9.

13. (a) $n(\{1, 1, 3, 5, 5, 5\}) = n(\{1, 3, 5\}) = 3$. This set has only three elements: 1, 3, and 5.
    (b) $n(\{0\}) = 1$. This set has 1 element: 0.
    (c) $n(\{a, b, g, x\}) = 4$. This set has four elements: a, b, g, and x.
    (d) $n(\{0, 1, 2, 3, 4, 5, 6, 7\}) = 8$. You can count its elements and see that there are eight of them.
    (e) $n(\emptyset) = 0$. The empty set has no elements.

14. (a) $\emptyset$ has no elements; {0} has one element, namely 0. Since the sets do not have exactly the same elements, they are not equal.
    (b) { } has no elements. {$\emptyset$} has one element, namely $\emptyset$. Since the sets do not have exactly the same elements, they are not equal.

15. (a) The set of digits is finite because when we count its elements the counting comes to an end. In this case the counting ends at 10.
    (b) The set of whole numbers is infinite because when we attempt to count its elements the counting never comes to an end.
    (c) Finite. The counting ends at 7.
    (d) Finite. If we started counting the books in the ELAC library, we would eventually finish counting them.

(e) Finite. Although this is a very large set, if we had some device for counting all the fish instantaneously, the counting would end.

16. (a) True (b) True (c) False (d) False
    (e) True

17. (a) {7, 12} because 7 and 12 are the only elements of U that are less than 15.
    (b) {23} because 23 is the only element of U that is greater than 20.

18. (a) {11}   (b) {5}

APPENDIX EXERCISES 2 (page 473)

1. (a) {3, 5} is a proper subset of M because each of its elements, 3 and 5, is an element of M; and M has at least one element, such as 2, that is not an element of {3, 5}.
   (b) {0, 1, 7} is not a subset of M because elements 0 and 7 are not elements of M.
   (c) ∅ is a proper subset of M because ∅ is a proper subset of every set except itself.
   (d) {2, 4, 1, 3, 5} is an improper subset of M because each element of C is an element of M, and M has no element that is not an element of C.

2. (a) Proper   (b) Improper   (c) Proper
   (d) Not a subset of P.

3. {R, G, Y} All the subsets with three elements
   {R, G}, {R, Y}, {G, Y} All the subsets with two elements
   {R}, {G}, {Y} All the subsets with one element
   { } All the subsets with no elements

4. {□, Δ}, {□}, {Δ}, { }

APPENDIX EXERCISES 3 (page 476)

1. (a) {1, 5, 7} ∪ {2, 4} = {1, 5, 7, 2, 4}
       {1, 5, 7} ∩ {2, 4} = { }
   (b) {a, b} ∪ {x, y, z, a} = {a, b, x, y, z}
       {a, b} ∩ {x, y, z, a} = {a}
   (c) { } ∪ {k, 2} = {k, 2}
       { } ∩ {k, 2} = { }
   (d) {river, boat} ∪ {boat, streams, down}
             = {river, boat, streams, down}
       {river, boat} ∩ {boat, streams, down}
             = {boat}

2. (a) {1, 3, 5, 7, 2, 4, 6}
   (b) {1, 2, 3, 4, 5, 6, 7}
   (c) { }
   (d) {6}

3. C and D are disjoint because they have no member in common. That is: $C ∩ D = ∅$. All other pairs of sets have at least one member in common.

4. (a) $P = \{c, d, k\}$ (b) $Q = \{k, j, f\}$
   (c) $P ∪ Q = \{c, d, k, j, f\}$ (d) $P ∩ Q = \{k\}$
   (e) $U = \{a, e, g, h, c, d, k, j, f\}$

5. (a) $X ∩ Y = \{5, 11\}$ because these are the only elements in both X and Y.
   (b) $Y ∩ X = \{5, 11\}$ for same reason as (a).
   (c) Yes. $X ∩ Y = Y ∩ X$ because they have exactly the same elements.

6. (a) $K ∩ L = \{4, b\}$ (b) $n(K ∩ L) = 2$
   (c) $L ∪ M = \{m, 4, 6, b, n, 7, t\}$
   (d) $n(L ∪ M) = 7$

7.
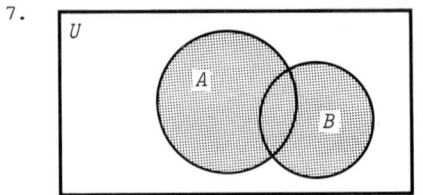
$A ∪ B$

8.
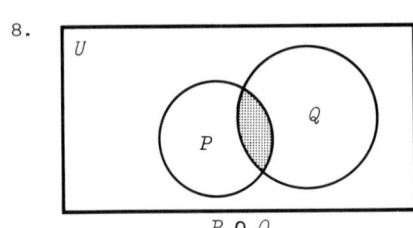
$P ∩ Q$

9. $R ∩ S$ because the shaded area is in both R and S.

10. $Y ∪ Z$

APPENDIX EXERCISES 4 (page 482)

1. $\dfrac{\overset{2}{\cancel{6}}}{\underset{3}{\cancel{9}}} = \dfrac{2}{3}$ 2. $\dfrac{3}{5}$

3. $\dfrac{49}{24}$ Already in lowest terms   4. $\dfrac{7}{8}$

5. $\dfrac{5}{2} = 2\overline{)5}^{\,2\ R1\ =\ 2\frac{1}{2}}$ 6. $1\dfrac{3}{8}$

7. $\dfrac{47}{25} = 25\overline{)47}^{\,1\ R22\ =\ 1\frac{22}{25}}$ with $\dfrac{25}{22}$ 8. $2\dfrac{4}{11}$

9. $3\dfrac{7}{8} = \dfrac{3 \cdot 8 + 7}{8} = \dfrac{24 + 7}{8} = \dfrac{31}{8}$ 10. $\dfrac{25}{9}$

11. $2\dfrac{5}{6} = \dfrac{2 \cdot 6 + 5}{6} = \dfrac{12 + 5}{6} = \dfrac{17}{6}$ 12. $\dfrac{43}{5}$

13. $\begin{aligned}\tfrac{2}{3} &= \tfrac{8}{12}\\ +\tfrac{1}{4} &= \tfrac{3}{12}\\ \hline &\ \ \tfrac{11}{12}\end{aligned}$ LCD = 12   14. $\dfrac{1}{2}$

15. $\begin{aligned}\tfrac{7}{10} &= \tfrac{7}{10}\\ -\tfrac{2}{5} &= -\tfrac{4}{10}\\ \hline &\ \ \tfrac{3}{10}\end{aligned}$ LCD = 10   16. $\dfrac{7}{20}$

17. $\dfrac{\overset{1}{\cancel{3}}}{\underset{4}{\cancel{16}}} \cdot \dfrac{\overset{5}{\cancel{20}}}{\underset{3}{\cancel{9}}} = \dfrac{5}{12}$ 18. $\dfrac{9}{28}$

19. $\dfrac{4}{3} ÷ \dfrac{8}{9} = \dfrac{4}{\underset{1}{\cancel{3}}} \cdot \dfrac{\overset{3}{\cancel{9}}}{\underset{2}{\cancel{8}}} = \dfrac{3}{2}$ 20. 4

21. $\begin{aligned}2\tfrac{2}{3} &= 2\tfrac{10}{15}\\ +1\tfrac{3}{5} &= 1\tfrac{9}{15}\\ \hline 3\tfrac{19}{15} &= 4\tfrac{4}{15}\end{aligned}$ 22. $7\dfrac{3}{4}$

578   Answers

23. $5\dfrac{4}{5} = 5\dfrac{8}{10}$

    $-3\dfrac{7}{10} = -3\dfrac{7}{10}$
                $2\dfrac{1}{10}$

24. $2\dfrac{1}{6}$

25. $4\dfrac{1}{5} \cdot 2\dfrac{1}{7} = \dfrac{\cancel{21}^{3}}{\cancel{5}} \cdot \dfrac{\cancel{15}^{3}}{7} = 9$

26. $10\dfrac{1}{2}$

27. $2\dfrac{2}{5} \div 1\dfrac{1}{15} = \dfrac{12}{5} \div \dfrac{16}{15}$

              $= \dfrac{\cancel{12}^{3}}{\cancel{5}} \cdot \dfrac{\cancel{15}^{3}}{\cancel{16}^{4}} = \dfrac{9}{4} = 2\dfrac{1}{4}$

28. $\dfrac{2}{3}$

29. $\dfrac{\frac{5}{8}}{\frac{5}{6}} = \dfrac{5}{8} \div \dfrac{5}{6} = \dfrac{\cancel{5}^{1}}{\cancel{8}^{4}} \cdot \dfrac{\cancel{6}^{3}}{\cancel{5}^{1}} = \dfrac{3}{4}$

30. $\dfrac{1}{2}$

31.   34.5
      1.74
   18.
    0.016
   54.256

32. 94.745

33. 356.40
    34.67
   321.73

34. 336.56

35. $100 \times 7.\underrightarrow{45} = 745$

36. 3540

37. $\dfrac{\overleftarrow{46.8}}{100} = 0.468$

38. 0.0895

39.   9 4.7 8 (2 decimal places)
         7 0.0 (1 decimal place)
        8 5 3 0 2
   6 6 3 4 6
   6 7 1 9.9 0 2 $\doteq$ 6719.9

40. 2798.5

41.   0.8 2 8 $\doteq$ 0.83
   $7.2\,5_{\wedge}\overline{\smash{)}6.0\,0_{\wedge}.7\,0\,0}$
        5 8 0 0
        2 0 7 0
        1 4 5 0
        6 2 0 0
        5 8 0 0
          4 0 0

42. 1.71

43. $5\dfrac{3}{4} = \dfrac{23}{4} = 4\overline{\smash{)}2\,3.\overset{3}{3}0^{2}0}$ 5.7 5

44. 4.6

45. $0.65 = \dfrac{\cancel{65}^{13}}{\cancel{100}_{20}} = \dfrac{13}{20}$

46. $\dfrac{1}{4}$

47. $5.9 = 5 + .9 = 5 + \dfrac{9}{10} = 5\dfrac{9}{10}$

48. $4\dfrac{3}{10}$

Index

Abscissa, 333
Absolute value, 12
Addition, 479, 482
   additive identity, 30
   associative property of, 26
   commutative property of, 24, 25
   of fractions, 287, 293
   of polynomials, 201, 202
   of signed numbers, 10, 13
   of square roots, 418, 419
   of zero, 30
Additive identity, 30
Algebra, 2
Algebraic expression, 68
   to simplify, 87
Area
   of rectangle, 263
   of square, 263
Arithmetic, 2
   brief summary, 479
Associative property
   of addition, 26
   of multiplication, 27

Bar, 51
Base, 32, 72, 154
Binomial, 198
   square of, 239
Boundary line, 361, 362
Braces
   grouping symbol, 51
   set notation, 469
Brackets, 51

Cardinal number(s), 470
Check-point, 336
Coefficient, 69, 198
   literal, 70
   numerical, 70, 198
Coin problems, 133
Commutative property
   of addition, 24, 25
   of multiplication, 25
Complex fraction, 298
   to simplify, 298, 482
Composite number, 224
Conditional equation, 114
Conjugate, 422
Consecutive numbers, 2
Consistent system of equations, 379
Constant, 68
   of proportionality, 161, 165
Coordinates, 331, 333
Corresponding values
   pair of, 161, 336

Cost, 158
Counting numbers, 2
Cross-multiplication rule, 142

Decimal (fraction), 5, 479
   addition of, 479
   decimal places, 5, 479
   division of, 480
   multiplication of, 480
   subtraction of, 479
Decimal places, 5, 479
Degree
   of equation, 257
   of polynomial, 199
   of term, 199
Denominator, 4, 277
   lowest common denominator, 289
Dependent system of equations, 381
Diagonal, 429
Digit, 4
Direct variation, 161, 162
Disjoint sets, 476
Distributive Rule, 76, 77
Dividend, 22
Divisibility, tests for, 226
Division, 480, 482
   involving zero, 31
   of fractions, 285, 482
   of polynomials, 211
   of signed numbers, 22
   of square roots, 417
Divisor, 22

Elements of set, 469
Empty set, 470
Equal sets, 470
Equal sign, 4
   approximately equal, 52
   meaning of, 97
Equation of line
   general form, 346
   point-slope form, 347
   slope-intercept form, 348
Equations, 97
   changing signs, 106
   to check, 99
   conditional equation, 114
   dependent, 381
   first-degree, 302
   graph of, 336, 341, 352
   identity (identical equation), 114
   independent, 379
   linear, 336, 341
   literal, 309
   parts of, 97

Lowest common denominator (LCD), 289
   to find, 290

Markup, 158
Master product, 253, 254
Means of proportion, 142
Member of set, 469
Mixed number(s), 4, 481
Monomial, 198
Multiplication, 480, 482
   associative property of, 27
   commutative property of, 25
   cross-multiplication rule, 142
   of fractions, 283, 482
   multiplicative identity, 19
   of polynomials, 207
   of signed numbers, 19, 20
   of square roots, 412, 415
   symbols, 19
   by zero, 30
Multiplicative identity, 19

Natural numbers, 2
Negative exponent(s), 179, 180
Negative number(s), 7
   powers of, 33
Negative of a number, 15
Null set, 470
Number
   composite, 224
   consecutive numbers, 2
   counting numbers, 2
   integers, 7
   irrational numbers, 408
   mixed numbers, 4, 481
   natural numbers, 2
   negative numbers, 7
   negative of, 15
   number line, 2, 330
   positive numbers, 7
   prime, 224
   rational numbers, 137, 407
   real numbers, 5
   rounding off, 479
   signed numbers, 7
   unknown, 97
   whole numbers, 2, 479
Number line, 2, 330
   real numbers, 5
Number pair, 331
Numerator, 4, 277

Odd power, 33
Order of operations, 48, 481
Ordered pair, 331
Ordinate, 333
Origin, 330, 333
Outer product, 242

Parallel lines, 380
Parentheses, 19, 51
Percent, 153
   amount, 154
   base of, 154
   percent proportion, 154
Percent proportion, 154
Perimeter, 139, 263
Polynomial, 198
   addition, 201, 202
   definition, 198
   degree of, 199
   descending powers, 200
   division, 211
   equation, 257
   factor, 228, 229
   multiplication, 207
   powers of, 210
   subtraction, 204
Polynomial equation, 257
   first degree, 257
   second degree, 257
Positive exponent(s), 176
Positive number(s), 7
Power(s)
   base, 32
   even, 33
   exponent, 32
   odd, 33
   of polynomials, 210
   of signed numbers, 32
   of zero, 33
Prime factorization, 223, 224
Prime number, 224
Principal square root, 36, 234,
     406, 431, 454
Product(s), 228
   of factors, 74, 223
   inner, 242
   Master, 253, 254
   outer, 242
   square of binomial, 239
   of sum and difference, 233
   of two binomials, 237, 238
   using Distributive Rule, 228
Proper subset, 473
Proportion, 141, 303
   extremes of, 142
   means of, 142
   related proportion, 162, 165
   to solve, 143
   terms of, 142
Pythagorean Theorem, 429

Quadratic equation(s), 257, 446
   general form of, 446
   graph of, 352
   incomplete, 452, 453, 455